A COMPREHENSIVE INTRODUCTION TO THE
PERIPHERAL NERVOUS SYSTEM

Charles A. Henderson, MD

MedTutor.com

MedTutor.com

1501 S. 40th Avenue
Hattiesburg, MS 39402

Technical Editors: Dan P. Childers, Betty Sugg

Cover and Poster Art: Bice Advertising, Inc.

Typesetting and Page Layout: Copy Cats Printing, Inc.

Indexer: Susan K. Cohen

Web-Based Applications: Open Sky Software, Inc.

A Comprehensive Introduction to the Peripheral Nervous System

ISBN# 978-0-9827485-0-3

Printed in the United States of America.

To my wife, Juliana, and to our children, Rachel and Tyler,

for their patience and love.

ACKNOWLEDGEMENTS

CONTENT EDITORS

Richard E. Clatterbuck, MD
Neurosurgeon
Hattiesburg Clinic
Forrest General Hospital
Hattiesburg, Mississippi

David J. Dzielak, PhD
Professor of Surgery
Professor of Health Sciences
Associate Professor of Physiology and Biophysics
University of Mississippi
Jackson, Mississippi

Michael J. Hammett, MD
Otolaryngologist
Hattiesburg Clinic
Forrest General Hospital
Hattiesburg, Mississippi

Keith P. Melancon, MD
Assistant Professor
Department of Orthopaedic Surgery
Louisiana State University
New Orleans, Louisiana

Charles E. Wall, Jr., MD
General Surgeon
Hattiesburg Clinic
Forrest General Hospital
Hattiesburg, Mississippi

TECHNICAL EDITORS
Dan P. Childers
Betty Sugg

CONTRIBUTORS
Ralph E. Abraham, MD; Horace Baggett, MD; Timothy L. Cole, MD; David J. Dzielak, PhD;
Keri H. Fischtziur; Leandra Jacobs; David L. Sicard, MD; Charles E. Wall, Jr., MD

ILLUSTRATORS
Rick Bice, Hank D'Aquilla, Crystal Davis, Donna B. Doherty,
Charles A. Henderson, Sophia A. Kerschbaum, Terry L. Lacy, Ethan Manning,
Sabrina S. Schuerger, Scott Stahler, Jay Temple, Tammy Thornhill

The author would like to acknowledge and thank Dover Publications and editor Jim Harter for the numerous illustrations that appear in this text, posters, and interactive applications of the website. These images were reproduced and modified with permission, *Harter, J.*: Medical and Anatomical Illustrations With Over 4800 Permission-Free Images, *2nd ed. Mineola, Dover, 2004.*

CONTENTS

FOUNDATIONS OF ANATOMY
AND PHYSIOLOGY

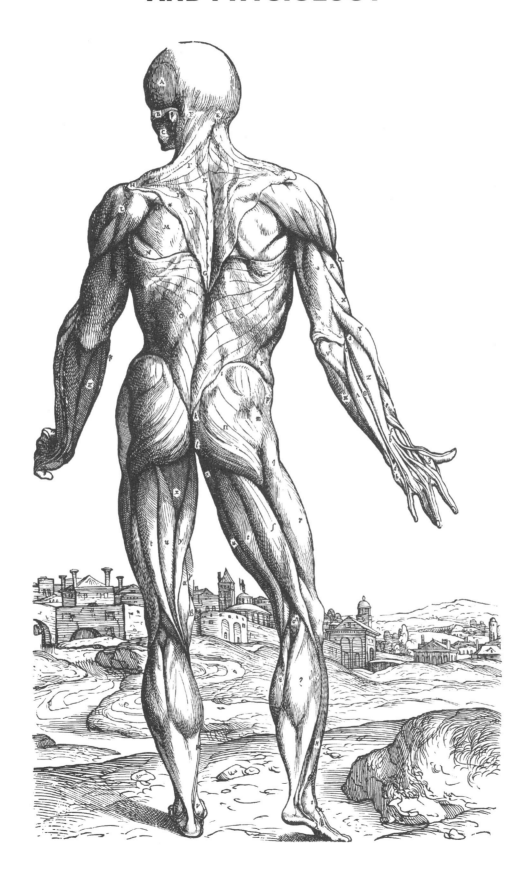

"Happiness lies in the absorption in some vocation which satisfies the soul."

– Sir William Osler

CHAPTER ONE

INTRODUCTION

Anatomy is at the core of health-related education. This book, accompanying posters, and interactive website form an educational system that teaches nerve anatomy without an instructor or formal classroom. The intent is to provide a mechanism to prepare for the first year of medical school and to serve as a compliment to formal medical education. The subject, nerve anatomy, is one of the more challenging topics faced by first year students and is found in several medial courses. The material is not difficult to learn, but the volume of information can become overwhelming. A student with a prior knowledge of medical language and nerve anatomy would have a significant advantage in school.

Although initially developed for students of medicine, the book has evolved into an educational system that could benefit any number of health professionals. Included are students and practitioners of medicine, nursing, dentistry, physical and occupational therapy, nurse anesthesia, physician assistance, and technicians from a variety of health care specialties. Because information is presented in a very basic manner, any lay reader can comprehend and digest the material. Virtually every nerve, muscle, and bone of the human body is taught. The goal is to identify information as relevant and present it to the reader in a simple and easy to understand format. To promote active learning, a variety of interactive mechanisms repetitively test the student.

Most textbooks merely present information. It is the responsibility of the reader to decipher what is written and determine what is important to learn. Anatomy books are considered especially tedious and difficult to follow. Without a cadaver to analyze or an instructor to learn from, it is difficult to learn anatomy by simply reading an anatomy textbook. It is too much material to learn without active participation in a systematic teaching process.

The importance of exams is usually linked to the determination of a grade and subsequent success or failure in reaching a particular benchmark. However, exams are particularly useful as a *teaching* method. At no point during the study process does a student know the material better than immediately after an exam. After reviewing the results of a test, a student is more knowledgeable about the topic than he/she was five minutes before the exam, at which point he/she may have studied for weeks and crammed the previous night in an attempt to prepare. One of the advantages of this course is the provision for teaching and testing without specific concern for grades. The student can actually learn the material as opposed to employing short-term memorization.

Before describing the interlinking components of the educational system, it is important to note the variability that exists in anatomy. Just as there is variability in anatomy from one individual to another, there is also variability in the way some of the fine details are taught. There are individuals who possess anatomic

relationships that vary from what is described here. There are also anatomy professors and texts which present certain anatomic details differently from what is described here. In addition, many anatomic structures have more than one name, owing much to language variations. The reader is encouraged to learn the material as it is presented here. The purpose of this course is to describe the *basics* of nerve anatomy. Anything taught differently in future anatomy courses can be easily addressed by simply modifying the existing knowledge base.

SKELETON POSTER

The skeleton forms the foundation of human anatomy and many anatomic structures are named with reference to certain bones. Thus, a high priority should be placed on learning the 206 bones of the human body as knowledge of the skeleton will expedite the study of anatomy. The comprehensive skeleton poster accompanying this text contains multiple bone images and hundreds of bone surface anatomy details that are labeled. Every bone is represented, including the twenty-one bones that form the skull, the eight that form the carpus (wrist), the seven that form the tarsus (ankle), and the nineteen that form each hand and foot. Various notches, foramina, heads, necks, tubercles, and tuberosities are examples of surface anatomy details that are also displayed.

As each nerve is described in the text, the muscles it innervates, if any, are also discussed. This discussion includes muscle origins and insertions to specific areas of certain bones. Therefore, while the skeleton poster compliments Chapter 3 in particular, it also serves as an essential reference for the remainder of the book and for the study of anatomy in general.

PERIPHERAL NERVE POSTER

The peripheral nerve poster is the centerpiece of the educational system. Every nerve is represented on the poster. To bolster learning, many nerves are color-coded; the colors are explained throughout the text. The poster should be considered an anatomic *chart* as opposed to an anatomically-correct *picture*. It is divided into six separate figures that represent common views of dissection. Nerves are drawn to be visually apparent in an arrangement that limits clutter. Other anatomic structures function as crude reference points. The book describes the peripheral nervous system and specifically explains how it is depicted on the poster. To facilitate the process of identifying individual nerves, every nerve is associated with a nerve number. The nerves are labeled and numbered in a counter-clockwise sequence in each of the six figures. Many nerves are present in more than one figure. As a particular nerve is described in the text, the nerve name is followed by one or more numbers in parenthesis. These nerve numbers correspond with each location the nerve appears on the poster. If more than one nerve number is present, the number with bold-faced font is the location of the nerve that is more applicable to the current text. Because of their relatively small size, the nerve names cannot be read from more than a few feet away from the poster. The student should place the poster in a location convenient for frequent viewing and repeatedly test and retest by attempting to identify nerves and moving closer to read the nerve names. With practice, an image of the poster becomes ingrained in the mind. This image becomes very useful during test time. Upon completion of the course, the poster can be used for continued review.

EXAMINATIONS

Each chapter includes two to three quizzes and a chapter test. To preserve questions for future review, answers should be recorded on a separate sheet of paper. All examinations are followed by correct answers and explanations. The explanations may present information in a different format or from a different perspective than the text. Many of the answers are intentionally redundant. It is said that the average person must be exposed to a new word six or seven times before it is remembered. The more times a particular topic is presented to the reader, the greater the likelihood it is learned. The purpose of the quizzes is to encourage the reader to slow down and master the information. The text material is very information dense. Most sentences include some fact that should be learned. The student should read the text slowly and attempt to learn it. Structures should be drawn out and/or listed on a separate sheet of paper. To maximize the learning experience, the quizzes and chapter tests should be treated as if a grade were administered in a formal course, and no exam should be taken until the student feels adequately prepared. This usually requires reading the text material several times, identifying the nerves by using the poster, drawing structures, and listing structures and their relationships. Because the information in the book tends to build on itself, the information contained within each chapter should be learned before continuing forward. The questions of each quiz should be reviewed prior to a chapter test. Missed chapter test questions require review prior to proceeding to the next chapter. Many times it is not until a particular chapter is completed that all elements seem to fit together and make sense.

Just as unclear segments of a particular chapter become more understandable once the chapter is completed, the book becomes more comprehensible when it is finished. The chapters tend to compliment one another. Each chapter is unique and different; each region of the body is unique and different. The variety of information contained in each chapter requires diverse methods of presentation.

BOXED LEARNING AIDS

Intermingled throughout the text are informal shaded *boxes* that contain helpful hints, mnemonics, and points of interest. At the conclusion of each chapter is a *summary of chapter boxes* which contains a synopsis of every box of the chapter. Although it may not be comprehensive for all information contained in a particular chapter, the summary provides an effective mechanism for review.

CLINICAL CORRELATIONS

Also found at the end of every chapter is a *clinical correlation*. The clinical correlation includes one or more clinical topics that relate in some form to material contained within the chapter. The intent is to make the information more interesting. Although the topics may reinforce the student's knowledge of the chapter and are independently important to know, they are provided for the student's insight only. No exam questions will come from information isolated to a clinical correlation.

WEB-BASED FINAL EXAM

After sufficient preparation, the student can go to the internet site and take the final examination. This examination mimics a board-type exam and includes 180 questions divided into two 90 question segments, part I and part II. The student has three hours to take the timed examination. A break is provided between part I and part II and additional breaks are available if needed. The test is immediately graded; answers and explanations are provided. Each question is categorized so the student knows how well he or she did in each anatomic category.

WEB-BASED INTERACTIVE LEARNING APPLICATIONS

After completion and review of the final exam, the student is encouraged to participate in four interactive learning applications found on the website. These applications include a random exam system, interactive posters, flashcard system, and medical crossword puzzles. The internet systems are useful for knowledge maintenance and continued learning. The student should proceed in the aforementioned manner: reading the book, referencing and identifying all nerves on the poster, and taking the quizzes and chapter tests as appropriate. The website should not be utilized until the final exam is taken. At this point, the student is considered adequately exposed to the material to proceed with more advanced learning. The internet applications are designed to provide a unique, efficient, and effective mechanism for enhancing study and learning. The goal is to employ a system that is easy and fun to use, thus encouraging frequent participation. Repetition is the key to success with anatomy.

RANDOMIZED EXAM APPLICATION

The randomized exam system includes a database of over 5,000 board-type questions related to information contained in this book. The student can sporadically and repeatedly prompt the system to assimilate a test of a certain number of randomized questions that are pulled from the question databank. This exam may contain questions specific to a particular chapter, to a group of chapters, or to the entire book. The student makes the determination. Like the final exam, each exam is timed and graded upon completion. Answers and explanations are provided. Each question is categorized to the specific area of nerve anatomy it applies. The system displays the number of questions and percentage correct for each of the various subdivisions. Similar to the subdivisions of math, science, and English on a college entrance exam, focus may then be placed on areas requiring improvement. The student may direct the system to create future exams from questions specific to the areas he or she feels deficient in.

INTERACTIVE POSTERS

The website includes several interactive posters, including two that replicate the peripheral nerve poster and two that replicate the skeleton poster. Each pair of interactive posters is composed of a "name-only" and "comprehensive" version. The *name-only* version of the peripheral nerve poster displays nerves that are associated with nerve numbers, but no nerve names are present. However, when the cursor is moved over the nerve number, the name appears on the screen. Using this method, a relatively large number of nerve names can be tested in a short period of time, ideal for a quick review immediately before an exam.

As the student becomes more proficient in nerve identification, the *comprehensive* peripheral nerve poster can be used. This poster depicts nerve names, images of supplied muscles, muscle names, images of supplied skin, and nerve compositions when prompted by the student. The images create an efficient mechanism for testing and learning the more in-depth associations between the nerves and various other body structures.

The *name-only* version of the skeleton poster contains images of bones that are associated with red and black dots. When the cursor is moved over a red dot, the name of the bone appears on the screen. When positioned over a black dot, the name of the associated surface anatomy detail appears.

Similar to the interactive peripheral nerve posters, bones of the *comprehensive* skeleton poster are associated with numbers. This poster displays bone names, images of bone surface details, names of bone details, images of bones with color-enhanced areas representing muscle origins and insertions, and muscle names when prompted by the student. With the comprehensive versions of the peripheral nerve and skeleton posters, an audio application furnishes the correct pronunciation of anatomic structures when requested by the student.

FLASHCARDS

The flashcard application contains thousands of flashcards related to virtually every fact presented in this text. Numerous flashcards contain color-enhanced images of anatomic structures. Every muscle and bone is represented. The student directs the system as to the number and type of flashcards to display during a particular sitting. Flashcards may be specific to a chapter, a group of chapters, the entire book, or a group of *Medtutor* books. Upon completion of a particular set of cards, the student may prompt the system to display the same set of cards backwards in order to show the back of each card first. The student has the ability to pass or fail him/herself on each flashcard. Failed flashcards are placed in a personalized databank and that can be accessed at any time. Cards that are passed are removed from the databank; failed cards remain.

CROSSWORD PUZZLES

The medical crossword puzzles are an informal way to continually review and learn new material. The system can be directed to create a puzzle specific to information contained in this book or some combination of other *Medtutor* books. If the answer to a crossword question is not known, the application provides a short explanation of the material when requested. A crossword puzzle can be worked online or printed and worked while away from the computer. The student can return to the internet site to check answers and obtain explanations. Among other utilities, the medical crossword puzzle is a fun and effective means to consistently review and maintain a tangible knowledge base long after the texts are finished. There is a significant amount of fundamental medical information presented in the *Medtutor* series; merely working one puzzle a day would greatly benefit any practitioner of a health-related profession. The interactive web-based systems and directions for their use will be covered in greater detail in the final chapter.

Upon completion of this course, the student will still have a substantial amount of material to learn in a formal anatomy class. This includes countless anatomic structures and three-dimensional relationships. Nevertheless, this one *Medtutor* course will equip the motivated student with knowledge of anatomic names, basic anatomic organizational structure, and an introduction to medical language. Armed with this, the student should accelerate the learning experience obtained in a formal course. The hope is that adequate preparation will permit future learning at an advanced level.

Perseverance is the key to success. The process is simple, but it is not easy. The student should work from quiz to quiz and chapter to chapter. Much will be gained by completing the course and participating in the web-based applications on a regular basis. Not only will the student attain an expanded knowledge base, but the exercise in self-discipline will mold routines beneficial in more advanced studies. Good luck.

– Charles A. Henderson, MD

"Men often become what they believe themselves to be. If I believe I cannot do something, it makes me incapable of doing it. But when I believe I can, then I acquire the ability to do it even if I didn't have it in the beginning."

– Mahatma Gandhi

CHAPTER TWO

BASICS OF ANATOMY

A significant amount of the challenge associated with the study of medicine may be attributed to the medical language. This text uses simplistic terms and descriptions to aid the beginning student in learning the course of peripheral nerves. Nevertheless, there are a number of descriptive terms which must be learned to facilitate the study of anatomy. These terms describe specific areas of the body, certain anatomic views, body positions, body movements, and anatomic relationships between structures. More specifically, they may describe how one anatomic structure relates to another in terms of function, direction, or location. These descriptive terms are not only important in anatomy but are an integral component of basic medical language. The sooner the language is mastered, the sooner advancement to further studies occurs.

An appropriate starting point is the **anatomic position**. This is the standardized position of the human body for the description of anatomy. The subject is standing and facing forward, toward the observer. Legs are straight and slightly apart. Feet are flat on the ground with the toes pointed forward. Arms are down, near the sides of the body. Hands are turned so the palms are facing forward, toward the observer.

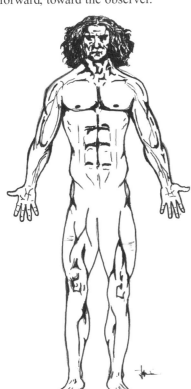

FIGURE 2.1

Derived from anatomic sketches by Leonardo Da Vinci (1452-1519), Fig. 2.1 serves as both an example of the anatomic position and a reminder of the classical nature of the study. Although Da Vinci lived some 500 years ago, his birth was preceded by thousands of years of anatomic studies.

Since the subject is facing the observer, it is important to realize that right-sided structures of the subject appear to the observer to be located on the left. In other words, the anatomic right-sided structures appear visually on the left. The anatomic left-sided structures appear visually on the right. For

instance, the right arm of the subject appears visually on the left as viewed by the observer. Again, this is because the subject and observer are facing one another. Although this initially may seem a simple concept, it is a common cause of confusion for the beginning student. It is not uncommon for exam questions to be missed merely because they are wrongly labeled as right or left.

DESCRIPTIVE TERMS OF ANATOMY

Note the following descriptive definitions. Most are paired with their opposite. This serves as an aid in learning their meanings. It is easier to remember what hot and cold are if it is known they are opposites. These opposites are designated with the letters (a) and (b). If a term does not have an opposite, it will not have a letter associated with it. One pair of descriptive terms may have the same basic meaning as another. This will be explained shortly. These similar pairs are grouped together.

1. (a) **Superior:** upward or above
    (b) **Inferior:** downward or below

2. (a) **Cephalic:** cranial, referring to or directed toward the cranium (the bones of the skull, excluding the mandible)
    Cephalad: toward the cranium
    (b) **Caudal:** referring to or directed toward the cauda (tail). In humans, this is toward the coccyx, the lowest bone of the vertebral column
    Caudad: toward the cauda

3. **Rostral:** toward the cerebrum of the brain. The word *rostrum* means beak.

FIGURE 2.2

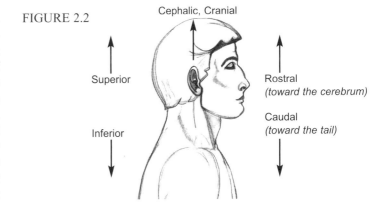

4. (a) **Anterior:**   toward the front
    (b) **Posterior:**   toward the back

5. (a) **Ventral:**   toward the abdomen (belly) surface
    (b) **Dorsal:**   toward the back

> Envision the ominous image of a shark's dorsal fin sticking out of the ocean surface. If you can remember that the dorsal fin is on the shark's back, you can remember that dorsal is posterior. The ventral or anterior aspect of the shark is opposite to this and is directed toward the underside or abdomen.

Why all the similarities in the anatomic descriptive terms? Anatomy is a fairly standardized discipline that applies not only to humans but to all animals. Although there are obvious anatomic differences between humans and other animals, the same anatomic descriptive terms are used.

FIGURE 2.3

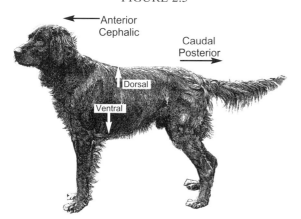

If a four-legged dog were facing the observer, the closest thing to the observer would be the head (cranial) end. The head is therefore the most anterior. The caudal direction is toward the tail and is posterior. The ventral direction is toward the abdomen. From other areas of the torso, this is inferior. The dorsal surface would be the most superior part of the torso.

In a two-legged human in the standing position, the ventral direction is also anterior. The dorsal direction is posterior. The cranial (cephalic, rostral) direction is also superior. Finally, the caudal direction is toward the inferior aspect of the trunk.

FIGURE 2.4

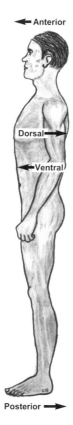

6. (a) **Superficial:** toward the surface of the body or structure
    (b) **Deep:** relatively "deep" into the structure – away from the surface

FIGURE 2.5

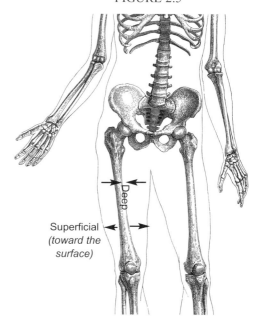

7. (a) **Medial:** toward the midline of the body or structure
    (b) **Lateral:** toward the sides of the body or structure, away from the midline

    Midline of body: separates the anatomic position of the external human body into two separate, symmetrical right and left halves

FIGURE 2.6

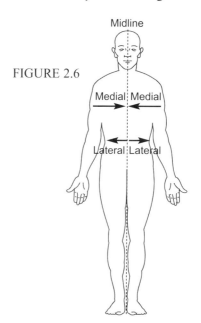

8. (a) **Ipsilateral:** on the same side of the body as a certain anatomic structure or reference point
    (b) **Contralateral:** on the opposite side of the body as a certain anatomic structure or reference point

The ip_si i_s on the _same _side

FIGURE 2.7

The subject's right hand is the reference point. It is shaded dark.

The ipsilateral foot has diagonal lines; the contralateral foot is shaded gray.

9. (a) **Proximal:** nearest to a reference point, a center, or an attachment point
   (b) **Distal:** farther removed from a reference point, a center, or an attachment point

The terms proximal and distal are often used to describe anatomy of the extremities (arms, legs). The reference point in this case is the attachment point of that extremity with the torso (body).

In Figure 2.8, the reference point is the attachment of the shoulder to the torso. With reference to that attachment point, the hand is distal to the elbow; it is farther removed from the attachment point than the elbow is. It can also be said that the elbow is proximal to the hand; it is closer to the attachment point than the hand is. If one were to start at the elbow and follow an anatomic structure (such as

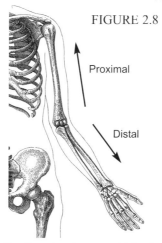

FIGURE 2.8

Proximal

Distal

a nerve or blood vessel) distally, the structure would be tracked toward the fingertips. If an anatomic structure were followed proximally, it would be tracked toward the shoulder.

The previous anatomic descriptions are basically directional in nature. They are helpful in describing how one anatomic structure is oriented to another anatomic structure. They are also used to describe how an anatomic structure (e.g. blood vessel, nerve, etc.) travels through the body. The following terms describe specific anatomic structures or regions of the human body:

1) **Caput:** the head
   Capitis: referring to the caput

2) **Occiput:** the back of the head
   Occipital: referring to the occiput

3) **Cranium:** the skull, excluding the mandible
   Cranial: referring to the cranium

4) **Cephalic:** (previously described) same as cranial

5) **Cervix:** the neck
   Cervical: referring to the cervix

6) **Collum:** neck
   Colli: referring to the collum

7) **Nucha:** the back of the neck
   Nuchal: referring to the nucha

> There are two terms for neck:
> collum (colli) and cervix (cervical).
> Additionally, the nucha is the back of the neck.

8) **Brachium:** upper arm (shoulder to elbow)
   Brachial: referring to the brachium

9) **Antebrachium:** forearm (elbow to hand)
   Antebrachial: referring to the antibrachium

10) **Axilla:** the armpit
    Axillary: referring to the axilla

11) **Palmar:** directed toward or referring to the palms of the hands
    Dorsal: directed toward or referring to the side of the hand opposite the palm (i.e. dorsum of the hand)

> Remember, in the anatomic position, the palms are facing the observer. The back of the hands are therefore dorsal.

12) **Thorax:** the chest. It extends from the neck to the diaphragm and is surrounded by the ribs. The diaphragm is the large muscle of respiration that separates the thorax from the abdomen.
    Thoracic: referring to the thorax

13) **Mediastinum:** the group of midline structures which divides the thorax into right and left compartments. The mediastinum includes the heart, great blood vessels, esophagus, trachea, thymus, and lymph glands.
    Mediastinal: referring to the mediastinum

14) **Loin:** the region of the back from the thorax to the pelvis. This is the posterior somatic region that extends from the diaphragm to the sacrum. It is not surrounded by ribs.
    Lumbar: referring to the loins

15) **Abdomen:** the region between the thorax and pelvis comprised of the abdominal cavity, visceral internal organs, and somatic anterior abdominal wall. It extends from the diaphragm superiorly,

to the pelvis inferiorly, and is anterior to the loins. Like the loins, the abdomen is also a portion of the trunk which is not surrounded by the ribs.

Abdominal: referring to the abdomen

16) **Pelvis:** the caudal (lower) part of the body trunk. It is surrounded by the sacrum posteriorly, the hip bones anteriorly and laterally, and the abdomen superiorly. Pelvic structures include the bladder, uterus, and rectum.

Pelvic: referring to the pelvis

17) **Sacrum:** the larger bone on the inferior aspect of the vertebral column that is formed by the fusion of five vertebrae. It forms the posterior boundary of the pelvis.

Sacral: referring to the area overlying the posterior side of the sacrum bone. The sacral area can be considered the area posterior to the pelvis.

18) **Perineum:** the floor of the pelvis. It is the area between the thighs which runs from the anus to the scrotum in the male and vulva in the female.

Perineal: referring to the perineum

19) **Peritoneum:** the membrane that surrounds the abdominal and pelvic cavities and contains internal organs. More about these cavities is discussed in the next chapter.

Retroperitoneal: referring to an area behind (posterior to) the peritoneum

Make it a point not to confuse perineum with peritoneum. Remember, the peri**t**oneum has a **"t"** in it because it is closer to the **t**horax.

20) **Groin:** the area at the junction of the thigh and abdomen

21) **Thigh:** upper leg (hip to knee)

22) **Popliteal:** referring to the area behind the knee

23) **Leg:** lower leg (knee to foot)

24) **Plantar:** directed toward or referring to the soles of the feet

Dorsal: directed toward or referring to the side of the foot opposite the sole. (i.e. dorsum of the foot)

The **plantar** surface of the foot is **planted** on the ground when walking.

FIGURE 2.9

ANTERIOR POSITION

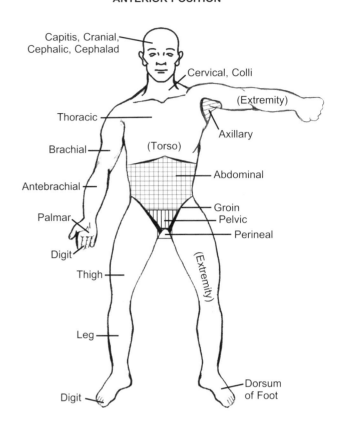

FIGURE 2.10

POSTERIOR POSITION

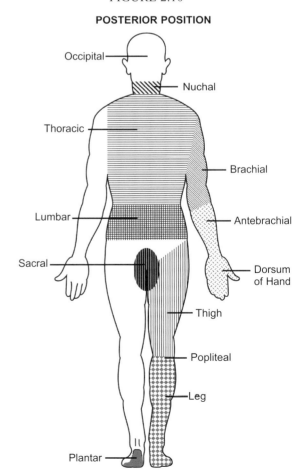

25) **Torso:**   the trunk of the body, excluding the head or extremities

> **T**runk = **T**orso
> No head or extremities

26) **Extremity:**   an arm or leg

27) **Digit:**   a finger or toe

In anatomy, the digits are assigned a number rather than a name (e.g. index finger). With the hand, the numbering starts with the thumb and proceeds to the little finger. Hence, the thumb is digit one (digit #1) and the little finger is digit five (digit #5). With the foot, the numbering begins with the great toe (digit #1) and ends with the little toe (digit #5).

> With the hands and feet, the numbering always starts with the "fat" digit. This includes the thumb of the hand and great toe of the foot.

FIGURE 2.11

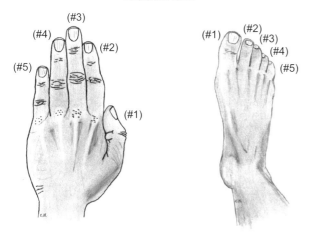

Thus far, two ways to organize and/or describe anatomic structures have been covered:

1) Directional anatomic descriptions, which are helpful in describing how one anatomic structure relates to another (e.g. anterior, posterior, medial, lateral, etc.)
2) Anatomic "areas" or body locations (e.g. cephalic, cervical, thoracic, etc.)

A third way to classify anatomic structures is by what the structure does with relation to a another structure. This is especially useful in the description of blood vessels and nerves.

Afferent: to carry an entity (e.g. blood, nerve transmission, etc.) toward another anatomic structure.

Efferent: to carry an entity (e.g. blood, nerve transmission, etc.) away from another anatomic structure.

As mentioned, the two descriptions are used to describe vessels and nerves. For example, consider the pancreas. The afferent blood vessels carry blood toward the pancreas. The efferent vessels carry blood away from the pancreas.

> The "A" in afferent comes before the "E" in efferent. Something must be carried to a structure before it can be carried away.
> OR
> "A" = arrive   And   "E" = exit

Finally, the fourth way to organize anatomic structures is by basic tissue function.

1) **Cutaneous:**   referring to or associated with the skin.
2) **Visceral:**   referring to or associated with a viscus.
   Viscus: an internal organ usually found in one of the body cavities (to be discussed later). Most commonly it refers to one of the hollow organs of the abdomen such as the stomach or gallbladder. The plural form of the word *viscus* is *viscera*.
3) **Somatic:**   referring to or associated with the body wall, as opposed to the viscera (internal organs).
   Soma: the body.

The skin is fairly self-explanatory. Although it is not considered a viscus, it is the largest organ of the body.

As mentioned above, the word root *soma* means body. The soma of a neuron is the cell body of that neuron. The word *somatic* refers to structures which make up the body wall. Primarily, the body wall is composed of bones and muscles. They are accompanied by tendons, ligaments, cartilage, fluid, fascia, etc. The body wall provides the structure of the body.

> **S**omatic provides **S**tructure.

The viscera represent a differentiation of tissue to provide a diverse number of highly specialized functions. Examples include gastric acid secretion, bile secretion, insulin release, maintenance of blood electrolytes, digestion, etc. For viscera to perform their respective functions, they require the ability to change shapes and sizes. Most viscera are therefore suspended in internal spaces of the body wall known formally as **body cavities**. Body cavities are formed by somatic structures and will be discussed in greater detail in the next chapter.

QUIZ 1
Descriptive Terms of Anatomy

Time for Quiz = 26 minutes.
For questions 1-16, choose the one best answer.

_____1) Which anatomic area includes the loin?
   a) the lumbar area
   b) the sacral area
   c) the thoracic area
   d) the abdominal area
   e) none of the above

_____2) On the hand, digit #2 is the
   a) thumb
   b) ring finger
   c) middle finger
   d) index finger
   e) none of the above

_____3) The plantar surface refers to
   a) the palms of the hands
   b) the surface of the back of the hand
   c) the soles of the feet
   d) the skin
   e) the surface of the head

_____4) With regard to the shaded area in the illustration,
   a) The left foot is ipsilateral to it.
   b) It is superior to the skull.
   c) The right foot is contralateral to it.
   d) It is proximal to the brachial area of the same extremity.
   e) None of the above

_____5) The cephalic area
   a) is medial to most structures
   b) is superior to most structures
   c) is rostral to most structures
   d) all of the above
   e) none of the above

_____6) With respect to a certain organ, an afferent blood vessel
   a) carries blood to the organ
   b) carries blood away from the organ
   c) both a and b
   d) travels in front of the organ
   e) none of the above

_____7) Which of the following is the Latin anatomic name for the head?
   a) the collum
   b) the cervix
   c) the nucha
   d) the loin
   e) none of the above

_____8) The rostrum is Latin for
   a) the head
   b) the back of the head
   c) the neck
   d) the back of the neck
   e) none of the above

_____9) On the foot, digit #1 is the
   a) little toe
   b) next to the little toe
   c) middle toe
   d) great toe
   e) none of the above

____10) Which of the following is the Latin anatomic name for the neck?
      a) the cervix
      b) the collum
      c) both a and b
      d) the rostrum
      e) none of the above

____11) Which of the following is the anatomic name for the back of the neck?
      a) the occiput
      b) the nucha
      c) the collum
      d) the rostrum
      e) none of the above

____12) Which structure forms the posterior border of the pelvis?
      a) the rostrum
      b) the caput
      c) the collum
      d) the nucha
      e) nonc of the above

____13) Which structure is formed by the fusion of five vertebrae?
      a) the occiput
      b) the nucha
      c) the sacrum
      d) the collum
      e) none of the above

____14) What is the anatomic name for the back of the head?
      a) the rostrum
      b) the caput
      c) the occiput
      d) the sacrum
      e) none of the abovc

____15) The loin coincides with which anatomic area?
      a) the somatic posterior area between the neck superiorly and the diaphragm inferiorly
      b) the visceral posterior area between the diaphragm superiorly and the pelvis inferiorly
      c) the somatic anterior area between the diaphragm superiorly and the pelvis inferiorly
      d) the visceral anterior area between the diaphragm superiorly and the pelvis inferiorly
      e) none of the above

____16) On the hand, digit #1 is the
      a) little finger
      b) index finger
      c) middle finger
      d) ring finger
      e) none of the above

For questions 17-26, use the following directions:
a.......1,2,3 are correct
b.......1,3 are correct
c.......2,4 are correct
d.......only 4 is correct
e.......all are correct

____17) The sacral region can be described as
      1. dorsal
      2. caudal
      3. posterior
      4. rostral

____18) The cephalic area
      1. is medial to most structures
      2. is superior to most structures
      3. is rostral to most structures
      4. is ventral to most structures

____19) As compared to structure B below, structure A is
      1. anterior
      2. superior
      3. cephalad
      4. medial

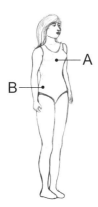

_____20) As compared to structure A in the Figure
    above, structure B is
        1. cephalic
        2. inferior
        3. posterior
        4. lateral

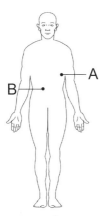

_____21) As compared to structure A in the Figure
    above, structure B is
        1. superior
        2. dorsal
        3. lateral
        4. caudal

_____22) Which statements concerning the peritoneum
    are true?
        1. It forms the floor of the pelvis.
        2. It is located between the thighs.
        3. It consists of tissue and structures
           located between the anus and
           genitalia.
        4. It is formed by a serous membrane.

_____23) Which of the following are mediastinal
    structures?
        1. esophagus
        2. thymus
        3. trachea
        4. great vessels

Use the following illustration for questions 24-26.

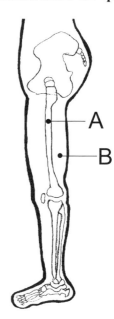

_____24) Structure A is within the substance of the
    femur bone. As compared to structure B,
    structure A is
        1. posterior
        2. proximal
        3. lateral
        4. deep

_____25) Structure A is within the substance of the
    femur bone. As compared to structure B,
    structure A is
        1. anterior
        2. superficial
        3. superior
        4. medial

_____26) Structure A is within the substance of the
    femur bone. As compared to structure B,
    structure A is
        1. deep
        2. medial
        3. superior
        4. distal

QUIZ 1: Descriptive Terms Answers and Explanations

1) a – The *loin* is the lumbar area. It is the somatic area of the posterior torso, which extends from the diaphragm superiorly to the pelvis inferiorly.

2) d – On the hand, the digits are numbered from the thumb (Digit #1) to the little finger (Digit #5).

3) c – People "plant" their feet on the ground. The palm of the hand is the palmar surface. The surface of the back of the hand is the dorsal surface. The word *cutaneous* refers to the skin. The surface of the head is known as the cranial or cephalic surface.

4) e – Remember, the subject's anatomic right-sided structures appear visually on the left. When you shake someone's hand, you reach to the left to shake the right hand because you are facing each other. In this case, the subject's right foot is ipsilateral to the shaded right hand because both are on the same side of the midline. The left foot is contralateral to the shaded right hand. In this position, the hand is inferior to the skull. The hand is distal to the arm (brachial area).

5) d – *Cephalic* describes the head or cranium. The cephalic direction is toward the head. Since the head is midline in the anatomic position, it is medial to most structures. It is also superior (above) and rostral (toward the cerebrum of the brain) to most structures.

6) a – With respect to a certain organ, an afferent blood vessel carries blood to the organ. An efferent vessel carries blood away from the organ. An *anterior* vessel would travel in front of the organ.

7) e – The *caput* is the Latin anatomic name for the head. *Capitis* is the descriptive form of the word. Both the *collum* and the *cervix* are Latin for the neck. *Nucha* is the specific name for the back of the neck. The *loin* is known as the lumbar area. It is the posterior aspect of the torso extending from the diaphragm superiorly to the pelvis inferiorly.

8) e – The word *rostrum* is Latin for beak. The rostral direction is toward the cerebrum of the brain. The head is the *caput*. The back of the head is the *occiput*. The neck has two names: the *cervix* and *collum*. The back of the neck is the *nucha*.

9) d – On the foot, the digits are numbered from the great toe (Digit #1) to the little toe (Digit #5).

10) c – Both the *cervix* and the *collum* are Latin names for the neck. The descriptive terms are *cervical* and *colli*, respectively. The word *rostrum* is Latin for beak. The rostral direction is toward the cerebrum of the brain.

11) b – The *occiput* is the back of the head. *Occipital* is the descriptive term. The *collum*, along with the *cervix*, is the Latin anatomic name for the neck. The descriptive terms are *colli* and *cervical*, respectively. The word *rostrum* is Latin for beak. The rostral direction is toward the cerebrum of the brain.

12) e – The posterior border of the pelvis is formed by the sacrum bone. The sacrum is made of 5 fused vertebrae and is part of the inferior portion of the vertebral column. The word *rostrum* is Latin for beak. The rostral direction is toward the cerebrum of the brain. The *caput* is the Latin anatomic name for the head. *Capitis* is the descriptive form of the word. The *collum*, along with the *cervix*, is the Latin anatomic name for the neck. The descriptive terms are *colli* and *cervical*, respectively. The *nucha* is the specific name for the back of the neck. *Nuchal* is the descriptive term.

13) c – The *sacrum* is at the inferior aspect of the vertebral column and forms the posterior border of the pelvis. The *occiput* is the back of the head. *Occipital* is the descriptive term. The *nucha* is the specific name for the back of the neck. *Nuchal* is the descriptive term. The *collum*, along with the *cervix*, is the Latin anatomic name for the neck. The descriptive terms are *colli* and *cervical,* respectively.

14) c – The *occiput* is the back of the head. *Occipital*

is the descriptive term. The word *rostrum* is Latin for beak. The rostral direction is toward the cerebrum of the brain. The *caput* is the Latin anatomic name for the head. *Capitis* is the descriptive form of the word. The *sacrum* is the bone formed by the fusion of five vertebrae and is located at the inferior aspect of the vertebral column. It forms the posterior border of the pelvis. *Sacral* is the descriptive term.

15) e – See #1 answer explanation.

16) e – Digit #1 is the thumb.

17) a – The *sacral area* is the area overlying the posterior aspect of the sacrum. The *sacrum* is a bone formed by the fusion of 5 sacral vertebrae at the distal end of the vertebral column. It is part of the vertebral column, so it is posterior or dorsal to many structures. It is near the distal end of the vertebral column, so it is caudal (toward the tail.) This is opposed to *rostral,* which is toward the top of the brain.

18) a – *Cephalic* means *toward the head* or *cranial.* Since the head is midline in the anatomic position, it is medial to most structures. It is also superior (above) and rostral (toward the top of the brain) to most structures. *Ventral* describes a direction toward the abdomen. The head is not near the abdomen. Humans, as compared to other animals, are two-legged. In humans, therefore, the ventral surface is also the anterior surface.

19) a – Structure A is toward the front or anterior of structure B. It is also above or superior to structure B. It is closer to the head or cranium, so it is also cephalad to structure B. Because this is a view of the side of the body (as opposed to the anatomic position), there is no way to tell where the midline is. Without knowing the midline, it is impossible to tell if one structure is medial (closer to the midline) or lateral (farther removed from the midline) as compared to another structure.

20) c – Because the subject shown here is facing somewhat toward the observer, the midline can be estimated. Structure A is closer to the midline or more medial than structure B. Hence, structure B is more lateral. There is no way to determine if one structure is anterior (ventral, front) or posterior (dorsal, back) because the subject is facing toward the observer. Structure A is closer to the head than structure B, so it is more cephalic (cranial, rostral, superior) than B (not vice versa, as implied in answer #1). Structure B is inferior (below, farther removed from the head) to structure A.

21) d – Structure B is inferior (below) structure A, not superior (above) to it. The subject is facing the observer, so it is impossible to tell if one structure is dorsal (posterior, in back of) or ventral (toward the abdomen, anterior, in front of) as compared to another structure. Structure B is closer to the midline, so it is more medial than structure A, not more lateral. Structure B is more caudal than structure A because it is closer to the coccyx, the bone at the lowest tip of the vertebral column.

22) d – The *peritoneum* is the serous membrane which surrounds the abdominal and pelvic cavities. These cavities contain internal organs. Do not confuse peritoneum with perineum. The perineum is the body area located between the thighs and extends from the anus to the genitalia. It forms the floor of the pelvis.

23) e – The *mediastinum* is a group of midline structures including the heart, great vessels, thymus, esophagus, trachea, and supporting structures. The mediastinum divides the thoracic cavity into right and left cavities, one for each lung.

24) c – Structure A is closer to the point of origin of the thigh from the torso, so it is more proximal than structure B. Since structure A is known to be within the substance of the femur, and structure B appears to be just under the posterior surface of the thigh, structure A is deep to structure B (structure B is superficial to structure A). Structure A is also anterior to structure B. The subject is not facing the observer, so there is no way to tell which structure is more medial or lateral.

25) b – Structure A is closer to the front of the thigh, so it is more anterior than structure B. It is also closer to the head, so it is more superior than structure B. The subject is not facing the observer, so there is no way to determine which structure is medial or lateral.

26) b – Since structure A is known to be within the substance of the femur and structure B appears just under the posterior surface of the thigh, structure A is deep to structure B (structure B is superficial to structure A). Structure A is above or closer to the head than structure B. Structure A is therefore superior to structure B (structure B is inferior to structure A). The subject is not facing the observer, so there is no way to determine which structure is medial or lateral. Structure A is closer to the point of origin of the leg from the torso, so it is more proximal than structure B (structure B is more distal than structure A).

ANATOMIC PLANES

An anatomic plane is a visual cut through a body or structure. It allows the observer to visualize a three-dimensional structure in two dimensions. Images of anatomic planes are commonly used in anatomic texts and presentations. Additionally, they are the images formed by radiologic studies such as magnetic resonance imaging (MRI) and computerized tomography (CT) scans.

The **frontal plane**, also known as the **coronal plane**, is a longitudinal plane running parallel to the long axis of the body. The longitudinal axis of the body is simply the long part of the body. It runs from head to foot. The frontal (coronal) plane separates the body or structure into anterior and posterior sections.

> The anatomic position has the subject with the front facing toward the observer. Imagine viewing the **frontal** plane as if you were viewing the anatomic position.

FIGURE 2.12 (Frontal or Coronal plane)

 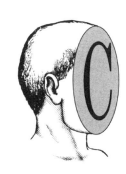

The **C**ap represents **C**oronal. The "**F**" on the cap represents **F**rontal.

The **C**oronal plane faces the front (frontal plane).

> The **frontal** plane divides the **"front"** or anterior portion from the "back" or posterior portion. It is also known as the coronal plane.

The **transverse plane** is a cross section, perpendicular to the longitudinal axis (long axis) of the body. It separates the body or structure into superior (upper) and inferior (lower) sections.

FIGURE 2.13 (Transverse plane)

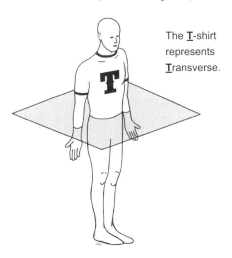

The **T**-shirt represents **T**ransverse.

> The prefix *trans* means "to go across." A transatlantic flight is a flight that goes across the Atlantic ocean. In the same fashion that a *trans*atlantic *plane* crosses the Atlantic, a *trans*verse *plane* crosses the long axis. The transverse plane is the only plane that "goes across" the long axis of the body. It is perpendicular to the long axis of the body. All the other planes discussed here are parallel to the long axis of the body. The transverse plane is therefore perpendicular to each of the other planes as well.

The **sagittal plane** is a longitudinal plane that runs from front (anterior) to back (posterior) and separates the body or structure into right and left sections. The **median plane** is a sagittal plane that occurs at the midline. It divides the exterior body or body wall into equal right and left halves. The median plane is often referred to as the **middle sagittal plane** and is useful for the radiologic evaluation of the spinal cord and vertebral column, among other things.

FIGURE 2.14 (Sagittal plane)

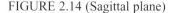
The **S**uit represents **S**agittal.

ANATOMIC POSITIONS AND MOVEMENTS

Certain body position and movement names are commonly used in basic medical language. Upright, standing, sitting, and lying are examples used by the general population. Other positions and movements are described below. The anatomic positions and movements will be paired with their opposites, where applicable.

1. (a) **Supine position:** the subject is lying flat on the back
   (b) **Prone position:** the subject is lying flat on the abdomen and anterior chest

> The word *supine* means face up.
> The word *prone* means face down.

2. (a) **Right lateral decubitus position:** the subject is lying on the side with the right side down
   (b) **Left lateral decubitus position:** the subject is lying on the side with the left side down

The word *decubitus* means lying down. An individual in the right lateral decubitus position has the right side lying down. A person in the left lateral decubitus position has the left side lying down. Debilitated patients, if left in the supine position, can develop pressure ulcers of the heels of the feet, sacral area, and back. These areas support the body weight. The skin over pressure points may necrose if no relief from the constant pressure is provided. Healthy individuals unconsciously turn in their sleep to prevent this from happening. These pressure ulcers of the skin and underlying tissue are known as **decubitus ulcers** because they occur on areas of the body on which the patient is "lying."

3. (a) **Adduction:** movement of the extremity toward the midline
   (b) **Abduction:** a movement of the extremity away from the midline or away from the rest of the body

In **add**uction, you **"add"** to the midline, or **"add"** to the rest of the body.

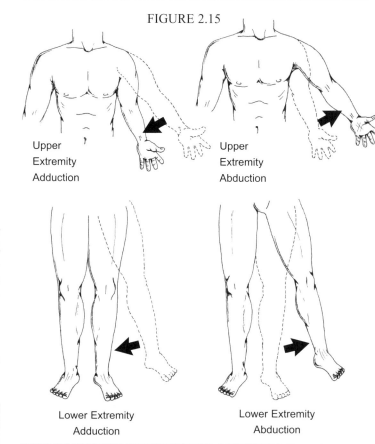

FIGURE 2.15

Upper Extremity Adduction

Upper Extremity Abduction

Lower Extremity Adduction

Lower Extremity Abduction

In **abduction,** movement is *away* from the mildine. An **abducted** person is taken *away.*

In addition to the extremities themselves, the digits of an extremity may be adducted and abducted. In this case, the midline of the extremity is used as "the midline." Adduction would move the fingers or toes toward the midline of the extremity. Again, with adduction one "adds" to the midline. Adduction of the fingers or toes brings the digits together. Abduction spreads the fingers or toes.

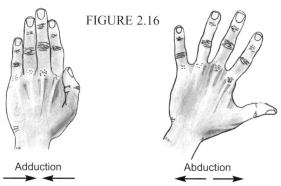

FIGURE 2.16

Adduction

Abduction

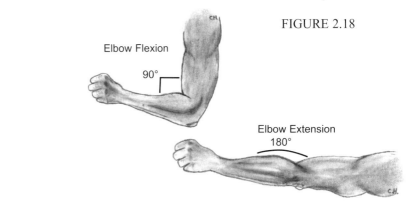

FIGURE 2.18

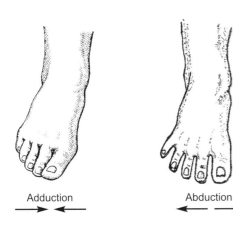

Adduction   Abduction

4. (a) **Ulnar deviation:** by way of the wrist joint, the hand deviates toward the same side as the ulna bone of the forearm (toward the little finger).

   (b) **Radial deviation:** by way of the wrist joint, the hand deviates toward the same side as the radius bone of the forearm (toward the thumb).

FIGURE 2.17

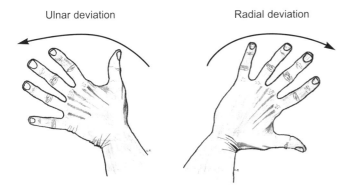

Ulnar deviation   Radial deviation

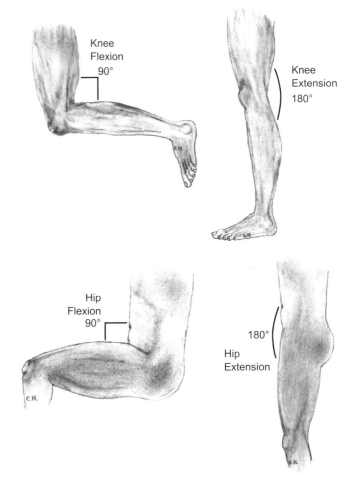

5. (b) **Flexion:** the joint is bent. The angle of the joint is decreased

   (a) **Extension:** the joint is straightened. The angle of the joint is increased

Flashback to geometry (See Figure 2.18). Recall that a right angle is 90° and a straight line is 180°. As a joint is bent, the angle of the joint becomes less, even though the amount of the bend in the joint becomes more acute. In other words, as a joint is straightened, the angle of the joint is increased. This is a cause of confusion for many.

6. (a) **Palmar flexion:** flexion of the wrist so the hand moves in the direction of the palm

   (b) **Dorsiflexion of hand:** *(Dorsal flexion of hand)* flexion of the wrist so the hand moves in the direction opposite of the palm, toward the dorsum of the hand

7. (a) **Plantar flexion:** flexion of the ankle so the foot moves in the direction of the sole. This is the same movement as pressing on a gas pedal in an automobile

   (b) **Dorsiflexion of foot:** *(Dorsal flexion of foot)* flexion of the ankle so the foot moves in the direction opposite the sole, toward the dorsum of the foot

FIGURE 2.19

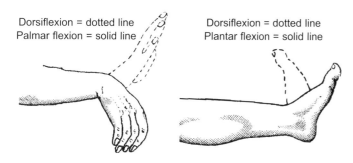

Dorsiflexion = dotted line
Palmar flexion = solid line

Dorsiflexion = dotted line
Plantar flexion = solid line

8. (a) **Inner rotation:**   also called **medial rotation**. This occurs at the shoulders or hips. The extremity is rotated inward, toward the midline

    (b) **Outer rotation:**   also called **lateral rotation**. The extremity is rotated outward or laterally

FIGURE 2.20

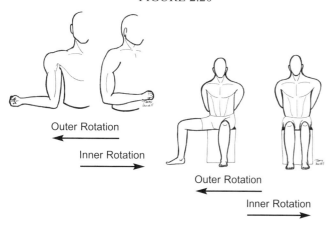

Outer Rotation

Inner Rotation

Outer Rotation

Inner Rotation

9. (a) **Inversion:**   the ankle is turned inward, as if attempting to stand on the outer side (little toe side) of the foot

    (b) **Eversion:**   the ankle is turned outward, as if attempting to stand on the inner side (great toe side) of the foot

FIGURE 2.21

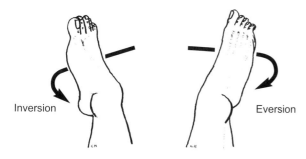

Inversion

Eversion

10. (a) **Supination:**   the forearm is rotated laterally, turning the hand so the palm of the hand is facing forward or up. The thumb is rotated laterally and becomes farther removed from the midline or trunk.

(b) **Pronation:**   the forearm is rotated medially, turning the hand so the dorsum of the hand is facing forward. The palm is facing backward or down. The thumb rotates medially to become closer to the midline of the trunk.

FIGURE 2.22

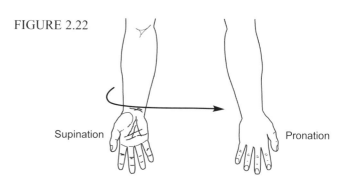

Supination

Pronation

The words *supinate* and *pronate* are derived from the word roots *supine* and *prone,* respectively. *Supine* means face up. *Prone* means face down. Each movement is made with reference to the palm of the hand. In *supination,* the palm faces up. In *pronation,* the palm faces down.

Supination is **super** because it is the position of the "anatomic position." Palms are facing forward. The thumbs are lateral (away from the body).

A person carrying **soup** has the hands in a **sup**inated position.

By contrast, a **pro** basketball player has the hand in a **pro**nated position as the ball is dribbled down the court.

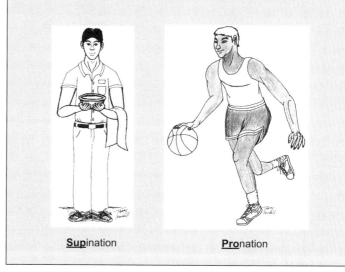

Supination

Pronation

Again, the terms covered in this chapter are used extensively, not only in the study of anatomy, but in the practice of medicine. For instance, if a student knew that *posterior* is a direction toward the back, *brachial* describes the upper arm, and *cutaneous* indicates skin, it would be easy to remember the innervation of the posterior brachial cutaneous nerve. It supplies skin on the back of the upper arm.

QUIZ 2
Anatomic Positions and Movements

Time for Quiz = 20 minutes.
For questions 1-17, choose the one best answer.

_____1) The hand is rotated so the palm of the hand is facing forward and the thumb is lateral. This is most consistent with
    a) inner rotation
    b) inversion
    c) supination
    d) pronation
    e) none of the above

_____2) With the heel touching the ground and foot in the air, the foot is pressed toward the ground, as if pressing down on a gas pedal. This movement is
    a) abduction
    b) pronation
    c) inversion
    d) palmar flexion
    e) none of the above

_____3) What is the body position of a patient lying flat on the back?
    a) decubitus
    b) prone
    c) supine
    d) lateral decubitus
    e) none of the above

_____4) Which movements are consistent with adduction?
    a) bringing the arm down to the side of the torso
    b) spreading the fingers
    c) lifting the leg out laterally
    d) all of the above
    e) none of the above

_____5) What is the body position of a patient lying on his/her right side?
    a) prone
    b) supine
    c) left lateral prone
    d) left lateral decubitus
    e) none of the above

_____6) Which movements are consistent with flexion?
    a) straightening the joint
    b) decreasing the angle of the joint
    c) both a and b
    d) increasing the angle of the joint
    e) none of the above

_____7) The arm is moved inward or medially by way of the shoulder joint. This movement is best described as
    a) pronation
    b) supination
    c) inner rotation
    d) abduction
    e) none of the above

_____8) What is the body position of a patient lying on his/her left side?
    a) prone
    b) supine
    c) left lateral supine
    d) right lateral decubitus
    e) none of the above

_____9) The arm is moved outward or laterally by way of the shoulder joint. This movement is best described as
    a) adduction
    b) inner rotation
    c) lateral rotation
    d) pronation
    e) none of the above

_____10) The leg is moved outward or laterally by way of the hip joint. This movement is consistent with
    a) inner rotation
    b) medial rotation
    c) both a and b
    d) adduction
    e) none of the above

_____11) Which movements are consistent with extension?
        a) straightening of a joint
        b) decreasing the angle of the joint
        c) both a and b
        d) bending the joint
        e) none of the above

_____12) Which movements are consistent with abduction?
        a) bringing the legs inward to touch at the knee
        b) sticking the thumb out, as if "hitch-hiking"
        c) bringing the arm down to the side of the torso
        d) all of the above
        e) none of the above

_____13) The hand is rotated so that the dorsum of the hand is facing forward and the thumb is the closest digit to the trunk. This is most consistent with
        a) inner rotation
        b) medial rotation
        c) pronation
        d) supination
        e) none of the above

_____14) What is the name of the body position in which the subject is lying flat on the abdomen and anterior chest?
        a) right lateral decubitus
        b) left lateral decubitus
        c) supine
        d) prone
        e) none of the above

_____15) The median plane
        a) is found in the transverse plane
        b) is found in the sagittal plane
        c) is found in the coronal plane
        d) is found in the frontal plane
        e) none of the above

_____16) The sagittal plane
        a) separates the body into right and left sections
        b) separates the body into anterior and posterior sections
        c) separates the body into superior and inferior sections
        d) is perpendicular to the long axis
        e) none of the above

_____17) The subject is facing the observer as in the anatomic position. The surface of the subject is removed so that the right lung is seen on the left and the left lung is on the right. Each is the same distance from the midline. Which of the following are true?
        a) This represents a coronal view.
        b) This represents a frontal view.
        c) This is perpendicular to a transverse view.
        d) All are correct
        e) None are correct

For questions 18-20, use the following directions:
a.......1,2,3 are correct   **d.......only 4 is correct**
b.......1,3 are correct   **e.......all are correct**
c.......2,4 are correct

_____18) Pronation
        1. involves the hip
        2. involves the shoulder
        3. is movement toward the body
        4. is a medial rotation

_____19) True statements concerning the coronal plane include which of the following?
        1. It is also known as the frontal plane.
        2. It separates the body into anterior and inferior sections.
        3. It is parallel to the long axis of the body.
        4. It divides the body into right and left sections.

_____20) The median plane
        1. occurs at midline
        2. is also known as the middle sagittal planc
        3. separates the body into right and left segments
        4. is perpendicular to the long axis of the body

QUIZ 2: Anatomic Positions and Movements Answers and Explanations

1) c – *Supination* is rotating the forearm laterally so the palm of the hand faces up or forward and the thumb is turned laterally, away from the midline. *Pronation* is rotation of the forearm in the opposite direction so the thumb is turned medially, toward the midline. The palm faces down or backward, depending on the orientation of the extremity. *Inner rotation* is also called *medial rotation*. This usually involves the shoulder or hip joint. The extremity is rotated inward, toward the midline. *Inversion* is turning the ankle inward, as if attempting to stand on the outer (lateral) side of the foot.

2) e – The movement described is *plantar flexion.* *Abduction* is movement of an extremity laterally, away from midline of the body. *Pronation* is movement of the wrist so the thumb is turned medially, toward the body. The dorsal aspect of the hand is facing forward. *Inversion* is turning the ankle inward, as if attempting to stand on the outer (lateral) side of the foot. *Palmar flexion* is flexion of the wrist to move the hand in the direction of the palm.

3) c – The word *supine* means face up. In the prone position, the person is lying flat on the abdomen and anterior chest. The right lateral decubitus position has the person lying on the right side. The right side is down. The left lateral decubitus position has the person lying on the left side. The left side is down.

4) a – *Adduction* is movement toward the midline. One "adds" to the midline. This is movement of the extremities medially, toward the midline of the body. With the digits (fingers and toes), it is movement toward the midline of the extremity. This brings the digits together. *Abduction* is movement away from the midline.

5) e – The right lateral decubitus position has the person lying on the right side. The right side is down. The left lateral decubitus position has the person lying on the left side. The left side is down. The prone position has the person lying flat on the abdomen and anterior chest. The supine position has the person lying flat on the back.

6) b – *Flexion* is bending of a joint. The angle of the joint is decreased. *Extension* is straightening of a joint. The angle of the joint is increased.

7) c – *Inner rotation* is also called *medial rotation.* This usually involves the shoulder or hip joint. The extremity is rotated inward, toward the midline. *Pronation* is rotation of the hand so the palms face down or backward. *Supination* is rotation of the hand so the palms face up or forward. *Abduction* is movement away from the midline.

8) e – See #5 answer explanation.

9) c – *Outer rotation* is also called *lateral rotation.* This usually involves the shoulder or hip joint. The extremity is rotated outward, or laterally, away from the midline. Inner rotation (medial rotation) involves rotation of the extremity inward, toward the midline. *Adduction* is movement toward the midline. One "adds" to the midline. *Pronation* is rotation of the hand so the thumb is turned medially and the palm faces down or back.

10) e – See #9 answer explanation.

11) a – See #6 answer explanation.

12) b – *Abduction* is movement away from the midline. This involves movement of an extremity out laterally, away from the midline of the body. With the digits (fingers and toes), it involves spreading them apart, or moving them outward, away from the midline of the extremity. *Adduction* is movement toward the midline. One "adds" to the midline.

13) c – See #1 answer explanation.

14) d – See #3 answer explanation. The word *prone* means face down. The word *supine* means face up. The supine position has the person lying flat on the back.

15) b – The median plane is a sagittal plane which occurs at the midline. It is also known as the middle sagittal plane. It divides the exterior body

into equal right and left halves. It runs parallel to the long axis of the body. The transverse plane separates the body into superior and inferior sections. The frontal (coronal) plane separates the body into anterior and posterior sections.

16) a – The frontal or coronal plane separates the body into anterior and posterior sections. The transverse plane separates the body into superior and inferior sections. The sagittal plane is parallel to the long axis of the body.

17) d – The frontal plane is also called the coronal plane. It separates the body into anterior and posterior sections. It is parallel to the long axis of the body

(head to foot). Because the transverse plane is perpendicular to the long axis of the body, the transverse plane is also perpendicular to the frontal (coronal) plane. The transverse plane separates the body into superior and inferior sections.

18) d – See #1 answer explanation.

19) b – The coronal plane separates the body into anterior and posterior sections (not anterior and inferior). The sagittal plane separates the body into right and left sections.

20) a – See #15 answer explanation.

"Winston, if I were your wife, I'd put poison in your coffee." – **Lady Nancy Astor**
"Nancy, if I were your husband, I'd drink it." – **Sir Winston Churchill**

CLINICAL CORRELATION

Figure 2.23 is an image obtained from the median plane of the head, neck, and upper torso. As discussed earlier, the median plane is also known as the middle sagittal plane and represents a cut through the midline of the body in the sagittal plane. It divides the body into equal right and left halves. This type of illustration may be used for teaching purposes in anatomic texts and slides. It is also the type of image obtained from diagnostic radiologic tests such as computer tomography (CT) and magnetic resonance imaging (MRI) scans.

There are a couple of clues that this indeed is a view of the middle sagittal plane, or at least very near to it. First, there is a good view of the spine on the left side of the image. The spine is a midline structure. The spinal cord (*u*) can be seen originating from the brain and traveling inferiorly or caudally. The bodies of the vertebrae are located anterior to the spinal cord and the spinous processes of the vertebrae are posterior to the cord. Secondly, there is a good view of the nasal cavity, yet neither eyeball is present. The cut is directly midline, between the two eyes.

The middle sagittal view is often used in radiologic studies evaluating various disease processes of the spine. These processes may involve traumatic injuries, osteoporosis, abscesses, or tumors. More commonly, the problem is related to compression of nerve tissue by other spinal structures. The radiologic study is usually performed to evaluate a new pain or neurological change, such as weakness or numbness. The cause is often found to be compression of nerve tissue by vertebral osteophytes and/or herniated ("slipped") intervertebral discs. An osteophyte is commonly known as a bone spur.

Like all bones which participate in movable joints, the bones of the vertebral column can develop arthritic changes or deformities secondary to injury. Bony outgrowths or osteophytes can enlarge and compress nerve tissue. This compression may be localized and involve only one small area of bone encroachment. Alternatively, multiple spinal levels can be affected. In fact, the process can become so severe that the overall diameter of the spinal canal becomes reduced, a condition known as spinal stenosis. The reduction of canal space compresses the spinal cord from essentially all sides. Depending on the progression of disease, the patient may experience severe pain, numbness, weakness, and even paralysis.

Nerve injury may also result from disc disease. An intervertebral disc is composed of thick connective tissue. It separates two successive vertebrae and acts as a shock absorber which prevents the bone of the vertebrae from grinding against one another. Because of injury or the aging process, one or more vertebral discs may herniate or "slide out" from between the two vertebrae. Disc material may then press on the spinal cord and/or spinal nerve root. This can cause muscular weakness, numbness, and pain which radiates to the area of the body supplied by the affected nerve structures.

Treatment depends on the severity of disease, symptoms, and coexisting diseases of the patient. Therapy may only consist of oral anti-inflammatory and pain medication if the nerve compression is mild and symptoms are tolerable. Even with severe spinal disease, the patient's poor health may eliminate surgery as a viable option. Some moderately-diseased patients respond well to epidural steroid injections and are thus able to avoid surgery. Steroids are strong anti-inflammatory medicines that, in certain circumstances, decrease the swelling and encroachment on nerve structures by inflamed tissues. The epidural space surrounds the spinal cord, so the medication is delivered specifically where needed. Many patients require surgery to physically remove the cause of compression. Laminectomy and discectomy serve as examples of such surgeries. During a laminectomy, the posterior arch of a vertebra is removed to create more space within the spinal canal. With a discectomy, only the offending disc is removed.

The middle sagittal view is useful in evaluation of spinal disease because it displays the bone of the vertebrae, the intervertebral discs, and the nerve tissue of the spinal cord. For example, Figure 2.23 displays an intervertebral disk (labeled IX), which lies between the seventh cervical vertebra (labeled III) and first thoracic vertebra (labeled IV). Should this disc herniate posteriorly and compress the spinal cord (labeled *u*), it would be evident on this view.

The sagittal plane is particularly useful in evaluating anterior-posterior and superior-inferior anatomic relationships. Other radiologic planes may also be utilized to finely pinpoint the specific structure or location in question. By obtaining a combination of views from different planes, the exact location of the diseased tissue can often be determined. Both the frontal (coronal) and transverse planes provide additional information on medial-lateral anatomic relationships. The frontal (coronal) plane is useful in determining superior-inferior and medial-lateral relationships. The transverse plane displays anterior-posterior and medial-lateral relationships. During the radiologic evaluation of spinal disease, images from the transverse plane are often used concurrently with those of the sagittal plane to pinpoint the location of the pathology.

FIGURE 2.23

This illustration depicts a large number of three dimensional structures in two dimensions. After a visual review of these structures, some appreciation of the interactive complexity of anatomy may be gained.

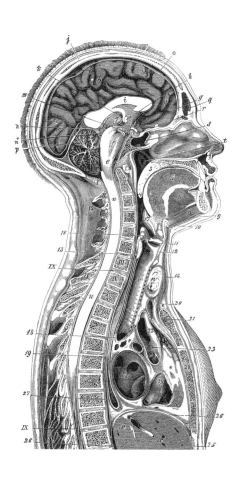

1. incisive fossa
2. hard palate
3. soft palate
4. uvula
5. tongue
6. genioglossus muscle
7. mandible
8. geniohyoid muscle
9. mylohyoid muscle
10. hyoid bone
11. vocal fold
12. thyroid cartilage
13. cricoid cartilage
14. sternohyoid muscle
15. ligamentum nuchae
16. arytenoid cartilage
17. epiglottis
18. hilum of trachea
19. esophagus
20. sternothyroid muscle
21. manubrium of sternum bone
22. ascending aorta artery
23. right pulmonary artery
24. body of sternum bone
25. xiphoid process of sternum bone
26. diaphragm muscle
27. pleural membrane
28. right atrium of heart
29. right ventricle of heart

I. Atlas bone (C1 vertebra)
II. Axis bone (C2 vertebra)
III. C7 vertebra
IV. T1 vertebra
IX. intervertebral disc

a. frontal lobe of brain
b. parietal lobe of brain
c. occipital lobe of brain
d. cerebellum
e. medulla oblongata
f. pons
g. optic chiasm
h. fornix
i. corpus callosum
j. skull bone
k. choroid plexus of 3rd ventricle
l. 3rd ventricle
m. mamillary body
n. quadrigeminal lamina
o. dura mater
p. straight sinus
q. frontal sinus
r. sella turcica
s. sphenoid sinus
t. pharyngeal orifice of auditory tube
u. spinal cord
v. trachea
w. thyroid gland
x. liver

SUMMARY OF CHAPTER BOXES

1) ***Dorsal* fin** of shark is on shark's back (***posterior)***. Ventral or anterior side is opposite to this and is directed toward the underside or abdomen.

2) Ip<u>si</u> is on <u>s</u>ame <u>si</u>de of midline...ipsilateral vs. contralateral

3) Two terms for the neck are **collum (colli)** and **cervix (cervical)**. Additionally, the **nucha** is the back of the neck **(nuchal)**.

4) Do not confuse peritoneum with perineum. The peri<u>t</u>oneum contains a **"t"** because it is closer to the <u>t</u>horax.

5) Palms are facing the observer in the anatomic position. The **back of the hands** are therefore **dorsal**.

6) **Plantar surface** is "planted" on the ground

7) **Trunk = Torso**...no head or extremities

8) **Numbering of digits** starts with the **"fat" digit** (thumb = digit #1, great toe = digit #1)

9) "A" = <u>a</u>rrive, "E" = <u>e</u>xit...The "A" in afferent comes before the "E" of efferent (something must be carried to a structure before it can be carried away). Afferent structures carry an entity toward a structure. Efferent structures carry an entity away.

10) <u>S</u>omatic provides <u>S</u>tructure

11) Anatomic position has **front** facing observer...this is the **frontal plane**. The frontal plane divides the front (anterior portion) from the back (posterior portion). It is also known as the **coronal plane**.

12) ***trans-* = "to go across."** A *trans*atlantic plane crosses the Atlantic Ocean. A ***transverse* plane crosses the long axis of the body**. This is the only plane discussed in this chapter which "crosses" the long axis. It is therefore perpendicular to the long axis. Because the other planes are all parallel to the long axis, the transverse plane is also perpendicular to the other planes.

13) Supine – to face up   Prone – to face down

14) **Decubitus – lying down. Right lateral *decubitus*** position has the right side lying down. **Left lateral *decubitus*** position has the left side lying down. Debilitated patients can develop ***decubitus*** ulcers over pressure points.

15) ***Adduction* "adds" to the midline** of the body or extremity.

16) **Abduction** is movement *away* from the midline. An **abducted** person is taken *away.*

17) Right angle = 90.° straight line = 180.° **As a joint is bent, the angle of the joint becomes less**, even though the amount of bend in the joint becomes more acute. **As a joint is straightened, the angle of the joint is increased**, even though the amount of bend is less.

18) <u>Sup</u>ination is <u>**super**</u> because it is the position of the hands in the anatomic position. A person carrying *soup* has the hands in a *supinated* position (supine = face up). A *pro* basketball player has the hands in a *pronated* position when dribbling the ball (prone = face down).

END OF CHAPTER TEST

Time for Exam = 50 minutes.
For questions 1-42, choose the one best answer.

_____1)   Where is the greater occipital nerve located?
    a) the front of the head
    b) the armpit
    c) the back of the head
    d) behind the knee
    e) none of the above

_____2)   Which movements are consistent with flexion?
    a) bending the joint
    b) decreasing the angle of the joint
    c) both a and b
    d) increasing the angle of the joint
    e) none of the above

_____3)   The hand is rotated so that the dorsum of the hand is facing forward and the thumb is closest to the trunk. This is most consistent with
    a) pronation
    b) inner rotation
    c) both a and b
    d) supination
    e) none of the above

_____4)   The rostrum is Latin for
    a) the head
    b) the back of the head
    c) the beak
    d) the back of the neck
    e) none of the above

_____5)   Where is the transversus colli nerve located?
    a) the arm
    b) the axilla
    c) the neck
    d) the thorax
    e) none of the above

_____6)   Correct statements include
    a) The wrist is distal to the fingers.
    b) Anatomically, the leg extends from the hip to the foot.
    c) Anatomically, the antebrachial region extends from the shoulder to the elbow.
    d) The mouth is rostral to the stomach.
    e) All of the above

_____7)   The loin coincides with which anatomic area?
    a) the sacral area
    b) the lumbar area
    c) the neck
    d) the thoracic area
    e) none of the above

_____8)   On the hand, digit #3 is the
    a) little finger
    b) index finger
    c) middle finger
    d) ring finger
    e) none of the above

_____9)   After a motor vehicle accident, a patient presents to the emergency room with nuchal rigidity. What is the most likely location of the injury?
    a) the neck
    b) the armpit
    c) the thorax
    d) the lower back
    e) none of the above

_____10) Where is the cervical plexus located?
    a) neck
    b) armpit
    c) arm
    d) groin
    e) none of the above

_____11) With respect to the brain, an efferent nerve may
    a) carry signals of sound perception
    b) transmit signals of pain from a hand laceration
    c) both a and b
    d) stimulate a muscle to contract
    e) none of the above

_____12) Which structure is formed by the fusion of five vertebrae?
    a) the cervix
    b) the occiput
    c) the sacrum
    d) the rostrum
    e) none of the above

____13) A person lying on his/her side, with the left side down is in which body position?
    a) supine
    b) prone
    c) left lateral decubitus
    d) right lateral decubitus
    e) none of the above

____14) A patient has an axillary abscess. Where is the abscess located?
    a) the neck
    b) the armpit
    c) the sole of the foot
    d) the back of the knee
    e) none of the above

____15) The coronal plane
    a) separates the body into superior and inferior sections
    b) separates the body into anterior and ventral sections
    c) separates the body into anterior and posterior sections
    d) separates the body into right and left sections
    e) is also known as the sagittal plane

____16) With the heel touching the ground and foot in the air, a person flexes his foot forward toward the ground, as if pressing down on a gas pedal. This movement is
    a) dorsiflexion
    b) palmar flexion
    c) plantar flexion
    d) inversion
    e) none of the above

____17) The frontal plane
    a) separates the body into right and left sections
    b) separates the body into anterior and inferior sections
    c) separates the body into superior and posterior sections
    d) is perpendicular to the long axis
    e) none of the above

____18) Where would a popliteal skin infection be found?
    a) the forearm
    b) the head
    c) behind the knee
    d) the armpit
    e) none of the above

____19) Which movements are consistent with adduction?
    a) lifting the leg out laterally
    b) lifting the arm out laterally
    c) bringing the toes together
    d) all of the above
    e) none of the above

____20) Which of the following is the Latin anatomic name for the head?
    a) the occiput
    b) the rostrum
    c) the collum
    d) the caput
    e) none of the above

____21) The leg is moved outward or laterally by way of the hip joint. This movement is consistent with
    a) outer rotation
    b) medial rotation
    c) both a and b
    d) adduction
    e) none of the above

____22) Where would a plantar wart be found?
    a) behind the knee
    b) the lower back
    c) the dorsum of the hand
    d) the sole of the foot
    e) none of the above

____23) Which of the following is the Latin anatomic name for the neck?
    a) the nucha
    b) the cervix
    c) the caput
    d) the occiput
    e) none of the above

_____24) Which movements are consistent with abduction?
     a) decreasing the angle of the joint
     b) moving the hip inward or medially
     c) rotating the hand counterclockwise
     d) bringing the fingers together
     e) none of the above

_____25) What structure do nerves of the brachial plexus supply?
     a) the head
     b) the abdomen
     c) the upper extremity
     d) the lower extremity
     e) none of the above

_____26) The arm is moved inward or medially by way of the shoulder joint. This movement is best described as
     a) pronation
     b) supination
     c) medial rotation
     d) abduction
     e) none of the above

_____27) Where is the lateral antebrachial cutaneous nerve located?
     a) the forearm
     b) the arm
     c) the thigh
     d) the lower leg
     e) none of the above

_____28) Which of the following is the anatomic name for the back of the neck?
     a) the cervix
     b) the collum
     c) the nucha
     d) the occiput
     e) none of the above

_____29) The leg is moved outward or laterally by way of the hip joint. This movement is consistent with
     a) adduction
     b) pronation
     c) medial rotation
     d) lateral rotation
     e) none of the above

_____30) What is the name of the nerve plexus that supplies the lower extremity?
     a) the cervical plexus
     b) the lumbosacral plexus
     c) the brachial plexus
     d) the thoracic plexus
     e) none of the above

_____31) Which movements are consistent with extension?
     a) straightening the joint
     b) increasing the angle of the joint
     c) both a and b
     d) decreasing the angle of the joint
     e) none of the above

_____32) What is supplied by the medial brachial cutaneous nerve?
     a) muscles of the forearm
     b) skin of the outer forearm
     c) skin of the outer arm
     d) muscles of the inner arm
     e) none of the above

_____33) The hand is rotated so the palm is facing forward and the thumb is lateral. This is most consistent with
     a) pronation
     b) outer rotation
     c) both a and b
     d) supination
     e) none of the above

_____34) Which of the following is the Latin anatomic name for the front of the brain?
     a) the rostrum
     b) the collum
     c) the occiput
     d) the sacrum
     e) none of the above

_____35) Which structure forms the posterior border of the pelvis?
     a) the cervix
     b) the collum
     c) the sacrum
     d) the nucha
     e) none of the above

_____36) Where is a palmar laceration located?
    a) the neck
    b) the hand
    c) the armpit
    d) the foot
    e) none of the above

_____37) What is the anatomic name for the back of the head?
    a) the nucha
    b) the rostrum
    c) the collum
    d) the occiput
    e) none of the above

_____38) Which of the following best describes the loin?
    a) the visceral posterior area between the diaphragm superiorly and the pelvis inferiorly
    b) the somatic posterior area between the diaphragm superiorly and the pelvis inferiorly
    c) the somatic anterior area between the diaphragm superiorly and the pelvis inferiorly
    d) the upper legs
    e) none of the above

_____39) On the hand, digit #4 is the
    a) ring finger
    b) thumb
    c) index finger
    d) middle finger
    e) none of the above

_____40) What is a sacral decubitus?
    a) a position with the patient lying on the anterior chest and abdomen
    b) a pressure ulcer of the posterior inferior trunk
    c) a position with the patient lying with the right side down
    d) a pressure ulcer of the back of the heel
    e) none of the above

_____41) What is the name of the position with the subject lying flat on the back?
    a) left lateral decubitus
    b) right lateral decubitus
    c) prone
    d) supine
    e) none of the above

_____42) On the foot, digit #5 is the
    a) little toe
    b) next to the little toe
    c) middle toe
    d) great toe
    e) none of the above

For questions 43-50, use the following directions:
a.......1,2,3 are correct   **d.......only 4 is correct**
b.......1,3 are correct   **e.......all are correct**
c.......2,4 are correct

_____43) True statements concerning a patient in the anatomic position include which of the following?
    1. The breast is medial to the elbow.
    2. The cervical vertebrae are superficial to the thoracic vertebrae.
    3. The heart is posterior to the sternum ("breast bone").
    4. The lumbar spine is anterior to the visceral organs of the abdomen.

_____44) With regard to the shaded area in the illustration
    1. Anatomically, it is known as the leg.
    2. It is proximal to the foot of the same extremity.
    3. It is superficial to the foot of the same extremity.
    4. It is contralateral to the right arm.

_____45) Which statements concerning the frontal plane are true?
    1. It is also known as the coronal plane.
    2. It separates the body into anterior and inferior sections.
    3. It is parallel to the long axis of the body.
    4. It separates the body into right and left sections.

_____46) The sagittal plane
    1. separates the body into superior and inferior sections
    2. contains the median plane
    3. is perpendicular to the long axis
    4. separates the body into right and left sections

_____47) With regard to the shaded area in the illustration
    1. It is distal to the antebrachial region.
    2. It is contralateral to the right foot.
    3. It is ipsilateral to the left hand.
    4. It is lateral to the ipsilateral nipple.

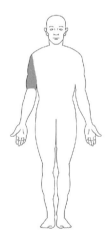

_____48) Which of the following are mediastinal structures?
    1. heart
    2. thyroid
    3. great vessels
    4. diaphragm

_____49) Structure A is within the substance of the femur bone. As compared to structure B, structure A is
    1. proximal
    2. superficial
    3. medial
    4. anterior

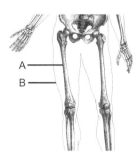

_____50) Which statements concerning the transverse plane are true?
    1. It divides the body into right and left sections.
    2. It divides the body into anterior and posterior sections.
    3. It contains the median plane.
    4. It is perpendicular to the long axis of the body.

END OF CHAPTER TEST: Answers and Explanations

1) c – The *occiput* is the back of the head. *Occipital* is the descriptive term. The greater occipital nerve supplies skin and muscles of the back of the upper neck and back of the head. The *axilla* is the armpit. *Axillary* is the descriptive term. *Popliteal* refers to the anatomic area behind the knee.

2) c – *Flexion* is bending of a joint. The angle of the joint is decreased. *Extension* is straightening of a joint. The angle of the joint is increased.

3) a – *Pronation* is rotating the forearm medially so the dorsum of the hand is facing forward and the thumb is the closest digit to the midline or trunk of the body. The palm faces down or backward, depending on the orientation of the extremity. *Supination* is rotation of the forearm in the opposite direction. The palm faces up or forward. *Inner rotation* is also called medial rotation. This usually involves the shoulder or hip joint. The extremity is rotated inward, toward the midline.

4) c – The word *rostrum* is Latin for beak. The rostral direction is toward the cerebrum of the brain. The head is the *caput*. The back of the head is the *occiput*. The back of the neck is the *nucha*.

5) c – Although this nerve has not yet been discussed, a student could at least make an educated guess on its location based on the name of the nerve. The *cervix* and *collum* are both Latin anatomic names for the neck. *Cervical* and *colli* are the descriptive terms, respectively. As will be later learned, the *transversus colli nerve* is a sensory nerve that "transverses" or goes across the front of the neck.

6) d – The words *proximal* and *distal* are used with reference to the trunk of the body. With this in mind, the wrist is proximal to the fingers. It is closer to the trunk. Although the leg is commonly considered as extending from the hip to the foot, anatomically, it actually extends only from the knee to the foot. The thigh extends from the hip to the knee. The antebrachial region (forearm) includes the area from the elbow to the hand. The brachial region (arm) extends from the shoulder to the elbow. *Rostral* means toward the top of the brain. The mouth is obviously rostral to the stomach.

7) b – The *loin* is the lumbar area. It is the somatic area of the posterior torso that extends from the diaphragm superiorly to the pelvis inferiorly.

8) c – The digits of the hand are numbered with the thumb as digit #1 and little finger as digit #5.

9) a – The *nucha* is the anatomic name for the back of the neck. Nuchal rigidity could be the result of neck muscle spasm following deceleration injuries sustained in certain motor vehicle accidents. *Whiplash* is the common name for such injury.

10) a – A *plexus* is a group of nerves. Although this material has not yet been covered, a student could choose the most likely answer based on an evaluation of the name of the plexus. The words *cervix* and *collum* are both Latin anatomic names for neck. *Cervical* and *colli* are the descriptive terms, respectively. The *cervical plexus* is a group of nerves which is formed in the neck.

11) d – With respect to the brain, efferent nerves are those that are carrying nerve transmission away from the brain. Included are motor nerves which supply voluntary muscles and/or smooth muscles of visceral structures. Afferent nerves are those which are carrying signals to the brain. These sensory nerves carry information that relates to touch, pain, position, balance, and the special senses.

12) c – The *sacrum* is the large bone found at the inferior aspect of the vertebral column. It is formed by the fusion of five vertebrae. The *cervix,* along with the *collum,* is the Latin name for neck. The descriptive terms are *cervical* and *colli,* respectively. The *occiput* is the back of the head. *Occipital* is the descriptive term. The word *rostrum* is Latin for beak. The rostral direction is toward the cerebrum of the brain.

13) c – The right lateral decubitus position has the person lying on the right side. The right side is down. The supine position has the person lying flat on the back. The prone position has the person lying flat on the abdomen and anterior chest.

14) b – The *axilla* is the armpit. *Axillary* is the descriptive from of the word.

15) c – The coronal plane is also known as the frontal plane. Anterior and ventral describe the same general direction in humans. The transverse plane separates the body into superior and inferior sections. The sagittal plane separates the body into right and left sections.

16) c – *Dorsiflexion* of the foot moves the toes up, toward the knee. *Palmar flexion* is flexion of the wrist in the direction of the palm. *Inversion* is rotation of the foot inward or medially, as if attempting to stand on the outer (lateral) side of the foot.

17) e – The frontal plane separates the body into anterior and posterior sections (not anterior and inferior). It is parallel to the long axis of the body.

18) c – The word *popliteal* refers to the anatomic area behind the knee.

19) c – *Adduction* is movement toward the midline. One

"adds" to the midline. This is movement of the extremities medially, toward the midline of the body. With the digits (fingers and toes), it is movement toward the midline of the extremity. This brings the digits together. *Abduction* is movement away from the midline.

20) d – See #12 answer explanation.

21) a – *Outer rotation* is also called *lateral rotation*. This usually involves the shoulder or hip joint. The extremity is rotated outward or laterally, away from the midline. *Inner rotation* is also called *medial rotation*. The extremity is rotated inward, toward the midline. *Adduction* is movement toward the midline. One "adds" to the midline.

22) d – The *plantar surface* is the bottom surface or sole of the foot.

23) b – The *cervix,* along with the *collum,* is the Latin name for neck. The descriptive terms are *cervical* and *colli,* respectively. The *nucha* is the specific name for the back of the neck. *Nuchal* is the descriptive term. The *caput* is the Latin anatomic name for the head. *Capitis* is the descriptive form of the word. The *occiput* is the back of the head. *Occipital* is the descriptive term.

24) e – *Abduction* is movement away from the midline. This involves movement of an extremity out laterally, away from the midline of the body. With the digits (fingers and toes), it involves spreading them apart or moving them outward, away from the midline of the extremity. *Flexion* is bending of a joint. The angle of the joint is decreased. *Inner rotation* is also called *medial rotation*. This usually involves the shoulder or hip joint. The extremity is rotated inward, toward the midline.

25) c – A *plexus* is a group of nerves. Because the word *brachial* describes the arm, the most likely answer is answer c. Indeed, the brachial plexus is responsible for innervation of the upper extremity.

26) c – See #3, #19 and #21 answer explanations.

27) a – Even though this nerve has not yet been

described, its location may be surmised by an evaluation of the nerve name. *Antebrachial* is a word that anatomically describes the forearm. The lateral antebrachial cutaneous nerve supplies skin on the lateral aspect of the forearm.

28) c – See #12 answer explanation.

29) d – See #3 and #21 answer explanations.

30) b – See #10 and #25 answer explanations. The word *thoracic* refers to the chest.

31) c – See #2 answer explanation.

32) e – *Brachial* is a word which describes the arm. Anatomically, the arm extends from the shoulder to the elbow. *Antebrachial* is a word which describes the forearm. The forearm extends from the elbow to the wrist. *Medial* means toward the midline. This corresponds to the inner aspect of the arm. *Cutaneous* means skin. The medial brachial cutaneous nerve supplies skin of the inner arm.

33) d – See #3 and #21 answer explanations.

34) a – See #12 answer explanation.

35) c – See #12 answer explanation.

36) b – *Palmar* is a word which describes the palm of the hand.

37) d – See #12 and #23 answer explanations.

38) b – See #7 answer explanation.

39) a – See #8 answer explanation.

40) b – *Sacral* is a word which describes the posterior area overlying the sacrum. The sacrum is a bone formed by the fusion of five vertebrae and is located at the inferior aspect of the vertebral column. The sacral area can be considered as the area near the anus. A decubitus ulcer is a pressure ulcer which forms on pressure points of debilitated patients. The sacral area is a frequent location of these ulcers, as it supports a significant amount of the weight of a patient lying in the supine position (on their back).

41) d – The word *supine* means face up. The word *prone* means to face down. The prone position has the person lying flat on the abdomen and anterior chest. The left decubitus position has the person lying on the left side. The left side is down. The right lateral decubitus position has the person lying on the right side. The right side is down.

42) a – On the foot, the digits are numbered from the great toe (digit #1) to the little toe (digit #5).

43) b – The breast is closer to the midline than the elbow, so it is more medial than the elbow. The heart is posterior (behind, dorsal) to the sternum. The cervical vertebrae are superior (above) to the thoracic vertebrae, but are no more superficial (closer to the surface) than the thoracic vertebrae. The lumbar spine is posterior (behind, dorsal) to the visceral organs of the abdomen.

44) c – Anatomically, the area is known as the thigh. It is closer to the origin of the extremity from the trunk than the foot is. It is therefore more proximal than the foot. Deep and superficial are terms that describe the anatomic relationship with reference to the surface of a body or structure. The closer a structure is to the surface, the more superficial it is. The thigh is no more superficial than the foot is. Since the thigh is above the foot in the standing position, it is more superior than the foot is. The subject is facing somewhat toward the observer so the right-sided anatomic structures appear visually on the subject's left. The right arm is contralateral to the shaded left thigh because it is on the opposite side of the midline. Ipsilateral structures are on the same side of the midline.

45) b – The frontal plane separates the body into anterior and posterior sections (not anterior and inferior). The sagittal plane separates the body into right and left sections.

46) c – The sagittal plane is parallel to the long axis and separates the body into right and left sec-

tions. The sagittal plane contains the median plane. The median plane occurs at the midline and is also known as the middle sagittal plane. It divides the external body into two equal right and left halves. The transverse plane is what separates the body into superior and inferior sections. It is therefore perpendicular to the long axis of the body.

47) d – The shaded area represents the anatomic arm. The arm is closer to the point of origin of the extremity from the torso than is the forearm (antebrachial region). It therefore is proximal to the antebrachial region. The subject is facing the observer, so the anatomic right-sided structures appear visually on the left. The shaded right arm is ipsilateral to the right foot because they are on the same side of the midline. The shaded arm is contralateral to the left hand because they are on opposite sides of the midline. The arm is lateral (away from the midline) as compared to the nipple, which is more medial (closer to the midline).

48) b – The mediastinum is formed by a group of midline structures including the heart, great vessels, thymus, esophagus, trachea, and supporting structures. The mediastinum divides the thoracic cavity into right and left cavities, one for each lung. The diaphragm is the large muscle of respiration that separates the thorax from the abdomen. The thyroid is an endocrine gland of the neck.

49) b – Structure A is closer to the point of origin of the leg from the trunk. It therefore is more proximal than structure B. Because structure A is within the substance of the femur, it is deep to structure B. Structure B appears near the lateral surface of the thigh, so it is superficial to structure A. Structure A is closer to the midline of the body, so it is more medial than structure B. Since the subject is facing the observer, there is no way to determine which structure is more anterior or posterior.

50) d – See #45 and #46 answer explanations.

*"Success is not measured by the position one has reached in life,
rather by the obstacles overcome while trying to succeed."*

– Booker T. Washington

CHAPTER THREE

THE SKELETON

The skeleton serves as the core body structure; it also forms the foundation for a study of anatomy. Other structures, including many nerves, are named for their relationship with certain bones. The femur is the thigh bone; there is also a femoral artery, femoral vein, and femoral nerve.

There are typically 206 bones in the adult human skeleton. The exact number varies in certain individuals, as some individuals may have an addition, absence, or fusion of one or more bones. The 206 bones found in most people will be covered here. Many of the more familiar bones will simply be depicted in illustrations and briefly mentioned. More attention will be given to bones less well-known. These include bones of the skull, wrist, hand, ankle, and foot.

The text is complimented by a comprehensive skeleton poster that includes multiple bone images and hundreds of bone surface anatomy details. All bones of the skeleton are represented and various notches, foramina, heads, necks, tubercles, and tuberosities are examples of surface anatomy details that are displayed and labeled in the poster. Although many of these details are not discussed in the text or included in exam questions, gaining a familiarity with them is still very important. As the student works through the material of the chapter, each described bone can be identified on the poster. Like the peripheral nerve poster, names of structures on the skeleton poster cannot be read from more than a few feet away. The student should place the poster in a location convenient for frequent viewing and repeatedly test and retest by attempting to identify several structures and moving closer to read the structure names. With perseverance, all bones and surface anatomy details will be learned. Throughout the remainder of the text, the poster can be used to reference various nerve locations, muscle origin points, and muscle insertion points. The bone poster is fairly detailed and will serve as a valuable, all-inclusive resource for future courses and clinical practice.

The skeleton can be divided into two portions: the axial and appendicular skeletons. The **axial skeleton** consists of the skull, vertebral column, ribs, and sternum. For this discussion, the vertebral column includes the sacrum and coccyx bones. Both are bones of the inferior vertebral column which are formed by the fusion of vertebrae. The axial skeleton is named with reference to the axis of the body. An *axis* is a line through a structure which serves as a point of revolution for the structure. The axial skeleton forms the head, neck and contributes to the torso. It is helpful to visualize a line which starts at the top of the skull and extends down the vertebral column. This line serves as the long axis of the body.

Long **axis** of body = **axial** skeleton

The **appendicular skeleton** is comprised of bones which form the extremities. The appendicular skeleton is named with reference to the appendages. An *appendage* is an outgrowth from a structure. The appendicular skeleton includes not only the bones of the arms and legs but also the bones of the trunk which serve as the limbs attachment points to the axial skeleton. The point of attachment for each limb is known as a girdle. A *girdle* is an encircling structure. Thus in clothing, a girdle is an undergarment which encircles the waist. In anatomy, the word also describes various encircling structures. Included are the two pairs of extremity attachment points. Each pair consists of bones which form the encircling socket of the ball and socket joints of the shoulder and hip. The **shoulder** or **pectoral girdle** is formed by the clavicle and scapula bones and is the attachment point for the upper extremity. The **pelvic girdle** is formed by the hip bone and is the attachment point of the lower extremity. In summary, any bone which is part of or serves as a girdle for an extremity is part of the appendicular skeleton. Any bone that is not part of or does not serve as a girdle for an extremity is part of the axial skeleton.

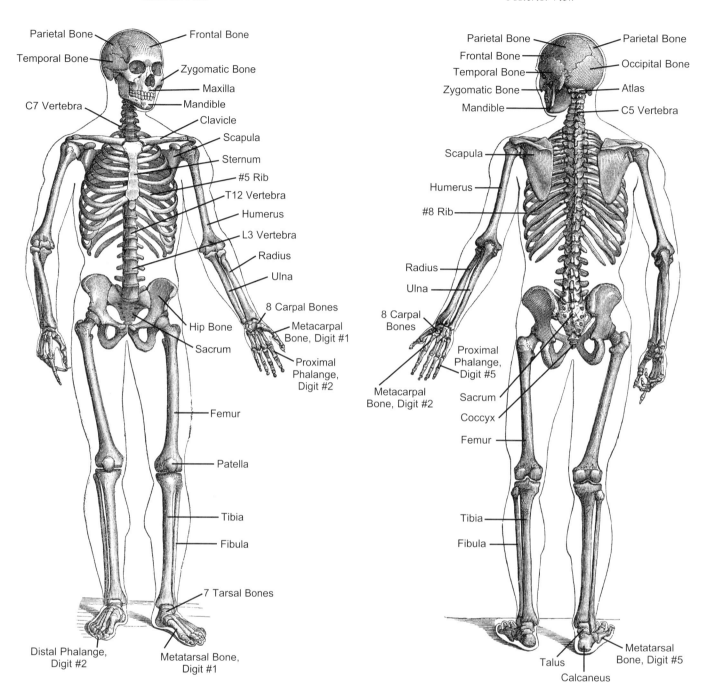

FIGURE 3.1
SKELETON
Anterior View

FIGURE 3.2
SKELETON
Posterior View

AXIAL SKELETON

SKULL

The skull is also known as the cranium. It is composed of 21 bones which fuse together to form one bony structure. The lower jaw or **mandible** would be the 22nd bone, depending on the classification. Because it is connected to the other 21 bones by way of a movable joint, the mandible is often classified as a bone separate from the skull.

As the bones of the skull fuse together, they form an exceedingly tortuous line of attachment with one another. The joint created by the skull bones is held together by fibrous tissue and is rendered immobile. These non-moving joints are known as **sutures**. They hold the bones of the skull together just as surgical sutures hold wound edges together.

A **foramen** is a passageway in a structure through which other structures or substances travel. With bones, a foramen serves as an opening in the bone through which nerves and blood vessels travel. The plural form of the word *foramen* is *foramina*. The skull has numerous foramina. The large **foramen magnum** is the opening at the base of the skull through which the spinal cord travels. Many of the foramina are named for the blood vessels or nerves that travel through them. Some foramina are rather small and appear as small holes in the bone of the skull. The specific names of the foramina will be covered as the nerves which travel through them are described.

There are five significant cavities in the skull. The largest, the **cranial cavity**, contains the brain. The top of the cranial cavity is known as the **calvaria**. The cranial cavity is the only large cavity of the skull that is a closed cavity. There is no passage to the outside world. The other four cavities have an opening to the outside and are called open cavities. These four open cavities are actually formed by two cavities which are paired (right and left; four cavities total). The open cavities include two **orbits** and two **nasal cavities**. The orbits are the eye sockets. They are so named because the eyes rotate within them, similar to a rotating planet in orbit.

In addition to the orbits and nasal cavities, there are smaller open cavities known as **paranasal sinuses.** The paranasal sinuses extend from the nasal cavities into nearby bones of the skull. These include the maxilla, ethmoid, frontal, and sphenoid bones. Because each sinus is named for the bone it inhabits, there are maxillary, ethmoid, frontal, and sphenoid sinuses, respectively.

Of the 21 bones of the skull, eight are paired (right and left, 16 bones total) and five are unpaired or single bones. The paired bones include the maxilla, lacrimal, nasal, inferior nasal concha, palatine, zygomatic, temporal, and parietal bones. The single bones are the frontal, occipital, vomer, ethmoid, and sphenoid bones.

Paired bones are "paired" because they require a right and left. The skeleton is symmetrical with regard to right and left but not with regard to front and back (anterior and posterior). The same holds true for the skull. Hence, the frontal bone ("front" of cranial vault) and occipital bone ("back" of cranial vault) do not require a right or left and are therefore unpaired. The vomer makes up part of the nasal septum and is unpaired. Both the ethmoid (resembling a sieve or strainer) and sphenoid (resembling a wedge) are located near the middle of the skull and are therefore unpaired. Remember, the "oids" are unpaired. Note that the sphenoid bone forms part of the lateral wall of the skull on both the right and left sides, even though the sphenoid bone is only one bone.

PAIRED BONES

1) **maxilla**: forms upper jaw, contains upper teeth; one on each side of nasal cavity beneath orbit.

2) **lacrimal**: pertaining to tears. Small thin bone in the upper medial corner of each orbit.

3) **nasal**: two bones, side-by-side, that form the bridge of the nose.

4) **inferior nasal concha**: one is connected to each side of the nasal cavity and extends inward and downward.

5) **palatine**: pertaining to the palate. Two bones, side-by-side, that form the posterior aspect of the hard palate.

6) **zygomatic**: forms upper cheek and lower lateral orbit on each side.

7) **temporal**: the temple. Forms parts of each side and part of bottom of skull. Contains the inner ear.

8) **parietal**: forms the upper lateral aspect of the skull.

SINGLE BONES

1) **frontal**: superior and anterior skull; the forehead.

2) **occipital**: posterior skull. Also forms a portion of the bottom or base of the skull. The occiput is the back of the head.

3) **vomer**: forms the lower part of the nasal septum.

4) **ethmoid**: forms the superior and medial nasal conchae and upper part of the nasal septum. The word *ethmoid* denotes that this bone is like a sieve or strainer.

5) **sphenoid**: forms part of each side and bottom of skull and a portion of the posterior wall of orbit. The word *sphenoid* means wedge-shaped.

FIGURE 3.3 **SKULL** *Anterior View*

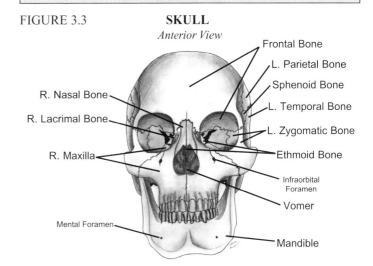

FIGURE 3.4 **SKULL** *Lateral view*

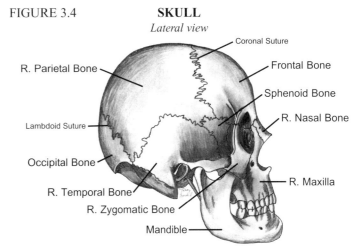

FIGURE 3.5 **SKULL** *Posterior View*

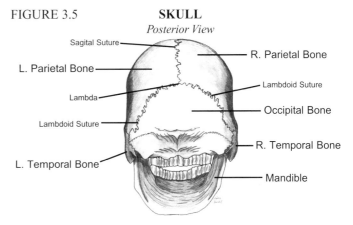

FIGURE 3.6 **SKULL**
Inferior view

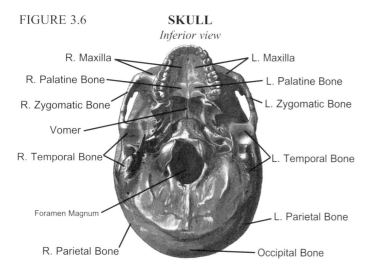

FIGURE 3.7 **RIGHT TEMPORAL BONE**
The temporal bone houses the inner ear. This image provides an example of the unique anatomic details bones possess.

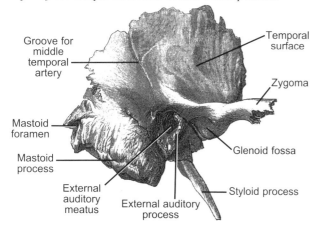

A concha is a shell-shaped object. Most people are familiar with a conch shell. The concha of the ear is the hollow portion of the external ear. The nasal conchae (concha = singular; conchae = plural) are extensions of tissue into the nasal cavity which increase the surface area exposed to inspired air. This warms, moistens, and filters the air. Three nasal conchae (superior, middle, and inferior) extend inward from the lateral side of each nasal cavity. There are therefore a total of six nasal conchae. The superior and middle nasal conchae are part of the ethmoid bone. There is only one ethmoid bone, as it is an unpaired bone. The inferior nasal concha is a separate bone which is paired (there is a right and left one). One inferior nasal concha extends inward from the lateral sides of each nasal cavity.

FIGURE 3.8 **INNER VIEW OF LEFT SKULL**

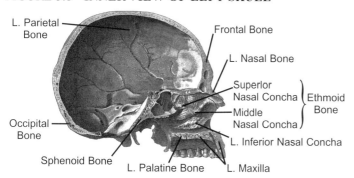

FIGURE 3.9 **ANTERIOR VIEW OF SKULL**
Anterior view of skull after removal of nasal bones and partial removal of maxillary and frontal bones.

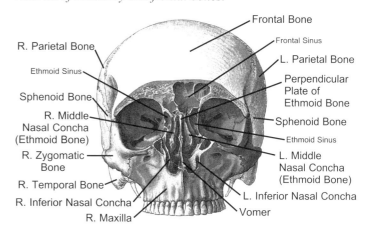

VERTEBRAL COLUMN

The **vertebral column** is the bony case protecting the actual nervous tissue, the **spinal cord**. The spinal cord extends from the brain, exits the skull via the foramen magnum, and travels inferiorly. The vertebral column consists of a total of **33 vertebrae**. Of these, 24 are true vertebrae grouped according to the region of the body they are located. There are **seven cervical vertebrae** (neck), **twelve thoracic vertebrae** (chest), and **five lumbar vertebrae** (loins/abdomen). In addition, five vertebrae below the lumbar vertebrae fuse to form the **sacrum**. Finally, the **coccyx** is a bone formed by the fusion of four vertebrae located below the sacrum. The coccyx forms the bony inferior tip of the vertebral column.

FIGURE 3.10
VERTEBRAL COLUMN
Posterior View

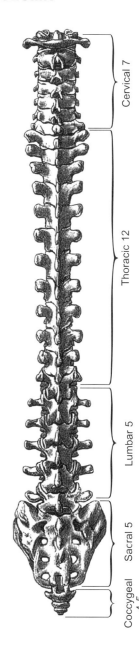

FIGURE 3.11
SACRUM
Anterior View

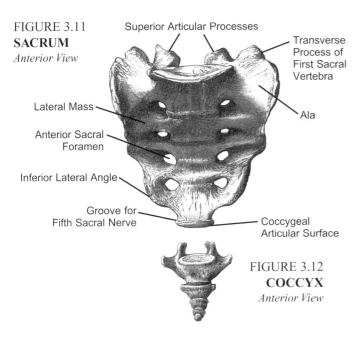

- Superior Articular Processes
- Transverse Process of First Sacral Vertebra
- Lateral Mass
- Anterior Sacral Foramen
- Inferior Lateral Angle
- Groove for Fifth Sacral Nerve
- Ala
- Coccygeal Articular Surface

FIGURE 3.12
COCCYX
Anterior View

are counted forward until the vertebra of question is reached. From the T12 vertebra, the vertebrae are counted backwards. Cervical and lumbar vertebrae are not associated with ribs. The seven vertebrae above the twelve thoracic vertebrae are cervical vertebrae. The five vertebrae below these twelve are lumbar vertebrae. To determine the specific location of a particular vertebra in question, the nearest vertebra associated with a rib is identified. For cervical vertebrae, this is the T1 vertebra. From the T1 vertebra, the vertebrae are counted backwards, starting at C7 and ending at the cervical vertebra of question. For lumbar vertebrae, the closest thoracic vertebra is T12. From T12, the vertebrae are counted forward, starting at L1 and ending at the lumbar vertebra of question.

Half and Half
This is a mnemonic which will be repeated throughout the text. The vertebrae serve as the first use of the mnemonic. There are 24 true vertebrae: half (12) articulate with ribs and half (12) do not.

Each bone of the vertebral column (excluding the sacrum and coccyx) is known separately as a *vertebra*. The plural form of this word is *vertebrae*. The seven cervical vertebrae are abbreviated C1 – C7; the fourth cervical vertebra is therefore the C4 vertebra. The twelve thoracic vertebrae are abbreviated T1 – T12. The five lumbar vertebrae are abbreviated L1 – L5. The only vertebrae with specific names are the top two. The C1 vertebra is the **atlas**. The C2 vertebra is known as the **axis**.

FIGURE 3.14
VERTEBRAL COLUMN AND RIB CAGE

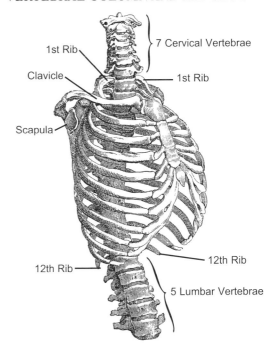

- 1st Rib
- Clavicle
- Scapula
- 7 Cervical Vertebrae
- 1st Rib
- 12th Rib
- 12th Rib
- 5 Lumbar Vertebrae

FIGURE 3.13
VERTEBRAL COLUMN
Lateral view

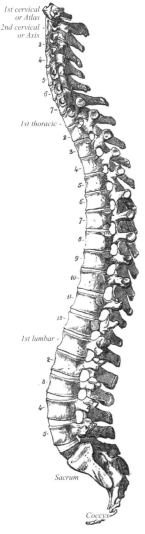

- 1st cervical or Atlas
- 2nd cervical or Axis
- 3
- 4
- 5
- 6
- 7
- 1st thoracic
- 2
- 3
- 4
- 5
- 6
- 7
- 8
- 9
- 10
- 11
- 12
- 1st lumbar
- 2
- 3
- 4
- 5
- Sacrum
- Coccyx

C1 comes before C2 and the "t" of atlas comes alphabetically before the "x" of axis. Additionally, Atlas was a character in Greek mythology who held the world up, just as the atlas holds the head up.

Each vertebra can be specifically identified by using thoracic vertebrae as a reference. The thoracic vertebrae are the only vertebrae which articulate or form joints with ribs. Each of the twelve thoracic vertebrae is associated with a pair of ribs. One rib emerges from each side of a vertebra. To correctly identify a particular thoracic vertebra of question, either the T1 or T12 vertebra is first located. The T1 vertebra is the first vertebra associated with ribs; the T12 vertebra is the last. From the T1 vertebra, the vertebrae

As mentioned earlier, the sacrum is a bone formed by the fusion of five sacral vertebrae. Superiorly, the sacrum articulates with the inferior aspect of the L5 vertebra. Inferolaterally, the sacrum forms a tight, rather immobile joint with the hip bone. The fusion of the five sacral vertebrae provides added strength which is valuable in transferring the weight of the upper body to the hip bone and subsequently, to the lower extremities. Inferiorly, the sacrum articulates with the coccyx. The coccyx is created by the fusion of four vertebrae and forms the bony inferior tip of the vertebral column.

THORACIC WALL

The two main functions of the rib cage are protecting vital organs and providing structure to enable respiration. There are twelve pairs of ribs. The first seven pair extend laterally from their respective vertebra. As they continue outward, they curve anteriorly and medially around the chest wall. Toward the end of each rib's length, the bone turns to cartilage. It is this **costal cartilage** of each of the first seven ribs that articulates directly with the sternum. The word root *cost(o)* means rib. The word *costal* refers to a rib. Because their costal cartilage articulate directly with the sternum, these first seven ribs are known as **true ribs**. The costal cartilages of the next three ribs (ribs #8, #9, #10) do not make it to the sternum but instead articulate with the anterior aspect of the rib immediately above or superior to it. These ribs are known as **false ribs**. Finally, the last two ribs (ribs #11, #12) do not articulate with the sternum or another rib. Each rib merely extends several inches laterally and inferiorly from their respective vertebra. These ribs are known as **floating ribs**.

FIGURE 3.15
RIB CAGE

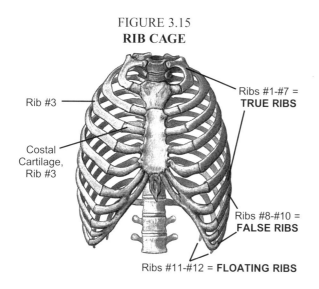

Rib #3

Costal Cartilage, Rib #3

Ribs #1-#7 = **TRUE RIBS**

Ribs #8-#10 = **FALSE RIBS**

Ribs #11-#12 = **FLOATING RIBS**

The **sternum** or breast bone is actually formed by the union of three bones. The larger, intermediately located bone is known as the **body of the sternum**. Superior to it is the **manubrium**. Inferior to the body of the sternum is the small **xyphoid process**. These three bones are separated by cartilaginous (cartilage) joints that permit limited movement during respiration.

FIGURE 3.16
STERNUM
Anterior View

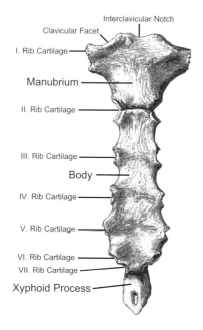

Interclavicular Notch
Clavicular Facet
I. Rib Cartilage
Manubrium
II. Rib Cartilage
III. Rib Cartilage
Body
IV. Rib Cartilage
V. Rib Cartilage
VI. Rib Cartilage
VII. Rib Cartilage
Xyphoid Process

OTHER BONES

There are four other small bones which also have no direct association with the extremities. The **hyoid bone** is a small bone of the upper anterior neck. It serves to protect the pharynx, larynx, and proximal trachea. It also serves as a point of attachment of small muscles used in swallowing and vocalization.

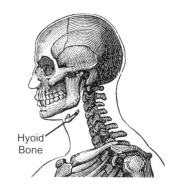

Hyoid Bone

FIGURE 3.17 **HYOID BONE**

The **hy**oid bone is the **high**est bone of the body which is not part of the skull or vertebral column.

Within the middle ear cavity of the temporal bone of the skull are three small, specialized bones used in hearing. The **malleus bone** is attached to the **tympanic membrane** or ear drum. The malleus bone transmits sound vibrations from the tympanic membrane to the **incus bone**. The incus, in turn, transmits this vibration to the **stapes bone**, and, subsequently, to the sound organs of the inner ear. These three bones are collectively known as the **ossicles of the ear**.

FIGURE 3.18
EAR OSSICLES

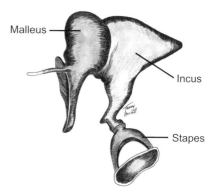

Malleus

Incus

Stapes

M I S = **m**alleus to **i**ncus to **s**tapes
stapes to **s**ound organs (**s**emicircular canals, cochlea)

QUIZ 1
The Axial Skeleton

Time for Quiz = 33 minutes.
For questions 1-22, choose the single best answer.

_____1) The axis bone is
       a) an ear ossicle
       b) the C1 vertebra
       c) the C2 vertebra
       d) a bone of the skull
       e) none of the above

_____2) The hyoid bone is
       a) a carpal bone
       b) a tarsal bone
       c) an ear ossicle
       d) a bone of the skull
       e) none of the above

_____3) The manubrium is
       a) part of the sacrum bone
       b) an ear ossicle
       c) the lower jaw
       d) the superiorly located component of the sternum bone
       e) none of the above

_____4) How many bones are typically present in the human skeleton?
       a) 219
       b) 184
       c) 306
       d) 242
       e) none of the above

_____5) How many skull bones are not paired (have only one bone – no right or left)?
       a) 3
       b) 6
       c) 5
       d) 8
       e) none of the above

_____6) What is the name of the jawbone?
       a) temporal bone
       b) maxilla
       c) mandible
       d) malleus
       e) none of the above

_____7) Bones of the skull are held together by
       a) calvaria
       b) foramen
       c) appendages
       d) glue
       e) none of the above

_____8) The T4 vertebra is which vertebra from the top?
       a) 7th
       b) 11th
       c) 6th
       d) 14th
       e) none of the above

_____9) How many vertebrae typically fuse to form the coccyx?
       a) 3
       b) 8
       c) 4
       d) none; the coccyx is a bone of the tarsus of the foot
       e) none of the above

_____10) The atlas bone is
       a) one of the skull bones
       b) the most superior part of the sternum
       c) the C1 vertebra
       d) the C2 vertebra
       e) none of the above

_____11) The top of the cranial cavity is known as the
       a) foramina
       b) calvaria
       c) suture
       d) noggin
       e) none of the above

_____12) Which of the following is an ear ossicle?
       a) scaphoid
       b) ischium
       c) ilium
       d) all of the above
       e) none of the above

_____13) The L6 vertebra is which number vertebra from the top of the vertebral column?
    a) 19th
    b) 23rd
    c) 24th
    d) there is no L6 vertebra
    e) none of the above

_____14) Which bone contains the inner ear?
    a) ethmoid
    b) maxilla
    c) temporal
    d) sphenoid
    e) none of the above

_____15) Which of the following statements about the sternum is true?
    a) It articulates with all the ribs.
    b) It is part of the axial skeleton.
    c) The manubrium is the intermediate-ly located, large component.
    d) It is part of the pectoral (shoulder) girdle.
    e) None of the above

_____16) How many bones are present in the skull (excluding the mandible)?
    a) 18
    b) 24
    c) 26
    d) 31
    e) none of the above

_____17) The xiphoid is
    a) the intermediately located, large part of the sternum bone
    b) the superiorly located part of the sternum bone
    c) the inferiorly located process of the sternum bone
    d) an ossicle bone of the ear
    e) none of the above

_____18) Which of the following statements concerning the rib cage are true?
    a) Rib #10 is a floating rib.
    b) Rib #11 is a false rib.
    c) Both a and b
    d) Rib #8 is a false rib.
    e) None of the above

_____19) How many skull bones are paired (have a right and left bone)?
    a) 8
    b) 6
    c) 5
    d) 10
    e) none of the above

_____20) Passageways in bone through which anatomic structures travel are known as
    a) calvaria
    b) foramina
    c) appendages
    d) sutures
    e) none of the above

_____21) How many large cavities are in the skull?
    a) 1
    b) 3
    c) 5
    d) 8
    e) none of the above

_____22) The L3 vertebra is which vertebra from the top?
    a) 18th
    b) 22nd
    c) 25th
    d) 20th
    e) none of the above

_____

For questions 23-33, use the following directions:
a.......1,2,3 are correct
b.......1,3 are correct
c.......2,4 are correct
d.......only 4 is correct
e.......all are correct

_____23) Which bones are part of the axial skeleton?
    1. incus
    2. sphenoid
    3. manubrium
    4. ischium

_____24) Which of the following are unpaired
bones of the skull?
1. vomer
2. ethmoid
3. occipital
4. sphenoid

_____25) Which bones form the orbit?
1. frontal
2. nasal
3. lacrimal
4. temporal

_____26) Which bones are ossicles of the ear?
1. ischium
2. scaphoid
3. ilium
4. incus

_____27) Which of the following are paired bones
of the skull?
1. frontal
2. vomer
3. occipital
4. zygomatic

_____28) Which statements about the sacrum bone
are true?
1. It is bound superiorly by the coccyx.
2. It transfers the weight of the upper
body to the lower extremities.
3. It is formed by the fusion of 3
vertebrae.
4. It is part of the axial skeleton.

_____29) Which statements about the coccyx bone
are true?
1. It is bound inferiorly by the sacrum.
2. It is part of the appendicular skeleton.
3. It is formed by the fusion of 6
vertebrae.
4. It technically is part of the vertebral
column.

_____30) Which of the following are unpaired
bones of the skull?
1. frontal
2. maxilla
3. occipital
4. parietal

_____31) Which statements about the vertebral
column are true?
1. The coccyx is formed by the fusion
of 4 vertebrae.
2. The sacrum is formed by the fusion
of 5 vertebrae.
3. There are a total of 33 vertebrae.
4. There are 8 cervical vertebrae.

_____32) Which of the following are unpaired
bones of the skull?
1. zygomatic
2. sphenoid
3. inferior nasal concha
4. ethmoid

_____33) Which of the following are paired bones
of the skull?
1. nasal
2. temporal
3. palatine
4. maxilla

QUIZ 1: The Axial Skeleton Answers and Explanations

1) c – The axis bone is the C2 vertebra. The atlas bone is the C1 vertebra. Ear ossicles include the malleus, incus, and stapes.

2) e – The hyoid bone is a small bone of the upper anterior neck which provides protection to the pharynx and larynx. It serves as an attachment point for several muscles that function in swallowing and phonation.

3) d – The sternum is formed by three components. The manubrium is the superiorly located component. The body is the largest component and is intermediately located. The xiphoid process is the small, inferiorly located component. The sacrum is a bone at the inferior aspect of the vertebral column. The ear ossicles include the malleus, incus, and stapes. The mandible is the lower jaw.

4) e – There usually are 206 bones in the human skeleton. This number may vary, depending on the possible absence, addition, or fusion of certain bones in certain individuals.

5) c – Excluding the mandible, there are 8 paired bones (16 total) and 5 unpaired bones of the skull. This brings the total number of skull bones to 21.

6) c – The mandible forms the lower jaw. The maxilla forms the upper jaw (M & M). The temporal bone is a paired bone of the skull. The malleus is one of the ossicles of the ear.

7) e – Bones of the skull are held together by sutures. The calvaria is the top of the cranial cavity. A foramen is a passage in bone through which anatomic structures travel. An appendage is an outgrowth from a structure. In anatomy, it generally refers to the extremities.

8) b – There are seven cervical vertebrae. Therefore, the fourth thoracic vertebra would be the eleventh vertebra from the top.

9) c – The coccyx is usually formed by the fusion of four vertebrae.

10) c – The atlas is the C1 vertebra. The axis is the C2 vertebra. The manubrium is the most superior part of the sternum.

11) b – The top of the cranial cavity is known as the calvaria. Foramina are passageways through bone. Sutures hold bones of the skull together.

12) e – The ossicles of the ear, from the tympanic membrane to the organs of sound, include the malleus, incus, and stapes. The scaphoid bone is a carpal bone. The ischium and ilium, along with the pubis, fuse to form the hip bone.

13) e – Granted, this is somewhat of a trick question. The take-home point is that there is a great deal of variability in anatomy. Although the vast majority of people have five lumbar vertebrae, there are individuals with 4, 6, or 7 lumbar vertebrae. In the case of L6, it would be the 25th vertebra from the top. Seven cervical + 12 thoracic + 6 lumbar = 25 vertebrae.

14) c – The temporal bone is a paired bone of the skull which houses the inner ear on each side.

15) b – There are seven pairs of true ribs, ribs #1-#7. The costal cartilage of each true rib articulates directly with the sternum. The sternum is formed by three components. The manubrium is the superiorly located component. The body is the largest, intermediately located component. The xiphoid process is the small, inferiorly located component. The pectoral (shoulder) girdle is formed by the scapula (shoulder blade) and clavicle (collar bone).

16) e – There are 21 bones in the skull, excluding the mandible.

17) c – See #3 answer explanation. The ossicle bones of the ear include the malleus, incus, and stapes.

18) d – There are a total of twelve pairs of ribs. There are seven pairs of true ribs, ribs #1-#7. The costal cartilage of each true rib articulates directly with the sternum. There are three pairs

of false ribs (ribs #8, 9, and 10). The costal cartilage of false ribs do not make it to the sternum, but instead articulate with the anterior aspect of the rib immediately above it. There are two pairs of floating ribs (rib #11 and 12). The floating ribs merely extend laterally and inferiorly from their respective vertebra. They do not articulate with any other structure.

19) a – There are 8 paired bones (16 total) and 5 unpaired bones of the skull. This brings the total number of skull bones to 21, excluding the mandible.

20) b – Foramina are passageways through bone (*foramen* is the singular form of the word). The calvaria is the top of the cranial cavity. Appendages are outgrowths from a structure. In anatomy, they generally refer to the extremities. Sutures hold the different bones of the skull together.

21) c – There are five relatively large cavities of the skull. The cranial cavity is the largest and only closed cavity. It is also the only unpaired cavity. The other four cavities are open cavities. They are *open* to the outside. They include the two orbits or eye sockets and the two nasal cavities. The orbits are named for the fact that the eyes *rotate* within them, similar to a rotating planet in orbit.

22) b – There are seven cervical vertebrae, twelve thoracic vertebrae, and five lumbar vertebrae. The L3 vertebra would therefore be the 22nd vertebra from the top (7 + 12 + 3 = 22).

23) a – The incus is an ossicle bone of the ear (along with the malleus and stapes). The sphenoid is an unpaired bone of the skull. The manubrium is the superiorly located component of the sternum bone. The ischium is a bone that fuses with the pubis bone and ilium bone to form the hip bone. The hip bone is part of the appendicular skeleton.

24) e – The vomer is an unpaired bone which forms the lower portion of the nasal septum. The ethmoid is an unpaired bone that forms the superior and medial nasal conchae and upper portion of the nasal septum. The occipital bone is an unpaired bone which forms the posterior skull. The sphenoid is an unpaired bone that forms part of the side and bottom of the skull. It also forms a portion of the posterior wall of the orbit.

25) b – The orbit is an open cavity of the skull which contains the eye. It is named for the fact that the eye *rotates* within it. It is formed by seven skull bones: the frontal, lacrimal, ethmoid, maxilla, zygomatic, sphenoid, and palatine bones.

26) d – See #12 answer explanation.

27) d – The zygomatic bone is a paired bone which forms the upper cheek and lower lateral orbit on each side of the face. The frontal bone is an unpaired bone which forms the forehead. The vomer is an unpaired bone which is part of the nasal septum. The occipital bone is an unpaired bone which forms the posterior skull.

28) c – The sacrum is bound inferiorly by the coccyx. The sacrum is formed by the fusion of 5 vertebrae.

29) d – The coccyx bone forms the bony inferior tip of the vertebral column. Hence, it is part of the axial skeleton. It forms an articulation or joint superiorly with the sacrum bone. The coccyx is formed by the fusion of 4 vertebrae.

30) b – The frontal bone is an unpaired bone that forms the forehead. The occipital bone is an unpaired bone which forms the posterior skull. The maxilla is a paired bone that forms the upper jaw and contains the upper teeth. There is one bone on each side of the nasal cavity. The parietal bone is a paired bone that forms the upper lateral aspect of each side the cranial cavity.

31) a – In most individuals, the vertebral column is formed by a total of 33 vertebrae. This includes 24 true vertebrae and two bones formed by the fusion of multiple vertebrae. The sacrum is formed by the fusion of five vertebrae and the coccyx by a fusion of four (7

cervical + 12 thoracic + 5 lumbar + 5 sacral + 4 coccygeal = 33 total vertebrae).

32) c – The sphenoid bone is an unpaired bone that forms part of the side and bottom of the skull. It also forms a portion of the posterior wall of the orbit. The ethmoid bone is an unpaired bone that forms the superior nasal conchae, middle nasal conchae, and part of the nasal septum. The zygomatic bone is a paired bone that forms the upper cheek and lower lateral orbit on each side of the face. The inferior

nasal concha is a paired bone; one is located on each side of the nasal cavity.

33) e – The nasal bone is a paired bone which forms the bridge of the nose. The temporal bone is a paired bone that forms the temple and contains the inner ear. The palatine bone is a paired bone forming the posterior aspect of the hard palate. The maxilla is a paired bone that forms the upper jaw and contains the upper teeth. There is one bone on each side of the nasal cavity.

APPENDICULAR SKELETON

The appendicular skeleton is comprised of bones that provide structure for the appendages or extremities. There are two pairs of appendicular skeletons. One pair forms the upper extremities; the other pair forms the lower extremities. There are several similarities between the two pairs which will be described shortly. Each of the two appendicular skeletons is divided into two sections. The **girdle** serves as the foundation for the extremity. It is part of the torso, articulates with the axial skeleton, and serves as the articulating base for the extremity. The shoulder joint is the girdle for the upper extremity. The hip joint is the girdle for the lower extremity. The **free limb** is the second segment of each appendicular skeleton. It is the section of each extremity which is distal to the articulating joint of the girdle.

UPPER EXTREMITY

The girdle of the upper extremity is the **shoulder girdle**. It is also known as the **pectoral girdle.** The word root *pectus* means breast. Derivations of the word are used in anatomy to describe structures associated with, or located near, the breasts. There are pectoralis major and pectoralis minor muscles. There are also medial pectoral and lateral pectoral nerves. The pectoral girdle consists of two bones, the **clavicle** (collar bone) and **scapula** (shoulder blade). The clavicle articulates with the sternum and cartilage of the first rib. Allowing more flexibility and range of motion of the upper extremity, the scapula has no articulating joint with the axial skeleton. It is bound by muscles only.

The **humerus** is the long bone of the arm. Proximally, it articulates with the scapula and clavicle by way of the shoulder joint. Distally, it articulates with the radius and ulna at the elbow joint.

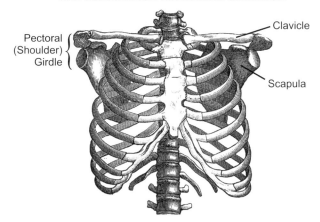

FIGURE 3.19
PECTORAL GIRDLE
AND ASSOCIATION WITH AXIAL SKELETON

Pectoral (Shoulder) Girdle

Clavicle

Scapula

The long bones of the forearm consist of the **radius** and **ulna**. In the anatomic position with the hands supinated, the radius is lateral to the ulna.

> In the distal forearm, the radius is the "thicker" bone. It is on the same side of the extremity as the "thickest" digit, the thumb.
>
> **Radius = thumb side...radial side = thumb side**

The **carpus** is the wrist joint. It is composed of eight bones. These bones are known as **carpal bones**. The presence of such a large number of bones in such a small area permits a great deal of flexibility and range of motion. The wrist joint allows the hand to move in virtually any direction. Although there are differences in sizes and shapes, the carpal bones can be considered to lie in two equally numbered rows.

Starting laterally and moving medially, the proximal row of carpal bones consists of the **scaphoid**, **lunate**, **triangular**, and **pisiform bones**. In the anatomic position, the palms are facing forward with the thumbs out laterally. The scaphoid bone is thereby on the thumb side of the wrist. The pisiform bone is most medial. It is closest to the little finger side. *Scaphoid* means boat-shaped. The lunate bone is named for its moon or crescent shape. The triangular bone has a three-sided shape. Finally, the pisiform bone is named for its pea size and/or shape.

Starting laterally and moving medially, the distal row of carpal bones consists of the **trapezium**, **trapezoid**, **capitate**, and **hamate** bones. A trapezium is a four-sided shape with irregular sides. A trapezoid is also a four-sided shape, but it has two parallel sides. The capitate bone is so named because it is shaped like a head (caput). Finally, the hamate bone is named for its hook-like appearance.

The prefix *meta* refers to *what is next.* It also denotes a period or structure of transition. The **metacarpal bones** are the bones that are immediately distal to the carpus or wrist. They can also be considered the transitory bones between the carpus and phalanges of the digits. There is one metacarpal bone for each digit, so each hand has five metacarpal bones. The metacarpal bones form the structure of the actual hand.

A **phalanx** is a bone located in the outgrowth or extension of a digit. In other words, any bone in a thumb, finger, or toe is a phalanx. *Phalanges* is the plural form of the word. Each finger has three phalanges. The thumb has only two. Each digit of the upper extremity is attached to the hand by way of a **metacarpophalangeal joint.** This is the junction between the metacarpal bone of a digit and the proximal phalanx of the same digit. The metacarpophalangeal joint forms the prominent *knuckle* of a clinched fist. The joints between two successive phalanges of the same digit are known as **interphalangeal joints** (inter = between). Because fingers have three phalanges, each finger has one metacarpophalangeal joint and two interphalangeal joints. The thumb has only two phalanges; it has one metacarpophalangeal joint and only one interphalangeal joint.

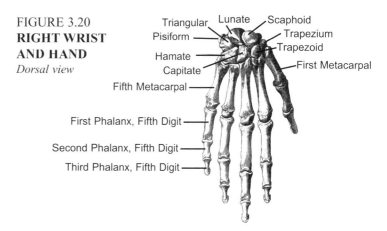

FIGURE 3.20
RIGHT WRIST AND HAND
Dorsal view

Labels: Triangular, Lunate, Scaphoid, Pisiform, Trapezium, Trapezoid, Hamate, Capitate, First Metacarpal, Fifth Metacarpal, First Phalanx, Fifth Digit, Second Phalanx, Fifth Digit, Third Phalanx, Fifth Digit

LOWER EXTREMITY

The **hip bone** forms the girdle of the lower extremity, the **pelvic girdle.** The hip bone actually consists of three fused bones. The **pubis** is the anterior bone. The **ischium** is the posterior and inferior bone. The large fan-shaped **ilium** is the posterior and superior bone. The superior aspect of the ilium is known as the iliac crest. The right and left hip bones are united at the anterior and inferior midline at the **pubic symphysis**. A symphysis is a type of fibrocartilaginous joint which is essentially immobile. The word *fibrocartilaginous* denotes that the joint is formed by fibrous tissue and cartilage. Posteriorly, both the right and left hip bones articulate with the sacrum. As opposed to the pectoral gir-

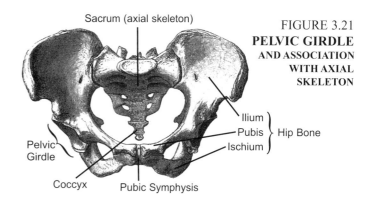

FIGURE 3.21
PELVIC GIRDLE AND ASSOCIATION WITH AXIAL SKELETON

Labels: Sacrum (axial skeleton), Ilium, Pubis, Ischium, Hip Bone, Pelvic Girdle, Coccyx, Pubic Symphysis

dle, in which the scapula is bound to the axial skeleton by muscle only and the clavicle articulates with only the sternum and first rib, the pelvic girdle forms a tight, highly immobile joint with the sacrum. The pelvic girdle has to bear the weight of the entire upper body; the pectoral girdle is only responsible for the weight of the upper extremity.

The free limb of the lower extremity will be considered next. The **femur** is the long bone of the thigh. At the knee, it articulates with the tibia and fibula bones of the leg. The **patella** or knee cap is a sesamoid bone that protects the joint of the knee. Sesamoid bones are located in areas of high friction and will be discussed later in the chapter. The **tibia** is the larger, medial bone of the leg. The **fibula** is the smaller, lateral bone of the leg.

The fibula is telling a "fib" in claiming to be the predominant bone of the leg.

Remember, the leg extends from the knee to the ankle. The femur is the long bone of the thigh. The tibia is the predominant long bone of the leg.

Just as the wrist is known anatomically as the carpus, the ankle joint is known as the **tarsus**. The seven bones of the ankle are therefore known as **tarsal bones**. They can be thought to exist in three layers from proximal to distal. The most proximal or superior bone of the tarsus is the **talus**. Below or inferior to the talus is the **calcaneus** or heel bone. The next distal layer is comprised of the **cuboid bone** laterally and the **navicular bone** medially. The cuboid bone is named for its cube shape. Like the word *scaphoid*, the word *navicular* also describes something which is shaped like a boat.

Each hand or foot contains "a boat." The scaphoid bone is a carpal bone located in the wrist. The navicular bone is a tarsal bone located in the ankle.

Because the laterally located cuboid bone extends to the lateral two metatarsal bones, the distal layer of tarsal bones consists of three bones which are relatively medially located. They include the **lateral cuneiform bone**, **intermediate cuneiform bone**, and **medial cuneiform bone**. The word *cuneiform* describes a structure which is shaped like a wedge.

FIGURE 3.22
RIGHT ANKLE AND FOOT
Lateral view

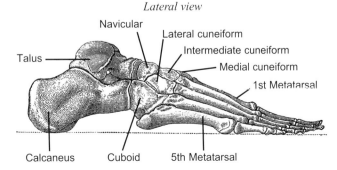

Just as the wrist plays a pivotal role in golf, the ankle is important for KICKING.

K I C K I N G = 7 tarsal bones
(1 2 3 4 5 6 7)

1st Layer	2nd Layer	3rd Layer	
2 +	2 +	3	= 7 tarsal bones
talus	*cuboid*	*lateral cuneiform*	
calcaneus	*navicular*	*intermediate cuneiform*	
		medial cuneiform	

The talus can be remembered as the most proximal bone because the beginning of its name sounds like the word *tarsal* (**ta**lus = 1st **ta**rsal). The word *kicking* contains two letters which serve as a reminder for the names of the other 6 tarsal bones. K I **C** K I **N** G

C = 5 tarsal bones with names beginning with the letter C = 5 C's ➡
1) **c**alcaneus (heel bone)
2) **c**uboid
3) lateral **c**uneiform
4) intermediate **c**uneiform
5) medial **c**uneiform

N = **n**avicular bone = boat-shaped bone

The tarsus thereby contains one boat (navicular bone) which "floats" in a sea of C's. It is bordered by each of the 5 C's. The calcaneous is proximal, the cuboid is lateral, and the three cuneiforms are distal.

From proximal to distal, the 5 C's also stay in a relative alphabetical order.

calcaneous ➡ cuboid ➡ 3 cuneiforms

Another way to remember this mnemonic is to relate kicking to its use in swimming. Because a boat is available in the sea of 5 C's, swimming is avoided.

Proximally, the metatarsal bones articulate with one cube and three wedges. This includes the cuboid (cube-shaped) bone for the lateral two metatarsals and the lateral, intermediate, and medial cuneiform (wedge-shaped) bones for the medial three metatarsal bones.

Similar to the carpus and metacarpal bones of the hands, the **metatarsal bones** of the foot are the bones just distal to the tarsus. There is one metatarsal bone for each digit or toe. The **metatarsophalangeal joint** is the articulation between the metatarsal bone and proximal phalanx of each digit. Every toe therefore has one metatarsophalangeal joint.

The toes have the same number of phalanges as the fingers and thumbs. Like the thumb, the great toe contains two phalanges. The other four toes, like the four fingers, each contains three phalanges. The interphalangeal joints are located between successive phalanges of each toe. The great toe therefore has only one interphalangeal joint. Each of the other four toes has two interphalangeal joints.

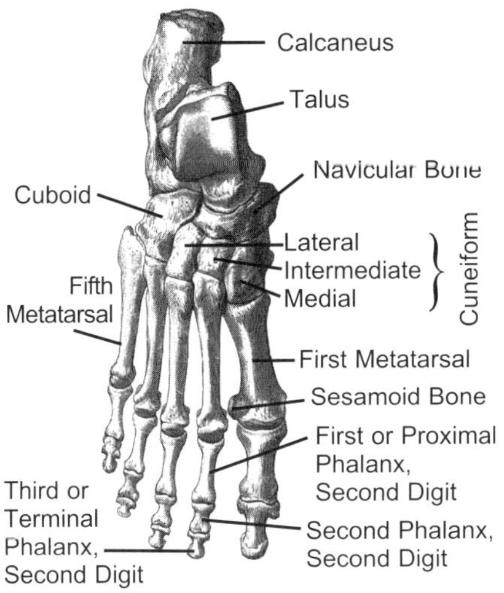

A comparison of the two appendicular skeletons reveals several similarities and differences of interest. First, the proximal component of each free limb contains only one long bone. The humerus is the long bone of the arm and femur is the long bone of the thigh. Each of these bones forms a ball and socket joint proximally with its respective girdle. Distally, each forms a type of hinge joint with the two bones of the second component of the extremity. The elbow serves as the hinge joint for the upper extremity, and the knee serves as the hinge joint for the lower extremity.

Hinge joints permit flexion in one direction only. In the anatomic position, the elbow flexes anteriorly, whereas the knee flexes posteriorly. The elbow joint has some differences which additionally permit pronation and supination. The lower extremity should be considered to remain in a constant pronated position. It is unable to supinate.

In both the upper and lower extremity, the second component of the extremity consists of two long bones. In the forearm, it is the radius and ulna bones. In the leg, it includes the tibia and fibula bones.

There are some differences to consider when evaluating the third joint of each extremity. The carpus contains eight carpal bones. The tarsus contains seven tarsal bones. The bony structure of the hand is formed almost entirely by the metacarpal bones. By contrast, the metatarsal bones form only the approximate distal half of the foot. The tarsal bones contribute much more to the mass of the foot than the carpal bones do in the hand. The tarsus must provide for weight-bearing activities. The carpus must provide for intricate, highly variable movements.

If one considers the hand in a pronated position, like the foot,

FIGURE 3.23
RIGHT ANKLE AND FOOT
Dorsal view

- Calcaneus
- Talus
- Navicular Bone
- Cuboid
- Lateral
- Intermediate
- Medial } Cuneiform
- Fifth Metatarsal
- First Metatarsal
- Sesamoid Bone
- First or Proximal Phalanx, Second Digit
- Third or Terminal Phalanx, Second Digit
- Second Phalanx, Second Digit

other similarities between the two extremities become apparent. In the distal aspect of the second component, the larger, more significant bone is medially placed. This includes the radius of the forearm and tibia of the leg. The center of gravity is more medial, requiring the heavier bone to be medially placed. Furthermore, in a pronated position, the short, "thick" digit of each extremity is also medial. This includes the thumb and great toe. Finally, both the thumb and great toe are formed by only two phalanges. All other digits, both fingers and toes, have three phalanges.

To remember this comparison, envision someone actually "walking" on his hands. Like the feet, the hands are in a pronated position. Both the soles of the feet and palms of the hands must face down to contact the ground. A **pro** walker, whether walking on his feet or hands, must have the feet or hands in a **pro**nated position.

Do not become confused by this description of the upper extremity in a pronated position. The lower extremity is in a constant state of pronation. This requires the upper extremity to also be in a pronated position to describe certain similarities. Remember, the anatomically correct description is provided from the anatomic position. In the anatomic position, the hands are supinated with the palms facing forward, toward the observer. The radius is actually lateral to the ulna. The thumb is also the most lateral digit.

No discussion of the skeleton would be complete without mention of sesamoid bones. Sesamoid bones are small, sporadically present bones located in areas of frequent friction. Such areas include tendon sheaths, bursae, and joint capsules. Sesamoid bones are named for their similarity to sesame seeds, although most are significantly larger. The patella or knee cap is actually a sesamoid bone, the largest in the body. The pisiform bone of the carpus is another example of a sesamoid bone. Because they are the only two sesamoid bones consistently present, the patella and pisiform are the only two sesamoid bones with specific anatomic names. Others are simply referred to as sesamoid bones.

Sesamoid bones are often present at the base of the thumb and great toe. These bones start out as cartilage which calcifies and ossifies over time. On x-ray, an older person may appear to have more bones than a young person does because the older person's sesamoids have ossified and are visible. Even though the typical human skeleton consists of 206 bones, a particular individual may have significantly more due to the presence of sesamoid bones.

FIGURE 3.24

AXIAL SKELETON

NAME	BONES		TOTAL NUMBER OF BONES
Skull	Paired bones (16 total)	Single bones (5)	21
	1. maxilla 4. inferior nasal concha 7. temporal 2. lacrimal 5. palatine 8. parietal 3. nasal 6. zygomatic	1. frontal 4. ethmoid 2. occipital 5. sphenoid 3. vomer	
Mandible			1
Ear ossicles	1. malleus 2. incus } per ear 3. stapes		6
Hyoid bone			1
Vertebral column	7 cervical (including atlas (C1) and axis (C2)) 12 thoracic 5 lumbar		24
Sacrum	Formed by fusion of 5 vertebrae		1
Coccyx	Formed by fusion of 4 vertebrae		1
Sternum	Formed by manubrium, body, and xyphoid		1
Ribs	12 pair		24

= **80 total bones**

APPENDICULAR SKELETON

EXTREMITY	BONES	TOTAL NUMBER OF BONES
UPPER (x 2)	Pectoral girdle	
	– scapula	2
	– clavicle	2
	Free Limb	
	– humerus	2
	– radius	2
	– ulna	2
	– carpal bones (8)	16

	1. scaphoid 5. trapezium
	    2. lunate 6. trapezoid
	    3. triangular 7. capitate
	    4. pisiform 8. hamate	

	– metacarpal bones (5)	10
	– phalanges (14)	28
LOWER (x 2)	Pelvic Girdle	
	– hip bone	2
	Formed by fusion of pubis, ischium, and ilium	
	Free Limb	
	– femur	2
	– patella	2
	– tibia	2
	– fibula	2
	– tarsal bones (7)	14

	1. talus 5. lateral cuneiform
	    2. calcaneus 6. intermediate cuneiform
	    3. cuboid 7. medial cuneiform
	    4. navicular	

	– mctatarsal bones (5)	10
	– phalanges (14)	28

= **126 total bones**

Axial skeleton (80 bones) + Appendicular skeleton (126 bones) = 206 total bones

QUIZ 2
The Appendicular Skeleton

Time for Quiz = 26 minutes.
For questions 1-17, choose the single best answer.

_____1) Of the distal row of carpal bones, which bone is the second most medial?
      a) trapezium
      b) capitate
      c) cuboid
      d) triangular
      e) none of the above

_____2) Which of the two long bones of the distal forearm is the smaller, thinner bone?
      a) tibia
      b) humerus
      c) fibula
      d) radius
      e) none of the above

_____3) What is the ilium?
      a) a bone of the skull
      b) a carpal bone
      c) a tarsal bone
      d) a part of the sternum bone
      e) none of the above

_____4) The pelvic girdle is formed by
      a) the clavicle bone
      b) the scapula bone
      c) both a and b
      d) the hip bone
      e) none of the above

_____5) Of these possibilities, which is the most lateral of the proximal row of carpal bones?
      a) trapezoid
      b) talus
      c) lunate
      d) triangular
      e) none of the above

_____6) Which tarsal bone is bounded by the calcaneus proximally and other tarsal bones distally?
      a) the cuneiform bone
      b) the cuboid bone
      c) the scaphoid bone
      d) the navicular bone
      e) none of the above

_____7) The long bone of the thigh is the
      a) humerus
      b) ulna
      c) femur
      d) tibia
      e) none of the above

_____8) Of the two long bones of the forearm, which is more lateral?
      a) tibia
      b) radius
      c) fibula
      d) ulna
      e) none of the above

_____9) Of the two long bones of the leg, which is the larger, thicker bone?
      a) tibia
      b) radius
      c) fibula
      d) ulna
      e) none of the above

_____10) Which of the following bones participate in the formation of the pectoral girdle?
      a) the scaphoid bone
      b) the sacrum bone
      c) the sternum bone
      d) the hip bone
      e) none of the above

_____11) What is the ischium?
      a) a carpal bone
      b) a tarsal bone
      c) one of the three bones which fuse to form the hip bone
      d) a component of the sternum bone
      e) none of the above

_____12) Which of the two long bones of the distal forearm is the larger, thicker bone?
    a) tibia
    b) radius
    c) fibula
    d) ulna
    e) none of the above

_____13) Of the two long bones of the leg, which is more lateral?
    a) tibia
    b) radius
    c) ulna
    d) fibula
    e) none of the above

_____14) The long bone of the arm is the
    a) femur
    b) tibia
    c) radius
    d) ulna
    e) none of the above

_____15) Of the proximal row of carpal bones, which bone is most medial?
    a) pisiform
    b) hamate
    c) cuboid
    d) scaphoid
    e) none of the above

_____16) Which tarsal bone forms the heel bone?
    a) the talus bone
    b) the calcaneus bone
    c) the navicular bone
    d) the capitate bone
    e) none of the above

_____17) Which bone extends from the calcaneus proximally to the metacarpal bones distally?
    a) scaphoid
    b) cuboid
    c) navicular
    d) cuneiform
    e) none of the above

For questions 18-26, use the following directions:
    a.......1,2,3 are correct
    b.......1,3 are correct
    c.......2,4 are correct
    d.......only 4 is correct
    e.......all are correct

_____18) Which bones are part of the upper extremity skeleton?
    1. the femur
    2. the capitate
    3. the fibula
    4. the hamate

_____19) Which bones are part of the lower extremity skeleton?
    1. axis
    2. cuboid
    3. ulna
    4. talus

_____20) Which statements about the hip bone are true?
    1. The pubis contributes to its formation.
    2. The ischium contributes to its formation.
    3. The ilium contributes to its formation.
    4. It is forms the pectoral girdle.

_____21) Which bones are part of the lower extremity skeleton?
    1. radius
    2. patella
    3. ulna
    4. femur

_____22) Which statements concerning the digits are true?
    1. Digit #1 of the foot has one interphalangeal joint.
    2. Digit #3 of the hand has two interphalangeal joints.
    3. Digit #2 of the hand is immediately distal to one metacarpophalangeal joint.
    4. Digit # 3 of the foot is distal to one metacarpal bone.

_____ 23) Which statements about the extremities are true?
1. The thumb has one metacarpophalangeal joint.
2. The thumb has one interphalangeal joint.
3. The great toe has two phalanges.
4. The great toe has one metacarpophalangeal joint.

_____ 24) Which bones are part of the appendicular skeleton?
1. ilium
2. ischium
3. patella
4. manubrium

_____ 25) Which bones could be classified as a sesamoid bone?
1. coccyx
2. pisiform
3. hyoid
4. patella

_____ 26) Which statements about Digit #1 of the foot are true?
1. It only has one interphalangeal joint.
2. It contains 3 phalanges.
3. It only has one metatarsophalangeal joint.
4. It is the most lateral of the digits.

QUIZ 2: The Appendicular Skeleton Answers and Explanations

1) b – The cuboid bone is a tarsal (ankle) bone extending from the calcaneus proximally to the lateral two (# 4 and 5) metatarsal bones distally. The other bones are carpal bones.

2) e – The ulna is the medial, smaller long bone of the distal forearm.

3) e – The ilium is a bone which fuses with the ischium bone and pubis bone to form the hip bone.

4) d – The hip bone forms the pelvic girdle of the lower extremity. The pectoral (shoulder) girdle of the upper extremity is formed by the scapula (shoulder blade) and clavicle (collar bone).

5) c – Of these possibilities, the lunate bone is more lateral than the only other carpal bone which is in the proximal row, the triangular bone. The trapezoid bone is located in the distal row of carpal bones. The talus is the most proximal of the tarsal bones.

6) d – The navicular bone extends from the calcaneus proximally to the cuneiforms distally. There are three (lateral, intermediate, and medial) cuneiform bones of the tarsus. They extend from the navicular bone proximally to the medial three (#1, 2, and 3) metatarsal bones distally. The cuboid bone extends from the calcaneus bone proximally, to the lateral two (#4 and 5) metatarsal bones distally. The scaphoid bone is a carpal bone.

7) c – The humerus is the long bone of the arm. The ulna is the medial long bone of the forearm. The tibia is the larger of the two long bones of the leg (below knee).

8) b – The radius is the lateral long bone of the forearm. In the anatomic position, the hands are supinated with the palms facing the observer. The radius would therefore be in a lateral position. The ulna would be medial. The tibia and fibula are long bones of the leg (below knee).

9) a – The tibia is the medial, thicker long bone of the leg (below knee). The fibula is the smaller long bone of the leg. The radius and ulna are the two long bones of the forearm.

10) e – The pectoral or shoulder girdle of the upper extremity is formed by the scapula (shoulder blade) and clavicle (collar bone). The scaphoid bone is a carpal bone. The sacrum is a bone at the inferior aspect of the vertebral column. The sternum is the breast bone. The hip bone forms the pelvic girdle of the lower extremity.

11) c – The ischium is a bone which fuses with the pubis and ilium bones to form the hip bone.

12) b – The radius is the lateral long bone of the forearm. The ulna is the medial forearm long bone. The tibia and fibula are long bones of the leg (below knee).

13) d – The fibula is the lateral, smaller long bone of the leg. The tibia is the larger, medially placed bone. The radius and ulna are long bones of the forearm.

14) e – The humerus is the long bone of the arm.

15) a – The hamate bone is the most medial of the distal row of carpal bones. The scaphoid is the most lateral of the proximal row of carpal bones. The cuboid bone is the tarsal bone extending from the calcaneus proximally to the lateral two (#4 and 5) metatarsal bones distally.

16) b – The talus is the most proximal of the tarsal bones. The navicular bone is distal to the calcaneus and proximal to the three cuneiform bones. The capitate is a carpal bone.

17) e – Sorry! This is a trick question. Do not think future instructors will not do the same. The answer would have been the cuboid bone if the question had asked which bone extended to the *metatarsal* bones instead of *metacarpal* bones. No bone extends from the calcaneus to the metacarpals. Make it a point to distinguish

metacarpal from metatarsal bones. The prefix *meta* infers a transition or something which is following something else. The metacarpals follow the carpus or carpal bones. The metatarsals follow the tarsus or tarsal bones.

18) c – The capitate is the second most medial bone of the distal row of carpal bones. The hamate is the most medial bone of the distal row of carpal bones. The femur is the long bone of the thigh. The fibula is the lateral, smaller bone of the leg.

19) c – The cuboid bone is a tarsal bone extending from the calcaneus proximally to the lateral two (#4 and #5) metatarsal bones distally. The talus is the most proximal of the tarsal bones. The axis is the C2 vertebra. The ulna is the medial long bone of the forearm.

20) a – The pubis, ischium, and ilium bones fuse to form the hip bone. The hip bone forms the pelvic girdle. The pectoral or shoulder girdle of the upper extremity is formed by the clavicle (collar bone) and scapula (shoulder blade).

21) c – The patella is a sesamoid bone also known as the knee cap. The femur is the long bone of the thigh. The radius is the lateral long bone of the forearm. The ulna is the medial bone of the forearm.

22) a – Digit #1 of the foot is the great toe. An interphalangeal joint is between to successive phalanges of the same digit. This digit may be a finger, thumb, or toe. With the exception of the thumb and great toe (both with only two phalanges each), every digit (finger or toe) has three phalanges. Because of this, each of these other digits has two interphalangeal joints. The thumb and great toe have only one interphalangeal joint each. The metacarpophalangeal joint is a joint of the hand between the metacarpal bone of a digit proximally and the first phalange of the same digit distally. This joint forms the prominent knuckle of a closed fist. Toes are distal to metatarsal bones. Fingers and thumbs are distal to metacarpal bones.

23) a – See #22 answer explanation.

24) a – The pelvic girdle of the lower extremity is formed by the hip bone. The three bones which fuse to form the hip bone are the pubis, ischium and ilium bones. The patella is a sesamoid bone which is also known as the knee cap. The manubrium is the superiorly located component of the sternum bone.

25) c – Named for their resemblance to sesame seeds, sesamoid bones are small, sporadically present bones that are located in areas of frequent friction. When present, they are found in tendon sheaths, bursae, and joint capsules. The pisiform bone is a carpal bone which is said to also be a sesamoid bone. The patella or knee cap is the largest sesamoid bone of the body. The coccyx is the bony inferior tip of the vertebral column. It is formed by the fusion of four vertebrae. The hyoid bone is a small bone of the anterior upper neck.

26) b – See #22 answer explanation. The great toe is the most medial of the lower extremity digits.

"Golf is a good walk spoiled."

– Mark Twain

CLINICAL CORRELATION

The knee joint is the largest joint of the body and is the articulation of two bones: the femur, superiorly, and tibia, inferiorly. The joint is protected anteriorly by the patella and supported laterally by the fibula, which articulates with the lateral aspect of the tibia just distal to the knee joint. It is not uncommon to hear of knee injuries. Joints of the lower extremity support the weight of the body and are more susceptible to injury as compared to those of the upper extremity. The other two major articulations of the lower extremity are the hip and ankle joints. The hip is a ball and socket joint that permits movement in a wide ranch of directions. The ankle is a complex joint that also provides a diverse movement pattern. The knee joint, by contrast, is a hinge joint that limits movement to two basic directions: flexion and extension. When forces cause movement outside of this range, damage to knee structures may occur. Not only does weight-bearing and the type of joint contribute to potential injury, but the location of the joint between two segments of long bones increases the forces of leverage and torque on the knee.

In addition to the aforementioned bones, several other connective tissue structures participate in the formation of the knee joint, including cartilage, ligaments, tendons, and minisci. **Cartilage** is a type of dense connective tissue. In the knee, it covers the articular surface of bones, providing a smooth surface with less friction during movement and protecting the bones from wear and tear. A **ligament** is a fibrous strand that connects bones and/or cartilages. A **tendon** is a fibrous strand that connects muscles to bones and/or cartilages. Ligaments are inherent to bone articulations, but both types of connective tissue strands may support and strengthen joints. The two **menisci** form the outer fibrocartilage rim of the knee joint and are located on the superior surface of the tibia. The lateral meniscus is positioned on the articular surface of the lateral condyle of the tibia and the medial meniscus is on top of the medial condyle. The knee is reliant on ligaments and adjacent muscles for strength and stability.

When a normal knee is in the anatomic position, the vertical alignment between the thigh and lower leg is fairly straight. *Valgus* is a Latin word that means *bent out* and is used to describe deformities that cause a deviation away from the body's midline. With the knee, this is commonly known as

FIGURE 3.25
THE LEFT KNEE JOINT AND BONES OF THE LEFT LOWER EXTREMITY

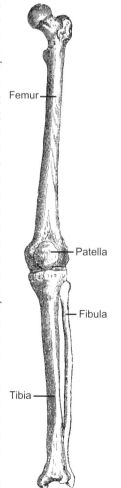

Femur

Patella

Fibula

Tibia

the "knock-knee" deformity. In a standing position the individual may not be able to place his or her feet together. The knees appear closer together than they should and the lower legs angulate slightly laterally as they travel distally from the knee. In contrast, *varus* means *bent in* and is associated with the "bow-leg" deformity of the knee. In the standing position with the feet together, the knees are separated by a wider distance than normal.

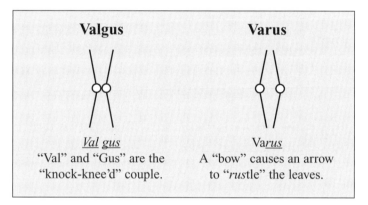

Valgus

Val gus
"Val" and "Gus" are the "knock-knee'd" couple.

Varus

Va*rus*
A "bow" causes an arrow to "*rus*tle" the leaves.

Traumatic injury may result in damage to one or more components of the knee. Each is associated with certain mechanisms of injury, clinical signs, and physical exam findings. Based on the history and physical, radiologic tests such as x-rays and magnetic resonance imaging (MRI) studies may be ordered to further delineate the extent of the injury. If significant, surgical intervention may be warranted.

■ **Cartilage**: To differentiate it from cartilage of the two menisci, knee "cartilage" can be more distinctly described as *articular* cartilage. Articular cartilage lines the joint surface and is found at the distal ends of the medial and lateral femoral condyles and the superior surface of the tibia, the tibial plateau. Damage to articular cartilage occurs with injury to the joint surface and is associated with twisting injuries, trauma, certain diseases, or gradual chronic changes over time. If there is notable loss of articular cartilage, the joint is said to have arthritis. The patient may note a "gritty" movement pattern, pain, swelling, catching, locking, and/or buckling of the knee.

■ **Ligaments:** There are four major ligaments of the knee joint, including two "internal" and two "external" ligaments. The internal ligaments include the anterior and posterior cruciate ligaments. Each travels from the middle of the superior tibia to one of the two femoral condyles. They cross one another within the knee joint, forming a *crucifix* (cross); hence, they are named the anterior and posterior *cruciate* ligaments. The external ligaments are the medial and lateral collateral ligaments. They are named *collateral* because each is located at one of the *lateral* aspects of the knee joint.

1) The **anterior cruciate ligament (ACL)** extends from the anterior portion of the middle of the superior tibia and

travels in a posterolateral direction to the lateral femoral condyle. Its purpose is to prevent excessive anterior movement of the tibia on the femur. The ligament is frequently damaged with hyperextension or pivoting injuries to the knee. **Hyperextension** injuries can occur when the knee is extended more than 10 degrees greater than full extension. **Pivoting injuries** may occur when the lower leg is excessively turned inward. ACL injury is clinically evaluated by the **anterior drawer test**. The patient is placed in the supine position with the ipsilateral hip flexed at 45 degrees and the suspected knee flexed at 90 degrees. The foot is immobilized while the examiner grasps the back of the tibia and attempts to move it forward, as if pulling a drawer open. The test is considered positive if there is excessive movement anteriorly. The **Lachman test** is thought to be a more accurate indicator of ACL instability and is performed in much the same fashion, except the knee is flexed at 15-30 degrees instead of 90 degrees.

2) The **posterior cruciate ligament (PCL)** extends from the posterior portion of the superior tibia and travels in an anteromedial direction to the medial femoral condyle. It prevents excessive posterior movement of the tibia on the femur. The mechanism of injury often involves acute posterior displacement of the tibia. This is seen with **dashboard injuries**, in which the dashboard of an automobile strikes the tibia during a motor vehicle accident. It also occurs in **contact sports** when the tibia is the first to strike the ground or another immobile object while the rest of the body continues forward. PCL injury occurs less often than ACL injury and there tends to be less knee instability, pain, and total disability. Unlike ACL injuries, a "pop" is seldom heard and the symptoms may have a gradual onset. Nevertheless, PCL injuries can be significant. Clinical evaluation involves the **posterior drawer test**, which is performed the same way as the anterior drawer test except the examiner attempts to displace the tibia in a posterior direction instead of an anterior direction.

3) The **medial collateral ligament (MCL)** extends from the medial (inner) aspect of the medial epicondyle of the femur to the medial side of the medial condyle of the tibia. The MCL resists abduction of the knee, preventing widening of the medial side of the knee joint. The ligament is often injured when the knee is struck from the lateral side, forcing unnatural abduction of the lower leg. This is commonly seen in **contact sports**. The patient has pain over the ligament and swelling. With more severe cases, the patient can have weakness and instability, feeling as if the knee could give way. Clinical evaluation is performed by placing the patient in the supine position and flexing the knee to about thirty degrees. From the lateral side, the knee is pushed in to **valgus** to determine the integrity of the MCL. Mild injuries may have pain, but limited movement. Complete tears will permit noticeable abduction. MCL tears are graded I-III.

- **Grade I MCL tear** – The tear is incomplete and the symptoms are minimal. Individuals usually return to normal activities in one to two weeks.
- **Grade II MCL tear** – The tear is also incomplete, but the damage is greater and the symptoms are more severe. Patients complain of pain and swelling and may experience instability when attempting to cut or turn sharply. Four to six weeks of rest may be required.
- **Grade III MCL tear** – This is a complete tear of the ligament and the patient usually experiences significant pain, swelling, and instability of the knee. The patient often requires a knee brace and follow-up physical therapy. Recovery could take at least six weeks.

FIGURE 3.27
OUTER STRUCTURES OF LEFT KNEE
Anteromedial view

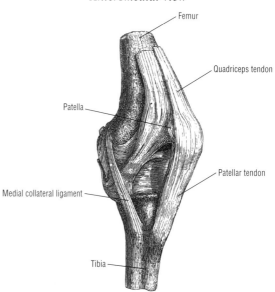

4) The **lateral collateral ligament (LCL)** extends from the lateral (outer) side of the lateral femoral epicondyle to the lateral aspect of the head of the fibula. The mechanism of injury and method of evaluation of a LCL injury are similar to that of a MCL injury, except everything is on the opposite side. The LCL resists adduction of the knee, preventing widening of the lateral side of the knee joint. The

FIGURE 3.26
FLEXED LEFT KNEE
Anterior view with patella and tendons removed

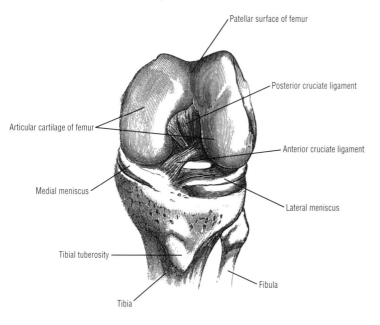

ligament is often injured when the knee is struck from the medial (inner) side, forcing unnatural adduction of the lower leg. Like MCL injury, damage to the LCL is often associated with **contact sports**. Clinical evaluation is performed the same way as that for MCL damage, except the knee is pushed out to **varus** from the medial side. Like MCL tears, LCL tears are also graded I-III. LCL tears usually don't heal as easily as MCL tears.

FIGURE 3.28
LATERAL COLLATERAL LIGAMENT
Anterior view of flexed left knee with patella and tendons removed

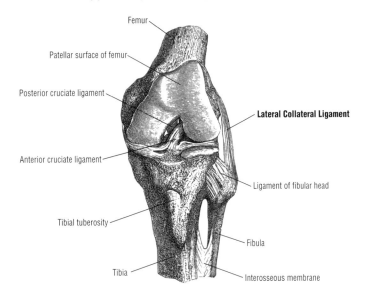

Tendons: There are multiple tendons that contribute to the function and stability of the knee joint, but the most obvious participants are the quadriceps and patellar tendons. The **quadriceps tendon** is the distal continuation of the rectus femoris tendon and inserts on the patella. The rectus femoris is one of the four muscles of the quadriceps femoris muscle group. The other three muscles are the vastus lateralis, vastus intermedius, and vastus medialis muscles. All four muscles of the quadriceps femoris are located in the anterior thigh and function to extend (straighten) the lower leg. The **patellar tendon** stretches from the patella to the tibial tuberosity and finalizes the connection between the quadriceps femoris and lower leg. As previously mentioned, the patella is the largest of the sesamoid bones and protects the articular surface of the knee from frictional forces created every time the leg is extended by this large muscle mass. It also serves to physically optimize the mechanics involved in leg extension. The quadriceps or patellar tendon could be damaged or torn with hyperflexion injuries. Such injuries may occur when the individual is jumping from a considerable distance with the knees bent. As the feet hit the ground, the quadriceps femoris intensely contracts in an attempt to break the fall and tremendous forces are applied to the quadriceps and patellar tendons. This may cause one of them to tear partially or completely. With severe injury, the patient will not be able to extend (straighten) the lower leg from a flexed position and may not be able to stand on the affected leg because the knee cannot be kept extended and will collapse. Partial tears can be treated with immobilization and

rest, but complete tears require surgical repair. If the quadriceps tendon is completely torn, the patella will be displaced inferiorly. If the patellar tendon is ruptured, the patella is displaced superiorly. If the patella is displaced laterally, patellar dislocation (subluxation) should be suspected, as most cases of patellar dislocation occur in the lateral direction. Both associated tendons may remain intact with patellar dislocation.

FIGURE 3.29
SURGICAL REPAIR OF TORN QUADRICEPS TENDON

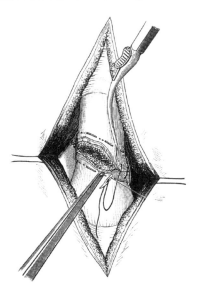

Menisci: The word *meniscus* is derived from the Greek word *meniskos*, which means *crescent*. The two menisci of the knee are the crescent-shaped fibrocartilage "pads" that are affixed to the superior surface of the tibia (tibial plateau) and form the outer rim of the knee joint. Each femoral condyle can be thought of as a cup which fits into the saucer created by a meniscus. Menisci differ from articular discs in that they don't cross the entire disc space. In addition to the knee, three other notable joints contain menisci: temporomandibular joint (lower jaw), sternoclavicular joint (sternum and clavicle), and acromioclavicular joint (acromion of scapula and clavicle). The menisci distribute weight and stress, and strengthen the knee against torsion. The medial meniscus is larger and forms a semicircle. The lateral meniscus is smaller and forms more of a complete circle.

FIGURE 3.30
LEFT KNEE TIBIAL PLATEAU
Superior view

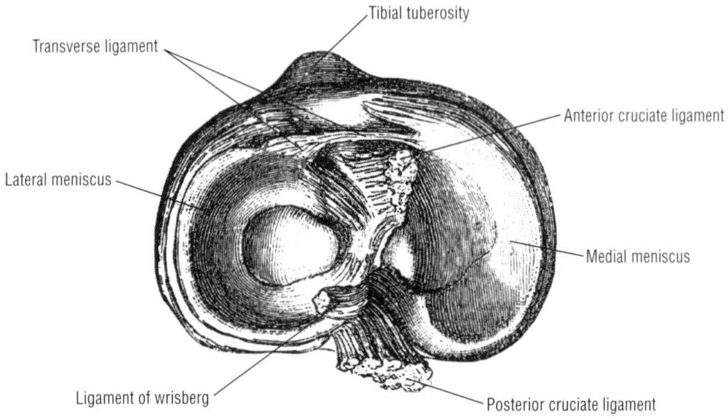

As previously mentioned, a significant portion of meniscus injuries are universally referred to as "cartilage" injuries by the lay public because the menisci are formed by fibrocartilage. Since there are two menisci and each meniscus essentially encircles its respective femoral condyle, there is a myriad of mechanisms for meniscus injury. Once injured, a flap of torn meniscus or loose body may get caught between the tibia and femur, preventing full extension of the knee. In such cases, the patient can experience severe pain and may collapse. The inability to straighten the knee is referred to as a **locked knee**. Later, the patient may feel a "pop" as the piece of meniscus slides out from between the two bones, permitting full extension of the knee. A **bucket handle tear** is a tear of a meniscus that periodically returns out from between the two bones, allowing intermittent normal knee motion. During these times of normal function, the flap of meniscus lies flat in its normal position, similar to a bucket handle that lies flat against the bucket when not in use. At times, the flap can slip back between the bones, just as the bucket handle can be lifted away from the bucket. In such situations, the patient will again not be able to straighten the leg.

SUMMARY OF CHAPTER BOXES

1) Long *axis* of body = *axial* skeleton

2) Paired bones of the skull are "paired" because they require two bones, a right and left. Bones located in the front, center, or back of the skull are unpaired. The "oids" are unpaired, although the sphenoid forms part of each lateral wall.

3) Concha = shell-shaped (conch shell). Nasal conchae are extensions of tissue into the nasal cavity to increase the surface area exposed to inspired air. This warms, moistens and filters the air. Ethmoid bone = superior and middle nasal conchae. Inferior nasal concha = separate, paired bone of the skull. One extends inward from each side of nasal cavity.

4) C1 comes before C2: the "*t*" of "a*t*las" comes before the "*x*" of "a*x*is." In Greek mythology, **Atlas held the world up**, just as the atlas holds the head up.

5) **HALF AND HALF:** 24 true vertebrae. half (12) articulate with ribs, half (12) do not.

6) *Hy*oid bone is *high*est bone which is not part of the skull or vertebral column

7) Ear ossicles = **MIS** = **M**alleus to **I**ncus to **S**tapes…stapes to **s**ound organs (**s**emicircular canals, cochlea)

8) Radius = thumb side. The radius is the "thicker" forearm long bone and is on the same side as the "thicker" digit, the thumb. **radial side = thumb side = lateral**

9) **HALF AND HALF:** 8 carpal bones. half (4) are in the proximal row, half (4) are in the distal row.

10) Wrist important in $G_1O_2L_3F_4$: four bones in each row. From lateral (radial) to medial (ulnar) :

Proximal row = **S**wing **L**ike **T**he **P**ros
(scaphoid) (lunate) (triangular) (pisiform)

Distal row = **T**ry **T**o **C**orrect **H**ook
(trapezium) (trapezoid) (capitate) (hamate = hook-shaped)

11) From lateral to medial, trape**zi**um comes before trape-z**o**id (alphabetical order)

12) **Pisiform** (means pea-sized or pea-shaped) and **Hamate** are the most **medial** carpal bones of proximal and distal rows, respectively. The more *peas* and *ham* one eats, the more one **"adds to the midline."**

13) *Fib*ula tells a *"fib"* in claiming to be the predominant long bone of leg (knee to ankle)

14) Each hand or foot contains a **"boat": scaphoid** = carpal bone, **navicular** = tarsal bone

15) Ankle important in $K_1I_2C_3K_4I_5N_6G_7$ = **7 tarsal bones**: proximal 2 (talus, calcaneus), intermediate 2 (cuboid, navicular), distal 3 (lateral, intermediate, and medial cuneiforms)

16) **5 C's** = **c**alcaneus, **c**uboid, lat. **c**uneiform, inter. **c**uneiform, med. **c**uneiform (alphabetical order from proximal to distal = calcaneus to cuboid to 3 cuneiforms) **Talus** = 1st **t**arsal bone. **Navicular = boat-shaped bone which "floats" in a sea of C's** (it is bordered by each of the 5 C's). Ankle is important in kicking, but because a boat is available, swimming is avoided.
Proximally, the metatarsal bones articulate with **1 cube and 3 wedges**.

17) A *pro* walker, whether walking on his feet or hands, must have the feet or hands in a *pro*nated position. The lower extremity is in a constant state of pronation. The upper extremity is described from a supinated position (anatomic position), but shares common characteristics with the lower extremity when pronated.

18) **CLINICAL CORRELATION:**

Val gus	Va*rus*
"Val" and "Gus" are the "knock-knee'd" couple.	A "bow" causes an arrow to "*rus*tle" the leaves.

END OF CHAPTER TEST

Time for Exam = 70 minutes.

MATCHING
Match each bone with one best answer

_____ 1. navicular bone	A. contains the inner ear
_____ 2. ethmoid bone	B. hook shaped
_____ 3. ulna bone	C. an ossicle bone of the ear
_____ 4. scaphoid bone	D. transfers the weight of the upper body to the lower extremities
_____ 5. temporal bone	E. a small bone of the upper anterior neck
_____ 6. fibula bone	F. a pea-shaped sesamoid bone of the carpus
_____ 7. calcaneus bone	G. medial to the radius bone
_____ 8. patella bone	H. pectoral girdle
_____ 9. mandible bone	I. the most lateral bone of the proximal row of carpal bones
_____10. hamate bone	J. false
_____11. talus bone	K. unpaired skull bone; wing-like; forms a portion of both sides of skull
_____12. capitate bone	L. long bone of the thigh
_____13. coccyx bone	M. lateral to the tibia bone
_____14. sacrum bone	N. formed by the fusion of 4 vertebrae
_____15. cuboid bone	O. one of the 3 bones which fuse to form the hip bone
_____16. hyoid bone	P. the largest sesamoid bone
_____17. pisiform bone	Q. floating
_____18. malleus bone	R. a boat-shaped tarsal bone
_____19. rib #11	S. located between the calcaneus proximally and metatarsal bones distally
_____20. scapula bone	T. located just lateral to the hamate bone
_____21. sphenoid bone	U. superior component of sternum bone
_____22. femur bone	V. heel bone
_____23. ischium bone	W. pelvic girdle
_____24. manubrium	X. most proximal of the tarsal bones
_____25. hip bone	Y. jaw bone
_____26. rib #10	Z. unpaired skull bone; sieve-like

For questions 27-54, choose the single best answer.

_____27) Of the proximal row of carpal bones, which is the second most medial?
    a) capitate
    b) triangular
    c) trapezoid
    d) navicular
    e) none of the above

_____28) How many bones are usually present in the human skeleton?
    a) 303
    b) 206
    c) 179
    d) 256
    e) none of the above

_____29) How many bones are present in the skull, excluding the mandible?
    a) 23
    b) 17
    c) 21
    d) 27
    e) none of the above

_____30) How many skull bones are paired (have a right and left bone)?
    a) 6
    b) 5
    c) 11
    d) 8
    e) none of the above

_____31) What is the name of the jawbone?
   a) maxilla
   b) malleus
   c) manubrium
   d) sphenoid
   e) none of the above

_____32) Of the two long bones of the leg, which is the smaller, thinner bone?
   a) tibia
   b) radius
   c) fibula
   d) ulna
   e) none of the above

_____33) The top of the cranial cavity is known as the
   a) calvaria
   b) magnum
   c) foramina
   d) noggin
   e) none of the above

_____34) The T4 vertebra is which vertebra from the top?
   a) 9th
   b) 13th
   c) 22nd
   d) 4th
   e) none of the above

_____35) How many vertebrae typically fuse to form the coccyx?
   a) 3
   b) 4
   c) 6
   d) none; the coccyx is a carpal bone.
   e) none of the above

_____36) What is the ischium?
   a) a bone of the skull
   b) a carpal bone
   c) a tarsal bone
   d) a part of the sternum
   e) none of the above

_____37) Passageways through which anatomic structures travel in bone are known as
   a) foramina
   b) calvaria
   c) magnums
   d) sutures
   e) none of the above

_____38) The L6 vertebra is which number vertebra from the top of the vertebral column?
   a) 20th
   b) 23rd
   c) 27th
   d) 25th
   e) none of the above

_____39) Which bone contains the inner ear?
   a) temporal
   b) parietal
   c) sphenoid
   d) ethmoid
   e) none of the above

_____40) Which statements concerning the rib cage are true?
   a) rib #6 is a true rib
   b) rib #8 is a false rib
   c) both a and b
   d) rib #10 is a floating rib
   e) none of the above

_____41) The pectoral girdle is formed by
   a) the clavicle bone
   b) the scaphoid bone
   c) both a and b
   d) the hip bone
   e) none of the above

_____42) The hyoid bone is
   a) an ear ossicle
   b) a small bone of the upper neck
   c) a carpal bone
   d) a tarsal bone
   e) none of the above

_____43) What is the ilium?
    a) a carpal bone
    b) a tarsal bone
    c) one of the three bones which fuse to form the hip bone
    d) a part of the sternum bone
    e) none of the above

_____44) Of the two long bones of the forearm, which is more medial?
    a) tibia
    b) radius
    c) fibula
    d) ulna
    e) none of the above

_____45) Which tarsal bone is bounded by the calcaneus proximally and metatarsal bones distally?
    a) the navicular bone
    b) the cuneiform bone
    c) the cuboid bone
    d) the capitate bone
    e) none of the above

_____46) Of the distal row of carpal bones, which bone is the most medial?
    a) hamate
    b) calcaneus
    c) pisiform
    d) trapezium
    e) none of the above

_____47) What is the total number of skull bones which are not paired (have only one bone – no right or left)?
    a) 11
    b) 6
    c) 8
    d) 4
    e) none of the above

_____48) What is the name of the three tarsal bones of the same name which have a lateral, intermediate, and medial member?
    a) the cuboid bones
    b) the calcaneus bones
    c) the capitate bones
    d) the cuneiform bones
    e) none of the above

_____49) Which statements about the sternum are true?
    a) The xyphoid is the superior process.
    b) It articulates with true ribs by way of costal cartilage.
    c) It transfers the weight of the upper body to the lower extremities.
    d) The manubrium is the intermediately located, large component.
    e) None of the above

_____50) Of the distal row of carpal bones, which bone is the second most medial?
    a) lunate
    b) talus
    c) trapezoid
    d) capitate
    e) none of the above

_____51) The manubrium is
    a) the large, intermediately located process of the sternum bone
    b) the lower jaw bone
    c) an ossicle bone of the ear
    d) a tarsal bone
    e) none of the above

_____52) Which of the following is the medial long bone of the leg?
    a) tibia
    b) femur
    c) fibula
    d) ulna
    e) none of the above

_____53) The axis bone is
    a) the C1 vertebra
    b) the C2 vertebra
    c) an ear ossicle
    d) a carpal bone
    e) none of the above

_____54) The pelvic girdle is formed by
    a) the femur
    b) the humerus
    c) the hip bone
    d) the scapula
    e) none of the above

For questions 55-70, use the following directions:
   a.......**1,2,3 are correct**
   b.......**1,3 are correct**
   c.......**2,4 are correct**
   d.......**only 4 is correct**
   e.......**all are correct**

_____55) Which statements concerning the sternum
         are true?
         1. The malleus forms the superior
            component.
         2. It is part of the appendicular skeleton.
         3. Nine true ribs articulate with it by
            way of costal cartilage.
         4. The xyphoid forms the small inferi-
            or component.

_____56) Which bones contribute to the formation
         of the orbit?
         1. ethmoid
         2. nasal
         3. sphenoid
         4. temporal

_____57) Which bones are ossicles of the ear?
         1. incus
         2. malleus
         3. stapes
         4. ischium

_____58) Which statements concerning the rib cage
         are true?
         1. There are seven pairs of true ribs.
         2. There are two pairs of floating ribs.
         3. All ribs articulate with thoracic
            vertebrae.
         4. There are three pairs of false ribs.

_____59) Which of the following are paired bones
         of the skull?
         1. vomer
         2. frontal
         3. ethmoid
         4. parietal

_____60) Which statements about the sacrum bone
         are true?
         1. It is formed by the fusion of five
            vertebrae.
         2. It is part of the axial skeleton.
         3. It is bound superiorly by the L5
            vertebra.
         4. It is bound inferiorly by the cuboid.

_____61) Which statements about the vertebral
         column are true?
         1. There are 5 lumbar vertebrae.
         2. There are 6 cervical vertebrae.
         3. There are 12 thoracic vertebrae.
         4. The axis is the C1 vertebra.

_____62) Which statements about the extremities
         are true?
         1. The thumb has 3 phalanges.
         2. The great toe has one metacarpal
            bone just proximal to it.
         3. The thumb is the most medial of the
            upper extremity digits.
         4. The little toe has 3 phalanges.

_____63) Which bones are part of the appendicular
         skeleton?
         1. pubis
         2. fibula
         3. scaphoid
         4. scapula

_____64) Which of the following bones could be
         classified as a sesamoid bone?
         1. first rib
         2. incus
         3. calcaneus
         4. pisiform

_____65) Which of the following are unpaired
         bones of the skull?
         1. ethmoid
         2. occipital
         3. sphenoid
         4. palatine

_____66) Which statements about Digit #1 of the foot are true?
   1. It has one metacarpal bone proximal to it.
   2. It only has one interphalangeal joint.
   3. It only has one metacarpophalangeal joint.
   4. It contains two phalanges.

_____67) Which statements about the pisiform bone are true?
   1. It is a carpal bone.
   2. Its name implies poor form.
   3. It is a sesamoid bone.
   4. It is hook-shaped.

_____68) Which bones are part of the axial skeleton?
   1. ethmoid
   2. scaphoid
   3. coccyx
   4. cuneiform

_____69) Which statements concerning the rib cage are true?
   1. There are nine pairs of true ribs.
   2. False ribs do not articulate with the sternum or any other rib.
   3. The bone of true ribs articulates directly with the sternum bone.
   4. There are three pairs of false ribs.

_____70) Which bones are part of the appendicular skeleton of the lower extremity?
   1. navicular
   2. sphenoid
   3. calcaneus
   4. vomer

END OF CHAPTER TEST: Answers and Explanations

1) R	8) P	15) S	21) K
2) Z	9) Y	16) E	22) L
3) G	10) B	17) F	23) O
4) I	11) X	18) C	24) U
5) A	12) T	19) Q	25) W
6) M	13) N	20) H	26) J
7) V	14) D		

27) b – When identifying carpal bones, a sport in which they play a vital role, golf, should be considered. The proximal row of carpal bones, from lateral to medial, can be remembered by "<u>S</u>wing <u>L</u>ike <u>T</u>he <u>P</u>ros." The second most medial carpal bone of the proximal row is thereby the <u>T</u>riangular bone. The navicular bone is a tarsal (ankle) bone that extends from the calcaneus proximally to the three cuneiform bones distally. The other bones are carpal bones. Where would each be located?

28) b – Some individuals may have more or less than 206 bones due to an addition, absence, or fusion of one or more bones.

29) c – Of the 21 bones, 5 are unpaired and 8 are paired. Paired bones are those which have both a right and left bone. 8 x 2 = 16 → 16 + 5 = 21

30) d – Excluding the mandible, there are 8 paired bones (16 total) and 5 unpaired bones of the skull which make the total number of skull bones 21.

31) e – The mandible forms the lower jaw. The maxilla is a paired bone of the skull which forms the upper jaw under both orbits. The malleus is one of the three ear ossicles. The manubrium forms the superior aspect of the sternum. Finally, the sphenoid is an unpaired bone of the skull.

32) c – The fibula is a lateral, smaller long bone of the leg. The fibula is telling a "fib" when it claims to be the predominant bone of the lower leg. The tibia is the medial, larger long bone of the leg. The radius and ulna are long bones of the forearm.

33) a – The top of the cranial cavity is known as the calvaria. Foramina are passageways through bone. The foramen magnum is the large passageway at the base of the skull through which the spinal cord travels.

34) e – There are seven cervical vertebrae. Therefore, the fourth thoracic vertebra would be the eleventh vertebra from the top.

35) b – The coccyx is usually formed by the fusion of four vertebrae.

36) e – The ischium is a bone which fuses with the pubis bone and ilium bone to form the hip bone.

37) a – *Foramina* are passageways through which other structures or substances travel. *Foramen* is the singular form of the word. The calvaria is the top of the cranial cavity. The foramen magnum is the large foramen at the base of the skull through which the spinal cord travels. Sutures hold the bones of the skull together.

38) d – Although the vast majority of people have five lumbar vertebrae, there are individuals with 4, 6, or even 7 lumbar vertebrae. In the case of L6, it would be the 25th vertebra from the top: 7 cervical + 12 thoracic + 6 lumbar = 25 vertebrae.

39) a – The temporal bone is a paired bone of the skull (there is a right one and left one) which houses the inner ear.

40) c – There are a total of twelve pairs of ribs. There are seven pairs of true ribs (ribs #1-#7). The costal cartilage of each true rib articulates

directly with the sternum. There are three pairs of false ribs (ribs #8, 9, and 10). The costal cartilage of false ribs do not make it to the sternum, but instead articulate with the anterior aspect of the rib immediately above it. There are two pairs of floating ribs (rib #11 and 12). The floating ribs simply extend laterally and inferiorly from their respective vertebra. They do not articulate with any other structure.

41) a – The pectoral (shoulder) girdle of the upper extremity is formed by the scapula (shoulder blade) and clavicle (collar bone). The scaphoid bone is a carpal bone. The hip bone forms the pelvic girdle for the lower extremity.

42) b – The hyoid bone is a small bone of the upper anterior neck which provides protection to the pharynx and larynx. It also serves as an attachment point for several muscles which function in swallowing and phonation.

43) c – The ilium is a bone which fuses with the ischium bone and pubis bone to form the hip bone.

44) d – The ulna is the medial long bone of the forearm. In the anatomic position, the hands are supinated with the palms facing the observer. The radius is on the same side as the thumb. The radius is therefore lateral; the ulna is medial.

45) c – The cuboid bone is bounded by the lateral two metatarsal bones distally. The navicular bone is bounded by the three cuneiform bones distally. The navicular bone is named for its boat-like appearance. Coincidently, it "floats" in a sea of C's. It is bordered by the 5 C's…calcaneus proximally, cuboid laterally, and 3 cuneiforms distally. The talus can be remembered as the most proximal of the tarsal bones because the beginning of its name is similar to the word *tarsal*. Finally, if the calcaneus can simply be remembered as the heel bone, the tarsal bones suddenly become easier to identify. The capitate bone is a carpal (wrist) bone.

46) a – When identifying carpal bones, a sport in which they play a vital role, golf, should be considered. The distal row of carpal bones,

from lateral to medial, can be remembered by "**T**ry **T**o **C**orrect **H**ook." The most medial bone would therefore be the **H**amate bone. The calcaneus (heel bone) is a tarsal (ankle) bone.

47) e – Excluding the mandible, there are 8 paired bones (16 total) and 5 unpaired bones of the skull. This brings the total number of skull bones to 21. The 5 unpaired or single bones of the skull include the frontal, occipital, vomer, ethmoid, and sphenoid bones.

48) d – There are three (lateral, intermediate, and medial) cuneiform bones of the tarsus (ankle). They extend from the navicular bone proximally to the medial three (#1, #2, and #3) metatarsal bones distally.

49) b – There are seven pairs of true ribs, ribs #1-#7. The costal cartilage of each true rib articulates directly with the sternum. The sternum is formed by three components. The manubrium is the superiorly located component. The body is the largest and intermediately located component. The xiphoid process is the small, inferiorly located component. Answer c is referring to the sacrum bone.

50) d – See #46 answer explanation. The second most medial carpal bone of the distal row is the **C**apitate bone. The talus is the most proximal of the tarsal (ankle) bones. The other bones are carpal bones.

51) e – The sternum is formed by three components. The manubrium is the superiorly located component. The body is the largest and intermediately located component. The xiphoid process is the small, inferiorly located component. The lower jaw is the mandible. The ear ossicles include the malleus, incus, and stapes.

52) a – The tibia is the medial, thicker long bone of the leg. The femur is the long bone of the thigh. The fibula is the lateral, smaller bone of the leg. The radius and ulna are long bones of the forearm.

53) b – The axis bone is the C2 vertebra. The atlas bone is the C1 vertebra.

54) c – The hip bone forms the pelvic girdle of the lower extremity. The pectoral (shoulder) girdle of the upper extremity is formed by the clavicle (collar bone) and scapula (shoulder blade).

55) d – The sternum is part of the axial skeleton and is also known as the breast bone. It is comprised of three components. The manubrium is the superiorly located component, the body is the largest, intermediately located component, and the xiphoid process is the small, inferiorly located component. Seven true ribs articulate with the sternum by way of costal cartilage. The malleus is an ear ossicle.

56) b – The orbit is an open cavity of the skull which contains the eyeball. It is named for the fact that the eye rotates within it, similar to planets rotating in an orbit. The orbit is formed by seven skull bones. This includes the frontal, lacrimal, ethmoid, maxilla, zygomatic, sphenoid, and palatine bones.

57) a – In sequential order, from the tympanic membrane to the organs of sound, the ossicles of the ear include the malleus, incus, and stapes (MIS). The ischium is a bone that fuses with the ilium and pubis bones to form the hip bone.

58) e – See #40 answer explanation. Each of the 12 ribs articulates with a thoracic vertebra.

59) d – The parietal bone is a paired bone which forms the upper lateral aspect of each side of the skull. The vomer bone is an unpaired bone which forms the lower part of the nasal septum. The frontal bone is an unpaired bone that forms the forehead. The ethmoid bone is an unpaired bone which forms the superior and medial nasal conchae and upper part of the nasal septum.

60) a – The sacrum is bound inferiorly by the coccyx bone, the bony inferior tip of the vertebral column. The cuboid bone is a tarsal bone.

61) b – The vertebral column consists of 7 cervical vertebrae, 12 thoracic vertebrae, and 5 lumbar vertebrae. The sacrum is formed by the fusion of 5 sacral vertebrae. Finally, the coccyx bone is formed by the fusion of 4 vertebrae. This brings the total number of vertebrae to 33 (7+12+5=24 free vertebrae + 5 sacral + 4 coccygeal = 33 total vertebrae). The atlas is the C1 vertebrae. The axis is the C2 vertebrae.

62) d – With the exception of the thumb and great toe (which have only two phalanges each), every digit (finger or toe) has three phalanges. Because of this, each of these digits has two interphalangeal joints. The thumb and great toe have only one interphalangeal joint each. The great toe has one metatarsal bone proximal to it. Metacarpal bones are in the hands. In the anatomic position, the hands are supinated with the palms facing forward. The thumb, therefore, is the most lateral of the hand digits.

63) e – The three bones which fuse to form the hip bone are the pubis, ischium, and ilium bones. The fibula is the lateral, smaller long bone of the leg. The scaphoid bone is the most lateral bone of the proximal row of carpal bones. The pectoral or shoulder girdle of the upper extremity is formed by the clavicle (collar bone) and scapula (shoulder blade).

64) d – Named for their resemblance to sesame seeds, sesamoid bones are small, sporadically present bones located in areas of frequent friction. When present, they are found in tendon sheaths, bursae, and joint capsules. The pisiform bone is a carpal bone which is said to also be a sesamoid bone. The patella is the largest sesamoid bone of the body. The incus, along with the malleus and stapes, is an ossicle bone of the ear. The calcaneus or heel bone is a tarsal bone.

65) a – The ethmoid bone is an unpaired bone that forms the superior and medial nasal conchae and part of the nasal septum. The occipital bone is an unpaired bone which forms the posterior skull. The sphenoid bone is an unpaired bone that forms part of each side and bottom of the skull. It also forms a portion of the posterior wall of the orbit. The palatine bone is a paired bone forming the posterior aspect of the hard palate.

66) c – See #62 answer explanation. Digit #1 of the foot is the great toe. It is the most medial of the

lower extremity digits. There is one metatarsal bone proximal to the great toe. Metacarpal bones are located in the hands. The metatarsophalangeal joint is a joint of the foot between the metatarsal bone of a toe proximally and the first phalange of the same toe distally. An interphalangeal joint is between two successive phalanges of the same digit. This digit may be a finger or toe.

67) b – The pisiform bone is the most medial bone of the proximal row of carpal bones. The name *pisiform* describes a resemblance to the size or shape of a pea. Although it is a carpal bone, the pisiform bone is also considered to be a sesamoid bone. Named for their resemblance to sesame seeds, sesamoid bones are small, sporadically present bones located in areas of frequent friction. When present, they are found in tendon sheaths, bursae, and joint capsules. The hamate bone is a carpal bone named for its hook-shape.

68) b – The ethmoid is an unpaired bone of the skull which forms the superior and medial nasal conchae and part of the nasal septum. The coccyx is the bony, inferior tip of the vertebral column. It is formed by the fusion of four vertebrae. The scaphoid bone is the most lateral bone of the proximal row of carpal bones. There are three (lateral, intermediate, and medial) cuneiform bones of the tarsus. They extend from the navicular bone proximally to the medial three (#1, #2, and #3) metatarsal bones distally.

69) d – See #40 answer explanation.

70) b – The navicular bone is a tarsal bone which extends from the calcaneus proximally to the three cuneiform bones distally. The calcaneus is a tarsal bone known commonly as the heel bone. Both the sphenoid and vomer are unpaired bones of the skull.

*"Your vision will become clear only when you look into your heart.
Who looks outside, dreams. Who looks inside, awakens."*

– Carl Jung

CHAPTER FOUR

BODY CAVITIES AND MAJOR ORGANS

Body cavities provide protected space for the various organs of the body. To accomplish their highly specialized functions, organs require the ability to change shape and size. The heart and lungs are in a constant state of movement and many other organs are fairly active. Peristaltic contractions of digestive organs move ingested contents through the alimentary canal. The bladder fills and empties. Body cavities provide this room while maintaining a high degree of protection to viscera from blows and shocks. They absorb G-force injury created by an impact or sudden change in the body's direction of movement. Suspension of visceral organs in cavities permits flexibility to bend, not break. Following an overview of body cavities, a description of the major organs will be provided in this chapter.

BODY CAVITIES

Body cavities are grossly divided into those that are closed and those that are open. Closed cavities have no direct communication to the outside of the body; open cavities do. Both types of cavities are surrounded by a membrane that is specific to the type of cavity it surrounds. The major closed cavities are surrounded by a *serosal* membrane. Open cavities are surrounded by a *mucosal* membrane.

Each of the larger closed cavities contributes to the formation of one of the two primary cavities: the ventral cavity and the dorsal cavity. As its name would imply, the **ventral cavity** is located in the ventral (anterior) aspect of the body. It is comprised of four smaller cavities that contain certain organs and supporting structures. The four cavities are the thoracic cavity, pericardial cavity, abdominal cavity, and pelvic cavity. The thoracic cavity contains the lungs and surrounds the pericardial cavity. The pericardial cavity contains the heart and base of the great vessels. The abdominal cavity holds digestive, urinary, and metabolic organs. The pelvic cavity can be considered the inferior portion of the abdominal cavity and contains the terminal portion of the digestive tract, urinary organs, and reproductive organs. Each of these four cavities is lined by a **serosal membrane (serosa)** and each membrane has a specific name. A serosal membrane secretes a watery substance that acts as a lubricant, preventing frictional tissue damage to moving visceral structures and the walls of the cavities in which they move.

> The word *serosa* is derived from the word *serous* which describes a substance that is like serum. Blood is composed of red cells, white cells, platelets, plasma, and the watery serum. Something that is described as being serous means that it is water-like, or serum-like.

Individual components of the ventral cavity are formed by the potential space that exists between the inner surface of the body wall (or membranous structure) and the outer surface of visceral organs. Each of these closed cavities can be considered to be formed by a continuous membrane that folds over on itself at the peripheral edges of the cavity, forming two layers. One layer covers the inner surface of the outer wall of the cavity. The other layer covers the outer surface of the visceral organs and their supporting structures. As mentioned, this surrounding membrane is a serosa and its watery secretion prevents frictional tissue damage from organ movement. In the truest sense, the actual cavity is within the two "coats" of membrane and has no visceral organ or structure within it. The cavity has no entrance or exit; it is a **closed cavity**.

The **thoracic cavity** contains the great blood vessels, lungs, and other tissues. In addition, it surrounds the pericardial cavity. The thoracic cavity is subdivided by the mediastinum into a right and left cavity, one cavity for each lung. The **mediastinum** is a group of midline structures comprised of the heart, great vessels, thymus, esophagus, trachea, and other supporting structures.

> Mediastinum is medial or midline

The serosa of the thoracic cavities is the **pleura**. The pleura lines the thoracic wall and folds over on itself to also cover the lungs. The portion that covers the inner surface of the chest wall, diaphragm, and mediastinum is known as the **parietal pleura.** The word *parietal* refers to the wall of a cavity. The **visceral pleura** covers the outer surface of the lungs, blood vessels, and supporting structures. Because the lungs comprise most of the surface area it covers, the visceral pleura is also commonly referred to as the **pulmonary pleura**.

> There are *two* lungs; they are the "plural" organ (in addition to the kidneys and adrenal glands) and are covered by the *pleura*.

The **pericardial cavity** contains the heart and base of the great vessels. It lies within the thoracic cavity. The pericardial and thoracic cavities are separated by the **membranous (fibrous) pericardium**, the sac-like structure that surrounds the heart. The serous membrane of the pericardial cavity is the **serous pericardial membrane (serous pericardium)**. Similar to the pleura, the serous pericardium lines the inner surface of the outer wall of the cavity and folds over on itself to also cover the outer surface of the visceral structures of the cavity. The portion that lines the inner surface of the membranous pericardium is the **parietal pericardial membrane**. The portion that lines the outer surface of the heart and proximal great vessels is the **visceral pericardial membrane**. The visceral pericardial membrane is also known as the **epicardium** and is external to the myocardium, the contracting muscle mass of the heart. The location where the visceral pericardial membrane folds back on itself to become the parietal pericardial membrane is known as the **reflection of the pericardium**.

The thoracic and pericardial cavities are separated from the abdominal and pelvic cavities by the diaphragm, the large dome-like muscle used to expand the lungs during inspiration. The **abdominal cavity** is inferior to the diaphragm and contains visceral organs of the digestive tract and urinary system. Included are the stomach, pancreas, small and large intestines, liver, gallbladder, spleen, and kidneys. The **pelvic cavity** can be considered the lower (inferior) portion of the abdominal cavity and contains the bladder, rectum, and reproductive organs. Both the abdominal and pelvic cavities are lined by the same serous membrane, the **peritoneum**. Because these two cavities are continuous and are lined by the same membrane, they are commonly considered one cavity, the **abdominopelvic cavity**.

The designations of the two portions of the peritoneum are similar to the designations of the other serosal membranes. The **parietal peritoneum** lines the inner surface of the abdominal and pelvic walls. It folds over on itself and becomes the **visceral peritoneum**, which lines the outer surface of the abdominal and pelvic organs and their supporting structures.

> Again, the word *parietal* refers to the wall of a cavity. Recall the paired parietal bones of the skull which form part of the wall of the cranial cavity.

The **dorsal cavity** is the second major closed cavity and lies in the dorsal (posterior) aspect of the body. It is comprised of two cavities: the cranial and spinal cavities. The **cranial cavity** contains the brain and associated structures. It lies within the bony skull. The **spinal cavity** contains the spinal cord and its associated structures. It lies within the bony protection of the vertebral column. The spinal cavity is also known as the spinal canal, vertebral cavity, and vertebral canal. The cranial and spinal cavities are continuous with one another and both are enclosed by a fibrous membrane, the **dura mater**. The space between the external layers of dura mater and structures of the central nervous system (brain and spinal cord) is filled with a fluid known as **cerebrospinal fluid**

(CSF). CSF acts as a shock absorber to cushion and protect the brain and spinal cord from injury sustained by G-forces associated with sudden changes in movement, direction, or blows.

In addition to the ventral and dorsal cavities, the body also contains numerous small closed cavities. Examples include the ventricles of the brain, blood vessels, inner ear ducts, eye ducts, and joint cavities.

FIGURE 4.1
BODY CAVITIES

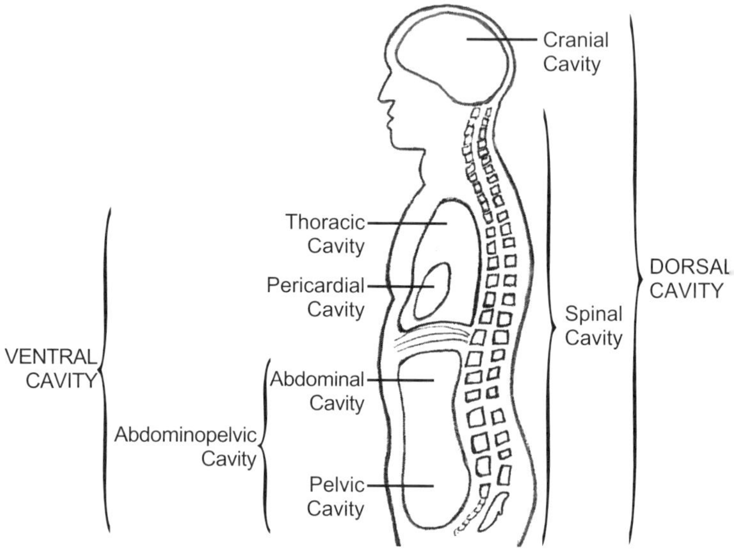

As previously indicated, in addition to these closed cavities, the body also contains **open cavities**, cavities that have an opening to the outside of the body. Open cavities include the inside lumen of viscera and certain bone cavities. The **oral cavity**, **digestive cavity**, **nasal cavity**, **respiratory cavity**, **urinary cavity**, **reproductive cavity**, and individual cavities formed by each of the **paranasal sinuses** are examples. In instances in which the open cavity is formed by the internal lumen of viscera, open cavities are often situated within the same body walls as closed cavities, but are differentiated by their portal into and out of the cavity. With the respiratory cavity, the trachea serves as both the passage into (inspiration) and out of (expiration) the lungs. With the digestive cavity, the esophagus is the portal of entry and the anus is the portal of exit. In addition, these open cavities are separated from closed cavities by the serosal membrane of the closed cavity (on the outer wall of the viscera), the tissue of the viscera, and the mucosal membrane of the open cavity (on the inner wall of the viscera).

The misconception that the serous membranes of closed cavities completely *surround* the visceral organs of their cavity should be avoided. On the contrary, they surround the potential space that exists between the outer surface of the organs and the inner surface of the body wall. In many instances, the serous membrane of a closed cavity covers only a portion of the outer wall of a visceral structure.

All open cavities are lined with a membrane called a **mucosa**. These mucosal membranes secrete a layer of mucous. The mucous serves as an aid in handling foreign substances which present to the body from the opening to the outside world. Examples of such substances include water, air, food, bacteria, viruses, and toxins. The mucous functions to "trap" unwanted foreign substances in its thick layer and to prevent their entrance into the interior of the body. The mucous and its trapped substances can then be returned to the external environment by way of the opening to the outside (digestive tract, respiratory tract, urinary tract, etc.). Unlike the serous membranes of the major closed cavities, the mucous membranes of the open cavities do not have specific names. Each is merely described as a mucous membrane of the cavity it lines.

> Mucosal membranes are usually covered with a layer of mucous, hence the name *mucosa*.

STRUCTURES OF THE THORACIC CAVITY

Intrathoracic organs are primarily responsible for receiving deoxygenated blood, oxygenating it, and returning the blood to the rest of the body for utilization as an energy source. To provide this function, a close functional and anatomic relationship exists between the heart and lungs. Although numerous other structures are present in the thorax, the focus of this section will be on the major intrathoracic components: the heart, great vessels, and lungs.

HEART AND GREAT VESSELS

Because the heart and great vessels possess specific anatomic relationships with nerves that are discussed later in the course, it is important to learn their basic anatomy. The heart and great vessels are located within the recently-described pericardial and thoracic cavities. The great vessels are the large blood vessels that carry blood into and out of the pericardial cavity.

FIGURE 4.2
HEART AND GREAT VESSELS

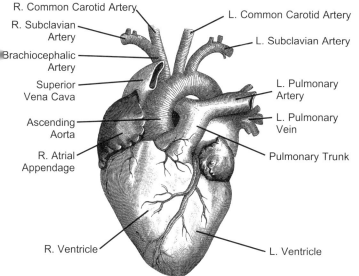

R. Common Carotid Artery
R. Subclavian Artery
Brachiocephalic Artery
Superior Vena Cava
Ascending Aorta
R. Atrial Appendage
R. Ventricle
L. Common Carotid Artery
L. Subclavian Artery
L. Pulmonary Artery
L. Pulmonary Vein
Pulmonary Trunk
L. Ventricle

Deoxygenated blood is returned to the heart by veins that coalesce to form the **superior vena cava** and **inferior vena cava**. The superior vena cava drains deoxygenated blood from the head, neck, upper extremities, and upper torso. In addition to draining blood from tissues that are positioned superior to the level of the heart, the superior vena cava also receives some blood from tissues that are inferior to the heart. This blood is drained from the chest wall and is delivered to the superior vena cava by the azygos vein. All blood that is returned to the heart by the inferior vena cava comes from

tissues that are inferior to the level of the heart.

Blood returning from each upper extremity travels by way of its respective **subclavian vein**. Deoxygenated blood returning from the head drains into the vertebral, external jugular, and internal jugular veins on each side. As it approaches the pericardium, the subclavian vein receives blood from the **vertebral** and **external jugular veins**. More blood arrives in the **internal jugular vein,** which combines with the subclavian vein to form the **brachiocephalic vein**. The brachiocephalic vein is also known as the **innominate vein**. Some prefer the name brachiocephalic because it describes where the blood is returning from (brachio = arm; cephalic = head). The word *innominate* means *something without a name.* The student should learn both names. The right and left brachiocephalic (innominate) veins join to form the **superior vena cava**.

Just prior to entering the pericardium, the superior vena cava receives the **azygos vein**. The azygos vein is positioned slightly to the right and drains deoxygenated blood from the chest wall at a level that is below the heart. The word *azygos* means unpaired. Although many individuals additionally have a left-sided azygos vein, the hemiazygos vein, it drains into the azygos vein early in its course.

Most of the deoxygenated blood of the lower torso returns by way of the **inferior vena cava**. Both the superior and inferior vena cava empty into the right atrium of the heart.

Blood returning to the heart enters the right atrium without having to cross a valve. From the right atrium, it is pumped through the tri-leaflet **tricuspid valve** and enters the stronger-contracting **right ventricle**. As the right ventricle contracts, it pushes the blood through the tri-leaflet **pulmonary valve** and into the pulmonary trunk. The **pulmonary trunk** is a large blood vessel which soon divides into the **right and left pulmonary arteries**. Each carries deoxygenated blood to its respective lung. Each pulmonary artery subdivides into smaller and smaller vessels until the deoxygenated blood reaches the **capillary beds** surrounding alveoli containing inspired air. At this level, gas exchange occurs and the blood becomes oxygenated.

Once oxygenated, the blood begins its trek back to the heart to be pumped out to the body. The oxygenated blood leaves the capillaries and enters progressively larger vessels to eventually reach a **pulmonary vein**. From the pulmonary vein, the oxygenated blood drains into the **left atrium** of the heart. The left atrium pumps the blood through the bi-leaflet **mitral valve** and into the **left ventricle** of the heart. The left ventricle is by far the strongest contracting heart chamber. It pumps oxygenated blood through the tri-leaflet **aortic valve** and into the **ascending aorta** to supply oxygenated blood to the body.

> Just as there are four heart chambers, there are four heart valves. Each chamber pumps blood through a valve. The tricuspid, pulmonary, and aortic valves are all tri-leaflet, meaning they are formed by three leaflets or cusps. Only the mitral valve is bi-leaflet, having two leaflets or cusps.
>
> <u>4</u> heart chambers with <u>4</u> valves
> <u>3</u> valves have <u>3</u> leaflets

> In sequence of blood flow,
> the valves are in reverse alphabetical order
>
> <u>T</u>ricuspid → <u>P</u>ulmonary → <u>M</u>itral → <u>A</u>ortic

FIGURE 4.3
HEART AND GREAT VESSELS

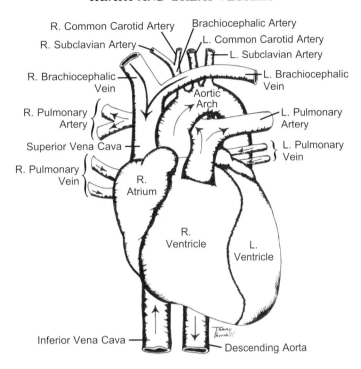

The ascending aorta travels a short distance before curving to the left and posteriorly, forming the **arch of the aorta**. Three important arterial branches come off the aortic arch.

The **brachiocephalic artery** is the first branch. Like the vein of the same name, the brachiocephalic artery is also known as the **innominate artery**. As opposed to the venous system, there is only one brachiocephalic (innominate) artery. The brachiocephalic travels a short distance before dividing into the right common carotid and right subclavian arteries. The **right common carotid artery** travels up the neck and separates into the **right internal** and **right external carotid arteries**. Both travel superiorly to supply blood to the neck and head. The **right subclavian artery** travels laterally to supply blood to the right upper extremity.

The second branch of the aortic arch is the **left common carotid artery**. Like the right, the left common carotid travels up the neck to divide into the **left internal and external carotid arteries**.

The third and final branch of the arch of the aorta is the left subclavian artery. The **left subclavian artery** travels laterally to

supply oxygenated blood to the left upper extremity.

After the takeoff of the left subclavian artery, the aorta continues posteriorly and inferiorly. From this point, it is known as the **descending aorta**. It travels posterior to the heart to supply the lower body with oxygenated blood.

A frequent cause of confusion is the lack of symmetry of the arterial system as compared to the venous system. The human skeleton and external body is symmetrical with regard to the right and left. However, the internal organs have different functions, sizes, and shapes. They cannot be symmetrical. Anyone who has ever placed the hand over the heart knows that the heart is slightly on the left side of the body. Because the veins drain to the right side of the left-positioned heart, the location where the vena cava drains into the heart is relatively midline. Hence, the venous system is relatively symmetrical and two brachiocephalic (innominate) veins exist.

The arterial system is less symmetrical. Not only does the aorta leave from the left heart (left ventricle), but the aortic arch curves to the left. In order to provide equal amounts of blood to the symmetrical body, the brachiocephalic (innominate) artery has to *carry* the right common carotid and right subclavian arteries to the right side of the body. In other words, there is only one vessel with the name brachiocephalic (innominate) in the arterial system. It is neither right nor left. It subsequently branches into the right common carotid and right subclavian arteries. Supplying structures on the left side of the body, the left common carotid and left subclavian arteries are already in the proper position. These vessels simply branch directly off the aortic arch.

FIGURE 4.5
ARTERIAL SYSTEM

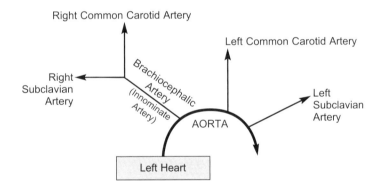

FIGURE 4.4
VENOUS SYSTEM
The venous system is not as symmetrical as depicted in this diagram.
The left brachiocephalic vein is actually longer
than the right brachiocephalic.

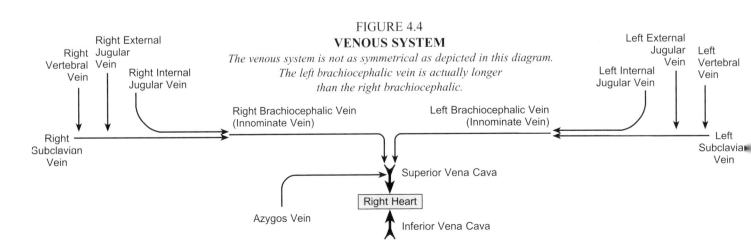

FIGURE 4.6
CIRCULATORY SYSTEM

Figure 4.7 is a generalized representation of the circulatory system. The student should attempt to identify each of the great vessels.

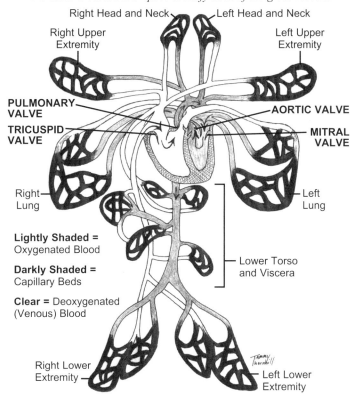

Lightly Shaded = Oxygenated Blood

Darkly Shaded = Capillary Beds

Clear = Deoxygenated (Venous) Blood

LUNGS

The paired lungs are organs that move air and exchange gasses between the atmosphere and blood. The basic component of the lungs is an **alveolus**, which is an air-containing terminal *sac* of the bronchial tree. Alveoli remain filled with air, even during expiration, and are responsible for much of the volume of the lungs. The **bronchial tree** is the network of branching airways that connect alveoli to the trachea, and thereby, the outer atmosphere. Alveoli are surrounded by capillary beds. The epithelium of an alveolus, also known as the **respiratory epithelium**, is where gas exchange occurs. Lung tissue is composed of three basic components: vessels that are carrying blood to and from the respiratory epithelium, airways that are carrying air to and from the respiratory epithelium, and connective tissue that holds the other two components together. In addition, supporting structures, such as blood vessels, nerves, and lymph vessels, are present.

Each lung is formed by an apex, base, and two surfaces. The **apex** is the rounded superior aspect of a lung that extends into the base of the neck. The **base** is the concave inferior portion that borders the superior aspect of the diaphragm. The **costal surface** is the outer surface that borders the chest wall. The **mediastinal surface** is the inner (medial) surface of each lung and borders the mediastinum. The **hilum** is a centrally-located area at the mediastinal surface of each lung and contains structures that form the root of the lung. The **root of the lung** is composed of the right or left bronchus, pulmonary artery, pulmonary veins, other blood vessels, lymphatic vessels, lymph nodes, nerves, and connective tissue.

> The *root* of the lung originates from the mediastinum, passes through the hilum, and sprouts out as the lung. The bronchial *tree* sprouts from the right or left main bronchus.

FIGURE 4.7
MEDIASTINUM AND ROOT OF LUNGS
Transverse Section

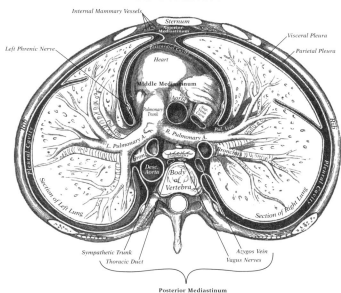

FIGURE 4.8
ROOT OF THE LUNGS
Posterior View

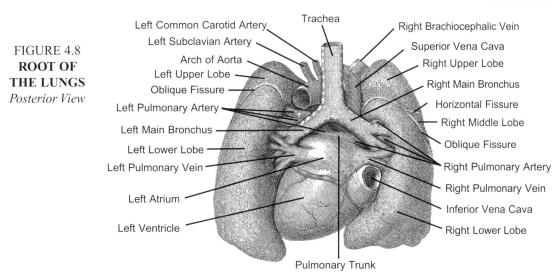

The right lung is bigger than the left and the two are separated by the mediastinum. Externally, each lung is divided into **lobes** by **fissures**. The right lung is formed by three lobes: **superior, middle,** and **inferior.** The **horizontal fissure** separates the superior and middle lobes; the **oblique fissure** separates the middle and inferior lobes. The left lung is divided into two lobes, the **upper lobe** and **lower lobe,** by the **oblique fissure.** On the anterior surface of the upper lobe is an inferior extension known as the **lingula.** *Lingu-* is a Latin word root for tongue and the lingula is named for its tongue-like extension from the anterior surface of the left upper lobe.

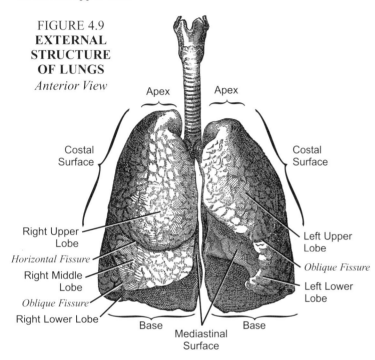

FIGURE 4.9
EXTERNAL STRUCTURE OF LUNGS
Anterior View

Apex
Apex
Costal Surface
Costal Surface
Right Upper Lobe
Horizontal Fissure
Right Middle Lobe
Oblique Fissure
Right Lower Lobe
Left Upper Lobe
Oblique Fissure
Left Lower Lobe
Base
Base
Mediastinal Surface

Both lungs curve down the thorax in an *oblique* fashion. Each lung has an *oblique* fissure. Each lung also has a lower lobe, and the oblique fissure is located just above it. Because the right lung is the only one with a middle lobe, it also is the only lung with a horizontal fissure (which is just above the middle lobe).

The heart is on the left. The left lung can be thought to be smaller to make room for the heart. Since it is smaller, the left lung only has only two lobes. Caution: The lingula is part of the upper lobe of the left lung, not a separate lobe.

The left lung is touchy about its smaller size and two lobes. It sticks its *tongue* out at you, while hoping you will mistakenly think the *lingula* is a separate, third lobe.

The **trachea** is formed by a series of approximately twenty C-shaped incomplete rings of cartilage and travels from the larynx to the carina. The cartilage reinforces the trachea and prevents its collapse during inspiration. The **carina** is the bifurcation of the trachea into the **right and left main bronchi** at the approximate level of the T4 – T5 vertebrae. *Carina* is Latin for *ridge-like*; the tracheal carina is formed by the posterior and inferior protrusion of the last tracheal ring, which creates a *ridge* between the origin of the right and left main bronchi. Consistent with the smaller size of the left lung, the left main bronchus is smaller in diameter than the right. It is also longer and departs from the trachea at a sharper, more acute angle due to the left-sided presence of the heart.

Any foreign material that is aspirated into the lungs will most likely go into the right lung. The right main bronchus is larger in diameter and follows a straighter path from the trachea.

Segments of the bronchopulmonary tree can grossly be divided into conductive, transitional, and respiratory airways. **Conductive airways** are those that function in conduction (movement) of air and do not participate in gas exchange. Each **main bronchus** is considered a *primary* bronchus and divides into **lobar bronchi,** which correspond to the external lobes of each lung. Because lobar bronchi branch from the primary bronchi, they are classified as *secondary* bronchi. **Segmental bronchi** originate from lobar bronchi and are also known as *tertiary* bronchi. As will be explained shortly, a segmental bronchus supplies a particular bronchopulmonary segment. Segmental bronchi progressively divide through several generations of smaller bronchi until the bronchioles are reached. **Bronchioles** are formed by connective tissue and smooth muscle cells and are the first airway components not to contain cartilage. Bronchioles continue to branch until reaching the **terminal bronchiole**, the final airway component that does not function in gas exchange.

FIGURE 4.10
DISTAL BRONCHI
The presence of cartilage differentiates distal bronchi from bronchioles. Note the irregular shape and placement of cartilage as compared to the cartilaginous rings of the trachea.

Transitional airways consist of respiratory bronchioles and alveolar ducts. **Respiratory bronchioles** arise from terminal bronchioles. Respiratory bronchioles are the first airway components to participate in gas exchange, but their function in this capacity is somewhat limited. Respiratory bronchioles are formed by walls of connective tissue and smooth muscle and contain sporadically-located outpockets of alveolar tissue. Respiratory bronchioles undergo several generations of branching before reaching alveolar ducts. Like other distal airway components, **alveolar ducts** undergo several generations of branches. There is no smooth muscle in the walls of alveolar ducts and each duct contains numerous openings to alveolar sacs along its entire length.

> Bronchi are the last component of the bronchial tree to contain cartilage. Bronchioles are the first component not to contain cartilage and the last component to contain smooth muscle.

> Most bronchioles are classified as conducting airways and function in air conduction exclusively. The last ones to do so are the *terminal* bronchioles. The next generation, the respiratory bronchioles, have a limited role in gas exchange and are classified as transitional airways. *Respiratory* bronchioles are the bronchioles most like the *respiratory* airways.

Respiratory airways are formed by alveolar sacs and alveoli. Like alveolar ducts, no smooth muscle is present in the walls of these structures. An **alveolar sac** is a relatively cavern-like structure into which an alveolar duct empties. Around the periphery of an alveolar sac are numerous small outpouches of alveolar tissue, each forming an **alveolus**. Gas exchange starts at the respiratory bronchioles and ends at the alveoli. An **acinus** is the terminal portion of the bronchial tree that is supplied by a particular terminal bronchiole. The word *acinous* is Latin for *grape-like*. Respiratory exchange occurs throughout the length of an acinus.

As described, **pulmonary arteries** carry deoxygenated blood from the right ventricle of the heart. While traveling toward the acini, a pulmonary artery progressively branches into smaller vessels until the capillary bed surrounding alveolar tissue is reached. Formation of pulmonary capillary beds begins at the level of the respiratory bronchiole and continues along the acinus to the alveolus. Carbon dioxide leaves the blood and enters the air in the alveolar tissue; oxygen leaves the air to enter the blood. The carbon dioxide is exhaled and the oxygenated blood travels in progressively larger **pulmonary veins** to reach the left atrium of the heart. Tissues of the lung, including connective tissue, bronchi, and visceral pleura, obtain oxygenated blood by way of **bronchial arteries.** These vessels arise from the descending aorta (or aortic arch). **Bronchial veins** carry deoxygenated blood away from lung tissue and drain into the azygos vein on the right, and hemiazygos vein on the left. A significant number of bronchial veins drain directly into the pulmonary vein, creating a physiologic shunt of deoxygenated blood that is mixed with oxygenated blood traveling back to the left atrium. The oxygen content of blood that is pumped out to the systemic circulation is therefore slightly less than it would be without the presence of this shunt.

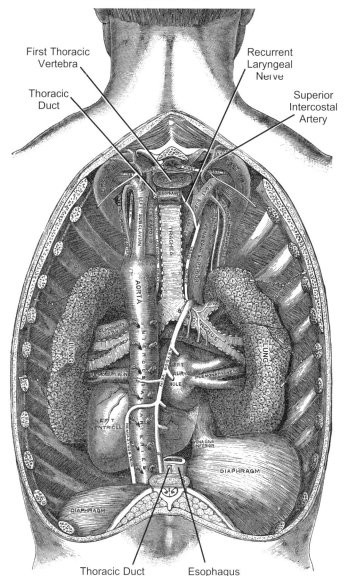

FIGURE 4.11
STRUCTURES OF THE THORACIC CAVITY
Posterior View

First Thoracic Vertebra
Thoracic Duct
Recurrent Laryngeal Nerve
Superior Intercostal Artery

Thoracic Duct   Esophagus

To participate in gas exchange, alveolar tissue must be tightly paired with capillary beds that are supplied by pulmonary arterioles and drained by pulmonary venules. This dictates a close relationship between bronchial and vascular structures. Each **segmental (tertiary) bronchus** is accompanied by a branch of the **pulmonary artery** and a branch of the **pulmonary vein.** Successive branches of these structures follow one another to eventually reach the respiratory epithelium and participate in gas exchange. The trio of the segmental bronchus, pulmonary artery, and pulmonary vein supplies one **bronchopulmonary segment**. A bronchopulmonary segment is therefore the wedge-shaped region of lung tissue that is supplied by a particular segmental bronchus and its corresponding pulmonary artery and vein branches. Each *segmental* bronchus supplies a specific bronchopulmonary *segment*. Certain disease processes, such as infection or tumor, may be isolated to a particular segment. Bronchopulmonary segments can be surgically separated.

> A *broncho**pulmonary** segment* is supplied by a *bronchus* and its accompanying **pulmonary** vessels (artery and vein).

The anatomy of the segmental bronchi is similar for each lung, despite obvious external differences. Even though the right lung is formed by three lobes and the left lung by two, each lung contains ten segmental bronchi. By combining two pairs of bronchi that exist on the right, it is frequently taught that eight segmental bronchi exist on the left. Both assortments will be explained. The name of each segmental bronchus corresponds to the bronchopulmonary segment it supplies.

The **right main bronchus** is the origin of three lobar (secondary) bronchi: right upper, right middle, and right lower bronchi. There is one lobar bronchus for each of the three lobes of the right lung. The **right upper lobe bronchus** gives off three segmental (tertiary) bronchi: the **apical**, **posterior**, and **anterior** bronchi. The **middle lobe bronchus** divides into the **lateral** and **medial** bronchi. The **right lower lobe bronchus** gives off the **superior** bronchus proximally. This bronchus branches from the posterior side of the right lower bronchus and supplies the superior aspect of the right lower lobe. The lobar bronchus continues distally to divide into the four segmental bronchi that supply the base of the right lung: the **anterior basal**, **medial basal**, **lateral basal**, and **posterior basal** bronchi.

The **left main bronchus** is the origin of two lobar bronchi, the left upper and left lower bronchi. The **left upper lobe bronchus** quickly divides into **two divisions**, the superior and inferior division bronchi. These bronchi correspond to the right

FIGURE 4.12
BRONCHI

There is significant variability in the bronchial branching patterns between different individuals. In addition, the anatomy may not be as uniform and easy to interpret as what is presented here (See Figures 4.13 and 4.14). Nevertheless, knowledge of how the bronchi should evolve will facilitate proper identification and diagnosis.

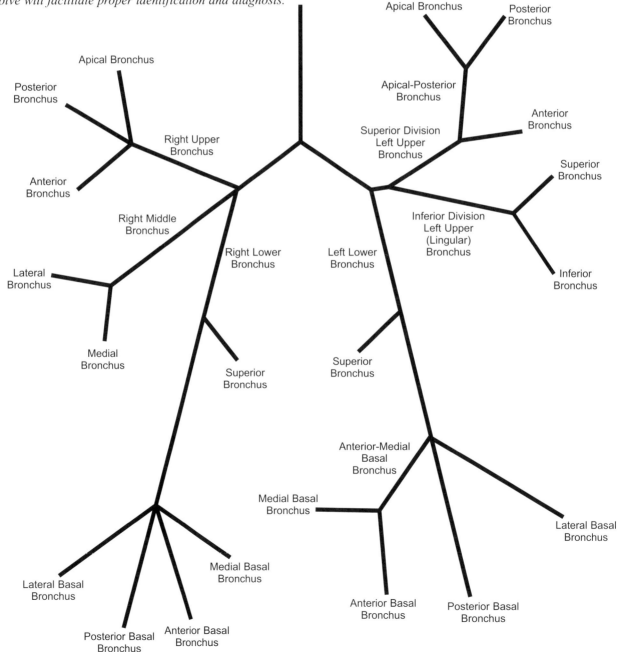

upper and right middle lobe bronchi, respectfully. Because there is no left middle lobe, and to prevent confusion with segmental bronchi, the bronchi are described as *divisions*. The **superior division** of the left upper lobe bronchus is the origin of the apical-posterior and anterior bronchi. The **apical-posterior** later branches into the **apical** and **posterior** segmental bronchi and is one of the reasons for the discrepancy in the number of segmental bronchi claimed for the left lung. The superior division also gives off the **anterior** bronchus.

In an effort to be fair and make up for the left lung's lack of three lobes, it was given two bronchus divisions. The right lung received none.

The **inferior division** of the left upper lobe bronchus is also known as the **lingular bronchus** and is the origin of two segmental bronchi, the **superior** and **inferior** bronchi. Like the right lower lobe bronchus, the **left lower lobe bronchus** is the origin of a **superior** bronchus, which branches early from the posterior side, and several basal bronchi. After the takeoff of the superior bronchus, the lobar bronchus continues distally and divides into three basal segmental bronchi: **anterior-medial basal**, **lateral basal**, and **posterior basal** segments. The anterior-medial basal bronchi later divides into the **anterior basal** and **medial basal** segmental bronchi and is the other reason for the two bronchi differential in the number of left lung segmental bronchi that exist among various descriptions.

FIGURE 4.13
PRIMARY (MAIN) AND SECONDARY (LOBAR) BRONCHI

FIGURE 4.14
TERTIARY (SEGMENTAL) BRONCHI

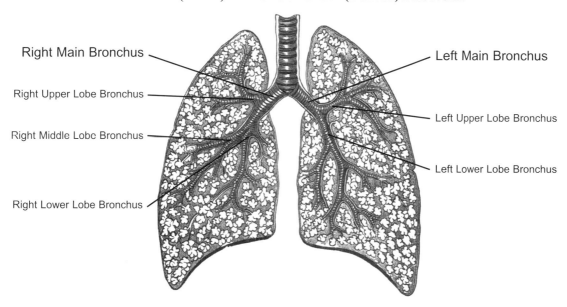

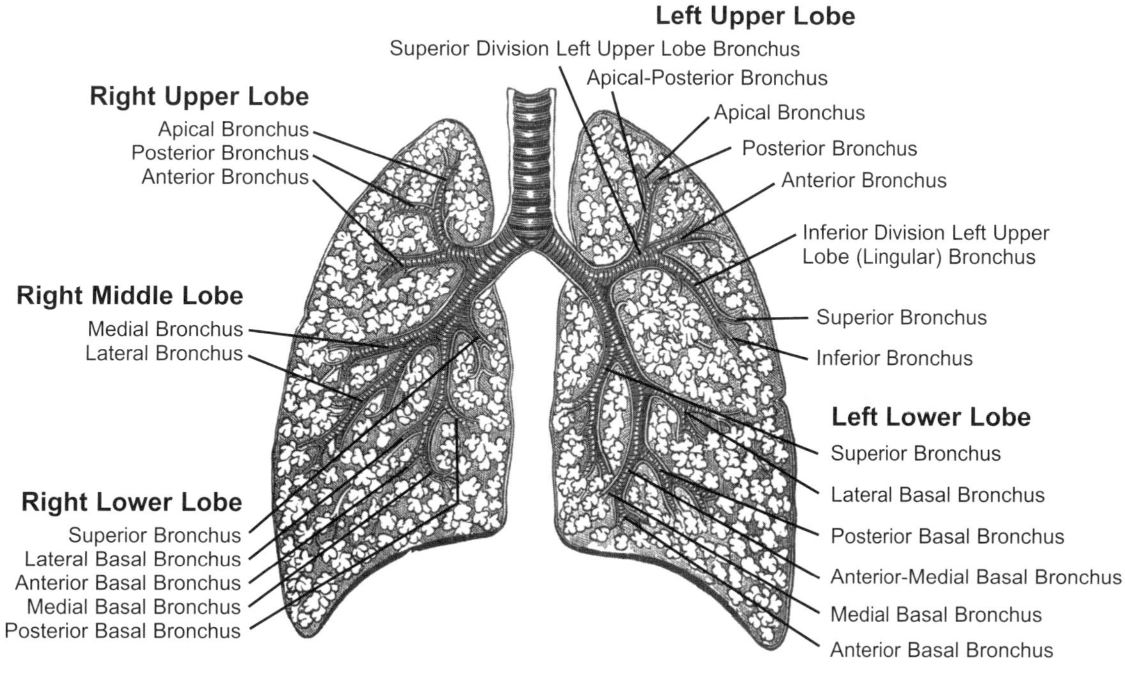

Two new directional descriptions were introduced in the discussion of the lung, apical (toward the apex [top]) and basal (toward the base [bottom]). Each lung has one apical segmental bronchus and four basal segmental bronchi (anterior basal, medial basal, lateral basal, and posterior basal). The base is bigger than the apex and should have more bronchi. Logically, the apical segments are in the upper lobes and the basal segments are in the lower lobes. In addition, the upper lobes have anterior and posterior bronchi; the lower lobes have superior bronchi. The final two bronchi locations in the lungs are the lateral and medial segmental bronchi of the right middle lobe and the superior and inferior segmental bronchi of the inferior division of the left upper lobe bronchus (lingular bronchus). The lingula can be thought of as a "mini-middle lobe" and all segmental bronchi that exist is the right middle lobe and lingula correspond to basic anatomic directions (right middle = medial and lateral, lingular [inferior division of left upper] = superior and inferior).

The lingula is the ***inferior*** extension of the left upper lobe and receives the ***inferior*** division of the left upper lobe bronchus (lingular bronchus). This bronchus continues the "inferior" pattern by separating into superior and ***inferior*** segmental bronchi.

The **m**iddle lobe of the right lung contains the **m**edial and lateral segmental bronchi. There is only one middle lobe and it is the only one to contain a medial (and a lateral) bronchus. *Note: Both the right and left lower lobes contain a medial *basal* and lateral *basal* bronchus.

Although it possesses a significant curvature, the base of the lung can be pictured as existing in a flat, two-dimensional plane. Like the transverse plane, there would be no superior or inferior direction to describe. Instead, the directional labels that can be applied are anterior, posterior, medial, and lateral. The *basal* bronchi supply the *base* of the lungs. Thus, the basal segmental bronchi include the anterior basal, posterior basal, medial basal, and lateral basal bronchi.

The apical and posterior segmental bronchi of the superior division of the left upper lobe bronchus are frequently combined into one bronchus, the apical-posterior bronchus. Likewise, the anterior basal and medial basal bronchi of the left lower bronchus may be combined as the anterior-medial basal bronchus. Each bronchus is paired with a bronchus that is not its "opposite." Apical (opposite = basal) is paired with posterior (opposite = anterior). Anterior basal (opposite = posterior basal) is paired with medial basal (opposite = lateral basal). Furthermore, each of the pairings includes one segmental bronchus that starts with the letter "A": *A*pical-posterior bronchus and *a*nterior-medial basal bronchus. Finally, with abbreviations, AP goes on top (in the left *upper* lobe) and AM goes on bottom (in the left *lower* lobe)

FIGURE 4.15
HEART AND LUNGS
Anterior View

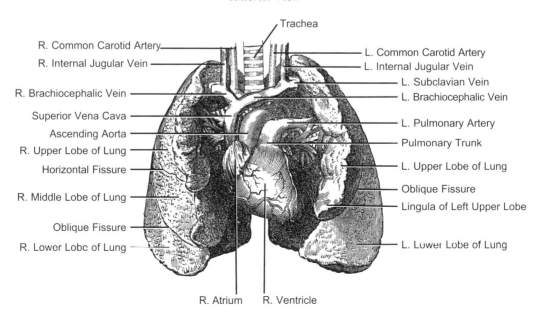

Trachea
R. Common Carotid Artery
R. Internal Jugular Vein
R. Brachiocephalic Vein
Superior Vena Cava
Ascending Aorta
R. Upper Lobe of Lung
Horizontal Fissure
R. Middle Lobe of Lung
Oblique Fissure
R. Lower Lobe of Lung
L. Common Carotid Artery
L. Internal Jugular Vein
L. Subclavian Vein
L. Brachiocephalic Vein
L. Pulmonary Artery
Pulmonary Trunk
L. Upper Lobe of Lung
Oblique Fissure
Lingula of Left Upper Lobe
L. Lower Lobe of Lung
R. Atrium   R. Ventricle

QUIZ 1
Body Cavities and Major Organs

Time for Quiz = 30 minutes.
For questions 1-24, choose the single best answer.

_____1) The serous membrane lining the inner surface of the chest wall is known as
   a) the parietal peritoneum
   b) the visceral pleura
   c) the parietal pleura
   d) the parietal perineum
   e) none of the above

_____2) What is another name for the right innominate vein?
   a) superior vena cava
   b) azygos vein
   c) inferior vena cava
   d) right subclavian vein
   e) none of the above

_____3) Examples of closed cavities include
   a) knee joints
   b) blood vessels
   c) inner ear ducts
   d) all of the above
   e) none of the above

_____4) The horizontal fissure separates
   a) the right upper and right middle lobes
   b) the left upper and left middle lobes
   c) the left upper and left lower lobes
   d) the right middle and right lower lobes
   e) none of the above

_____5) What is the correct order of venous drainage for blood returning from the left (L.) internal jugular vein?
   a) L. brachiocephalic, superior vena cava, L. atrium
   b) L. subclavian, L. brachiocephalic, azygos vein
   c) L. brachiocephalic, superior vena cava, R. atrium
   d) L. subclavian, L. brachiocephalic, inferior vena cava
   e) None of the above

_____6) The dorsal cavity consists of
   a) the thoracic cavity
   b) the pericardial cavity
   c) the abdominopelvic cavity
   d) all of the above
   e) none of the above

_____7) Which structures carry deoxygenated blood?
   a) azygos vein
   b) pulmonary artery
   c) both a and b
   d) left atrium
   e) none of the above

_____8) The serous membrane lining the inner surface of the abdominal wall is known as
   a) the visceral pleura
   b) the parietal pleura
   c) the visceral perineum
   d) the parietal perineum
   e) none of the above

_____9) What is characteristic of terminal bronchioles?
   a) They do not contain cartilage.
   b) They are the first airway component to participate in gas exchange.
   c) Both a and b
   d) They do not contain smooth muscle.
   e) None of the above

_____10) To reach the right (R.) internal carotid artery, what is the correct sequence of structures through which blood must flow?
   a) aortic valve, descending aorta, brachiocephalic artery
   b) ascending aorta, R. subclavian artery, R. common carotid artery
   c) aortic valve, ascending aorta, brachiocephalic artery
   d) subclavian artery, R. brachiocephalic artery, R. common carotid artery
   e) none of the above

_____11) The serous membrane lining the outer surface of the thoracic organs is known as
    a) the parietal pleura
    b) the pulmonary pleura
    c) both a and b
    d) the visceral peritoneum
    e) none of the above

_____12) What is another name for the left innominate vein?
    a) superior vena cava
    b) azygos vein
    c) there is no left innominate vein
    d) left subclavian vein
    e) none of the above

_____13) Which bronchus may be found in the lingula?
    a) medial segmental bronchus
    b) inferior segmental bronchus
    c) lateral basal segmental bronchus
    d) apical segmental bronchus
    e) none of the above

_____14) Examples of open cavities include
    a) the dorsal cavity
    b) blood vessels
    c) the lungs
    d) all of the above
    e) none of the above

_____15) What is the correct sequence of heart valves through which blood must flow?
    a) mitral, pulmonary, tricuspid, aortic
    b) pulmonary, tricuspid, mitral, aortic
    c) tricuspid, mitral, pulmonary, aortic
    d) tricuspid, pulmonary, mitral, aortic
    e) none of the above

_____16) The serous membrane lining the outer surface of the abdominal organs is known as
    a) the visceral pleura
    b) the parietal pleura
    c) the visceral perineum
    d) the parietal perineum
    e) none of the above

_____17) Which structure serves as the immediate origin of an acinus?
    a) tertiary bronchus
    b) respiratory bronchiole
    c) terminal bronchiole
    d) alveolar duct
    e) none of the above

_____18) What is the other name for the left innominate artery?
    a) left brachiocephalic artery
    b) there is no left innominate artery
    c) left subclavian artery
    d) left vertebral artery
    e) none of the above

_____19) Which heart valves are tri-leaflet (have three leaflets or cusps)?
    a) pulmonary
    b) aortic
    c) both a and b
    d) mitral
    e) none of the above

_____20) Which venous structures return blood to the heart from below (inferior to) the level of the heart?
    a) superior vena cava
    b) inferior vena cava
    c) both a and b
    d) jugular vein
    e) none of the above

_____21) The lingular bronchus corresponds to the
    a) superior division of the left upper lobe bronchus
    b) inferior division of the right upper lobe bronchus
    c) inferior division of the left upper lobe bronchus
    d) superior division of the left lower lobe bronchus
    e) none of the above

____22) In order to reach the left (L.) subclavian artery, what is the correct sequence of structures through which blood must flow?
- a) ascending aorta, brachiocephalic artery, L. common carotid artery
- b) aortic valve, ascending aorta, brachiocephalic artery
- c) mitral valve, ascending aorta, innominate artery
- d) mitral valve, aortic valve, ascending aorta
- e) none of the above

____23) Which structures carry oxygenated blood?
- a) aorta
- b) pulmonary vein
- c) both a and b
- d) vena cava
- e) none of the above

____24) To reach the right (R.) subclavian artery, what is the correct sequence of structures through which blood must flow?
- a) aortic valve, ascending aorta, L. innominate artery
- b) ascending aorta, L. innominate artery, common carotid artery
- c) aortic valve, descending aorta, innominate artery
- d) the right subclavian artery branches directly off the aorta
- e) none of the above

For questions 25-30, use the following directions:
- **a.......1,2,3 are correct**
- **b.......1,3 are correct**
- **c.......2,4 are correct**
- **d.......only 4 is correct**
- **e.......all are correct**

____25) Which of the following could be classified as a conductive airway?
1. tertiary bronchi
2. terminal bronchioles
3. lobar bronchi
4. alveolar ducts

____26) Which of the following is true?
1. The trachea corresponds to a primary bronchus.
2. A lobar bronchus corresponds to a secondary bronchus.
3. The right main bronchus is longer than the left main bronchus.
4. A segmental bronchus corresponds to a tertiary bronchus.

____27) Membranes which surround closed cavities include the
1. pleura
2. perineum
3. dura mater
4. mucosal membranes

____28) Which statements concerning the thoracic cavity are true?
1. It is part of the dorsal cavity.
2. It is lined by the pleura.
3. It is divided into ventral and dorsal components by the mediastinum.
4. It surrounds the pericardial cavity.

____29) A bronchopulmonary segment is formed by branches of a
1. bronchial artery
2. lobar bronchus
3. bronchial vein
4. segmental bronchus

____30) Which of the following are true?
1. A superior segmental bronchus is located in the right middle lobe.
2. A lateral segmental bronchus is located in the lingula.
3. An inferior basal segmental bronchus is located in the left lower lobe.
4. A superior segmental bronchus is located in the right lower lobe.

QUIZ 1: Body Cavities and Major Organs

1) c – *Visceral* refers to the internal organs. *Parietal* refers to an outer wall of a cavity. Just as the parietal pleura lines the inner surface of the chest wall, the parietal peritoneum lines the inner surface of the abdominal wall. The visceral pleura lines the outer surface of the thoracic organs (lungs). The perineum is not a serous membrane, but an area of the body which forms the floor of the pelvis. An effort should be made not to confuse the word *perineum* with *peritoneum*.

2) e – The right innominate vein is also known as the right brachiocephalic vein. Because the venous system drains to the right side of the left positioned heart, it is draining toward the midline of the body. This allows it to be relatively symmetrical with regard to right and left. Hence, there is both a right and left innominate (brachiocephalic) vein. This is in contrast to the arterial system which only has one innominate (brachiocephalic) artery. This artery *carries* the right common carotid and right subclavian artery from the left heart to the right side of the body.

3) d – Closed cavities have no opening to the outside of the body. Open cavities have an opening to the outside and are lined with a mucosal membrane. Mucosal membranes are named for their production of mucous, which traps and subsequently disposes of foreign molecules entering the body via the outside opening.

4) a – The right lung has three lobes and the left lung has only two. There is no left middle lobe. The horizontal fissure separates the right upper and right middle lobes. The oblique fissure separates the right middle and right lower lobes. Likewise, the left lung also has an oblique fissure that separates the left upper and left lower lobes.

5) c – As it is traveling back to the heart, the left (L.) internal jugular vein combines with the left subclavian vein to form the left brachiocephalic (L. innominate) vein. The right and left brachiocephalic (innominate) veins subsequently combine to form the superior vena cava. The superior vena cava receives the azygos vein (which drains blood from below the level of the heart) prior to emptying into the right atrium of the heart.

6) e – The dorsal cavity consists of the cranial cavity and the spinal cavity. The thoracic cavity, pericardial cavity, and abdominopelvic cavity together form the ventral cavity.

7) c – All of the systemic veins return deoxygenated blood to the superior and inferior vena cava, both of which drain directly into the right atrium of the heart. From there, the deoxygenated blood travels through the right ventricle and pulmonary artery to reach the lungs and become oxygenated. The oxygenated blood returns to the left atrium via the pulmonary vein. From the left atrium, the oxygenated blood is pumped through the left ventricle and ascending aorta to reach the systemic arteries. Note that the pulmonary artery is the only artery that carries deoxygenated blood. Likewise, the pulmonary vein is the only vein which carries oxygenated blood.

8) e – See #1 answer explanation.

9) a – Bronchioles are the first airway components that do not contain cartilage. Terminal bronchioles are the terminal components of the conducting airways, the portion of the bronchial tree that does not participate in gas exchange. Terminal bronchioles contain smooth muscle and connective tissue. Alveolar ducts are the first airway components not to contain smooth muscle.

10) c – Because the heart is located on the left side of the thorax and the arterial system comes off the left side of the heart (left ventricle), the proximal arterial system is somewhat asymmetric. This is required to provide oxygenated blood to the symmetric body (with regard to right and left). The left common carotid and left subclavian arteries simply branch off the arch of the aorta because they are already in the proper position on the left side of the body. The right common carotid and right subclavian arteries require the assistance of the brachiocephalic (innominate) artery, which *carries* them to the proper position on the right side of the symmetrical body. By contrast, the venous system drains to the right side of the heart. This is

much closer to the midline, so the venous system is more symmetrical as compared to the arterial system. Hence, there are two brachiocephalic (innominate) veins, a right and left one. There is only one brachiocephalic (innominate) artery.

11) b – *Visceral* refers to the internal organs. *Parietal* refers to an outer wall of a cavity. The visceral pleura lines the outer surface of the thoracic organs. Because the lungs comprise most of this surface area, the visceral pleura is often called the pulmonary pleura. The parietal pleura lines the inner surface of the chest wall. The visceral peritoneum lines the outer surface of the abdominal organs.

12) e – See #2 answer explanation.

13) b – The lingula is the inferior extension of the left upper lobe and contains a superior and inferior segmental bronchus.

14) c – Open cavities have an opening to the outside and are lined with a mucosal membrane. These membranes are named for their production of mucous. Mucous helps the body handle foreign molecules by trapping and subsequently disposing of them. Both the dorsal cavity (consisting of the cranial cavity and the spinal cavity) and the blood vessels are closed cavities. They have no direct opening to outside the body.

15) d – There are four chambers of the heart. Each heart chamber must pump blood through a valve. Hence, there are four valves. The tricuspid valve is between the right atrium and right ventricle. The pulmonary valve is between the right ventricle and pulmonary artery. The mitral valve is between the left atrium and left ventricle. Finally, the aortic valve is between the left ventricle and ascending aorta.

16) e – See #1 answer explanation. The visceral peritoneum lines the outer surface of abdominal organs.

17) c – A terminal bronchiole is the final airway component that does not function in gas exchange and is the origin of airway structures that form an acinus. Structures within an acinus participate in gas exchange. In sequential order, these structures include respiratory bronchioles, alveolar ducts, alveolar sacs, and alveoli. A tertiary bronchus is a segmental bronchus, which is located multiple generations of branches proximal to an acinus.

18) b – See #2 answer explanation.

19) c – Of the four heart valves, the mitral valve is the only valve which is bicuspid, meaning it has only two cusps or leaflets. It is located between the left atrium and left ventricle. The other three valves, the tricuspid, pulmonary, and aortic valves, have three cusps each. The tricuspid valve is actually named for its three cusps. Both the pulmonary and aortic valves are named for the arteries they open into.

20) c – Deoxygenated blood from the chest wall, including areas below or inferior to the heart, drains into the azygos vein. The azygos vein subsequently drains into the superior vena cava just before the superior vena cava enters the pericardium to empty into the right atrium of the heart. Deoxygenated blood from other areas of the lower body returns to the heart via the inferior vena cava.

21) c – The left upper lobe bronchus divides into a superior and an inferior division bronchus. The superior division is the origin of the apical-posterior and anterior segmental bronchi. The inferior division bronchus is also known as the lingular bronchus and provides superior and inferior segmental bronchi, which supply the lingula of the left upper lobe.

22) d – Like the left common carotid artery, the left subclavian artery branches directly off the aortic arch. Both the right subclavian and right common carotid arteries must be *carried* over to the right side of the body by the brachiocephalic (innominate) artery.

23) c – See #6 answer explanation.

24) e – See #8 answer explanation.

25) a – Conductive airways are those that function in conduction (movement) of air and do not participate in gas exchange. They include the trachea, right and left main (primary) bronchi,

lobar (secondary) bronchi, segmental (tertiary) bronchi, smaller bronchi, and most bronchioles. A terminal bronchiole is the final airway component that does not function in gas exchange. Alveolar ducts are classified as transitional airways and participate in gas exchange in a limited capacity. They contain no smooth muscle and are lined with numerous openings to alveolar sacs along their length.

26) c – The right and left main bronchi are the primary bronchi; they are the first bronchi to branch from the trachea. Lobar bronchi branch from main bronchi and are also described as secondary bronchi. Each *lobar* bronchus supplies a *lobe* of the lungs. Segmental bronchi branch from lobar bronchi and are also known as tertiary bronchi. Each *segmental* bronchus supplies a particular bronchopulmonary *segment.* As compared to the left main bronchus, the right main bronchus has a larger diameter, is shorter, and branches from the trachea at a less acute angle. Because of these structural differences, substances that are aspirated into the lungs are often deposited in the right lung.

27) b – The pleura is a serosal membrane that lines the thoracic cavity. The dura mater is the fibrous membrane that lines the dorsal cavity (consisting of the cranial and spinal cavities). The perineum is the area between the thighs extending from the anus to the external genitalia. It forms the floor of the pelvis. Mucosal membranes surround open cavities. They form a layer of mucous that aids in the handling of foreign substances that present via the opening to the outside of the body.

28) c – The thoracic cavity is part of the ventral cavity. It is lined by a serous membrane, the pleura, which folds over on itself. The mediastinum is a group of midline structures including the heart, great vessels, esophagus, trachea, and thymus. The mediastinum divides the thoracic cavity into left and right cavities, one for each lung. The pericardial cavity is within the thoracic cavity. The two cavities are separated by the membranous pericardium.

29) d – A bronchopulmonary segment is a particular area of lung tissue that is supplied by a *segmental* bronchus and its corresponding *pulmonary* artery and *pulmonary* vein branches. The segmental bronchus provides air, which eventually reaches capillary beds of the respiratory epithelium and participates in gas exchange. Branches of the pulmonary artery transport deoxygenated blood to the capillary beds. This blood is oxygenated and drains to pulmonary veins. Bronchial arteries carry oxygenated blood to tissues that form the lung. Bronchial veins drain deoxygenated blood from these tissues.

30) d – The right middle lobe contains a medial and lateral segmental bronchus. The lingula contains a superior and inferior segmental bronchus. The left lower lobe contains a superior segmental bronchus and three basal segmental bronchi: anterior-medial basal, posterior basal, and lateral basal bronchi. The right lower lobe contains a superior segmental bronchus and four basal segmental bronchi: anterior basal, medial basal, posterior basal, and lateral basal bronchi.

STRUCTURES OF THE ABDOMINOPELVIC CAVITY

Although visceral structures exist throughout the body, when the terms *viscus* or *viscera* are used, they are frequently describing the large, hollow organs of the abdominopelvic cavity. Digestive and urogenital organs form most of the visceral mass of the cavity. Many of these organs have multiple functions and important metabolic roles. The viscera interact with one another in a very complex fashion that is beyond the scope of this text. Instead, this book is focused on the anatomy and basic function of each of the major organs.

FIGURE 4.16
ABDOMINAL ORGANS

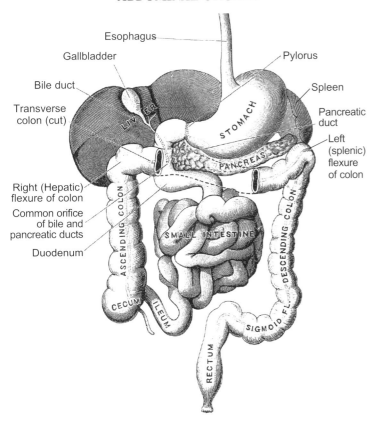

ESOPHAGUS

The esophagus is the muscular conduit stretching inferiorly from the pharynx to the stomach. The esophagus is approximately 25 cm long and less than ten percent of its length is located in the abdomen. In the neck and thorax, the esophagus travels posterior the trachea, near the anterior aspect of the spine. As opposed to the trachea, which is held open by cartilaginous rings, the esophagus usually remains in a closed state. The anterior wall remains flattened against the posterior wall except when something is swallowed. Although gravity facilitates the downward movement of food, coordinated muscular contractions are largely responsible for the transport of swallowed food into the stomach. This is evidenced by an individual's ability to swallow both solids and liquids while in an upside-down position. The esophagus passes posterior to the heart and enters the abdomen by passing through the **esophageal hiatus** of the diaphragm. At the approximate level of the T-10 vertebra, the esophagus deviates to the left and unites with the cardia of the stomach. The **cardiac sphincter** is located at the junction of the esophagus and stomach. It functions to prevent regurgitation of gastric contents up the esophagus.

STOMACH

The stomach is the pouch-like dilation of the digestive tract just below the diaphragm in the left upper quadrant of the abdomen. The stomach functions as a mixer; peristaltic contractions agitate and blend consumed food, liquids, saliva, and gastric secretions. The resulting homogenous mixture is known as **chyme**, which is intermittently released into the duodenum of the small intestine for further digestion.

The stomach is divided into seven portions. The previously-mentioned cardiac sphincter separates the esophagus from the stomach. Adjacent to the cardiac sphincter is the **cardia**. The **fundus** is the portion of the stomach that is superior and lateral (to the left) of the esophageal opening. The portion that is below the opening is known as the **body** of the stomach. The body continues down to the **pyloric antrum**, the funnel-shaped entry to the pyloric canal. The **pyloric canal** leads to the **pylorus**, which is the area immediately adjacent to the pyloric sphincter. The **pyloric sphincter** separates the stomach from the duodenum and periodically opens and closes to release chyme to the duodenum.

The stomach possesses several surface anatomy details that also require attention. The left-positioned organ curves to the right, forming a greater and lesser curvature. The **greater curvature** of the stomach is formed by its lateral (left) border and is convex to the left. The **lesser curvature** is created by the medial (right) border and is concave to the right. The **cardiac notch** is created by the acute angle of the junction of the left side of the esophagus with the stomach. The tip of the cardiac notch marks the division between the fundus, which is the portion of stomach located to the left and above the notch, and body, which is below the notch. The **angular notch** is found at the base of the lesser curvature and marks the border between the body and pyloric antrum. The borders between other regions of the stomach are fairly indistinct.

FIGURE 4.17
THE STOMACH

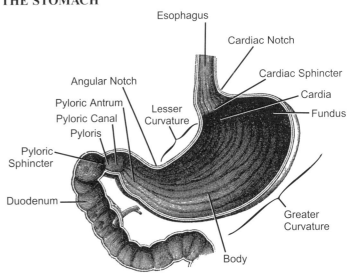

SMALL INTESTINE

The small intestine is the coiled tube that functions in the absorption of ingested food. When uncoiled, it can be up to ten meters long. The small intestine is composed of three sections: the duodenum, jejunum, and ileum. The **duodenum** is relatively compact and immobile. It receives gastric contents from the stomach, digestive enzymes from the pancreas, and bile from the liver and gallbladder. The **jejunum** and **ileum** function in the absorption of food; inner mucosal folds known as **villi** increase the absorptive surface area exposed to intestinal contents. The small intestine is suspended from the posterior abdominal wall by the **mesentery**. This structure allows a greater degree of mobility of the jejunum and ileum as compared the duodenum. The transition between the duodenum and jejunum occurs at the **duodenojejunal flexure**, which is located left of the L2 vertebra. The border between the jejunum and ileum is less distinct. The jejunum comprises the proximal two-fifths of the small intestine between the duodenojejunal flexure and large intestine; the ileum forms the distal three-fifths.

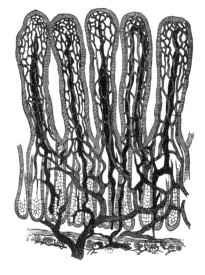

FIGURE 4.18
INTESTINAL VILLI

LARGE INTESTINE

The large intestine, also known as the colon, is approximately 1½ meters long, stretching from the ileocecal junction to the anus. In sequence, the large intestine is composed of the cecum, appendix, ascending colon, transverse colon, descending colon, sigmoid colon, rectum, and anus. With a little imagination, the large intestine can be thought to form a square within the abdominal cavity. The ascending colon forms the right side, the transverse forms the top, the descending forms the left side, and the sigmoid colon forms the bottom. Within the space of this square are loops of small bowel. The large intestine functions to absorb fluid and electrolytes and convert the liquid contents of the small intestine into semisolid fecal material. The ascending colon, descending colon, and rectum are attached to the posterior abdominal wall. The transverse colon and sigmoid colon are suspended from mesentery and are therefore permitted significantly more flexibility and mobility.

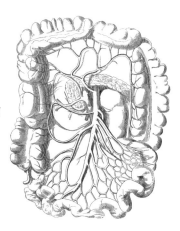

FIGURE 4.19
THE LARGE INTESTINE
Anterior View
The Sigmoid colon is covered externally by the jejunum and ileum in this view.

The **cecum** is the pouch-like beginning of the large intestine in the right lower quadrant of the abdomen. Because the ascending colon is attached to the posterior wall, the cecum is relatively immobile. At the opening of the ileum into the cecum are a pair of tissue flaps that form the lip-like **ileocecal valve**. This valve functions to maintain forward flow of colonic contents by preventing their return back up the ileum.

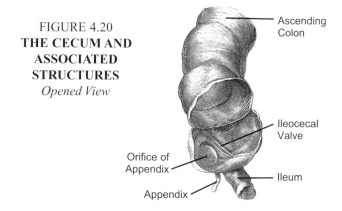

FIGURE 4.20
THE CECUM AND ASSOCIATED STRUCTURES
Opened View

Ascending Colon

Ileocecal Valve

Orifice of Appendix

Ileum

Appendix

The **appendix** is suspended from the posterior surface of the cecum and may be five to twenty centimeters long. In addition to its origin from the cecum, the appendix is also attached to the distal ileum by its own mesentery, the **mesoappendix**, which contains the appendicular artery and vein. The exact function of the appendix remains uncertain. Within its dense walls are numerous lymphoid follicles. Its narrow lumen predisposes to stagnant flow, infection, and inflammation. Although it is most frequently associated with right lower quadrant pain, the clinical picture of appendicitis may vary; the length and position of the appendix are inconstant.

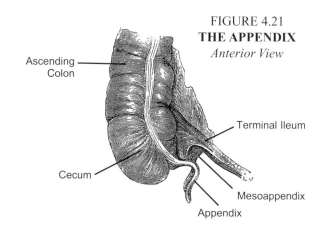

FIGURE 4.21
THE APPENDIX
Anterior View

Ascending Colon

Terminal Ileum

Cecum

Mesoappendix

Appendix

The **ascending colon** extends from the ileocecal valve to the liver, where it makes a sharp left turn to become the transverse colon. This sharp turn is known as the **right colic (hepatic) flexure** and occurs anterior to the right kidney. The **transverse colon** runs from the right colic (hepatic) flexure to the **left colic (splenic) flexure.** The left colic flexure is in a more superior position as compared to the right. Because the transverse colon is suspended by mesentery, it tends to hang down in front of the small intestine. Like the ascending colon, the **descending colon** is also affixed to the posterior abdominal wall. It leaves the left colic flexure and near the left iliac crest, it again picks up a mesentery and thereafter is known as the **sigmoid colon.** The sigmoid is named for its resemblance in shape to the Greek letter *sigma.* Near the third sacral vertebra the sigmoid colon again loses its mesentery, at which point it becomes the **rectum.** The rectum leads to the **anal canal,** which ends at the **anus.**

LIVER AND GALLBLADDER

Weighing one to two kilograms, the liver is the largest gland and second largest organ of the body. The skin is considered the largest organ. The liver has numerous vital functions. It has multiple roles in metabolism, secretes hormones, stores glucose, secretes bile, metabolizes drugs and toxins, filters digestive products, and synthesizes lipids and proteins. The liver is located in the right upper quadrant of the abdomen, largely under cover of the ribcage.

The **LIVER** is to the **RIGHT** and does **5** major things

1) **stores and releases** carbohydrates (glucose), proteins, and lipids
2) **transforms amino acids** into carbohydrates (gluconeogenesis) and urea
3) **creates bile** from water, salts, and pigments
4) **metabolizes** drugs (cytochrome P450)
5) **detoxifies** ingested substances

The appendix, cecum, ascending colon, and right kidney/adrenal gland are also on the right. The stomach, spleen, descending colon, sigmoid colon, and left kidney/adrenal gland are on the left. Everything else is in the "middle."

The liver has two surfaces: the diaphragmatic and visceral surfaces. The **diaphragmatic surface** is the superior aspect that borders the diaphragm. On this surface are the peritoneal ligaments that attach the liver to the diaphragm and the inferior vena cava. The vena cava is actually implanted in liver tissue. The **visceral surface** faces inferiorly and is divided by fissures. Included is the fissure for the ligamentum venosum, fissure for the ligamentum teres (round ligament), and the porta hepatis. Also located on the visceral surface is the gallbladder.

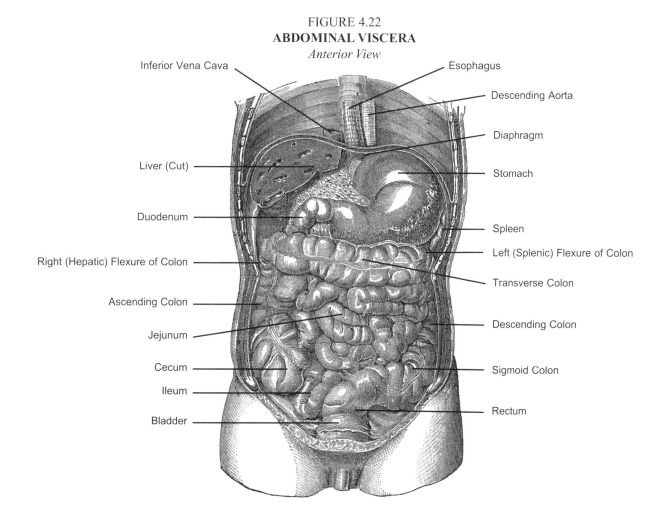

FIGURE 4.22
ABDOMINAL VISCERA
Anterior View

Inferior Vena Cava

Esophagus

Descending Aorta

Diaphragm

Liver (Cut)

Stomach

Duodenum

Spleen

Right (Hepatic) Flexure of Colon

Left (Splenic) Flexure of Colon

Transverse Colon

Ascending Colon

Descending Colon

Jejunum

Cecum

Sigmoid Colon

Ileum

Rectum

Bladder

FIGURE 4.23
DIAPHRAGMATIC SURFACE OF THE LIVER
Anterior View

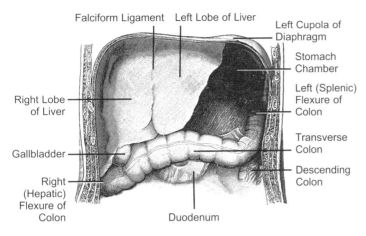

Based on surface anatomy divisions by ligaments and fissures, the liver can be divided into four lobes. On the diaphragmatic surface, the **falciform ligament** separates the right and left lobes. The right lobe molds the base of the liver and is approximately five times the size of the left. On the visceral surface, the **right lobe** is right of the gallbladder. The **left lobe** is left of the fissures for the ligamentum teres (round ligament) and ligamentum venosum. The **quadrate lobe** is between the gallbladder and fissure for the ligamentum teres, anterior to the porta hepatis. The **caudate lobe** is posterior to the porta hepatis and between the vena cava and fissure for the ligamentum venosum.

FIGURE 4.24
VISCERAL SURFACE OF THE LIVER
Inferior View
The bare area is the area of the liver that abruptly borders the diaphragm and is not covered by peritoneum.

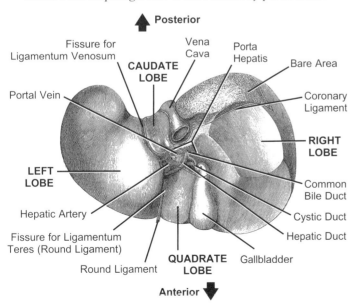

The liver has a dual blood supply. The **hepatic artery** is a branch of the celiac trunk of the aorta and supplies oxygenated blood to cells of the liver. Twenty-percent of blood is obtained via the hepatic artery, yet this blood provides eighty-percent of the oxygen requirement of the liver. The **portal vein** drains the intestines and transports recently-digested food, vitamins, toxins, and electrolytes for processing by the liver. Eighty-percent of blood arriving to the liver is by way of the portal vein. Portal blood provides only twenty-percent of the liver's oxygen requirement.

One of the numerous responsibilities of the liver is production of bile. **Bile** is produced by the liver and stored in the gallbladder. It is intermittently released into the duodenum by way of bile ducts and functions in the digestion of intestinal contents. Greater than 90% of bile is composed of water. It also contains bile salts and pigments obtained by the breakdown of hemoglobin in the spleen. Bile is secreted by cells of the liver, **hepatocytes**, into nearby small canals known as **bile canaliculi**. Canaliculi combine to form **bile ductules** which drain into **bile ducts**. Similar to the relationship of a pulmonary bronchus with branches of the pulmonary artery and pulmonary vein, bile ducts travel in close proximity to branches of the hepatic artery and portal vein, forming a **portal triad**. Although it is classically termed a *triad*, the portal triad also contains lymph vessels. Lymphatic vessels commonly accompany blood vessels in other areas of the body and will be described in more detail later in the chapter.

FIGURE 4.25
LIVER CIRCULATION
Note the portal vein is formed by the combination of the superior mesenteric and splenic veins. The superior mesenteric carries digested substances from the intestines for processing. The splenic carries bile pigments from the breakdown of hemoglobin in the spleen. These pigments are used by hepatocytes in the production of bile.

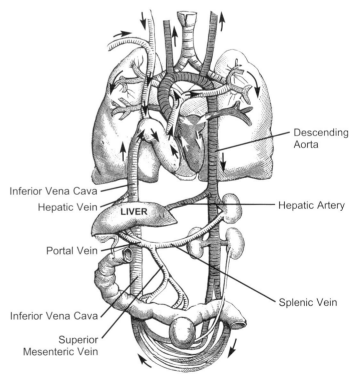

A **liver lobule** is the basic structural component of the liver and is formed by a group of hepatocytes that surround a **central vein**. Around the periphery of the lobule are several portal triads that run in the same direction as the central vein. Blood flows from the portal vein and hepatic artery through the meshwork of hepatocytes to reach the central vein. Blood from the portal vein travels in **sinusoids** that surround the hepatocytes and provides recently-digested materials for processing. Blood from the hepatic artery provides oxygen to meet the metabolic demands of the liver cells. Hepatocytes absorb substances from the sinusoids and discharge metabolic by-products and other chemicals into them. Sinusoids drain to the central vein, which subsequently merges with other central veins. Venous branches continue to join, forming **hepatic veins**, which drain into the inferior vena cava.

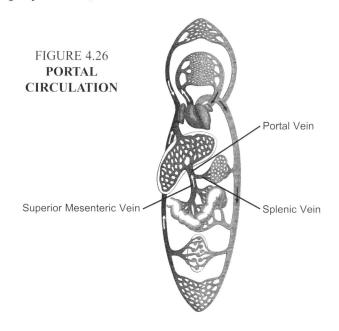

FIGURE 4.26
**PORTAL
CIRCULATION**

Portal Vein

Superior Mesenteric Vein

Splenic Vein

Traveling in the opposite direction, bile leaves the hepatocytes and travels in canaliculi and ductules to reach bile ducts at the periphery of the lobule. Bile travels in progressively larger ducts and leaves the liver in the **right** and **left hepatic ducts**. These ducts converge at the porta hepatis, forming the **common hepatic duct**. The **porta hepatis** was previously mentioned as a fissure that divides the visceral surface of the liver into lobes. More importantly, this fissure is the location of structures that form the **pedicle of the liver** and are inherent to the responsibilities of the organ. Through the porta, the hepatic artery and portal vein enter the liver and the hepatic duct leaves it.

> A *porta* is an entrance or *portal*
> into an object, structure, or place.
>
> The word is frequently used in anatomy to describe the point of entrance of supplying structures (blood vessels, nerves, etc.) into an organ. Although the porta hepatis is a fissure on the underside or visceral surface of the liver, it is named for the fact that it is also the point of entry of the hepatic artery and portal vein and point of departure of the hepatic duct.

Inferior to the porta hepatis, the hepatic duct is joined by the **cystic duct** from the gallbladder. The gallbladder functions to store bile and inject it as needed with the passage of ingested contents. The combination of the hepatic and cystic ducts forms the **common bile duct.** The common bile duct is later joined by the **pancreatic duct**, which carries digestive enzymes from the pan-

creas. The union of the common bile and pancreatic ducts may occur within the substance of the head of the pancreas or below the pancreas. The two ducts empty into the posterior duodenum via the **ampulla of Vater**. An *ampulla* is a funnel-like dilation of a tube and the ampulla of Vater is the dilation of the hepatopancreatic duct at its union with the posterior wall of the duodenum. The ampulla projects into the duodenal lumen, creating the **major duodenal papilla**. A *papilla* is a nipple-shaped protrusion. Surrounding the ampulla are strands of smooth muscle fibers that are independent of the regular duodenal smooth muscle wall. These fibers form the **sphincter of Oddi**, which remains closed when the stomach and duodenum are empty. During this time, the bile that is produced by the liver travels down the hepatic duct and is forced up the cystic duct for storage and concentration in the gallbladder. The discharge of stomach contents into the duodenum triggers the duodenal wall to release the hormone **cholecystokinin** and other hormones. Cholecystokinin relaxes the sphincter of Oddi and induces peristaltic contractions of the gallbladder. Bile is forced out of the organ and into the duodenum by way of the cystic and common bile ducts. Within the duodenum, bile is mixed with intestinal contents, raises the pH, and emulsifies fats. The emulsification of fats increases their water solubility and makes them easier to break down and digest. Digestive enzymes from the pancreas are also permitted entry and include peptidases (for the breakdown of proteins), amylases (for the breakdown of carbohydrates), and lipases (for the breakdown of fats).

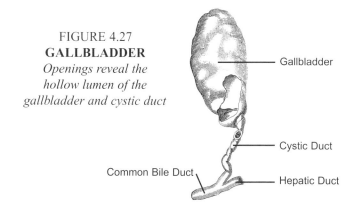

FIGURE 4.27
GALLBLADDER
*Openings reveal the
hollow lumen of the
gallbladder and cystic duct*

Gallbladder

Cystic Duct

Common Bile Duct

Hepatic Duct

> "Chole" is a Greek word root for "bile." "Gall" is another word for the bile. "Cyst(o)" is a Greek word root for "bladder." The Greek combining form "–ectomy" refers to "excision" or "surgical removal." Thus, a *cholecystectomy* is surgical removal of the gallbladder.
>
> "Kine" is a Greek combining form for "movement" (e.g. kinetics). A *kinin* is a peptide that induces contraction of smooth muscle.
>
> ***Cholecystokinin*** is a polypeptide hormone that induces contraction of the gallbladder (as well as secretion of pancreatic enzymes).

FIGURE 4.28
COMMON BILE AND PANCREATIC DUCTS

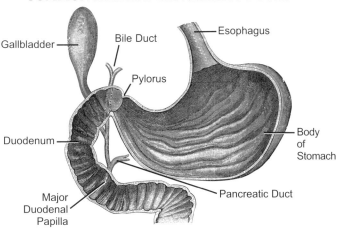

metabolic effects of these hormones are discussed in greater detail in Chapter Six.

Grossly, the pancreas is composed of a head, neck, body, and tail. The rounded **head** is tightly positioned within the turn of the duodenum. The **neck** is continuous with the head and is narrowed by branches of the superior mesenteric artery and vein. The **body** stretches to the left and is positioned superior to the duodenojejunal border. Finally, the **tail** narrows as it extends over the left kidney and ends next to the spleen.

FIGURE 4.30
THE PANCREAS
Anterior View

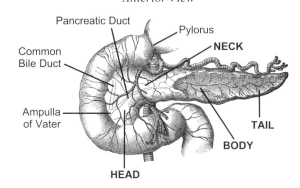

PANCREAS

The pancreas is a large gland located in the upper abdomen behind the stomach and transverse colon and is closely associated with the duodenum. It has both exocrine and endocrine glandular functions. **Exocrine** glands secrete externally by way of a duct. The exocrine functions of the pancreas have been mentioned and include release of digestive enzymes into the pancreatic duct and duodenum. **Endocrine** glands secrete hormones "internally" via the blood. The pancreas releases hormones that regulate carbohydrate metabolism into the venous blood. Histologically, separate cell groupings are responsible for the two glandular functions. Cells that secrete digestive enzymes are found in **pancreatic acini**. Cells that secrete metabolic hormones are located in **islets of Langerhans**.

FIGURE 4.29
FRAMEWORK OF THE PANCREATIC DUCT

An acinus is a sac-like dilatation of a structure. As previously mentioned, *acinous* is a Latin word for *grape-like*. Pulmonary acini are the sac-like dilations of the terminal aspect of the bronchial tree. Pancreatic acini are formed by outpouches of pancreatic cells that line channels to the pancreatic duct. Secreted digestive enzymes follow these channels to eventually reach duodenum.

Amongst the channel-bordering acini are isolated groupings of cells known as islets of Langerhans. Cells in the islets have no connections to the duodenum and secrete their hormones straight into venous blood. In addition to other responsibilities, these hormones regulate carbohydrate metabolism. The pancreatic vein drains into the portal vein, allowing the hormones to first be taken to the organ on which they exert the most meaningful effect, the metabolically-active liver. The islets are named for their histological appearance as tiny cell "islands" dispersed through the acini. These islets are composed of several different cell types. **Alpha cells** secrete the hormone glucagon. **Beta cells** secrete insulin. **Delta cells** secrete somatostatin. There are also other, less plentiful cell types. More than 50% of all islet cells are beta cells. The

SPLEEN

The spleen is a lymphoid organ found in the upper left abdomen between the stomach and diaphragm, immediately above the left kidney. It is completely covered by the ribcage and is positioned at the approximate level of the 11th and 12th ribs. Though it can vary significantly in size, the spleen is usually about the size of a closed fist. Similar to the liver, its **diaphragmatic surface** is fairly smooth, rounded, and convex. The **visceral surface** is concave. Whereas the diaphragmatic surface of the liver is in more of an anterior position and the visceral surface a posterior position, the diaphragmatic surface of the spleen is in more of a lateral orientation and the visceral surface a medial orientation. The visceral surface contains the **hilum**, a longitudinal fissure where the splenic artery and vein enter and exit the organ, respectively.

FIGURE 4.31
**TRANSVERSE SECTION OF ABDOMEN
AT THE L1 VERTEBRAL LEVEL**
Superior View

The spleen functions as a component of the **immune system**. Other than its transfer of bile pigments from the breakdown products of hemoglobin to the liver for the creation of bile, the spleen has little role in the digestive process. The outer wall of the spleen is the **splenic capsule**. Inward projections from the capsule form fibrous, sponge-like **trabeculae**, which provide the supporting structure of the organ. The spleen contains a seemingly endless supply of red and white blood cells that percolate through the arterioles, lymphoid follicles, sinusoids, and venules. Blood is provided to this "filter" by the splenic artery and leaves via the splenic vein. Phagocytosis and antibody production are primary functions of the spleen. Old or damaged red blood cells are destroyed by phagocytes. Antigens are filtered and an antibody response may be mounted against a common pathogen. Because of its immunologic function, the size of the spleen may increase considerably during times of infection or with certain blood disorders. The condition of an enlarged spleen is known as **splenomegaly**.

Another function of the spleen is the **sequestration of blood cells** for their use during times of acute, potentially life-threatening events. As will be discussed in Chapter 6, sympathetic stimulation causes splenic capsule contraction. This forces additional blood into the systemic circulation, increasing the oxygen carrying capability of the blood and immune response of the body.

There is significant vascular pressure within the spleen and the capsule is often taut with tension. This predisposes it to tear or rupture with blunt trauma. Because of its vascular nature, once the spleen is damaged, bleeding can be difficult to control and stop. It is not uncommon that surgical removal of the spleen, a procedure known as **splenectomy**, is required to control hemorrhage following traumatic injuries. In many instances of "internal bleeding" associated with trauma, the spleen is the source of the hemorrhage. Splenectomy may also be performed as required to treat certain blood disorders. Although it appears that the spleen plays a vital role in the immune response, most patients do quite well without it.

KIDNEYS AND BLADDER

The paired kidneys are the bean-shaped organs that maintain the fluid, electrolyte, and acid-base balance of the body. They control the concentration and amount of urine that is excreted. In addition, the kidneys have other functions including regulation of blood pressure, roles in blood cell generation, and serving as a site for gluconeogenesis.

The kidneys are located behind (posterior to) the parietal peritoneum and are therefore said to be in the **retroperitoneum**. Also found in the retroperitoneum are the descending aorta and inferior vena cava. This necessitates the crossing of the peritoneum by blood vessels that supply structures of the peritoneal cavity. The fibromuscular urinary bladder and other pelvic viscera are below the parietal peritoneum. The right and left **ureters** are the conduits that transport urine from the kidneys to the bladder for storage. They leave the kidneys and travel inferiorly in the retroperitoneum to attach to the posterior and inferior portion of each side of the bladder. The major components of the urinary system therefore remain outside the peritoneum. The **urethra** is located at the anterior and inferior portion of the bladder and is the conduit that transports urine out of the body. The triangle-shaped area of bladder wall between the two ureteral openings (orifices) into the bladder and urethral orifice out of the bladder is known as the **trigone** of the bladder.

The *tri*gone is the *tri*angle between the *three* orifices of the bladder (the two ureteral and one urethral).

Similar to the liver and spleen, the kidney can be considered a blood "filter." In addition to other functions, the liver filters digestive contents of the blood; the spleen filters cellular and antigenic contents. The kidney can be thought to filter the water and electrolytes of the blood and maintain proper acid-base balance. The kidney removes certain electrolytes and molecules from the blood. Others are returned. What remains is waste that is transported by the ureter to the bladder for storage and eventual excretion.

FIGURE 4.32
STRUCTURES OF POSTERIOR ABDOMEN
Removal of stomach and transverse colon reveals the underlying pancreas and spleen.

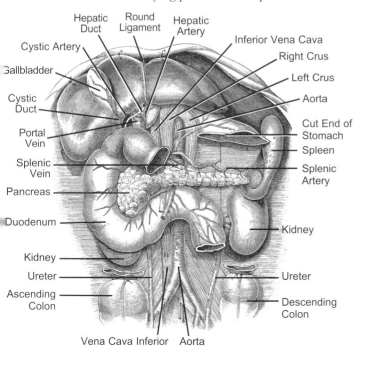

FIGURE 4.33
THE "VASCULAR FILTERS"

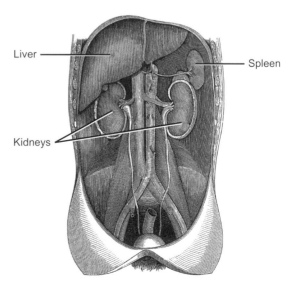

Grossly speaking, each kidney possesses a superior (upper) and inferior (lower) **pole**, a medial and lateral **margin**, and an anterior and posterior **surface**. At the medial margin is the longitudinally-directed **hilum**, which is the point of entry or exit for the renal artery, renal vein, nerves, lymphatic vessels, and the ureter. The **renal sinus** is the space created by the semicircle of surrounding kidney tissue and contains the structures of the hilum, including the **renal pelvis**. The pelvis is the dilated, funnel-shaped superior end of the ureter.

> Like the earth, each kidney has a north pole (superior pole) and south pole (inferior pole). A *margin* is an *edge*. Because of the shape of the kidney, it is logical that the lateral and medial borders would form the *margins*.

> A *sinus* is a *cavity* or *channel* (e.g. maxillary sinus). The **renal sinus** is the *cavity* within the tissue of the kidney through which structures of the renal hilum travel. A *pelvis* is a *basin-shaped* structure (e.g. human pelvis). The **renal pelvis** is the *basin* to which urine drains.

FIGURE 4.34
THE KIDNEY

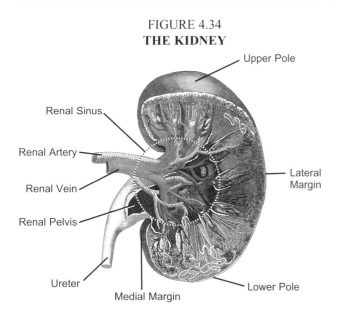

Upper Pole
Renal Sinus
Renal Artery
Renal Vein
Renal Pelvis
Lateral Margin
Ureter
Medial Margin
Lower Pole

The kidney is composed of an outer fibrous **capsule** and an inner **parenchyma**. A *parenchyma* is the *functional tissue* of an organ and performs the duties required to fulfill the responsibilities of the organ. This is opposed to the structural tissue or framework of the organ. The renal parenchyma is formed by tightly interwoven renal tubules and blood vessels and contains two parts: the outer **cortex** and inner **medulla**. A *cortex* is an *outer layer*; a *medulla* is the *innermost portion*. The renal cortex is a continuous strip of parenchyma located beneath the capsule. The medulla is divided into several portions by extensions of cortex that travel from the periphery toward the renal sinus. These strands of cortex are known as **renal columns**. Between the renal columns are fan-shaped areas of medulla that appear to expand from the renal sinus. These inverted pyramids of medulla are known as **renal pyramids**. Each kidney may contain 5 to 15 renal

pyramids. Each renal pyramid, together with the cortex that extends from the base of the pyramid to the capsule, creates a **lobe** of the kidney. There are therefore 5 to 15 lobes in a kidney.

A **renal tubule** is a basic functional structure of the kidney and is formed by a **nephron** and a **collecting tubule**. Blood arrives to the kidney via the renal artery and generations of branches eventually provide an afferent arteriole to a particular nephron. Blood enters the capillary beds (glomerulus) of the filtering capsule (Bowman's capsule) of the nephron and undergoes various electrolyte and molecular exchanges. An efferent arteriole then drains the "filtered" blood. The resulting solution that remains in the nephron tubule continues through a series of twists and turns (convoluted portion) as well as a straight portion (loop of Henle) of the tubule. During this trek, various electrolyte and molecular exchanges continue. The nephron ends by draining into the collecting tubule and what remains in the tubule is waste. Less than 1% of filtered plasma becomes urine; the kidneys function to conserve water and maintain electrolyte balance. Collecting tubules merge to form **collecting ducts**.

The cortex visually appears rather homogenous and is primarily composed of glomeruli, filtering capsules, and convoluted portions of nephrons. The medulla (renal pyramids) is darker and contains striations that appear to course toward or away from the renal sinus. The medulla is primarily composed of ascending and descending limbs of nephrons (loop of Henle), collecting tubules, and collecting ducts.

The apex of each renal pyramid (area of medulla) points toward the renal sinus and is called a **renal papilla**. As with its use in the name of the major duodenal papilla, a *papilla* is a *nipple-shaped* protrusion. Collecting tubules and ducts empty into the renal pelvis at the renal papillae. Urine is first drained into the **minor calices**. A particular minor calix may obtain urine from several renal papillae. The Latin word *calix* describes a *cup-shaped* structure or cavity. Minor calices empty into the two or three major calices a kidney may have. The urine then enters the renal pelvis and flows through the ureter to be stored in the bladder.

> Renal nomenclature can be confusing. However, once the meanings of the words in the names are known, the names of the structures become self-apparent. Consider the following:
>
> The *functional tissue* (**parenchyma**) has an *outer layer* (**cortex**) and *innermost portion* (**medulla**). The medulla is separated by *pillars of cortex* (**renal columns**) that travel from the periphery toward the *cavity* formed by the curve of the kidney (**renal sinus**). These columns create *pyramid-shaped areas of medulla* (**renal pyramids**). The cortex contains glomeruli, filtering capsules, and convoluted portions of nephrons. The medulla contains ascending and descending limbs of nephrons (loop of Henle), collecting tubules, and collecting ducts. Urine flows down the pyramid and is secreted at its *nipple* (**renal papilla**) into a *small cup* (**minor calix**) which drains into a *larger cup* (**major calix**) and finally into a *basin* (**renal pelvis**). It leaves the kidney in the ureter and travels to the bladder for storage and excretion.

FIGURE 4.35
THE KIDNEY AND ADRENAL GLAND

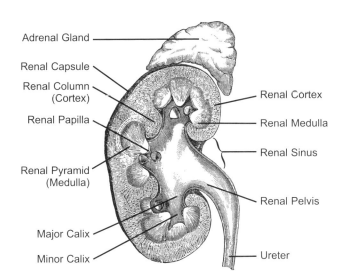

Adrenal Gland

Renal Capsule

Renal Column
(Cortex)

Renal Papilla

Renal Pyramid
(Medulla)

Major Calix

Minor Calix

Renal Cortex

Renal Medulla

Renal Sinus

Renal Pelvis

Ureter

ADRENAL GLAND

The adrenal gland is also known as the **suprarenal gland** and is an endocrine gland found just above the superior pole of each kidney in the retroperitoneum. Each gland is pyramidal in shape with a slightly concave base that abuts the superior pole of its associated kidney. The hilum is located in an anterior position and contains only one vein. Arterial branches enter the gland from various directions.

The adrenal gland has vital hormonal roles. Similar to the kidney, its parenchyma is composed of an outer cortex and inner medulla. The cortex secretes steroid hormones and the medulla secretes adrenergic hormones. As a result of nerve or other hormonal stimulation, hormones are secreted and leave the gland in the lone vein of the hilum. Steroid hormones facilitate the body's stress response while promoting growth and healing. Adrenergic hormones include adrenaline (epinephrine) and norepinephrine. These hormones contribute substantially to the sympathetic fight or flight response, which will be covered in Chapter Six.

FIGURE 4.36
CIRCULATORY AND UROLOGIC STRUCTURES

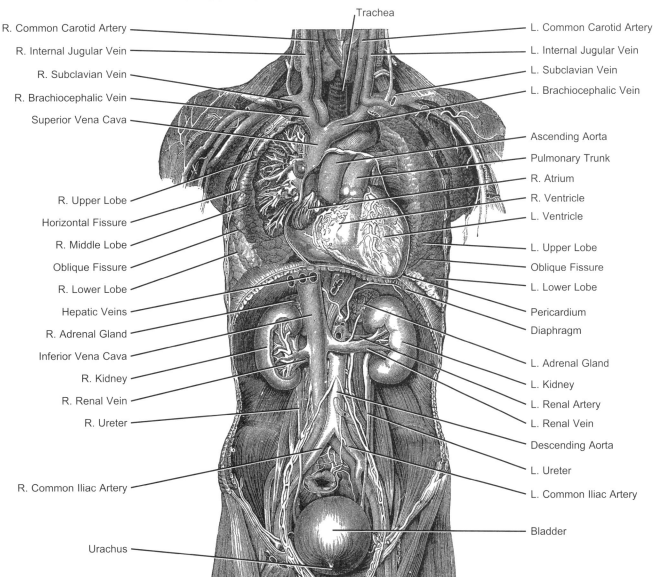

Trachea

R. Common Carotid Artery

R. Internal Jugular Vein

R. Subclavian Vein

R. Brachiocephalic Vein

Superior Vena Cava

R. Upper Lobe

Horizontal Fissure

R. Middle Lobe

Oblique Fissure

R. Lower Lobe

Hepatic Veins

R. Adrenal Gland

Inferior Vena Cava

R. Kidney

R. Renal Vein

R. Ureter

R. Common Iliac Artery

Urachus

L. Common Carotid Artery

L. Internal Jugular Vein

L. Subclavian Vein

L. Brachiocephalic Vein

Ascending Aorta

Pulmonary Trunk

R. Atrium

R. Ventricle

L. Ventricle

L. Upper Lobe

Oblique Fissure

L. Lower Lobe

Pericardium

Diaphragm

L. Adrenal Gland

L. Kidney

L. Renal Artery

L. Renal Vein

Descending Aorta

L. Ureter

L. Common Iliac Artery

Bladder

FEMALE REPRODUCTIVE ORGANS

The **uterus** is the muscular, pear-shaped gestational organ located posterior to the bladder and anterior to the rectum. Within it is the triangular **uterine cavity**, which remains fairly collapsed except during pregnancy. The uterus has an incredible capacity to expand as needed during pregnancy and return to its previous size afterward. There are two **fallopian tubes** and each extends laterally from the upper portion of the uterus and curls to reach one of the two **ovaries**. The uterus, fallopian tubes, and ovaries are affiliated with the **broad ligament**, which suspends the fallopian tubes and ovaries from the floor of the pelvis. The suspension of these structures by the broad ligament is similar to the suspension of the intestines from the abdominal wall by the mesentery.

FIGURE 4.37
SAGITTAL SECTION THROUGH THE FEMALE PELVIS

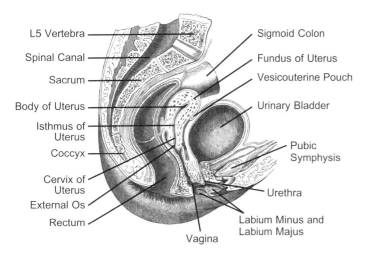

L5 Vertebra
Spinal Canal
Sacrum
Body of Uterus
Isthmus of Uterus
Coccyx
Cervix of Uterus
External Os
Rectum
Vagina
Sigmoid Colon
Fundus of Uterus
Vesicouterine Pouch
Urinary Bladder
Pubic Symphysis
Urethra
Labium Minus and Labium Majus

The uterus is composed of a body, fundus, cervix, and isthmus. The **body** (corpus) is the upper, wide portion. Superior to it is the dome-like **fundus**. Similar to the way the fundus of the stomach extends above the entrance of the esophagus, the fundus of the uterus extends above the entrance of the fallopian tubes. Inferior to the body is the narrowed **cervix**, which projects into the vagina. The **vaginal portion** of the cervix extends into the vagina; the **supravaginal cervix** does not. The lumen of the vagina that borders the cervix is known as the **fornices of the vagina**. A fornix is a vault-like or arch-like space. The lower portion of the body that borders the supravaginal cervix is the **isthmus** or **lower uterine segment**.

The cervix has two openings separated by a canal. The **external os** opens into the vagina and appears as a crevice formed by an anterior lip (labia) and posterior lip. The **internal os** opens into the uterine canal. The two are separated by a narrow passage, the **cervical canal**, which remains semi-closed except during childbirth. Although the fundus, body, and isthmus enlarge throughout pregnancy, the cervical canal does not begin to dilate until the second stage of labor.

> *Os* is a shortened form of the word ***ostium***, which is Latin for *orifice* or *mouth*.

Each fallopian tube is about ten centimeters long. The **uterine** or **intramural** portion of the tube leaves the uterus at the **uterine ostium**. The **isthmus** is the narrow portion that continues away from the uterus. The tube again begins to dilate and becomes tortuous at the **ampulla**. The dilation becomes more prominent and forms the funnel-shaped **infundibulum** at the terminal aspect of the tube, near the ovary. Within the infundibulum is the opening to the lumen of the tube, the **ostium of the fallopian tube**. Numerous small, fringe-like projections extend from the edge of the infundibulum and are known as **fimbriae**, which is Latin for fringe or border. At least one of the fimbriae, the **ovarian fimbria**, stretches from the infundibulum to the ovary.

With the Exception of the <u>C</u>ervix, Components of the Female System Starts With Vowels

<u>E</u>xternal <u>O</u>s → <u>I</u>nternal <u>O</u>s → <u>U</u>terus → <u>U</u>terine <u>O</u>stium → <u>U</u>terine (<u>I</u>ntramural) portion of tube → <u>I</u>sthmus → <u>A</u>mpulla → <u>I</u>nfundibulum

IAI: The ampulla is between the two "I's, the isthmus and infundibulum.

Infundibulum means *funnel*

An ovary is the female gonad, which is a gland that produces gametes. Ovaries are named for their production of ova (eggs). Ova are female germ cells. In addition, the ovaries are also endocrine glands and secrete hormones. Each oval-shaped ovary is about three centimeters long and attaches to the broad ligament via the **mesovarium**. Each ovary is also supported laterally and anteriorly by its respective fallopian tube. The mesovarium can be considered the mesentery of the ovary and contains the nerves, arteries, and veins that supply the organ. These structures enter the ovary at the ovarian **hilum**.

In order to cause pregnancy following intercourse, sperm must pass through the cervix, uterus, fallopian tube, and ovarian fimbria to reach the ovary and potentially meet with the right egg at the right time. Odds are against it, yet here we are.

A **bilateral tubal ligation (BTL)** is the surgical sterilization procedure for the female. Each (*bilateral*) fallopian tube (*tubal*) is ligated (*ligation*). To ligate something is to constrict and close off the lumen of a structure by tying a ligature (string, suture, wire) around it.

FIGURE 4.38
FEMALE REPRODUCTIVE ORGANS

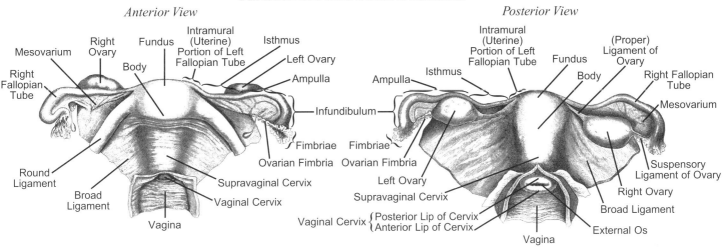

Anterior View   *Posterior View*

MALE REPRODUCTIVE ORGANS

Because organs of the male reproductive system have less of a presence in the ventral cavity, their discussion here will be limited. The male gonads are the **testes** (testicles) and the gametes they produce are spermatozoa. Like ovaries, the testes are also endocrine glands and secrete hormones. Interestingly, maturation of the male germ cells (spermatozoa) requires a temperature that is a little less (95° F) than normal body temperature (98.6° F). This necessitates the suspension of the testes in the skin and muscular tissue of the **scrotum**, which distances them from the warmer body cavities. The temperature of the testes can be modified by contraction and relaxation of the smooth muscle of the scrotal wall, the **dartos muscle**. Contraction elevates the testes closer to the pelvic cavity and increases their temperature; relaxation lowers their temperature. Nerves, blood vessels, and lymph vessels enter and exit the testes from the posterior border.

Within a testicle, spermatozoa are produced and transported from the **seminiferous tubules** to a series of interwoven channels of the posterior testis, the **rete testis**. The posterior portion of the testicle that contains the rete testis and receives the supporting structures is known as the **mediastinum testis**. Mature spermatozoa travel by way of **efferent ductules** to be stored in the nearby **epididymis**. The epididymis appears as a mass of tightly coiled tubules held together by loose connective tissue. The **head** is the thick portion that receives the efferent ductules from the testis. The **body** trails away from the testis. The **tail** is the thin portion that turns to begin its course out of the scrotum. The tail of the epididymis is continuous with the **ductus (vas) deferens**.

> Epididymis: the Greek word *didymos* = the Latin word *testis*

The ductus (vas) deferens takes a rather circuitous route to reach and join the urethra. The ductus leaves the scrotum and courses anterior and superior to the pubic bone. It passes through the abdominal wall to enter the pelvic cavity by way of the inguinal canal. Here it travels with the testicular artery, testicular vein, nerves, and lymphatic vessels. The group of structures is surrounded by membrane and forms the **spermatic cord**.

> A **vasectomy** is the male surgical sterilization procedure. During the procedure, the spermatic cord on each side is located and the ductus (vas) deferens is separated from the other structures and divided (cut). A *vas*ectomy is cutting of the *vas* deferens and it must be done on both sides.

The ductus enters the **prostatic urethra** via the **ejaculatory duct**. The prostatic urethra is the portion of the male urethra that courses through the tissue of the prostate gland and is located between the urinary bladder and penis. At the prostate, each ductus receives a corresponding duct from an exocrine gland, the **seminal vesicle**. There are two seminal vesicles, one for each ductus. Once stimulated, rhythmic contractions of the smooth muscle wall of the ductus deferens propel spermatozoa forward. The spermatozoa are mixed with zinc-rich secretions from the prostate and secretions from the seminal vesicles to create semen. Sixty percent of the volume of semen is obtained from the seminal vesicles and these secretions are rich in sugars, proteins, enzymes, vitamins, and other chemicals. Much of the initial ejaculate is composed of spermatozoa and prostatic secretions. The seminal secretions arrive relatively late. Between the prostate and penis, ducts from small exocrine glands, the **bulbourethral glands**, join the urethra. During arousal, secretions from these glands produce the pre-ejaculate, which lubricates the urethra and neutralizes urethral acidity caused by urine. Both actions facilitate spermatozoa delivery.

> 60% of the volume of *sem*en is secreted by the *sem*inal vesicle.

Figure 4.39
Male Urogenital Structures
Sagittal View

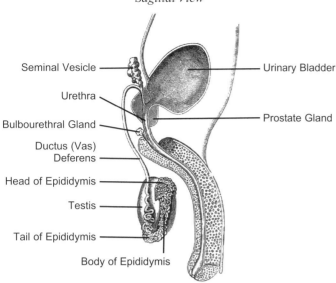

Seminal Vesicle

Urethra

Bulbourethral Gland

Ductus (Vas) Deferens

Head of Epididymis

Testis

Tail of Epididymis

Body of Epididymis

Urinary Bladder

Prostate Gland

THE LYMPHATIC SYSTEM

Vessels of the lymphatic system have been mentioned and require description. **Lymphatic vessels** course throughout the body and are not confined to the cavities. At different points, certain lymph vessels are filtered by **lymph nodes**. The majority of the body is composed of water; the lymphatic system assists the venous system in draining fluids from body tissues. It also transports lipids (fats) and immune cells.

Water forms about sixty-percent of the body mass and is found in various *spaces*: the intravascular, extravascular, intracellular, and extracellular spaces. This water is circulated through the spaces and participates in the transportation of cells, enzymes, nutrients, hormones, and the numerous chemical mediators required to sustain life. Circulation also permits the filtering and removal of metabolic byproducts, toxins, and infectious agents. **Lymph** is a clear, yellowish fluid that collects in tissue spaces and must be returned to the intravascular space for redistribution. The extravascular, extracellular space is the **interstitial space**, which is the tissue space where lymph accumulates. Lymph contains fluid, lipids, and **lymphocytes**, which are vital cells of the

FIGURE 4.40
THE VISCERA
Anterior View

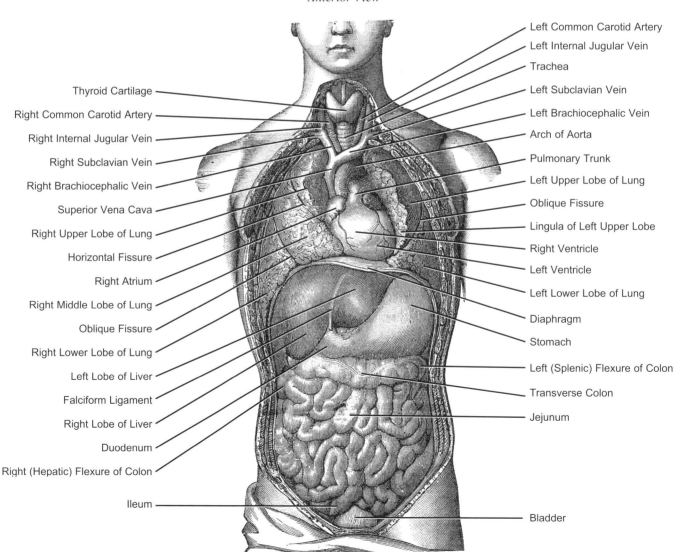

Thyroid Cartilage

Right Common Carotid Artery

Right Internal Jugular Vein

Right Subclavian Vein

Right Brachiocephalic Vein

Superior Vena Cava

Right Upper Lobe of Lung

Horizontal Fissure

Right Atrium

Right Middle Lobe of Lung

Oblique Fissure

Right Lower Lobe of Lung

Left Lobe of Liver

Falciform Ligament

Right Lobe of Liver

Duodenum

Right (Hepatic) Flexure of Colon

Ileum

Left Common Carotid Artery

Left Internal Jugular Vein

Trachea

Left Subclavian Vein

Left Brachiocephalic Vein

Arch of Aorta

Pulmonary Trunk

Left Upper Lobe of Lung

Oblique Fissure

Lingula of Left Upper Lobe

Right Ventricle

Left Ventricle

Left Lower Lobe of Lung

Diaphragm

Stomach

Left (Splenic) Flexure of Colon

Transverse Colon

Jejunum

Bladder

immune system. Lymphocytes are one of five types of leukocytes (white blood cells). The other four types are monocytes, eosinophils, neutrophils, and basophils. Lymphocytes are created in the **thymus**, a gland of the anterior mediastinum, and **bone marrow**, the soft, hematopoietic center of certain bones.

Lymph contains *lymphocytes*

Lymphocytes are disseminated in a pattern that optimizes exposure to both infective agents and other immune system components. The immune cells leave their generative organs in venous blood, travel to the heart, and are delivered to body tissues in arterial blood. Lymphocytes leave arterial capillaries to enter the tissue they are to "patrol." Many are concentrated in lymphoid tissues, which are tissues strategically positioned to detect and respond to an infectious intrusion. Examples of lymphoid tissues include lymph nodes, pharyngeal tonsils, adenoids, the spleen, Peyer's patches of the ilium, and the appendix. Others lymphocytes seep through peripheral tissues and enter lymphatic vessels for redistribution in the systemic circulation or transport to lymphatic tissues. If an infective agent is detected, an immune response is triggered.

Unlike the arterial and venous systems, which form a closed loop with the capillary beds serving as the intermediary between the two, the lymph system is closed at one end. Lymph capillaries start out as blind pouches located in peripheral tissues. Lipid-containing interstitial fluid crosses the capillary membrane and lymphocytes migrate through it. The capillaries merge and progressively larger lymphatic vessels form a dense network of interweaving channels. Lymphatic walls are so thin that the vessels often cannot be delineated from the tissue they travel through. They simply appear as narrow areas of space within tissue substance.

Flowing toward large veins of the neck, lymph travels through regionally-situated groupings of lymph nodes. Lymph nodes are particularly numerous in the lateral neck, axilla, groin, and mediastinum. These groupings are known as the cervical, axillary, inguinal, and mediastinal nodes, respectively. Lymph nodes can become inflamed, swollen, and tender when an area they drain becomes infected. They can also be the first structures to receive metastatic cells from a cancer that is located in their drainage zone. Many times, **lymphadenopathy** (swollen lymph nodes) is the first sign that an infection or a tumor is present.

FIGURE 4.41
SECTION THROUGH A LYMPH NODE

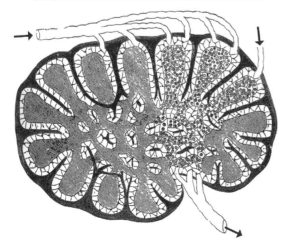

> **Point of Interest**
>
> Elephantiasis is a parasitic disease caused by filarial worms that gain entrance into the lymphatic system and obstruct the flow of lymph, causing edema and massive tissue swelling.

The **cisterna chyli** is a relatively large lymph sac positioned deep in the abdomen, anterior to the descending aorta at the level of the L1 vertebra. A *cistern* is a space that serves as a fluid reservoir. *Chyle* is a fluid obtained from the intestines during digestion and contains lipids and lymph. **Lacteals** are lymphatic vessels that drain the intestines and transport chyle. During digestion, the higher hydrostatic pressure of the venous system prevents large lipid molecules like fatty acids from passing through venous walls. Smaller sized digestive products like carbohydrates and amino acids are permitted direct entry. Fatty acids are able to penetrate the thin walls of the low-pressure lymphatic system and must use the lymphatics as an indirect route for vascular entry following digestion.

FIGURE 4.42
LYMPHATIC DRAINAGE OF THE LOWER EXTREMITY, PELVIS, AND LOWER ABDOMEN

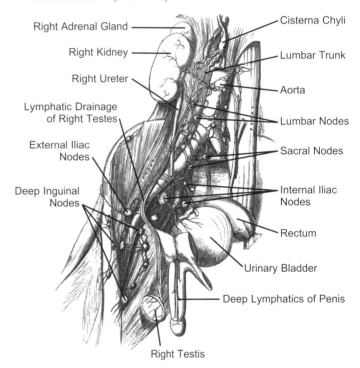

Right Adrenal Gland — Cisterna Chyli
Right Kidney — Lumbar Trunk
Right Ureter — Aorta
Lymphatic Drainage of Right Testes — Lumbar Nodes
External Iliac Nodes — Sacral Nodes
Deep Inguinal Nodes — Internal Iliac Nodes
Rectum
Urinary Bladder
Deep Lymphatics of Penis
Right Testis

Lymphatic vessels converge to form lymphatic trunks, which drain body regions. The cisterna chyli receives the paired **lumbar trunks**, **intestinal trunks**, and **lower intercostal trunks**. Lymph from the lower extremities, back, abdomen, and lower thorax drains to the cisterna chyli. The **thoracic duct** extends from the upper aspect of the cisterna chyli and travels superiorly along the anterior spine. In the neck, it receives the **left jugular trunk**, **left subclavian trunk**, and **left bronchomediastinal trunk**. The left jugular trunk transports lymph from the left side of the head and neck. The left subclavian trunk drains the left upper extremity and left chest wall. The left bronchomediastinal trunk carries lymph from the mediastinum and left lung. After receiving these trunks, the thoracic duct drains into the **left subclavian vein** at its merger with the left internal jugular vein. It is by this circuitous route that digested fatty acids enter the systemic circulation.

Likewise, the **right lymph duct** receives the **right jugular trunk**, **right subclavian trunk**, and **right bronchomediastinal trunk** and drains into the **left subclavian vein** at a similar location. The right duct can be considered the counterpart of the thoracic duct, except it is responsible for much less body area and does not drain chyle from the intestines. As compared to the right duct, the thoracic duct additionally transports chyle and lymph from the lower extremities, abdomen, and lower thorax.

FIGURE 4.43
MAJOR LYMPHATIC STRUCTURES

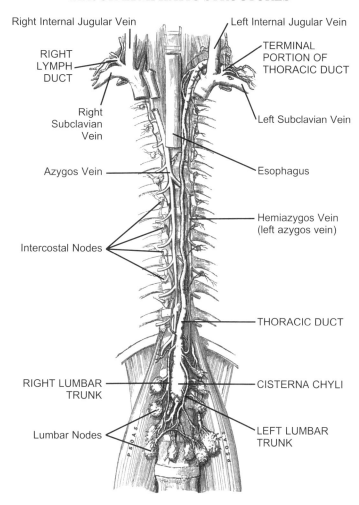

FIGURE 4.44
THE LYMPHATIC SYSTEM

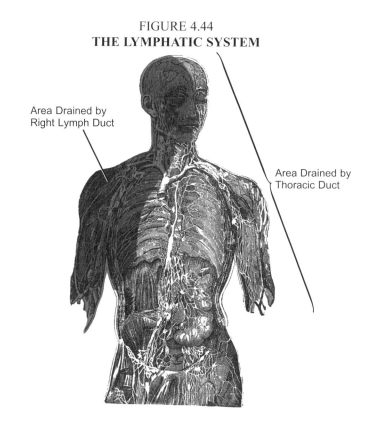

DUCT = LEFT = MOST
Each word contains four letters. The *thoracic duct* is on the *left* and drains lymph from *most* of the body.

CC right —AH→ left @ T5 to L. SC/IJ
The **thoracic duct** forms at the **C**isterna **C**hyli (T12-L2) on the **right** side of the abdominal aorta. It passes through the **A**ortic **H**iatus of the diaphragm (T10-T12) and ascends between the aorta and azygos vein, posterior to the esophagus and anterior to the vertebral column. It crosses over to the **left** at the **T5** level and joins the junction of the left **S**ub**C**lavian and **I**nternal **J**ugular veins.

STRUCTURES OF THE DORSAL CAVITY

The dorsal cavity contains the central nervous system (CNS), which is composed of the brain and spinal cord. Both components are enclosed within three membranes that separate these structures from bones of the skull and vertebrae, respectively. The three membranes include the pia mater, arachnoid, and dura mater. Together, these membranes form the meninges. The word *mater* infers *substance*, similar to the use of the word *matter* in the description of gray and white matter of the brain. The descriptor is often omitted and the membranes are simply referred to as the pia, arachnoid, and dura.

The **pia mater** is applied directly to the outer surface of brain and spinal cord tissue. It contains numerous blood vessels that supply nervous tissue. The arachnoid is located between the pia and dura. The **arachnoid** contains "strands" of connective tissue, no blood vessels, and is named for its spider-web appearance. The arachnoid is separated from the pia by the subarachnoid space which is filled with cerebrospinal fluid (CSF). The **dura mater** is the thick, outer layer of the meninges. It is separated from the arachnoid by the subdural space.

The CNS is surrounded by a PAD
From internal to external: Pia → Arachnoid → Dura

BRAIN

The brain is known as the **encephalon**. The Greek word root *encephal(o)* means *brain*. Based on embryologic development, the brain is formed by the telencephalon, diencephalon, mesencephalon, metencephalon, and myelencephalon. The **telencephalon** is formed by two cerebral hemispheres. The telencephalon, along with the **diencephalon**, constitutes the cerebrum. The **mesencephalon** is commonly known as the midbrain. The **metencephalon** is comprised of the pons and cerebellum. Finally, the **myelencephalon** is formed by the medulla oblongata.

The brain is commonly subdivided into the cerebrum, diencephalon, basal ganglia, cerebellum, and brain stem. The **cerebrum** forms the largest portion of the brain and is composed of **two hemispheres** that are joined by the **corpus callosum.** Each hemisphere contains **four lobes:** frontal, temporal, parietal, and occipital. The surface elevations are known as **gyri** (gyrus); the grooves between elevations are **sulci** (sulcus).

The diencephalon and basal ganglia are located between the cerebrum and brain stem. The **diencephalon** includes the thalamus, epithalamus, hypothalamus, and subthalamus. The **basal ganglia** is formed by the caudate nucleus, putamen, globus pallidus, and substantia nigra. The **cerebellum** is located posterior to the brain stem and is attached by six cerebellar peduncles, three on each side. The cerebellum consists of three lobes: a middle lobe known as the vermis and two outer lobes. The **brain stem** is composed of three components. The **midbrain** forms the superior aspect of the brain stem. The **pons** is in an intermediate position and the **medulla oblongata** is the inferior component. The brain is the origin of twelve pairs of nerves that branch directly from it. These are the twelve cranial nerves and are described in Chapter Seven.

The Embryologic Designations for Brain Stem Components are in Alphabetical Order

Proximal	**Intermediate**	**Distal**
midbrain = **mes**encephalon	pons = **met**encephalon *(along with cerebellum)*	medulla = m**ye**lencephaion

---

1) The lobes of the cerebrum correspond to four bones of the skull
2) The diencephalon is full of four "thalamus's" : thalamus, epi-, hypo-, and sub-
3) The basal ganglia asks, "**C**an **P**utamen **G**et **S**mart?" = **C**audate nucleus, **P**utamen, **G**lobus pallidus, and **S**ubstantia nigra
4) The cerebellum is formed by **3** lobes and attaches to brain stem by **3** cerebellar peduncles on each side (6 total)
5) The brain stem is composed of **3** components. The mid-*brain* is in the superior position because it is closest to the *brain*. The pons is in an intermediate position between the two "m's" (midbrain and medulla)

Any student that knows the anatomic outline of the preceding paragraphs would have a significant advantage at the onset of a neuroanatomy course.

SPINAL CORD

The spinal cord is the tubular protrusion of central nervous tissue into the bony vertebral column. It is continuous with the medulla oblongata and passes through the **foramen magnum** of the skull. The spinal cord is the origin of thirty-one pairs of **spinal nerves**, which are the focus of much of this text. Although the true spinal cord ends at the approximate L1-L2 vertebral level, spinal nerve roots leave the cord and continue inferiorly within the vertebral canal. The spinal cord is discussed in greater detail in Chapter Eight and much of the subsequent text is devoted to the description of the thirty-one pairs of spinal nerves that originate from it.

FIGURE 4.45
MIDDLE SAGITTAL VIEW OF BRAIN

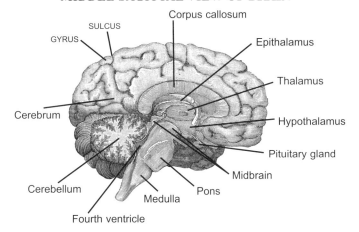

FIGURE 4.46
BRAIN STEM AND ASSOCIATED STRUCTURES

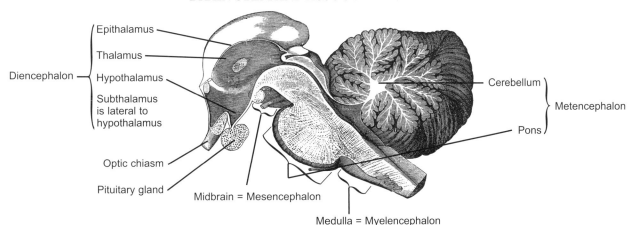

QUIZ 2
Body Cavities and Major Organs

Time for Quiz = 20 minutes.
For questions 1-15, choose the single best answer.

_____1) Which cells secrete insulin?
    a) cells of pancreatic acini
    b) alpha cells
    c) beta cells
    d) delta cells
    e) none of the above

_____2) What is the terminal portion of the small bowel?
    a) the cecum
    b) the ileum
    c) the jejunum
    d) the duodenum
    e) none of the above

_____3) Which lobe of the liver is bordered by the gallbladder?
    a) caudate lobe
    b) quadrate lobe
    c) left lobe
    d) all of the above
    e) none of the above

_____4) What tissue forms renal pyramids?
    a) renal parenchyma
    b) renal medulla
    c) both a and b
    d) renal cortex
    e) none of the above

_____5) Which is a component of the metencephalon?
    a) pons
    b) midbrain
    c) both a and b
    d) medulla
    e) none of the above

_____6) Within a liver lobule, which fluids flow in the same direction?
    a) blood from the hepatic artery and bile
    b) blood from the portal vein and bile
    c) blood from the hepatic artery and portal vein
    d) blood from the hepatic vein and bile
    e) none of the above

_____7) Where is the epididymis located?
    a) at the entry of the ductus deferens into the prostate
    b) in the spermatic cord
    c) near the urethra between the prostate and penis
    d) at the ampulla of Vater
    e) none of the above

_____8) From where is epinephrine secreted?
    a) renal cortex
    b) adrenal medulla
    c) adrenal cortex
    d) renal medulla
    e) none of the above

_____9) Which component of a fallopian tube is closest to the origin of the tube from the uterus?
    a) isthmus
    b) infundibulum
    c) fimbria
    d) intramural portion
    e) ampulla

_____10) Of the following membranes, which is closest to the outer surface of CNS nervous tissue?
    a) arachnoid
    b) meninges
    c) pia
    d) dura
    e) none of the above

____11) Where is an internal os located?
    a) between the cervical canal and vaginal fornices
    b) between the cervical and uterine canals
    c) beween the uterus and uterine portion of the fallopian tube
    d) beween the ampulla and infundibulum
    e) none of the above

____12) Within a liver lobule, which structures transport bile?
    a) portal vein
    b) trabeculae
    c) branches of the cystic duct
    d) canaliculi
    e) none of the above

____13) Which male reproductive structure is responsible for secreting the pre-ejaculate?
    a) bulbourethral gland
    b) epididymis
    c) testis
    d) prostate
    e) seminal vesicle

____14) To which structure is the head of the pancreas closely associated?
    a) the spleen
    b) the duodenum
    c) the jejunum
    d) the right kidney
    e) none of the above

____15) Which is the largest lobe of the liver?
    a) right lobe
    b) left lobe
    c) quadrate lobe
    d) caudate lobe
    e) upper lobe

For questions 16-20, use the following directions:
  a.......1,2,3 are correct
  b.......1,3 are correct
  c.......2,4 are correct
  d.......only 4 is correct
  e.......all are correct

____16) Components of the basal ganglia include the
    1. caudate nucleus
    2. hypothalamus
    3. putamen
    4. medulla oblongata

____17) The caudate lobe of the liver is bordered by the
    1. fissure for ligamentum venosum
    2. vena cava
    3. porta hepatis
    4. gallbladder

____18) What may be readily found within the cisterna chyli?
    1. white blood cells
    2. chyme
    3. fatty acids
    4. red blood cells

____19) Which organ has its own mesentery?
    1. appendix
    2. liver
    3. ovary
    4. spleen

____20) Which components of a renal tubule may be found in great abundance in the renal cortex?
    1. ascending limb of the loop of Henle
    2. collecting tubules
    3. descending limb of the loop of Henle
    4. glomeruli

QUIZ 2: Body Cavities and Major Organs

1) c – Insulin is secreted by beta cells of the islets of Langerhans of the pancreas. Other islet cells include alpha cells (which secrete glucagon) and delta cells (which secrete somatostatin). There are additional, less well-known cell types that also exist in the islets. Cells of the pancreatic acini secrete digestive enzymes that travel in the pancreatic duct to reach the duodenum.

2) b – The small intestine is composed of three portions. The duodenum is the proximal component that receives gastric contents from the pylorus of the stomach. The jejunum is the long, intermediate portion. The ileum is the terminal component and empties into the cecum of the large bowel.

3) b – The quadrate lobe is positioned between the fissure for ligamentum teres (round ligament) and the gallbladder, anterior to the porta hepatis. The right lobe is right of the gallbladder.

4) c – As opposed to the structural tissue of an organ, the parenchyma is the functional tissue of an organ. The renal parenchyma is formed by tightly interwoven renal tubules and blood vessels and consists of two portions: the outer cortex and inner medulla. The medulla is divided into several portions by extensions of cortex (renal columns) that travel from the periphery toward the renal sinus. Between the renal columns are pyramid-shaped areas of medulla known as renal pyramids.

5) a – The metencephalon is formed by the pons and cerebellum. The mesencephalon is formed by the midbrain. The myelencephalon is formed by the medulla.

6) c – A liver lobule is formed by a group of hepatocytes that are surrounded by several portal triads at the periphery. A portal triad consists of branches of the hepatic artery, portal vein, and bile duct (as well as lymph vessels). In the center of the lobule is a *central* vein that is oriented in the same direction as the portal triads. Blood leaves from the portal vein and hepatic artery and flows through the hepatocytes of the lobule. It eventually drains to the central vein. Central

veins empty into hepatic veins, which drain to the vena cava. Bile flows in the opposite direction in a liver lobule. Bile is produced by hepatocytes and flows in canaliculi to reach bile ducts in the portal triads at the periphery of the lobule. Bile drains to the hepatic duct and is subsequently stored in the gallbladder where it is concentrated.

7) e – The epididymis is located in the scrotum and stores mature spermatozoa. The epididymis obtains spermatozoa via efferent ductules from the rete testis of its affiliated testis. The seminal vesicles are located at the entry of the ductus deferens into the prostate. The spermatic cord contains the ductus (vas) deferens, testicular artery, testicular vein, nerves, and lymph vessels. The bulbourethral glands are near the urethra between the prostate and penis. The ampulla of Vater is the dilation of the hepatopancreatic duct at its union with the posterior wall of the duodenum.

8) b – Epinephrine (adrenalin) and norepinephrine are secreted by cells of the adrenal medulla. Cells of the adrenal cortex secrete steroid hormones. The renal cortex and medulla contain various components of renal tubules and function in maintenance of water, electrolyte, and acid-base balance.

9) d – From proximal to distal, a fallopian tube is composed of an intramural (uterine) portion, isthmus, ampulla, infundibulum, and fimbriae. The intramural portion leaves the uterus at the uterine ostium. The isthmus is the narrow portion that continues away from the uterus. The tube dilates and becomes tortuous at the ampulla. The funnel-shaped infundibulum is located at the terminal aspect of the tube, near the ovary. Numerous small, fringe-like projections extend from the edge of the infundibulum and are known as fimbriae. Fimbria is the singular form of the word.

10) c – The three membranes, the pia, arachnoid, and dura, together form the meninges. From internal to external, the CNS is surrounded by a PAD. The pia is adherent to the outer layer of

nerve tissue, the arachnoid is in an intermediate position, and the dura forms the outer layer.

11) b – The cervix is the neck of the uterus and has two openings that are separated by the narrow cervical canal. The external os opens into the vagina and appears as a crevice formed by anterior and posterior lips. The internal os opens into the uterine canal. The uterine (intramural) portion of the fallopian tube leaves the uterus at the *uterine* ostium. No os exists between the ampulla and infundibulum of the fallopian tube.

12) d – Bile is secreted by hepatocytes into small canals known as bile canaliculi. Canaliculi combine to form bile ductules, which drain into bile ducts in portal triads at the periphery of a liver lobule. Merging of ducts continues until the common hepatic duct is formed at the porta hepatis. The hepatic duct leaves the liver and is soon joined by the cystic duct from the gallbladder. This combination creates the common bile duct, which is later joined by the pancreatic duct and empties into the duodenum.

13) a – During arousal and before ejaculation, bulbourethral glands secrete the pre-ejaculate, which lubricates the urethra and neutralizes urethral acidity caused by urine. The testis generates spermatozoa, which are then stored in the epididymis. The prostate secretes a zinc-rich solution into the ejaculate. The seminal vesicle secretes a fluid rich in nutrients, vitamins, and enzymes into the ejaculate.

14) b – The head of the pancreas is tightly positioned in the turn made by the duodenum. The pancreatic duct usually joins the common bile duct and the two dilate into the ampulla of Vater at the posterior wall of the duodenum. The tail of the pancreas extends over the left kidney and often borders the spleen.

15) a – The four lobes of the liver are the right, left, quadrate, and caudate lobes. The right lobe forms the base of the liver and is up to five times larger than the left lobe. The left lobe is larger than the quadrate and caudate lobes. There is no upper lobe of the liver.

16) b – The basal ganglia is formed by the caudate nucleus, putamen, globus pallidus, and sub-

stantia nigra. Along with the other three "thalami," the hypothalamus is part of the diencephalon. The medulla forms the myelencephalon and is one of the three components of the brain stem.

17) a – On the visceral surface of the liver, the caudate lobe is positioned between the fissure for ligamentum venosum and the vena cava, posterior to the porta hepatis. The quadrate lobe is positioned between the fissure for ligamentum teres (round ligament) and the gallbladder, anterior to the porta hepatis. The right lobe is right of these structures and the left lobe is left of them.

18) b – The cisterna chyli is a lymph-containing sac in the deep abdomen and is the origin of the thoracic duct. Lymph is composed of fluid, lipids (fatty acids) and lymphocytes. Lymphocytes are one of five types of white blood cells. The four others are monocytes, eosinophils, neutrophils, and basophils. The *chyli* portion of the name relates to the fact that the citerna chyli receives chyle from lymphatic drainage of the intestines during digestion. Chyle contains lymph and fatty acids. Fatty acids are relatively large molecules and cannot penetrate the walls of the higher-pressure venous system. Instead, they cross the thin walls of lymphatic vessels and are transported to the cisterna chyli by lymphatic vessels known as lacteals. From the cisterna chyli, they travel by way of the thoracic duct and enter the systemic blood circulation at the left subclavian vein. Chyme is the partially-digested semifluid mixture that enters the duodenum from the stomach.

19) b – A mesentery is a membrane that loosely attaches organs to the body wall. The mesoappendix attaches the appendix and a mesovarium attaches each ovary. Each of these two organs obtains its nerve innervation, vascular supply, and lymphatic drainage by way of its respective mesentery.

20) d – See #4 answer explanation. The renal cortex is primarily composed of glomeruli, filtering capsules (Bowman's capsules), and convoluted portions of nephrons. The medulla (renal pyramids) is primarily composed of collecting tubules, collecting ducts, and the ascending and descending limbs of the loop of Henle of nephrons.

"I merely took the energy it takes to pout and wrote some blues"

– Duke Ellington

CLINICAL CORRELATION

Numerous disease processes promote the movement of fluid out of the vasculature and into the tissues. This movement may be evidenced by generalized tissue swelling and edema. It also may involve fluid accumulation in closed cavities. Closed cavities have no direct opening to the outside; there is no place for the additional fluid to go. In fact, fluid accumulation in closed cavities may be the first sign that a pathologic process is present.

The word *effusion* describes an accumulation of fluid. In the face of heart failure, kidney failure, liver failure, malignancy, electrolyte disorders, and lung injury, fluid can accumulate in the thoracic cavity in the form of a **pleural effusion**. Accumulation of fluid in the pericardial cavity is called a **pericardial effusion**. Within the abdominopelvic cavity, the accumulation is known as **ascites**.

Disease processes such as liver failure, kidney failure, poor nutrition, and various metabolic diseases may cause electrolyte disorders and lower the oncotic pressure of the blood. Oncotic pressure can be thought of as the osmotic pressure of the blood formed by dissolved compounds in blood plasma. Large protein molecules create an oncotic pressure of the intravascular fluid which promotes retention of fluid within vessel walls. A decrease in these proteins, occurring with the previously mentioned disease processes, would cause a decrease in oncotic pressure. This decrease would favor movement of fluid out of vessels and into the tissues, accumulating in body cavities.

Autoimmune diseases are another group of diseases which can cause fluid movement from the vessels to tissues. These diseases may cause the inner lining of the blood vessels to become "leaky" and may promote movement of fluid out of the intravascular space and into the tissues. Autoimmune diseases include various pathologic states in which the body's immune system is mistakenly directed against its own tissues. In some cases, the blood vessel walls become damaged and intravascular fluid is able to leak out. Examples of such diseases are systemic lupus erythematosus (lupus), vasculitis (inflammation of the vasculature), sarcoidosis, and Kawasaki disease. With these diseases, additional fluid may leak from the vasculature even though the oncotic pressure of the blood may be normal.

Another cause for the fluid collection could be of a mechanical nature. For some reason, the hydrostatic pressure of the intravascular fluid becomes elevated. Hydrostatic pressure can be considered the amount of *fluid pressure* within the intravascular space. A high hydrostatic pressure favors movement of fluid out of the vessels and into the tissues and cavities. The fluid is simply pushed out of the vessels. In heart failure, the heart may not be able to adequately pump the blood. The blood backs up in the heart and lungs and predisposes to the development of pericardial and pleural effusions, respectively. In cirrhosis of the liver, there is a fibrous scarring of the liver. This slows the flow of blood

through the liver, backs up the portal circulation, and predisposes to the development of ascites. Both heart failure and liver cirrhosis increase the hydrostatic pressure of intravascular fluid, favoring movement of fluid out of the vessels and into the tissues and cavities.

Direct tissue injury to structures within the cavity could also result in accumulated cavity fluid. A pleural effusion may be due to a pulmonary contusion after blunt trauma to the chest sustained in a motor vehicle accident. A pericardial effusion may follow a myocardial infarction (heart attack). One may develop "fluid on the knee" following a knee injury. In this case, the fluid accumulates within the closed cavity of the joint space. Another potential cause of fluid accumulation is malignancy, which could involve any of the cavities.

Patients may present with complaints of weakness, fatigue, shortness of breath, and tachycardia (elevated heart rate). Radiologic exams such as x-rays, computerized tomography (CT), and/or magnetic resonance imaging (MRI) often reveal the fluid accumulation. Next, the area of fluid accumulation is approached by needle to obtain fluid specimens. These specimens may provide clues to the specific cause of the problem. Fluid removal by needle is often referred to as a **tap**. In this situation, the fluid is being removed in an effort to provide a diagnosis; the procedure is therefore called a **diagnostic tap**.

There are two basic types of classification for the *tapped* fluid: an exudate or a transudate. An **exudate** has a higher level of cellular debris and protein. This is because there has been an actual injury to the inner lining of the blood vessels and they become "leaky." The cellular debris and proteins are able to leave the vessels and accumulate with the fluid. This is indicative of an inflammatory cause such as autoimmune disease (e.g. lupus), infection, or malignancy. By contrast, a **transudate** contains little, if any, cellular debris and protein. With a disease process that produces a transudate, the vascular integrity of the vessels remains intact. The cause may be due to the decreased osmotic pressure (e.g. poor nutrition, liver disease, electrolyte disorders) or increased hydrostatic pressure (e.g. heart failure, cirrhosis of the liver). Based on whether the fluid is an exudate or transudate, further diagnostic tests would be done to narrow down the etiology.

A **trans**udate is simply a fluid that has gone **trans**membrane or has crossed a membrane (similar to a simple osmotic pressure experiment) as opposed to an exudate which has leaked. An **ex**udate has crossed the membrane by the use of **ex**its.

The word *therapeutic* describes a procedure or process performed in an effort to provide a therapy or treatment. This is opposed to the word *diagnostic* which describes a test or procedure which is performed to provide a diagnosis. Patients typically undergo diagnostic procedures first. Once the diagnosis is established, the proper therapeutic maneuvers may then be employed. Even though a diagnosis is desired before treatment is performed, a diagnosis is not always possible. Patients can become so symptomatic that treatment must be performed, even though a diagnosis is not yet known. For example, a severe pericardial effusion can cause **cardiac tamponade**, a condition in which excessive fluid trapped within the pericardium prevents the passive return of venous blood to the heart. Hence, the heart does not adequately fill. Because it does not adequately fill, the heart cannot adequately contract, causing hypotension or low blood pressure. This is a life threatening condition which may require a therapeutic opening or tapping of the pericardium to drain the fluid and improve cardiac function. Pleural and peritoneal fluids may also require a therapeutic tap. Regardless of whether it is diagnostic or therapeutic, needle removal of pericardial fluid is called a **pericardiocentesis**. Needle removal of pleural fluid is a **thoracentesis**. Needle removal of peritoneal fluid (ascites) is called a **peritoneocentesis**.

What about the dorsal cavity? The cavity is already filled with fluid, cerebrospinal fluid (CSF). This fluid is frequently obtained by needle aspiration for evaluation of unexplained fever, headache, pain, or neurologic changes such as weakness, numbness, or bowel and/or bladder dysfunction. The fluid is examined for such things as bacterial count, culture, cell count, protein content, and glucose content. The results of these tests will provide clues as to what is causing the problem. Further diagnostic or therapeutic procedures may then begin. The procedure of obtaining CSF by needle removal is called a **lumbar puncture** or **L.P.** This is also commonly called a **spinal tap** by the lay public.

SUMMARY OF CHAPTER BOXES

1) The word *serosa* is derived from the word *serous*, which describes a substance that is like serum or water.

2) **M**ediastinum is **m**edial or **m**idline

3) There are *two* lungs; they are the "plural" organ and are covered by the *pleura*.

4) The word *parietal* refers to the *wall of a cavity*. The word *visceral* relates to a *viscus*.

5) *Mucosal* membranes are usually covered with a layer of *mucous*.

6) **4 heart chambers,** so **4** valves. **3** valves have **3** leaflets (tricuspid, pulmonary, aortic). Mitral valve is the only bi-leaflet (has 2 leaflets) valve.

7) In sequence of blood flow, the valves are in reverse alphabetical order
Tricuspid → **P**ulmonary → **M**itral → **A**ortic

8) The *root* of the lung originates from the mediastinum, passes through the hilum, and sprouts out as the lung. The bronchial *tree* sprouts from the right or left main bronchus.

9) Both lungs curve down the thorax in an *oblique* fashion and each lung has an *oblique* fissure. Each lung also has a lower lobe, and the oblique fissure is located just above it.

10) The left lung attempts to make room for the slightly left-placed heart by providing only two lobes. To make up for the difference, the lingula sticks its tongue out at you from its origin at the left upper lobe.

11) Any foreign material that is aspirated into the lungs will most likely go into the right lung.

12) Bronchi are the last component of the bronchial tree to contain cartilage. Bronchioles are the first component not to contain cartilage and the last component to contain smooth muscle.

13) Most bronchioles are classified as conducting airways and function in air conduction exclusively. The last ones to do so are the *terminal* bronchioles. The next generation, the respiratory bronchioles, have a limited role in gas exchange and are classified as transitional airways. *Respiratory* bronchioles are the bronchioles most like the *respiratory* airways.

14) A **bronchopulmonary** segment is supplied by a *bronchus* and its accompanying <u>pulmonary</u> vessels (artery and vein).

15) In an effort to be fair and make up for the left lung's lack of three lobes, it was given two bronchus divisions. The right lung received none.

16) **SEGMENTAL BRONCHI:**
right upper lobe = apical, posterior, anterior
right <u>m</u>iddle lobe = <u>m</u>edial and lateral
right lower lobe = superior, anterior basal, medial basal, lateral basal, posterior basal

left upper lobe = *superior division*: apical-posterior (**AP**), anterior
<u>inferior</u> division (*lingular* bronchus): superior, <u>inferior</u>
left lower lobe = superior, anterior-medial (**AM**) basal, lateral basal, posterior basal
*AP is on top, AM is on bottom

17) The word ***liver*** contains 5 letters, is to the **right** (5 letters), and does **5** major things: (1) **stores and releases** digestive products (2) **transforms amino acids** (3) **creates bile** (4) **metabolizes** drugs (5) **detoxifies** ingested agents

18) ***Porta*** = entrance or ***portal***. The **porta hepatis** is a fissure on the underside (visceral) surface of the liver where the hepatic artery and portal vein enter and the hepatic duct exits the liver.

19) ***Cholecystokinin*** is a polypeptide hormone that induces contraction of the gallbladder (as well as secretion of pancreatic enzymes). *Chole* = bile; *kine* = movement

20) The <u>tri</u>gone is the <u>tri</u>angle of the bladder wall created by its ***three*** orifices (two ureteral and one urethral).

21) Each kidney has an upper (superior) pole and lower (inferior) pole. A *margin* is an *edge*. Each kidney also has a lateral margin and medial margin.

22) A *sinus* is a *cavity*. The renal sinus is the *cavity* within the tissue of the kidney through which structures of the renal hilum travel. A *pelvis* is *basin-shaped* structure. The renal pelvis is the basin to which urine drains.

23) **Renal nomenclature:**
The *functional tissue* (**parenchyma**) has an *outer layer* (**cortex**) and *innermost portion* (**medulla**). The medulla is separated by *pillars of cortex* (**renal columns**) that travel from the periphery toward the *cavity* (**renal sinus**) formed by the curve of the kidney. These columns create *pyramid-shaped areas of medulla* (**renal pyramids**). Urine flows down the pyramid and is secreted at its *nipple* (**renal papilla**) into a *small cup* (**minor calix**) which drains into a *larger cup* (**major calix**) and finally into a *basin* (**renal pelvis**). It leaves the kidney in the ureter and travels to the bladder for storage and excretion.

24) ***Os*** is a shortened form of ***ostium***, which is Latin for *orifice* or *mouth*

25) **Female System starts with vowels**: *E*xternal *O*s → *I*nternal *O*s → *U*terus → *U*terine *O*stium → *U*terine (*I*ntramural) portion of tube → *I*sthmus → *A*mpulla → *I*nfundibulum (*Infundibulum – funnel*).
IAI: The ampulla is between the two "I's."

26) A **bilateral tubal ligation (BTL)** is the surgical sterilization procedure for the female. Each (*bilateral*) fallopian tube (*tubal*) is ligated (*ligation*).

27) Epididymis: the Greek word *didymos* = the Latin word *testis*

28) A **vasectomy** is a surgical sterilization procedure for males. The ductus (vas) deferens is separated from other structures of the spermatic cord and divided (cut). A *vas*ectomy is cutting of the *vas* deferens.

29) 60% of the volume of *sem*en is secreted by the *sem*inal vesicle.

30) The CNS is surrounded by a **PAD**: From inner to outer: **P**ia → **A**rchnoid → **D**ura

31) Embryologic designations for brain stem components are in alphabetical order:
Proximal: midbrain = m**es**encephalon
Intermediate: pons = m**et**encephalon (along with cerebellum)
Distal: medulla = m**ye**lencephalon

32) (1) The lobes of the cerebrum = four bones of the skull. (2) The diencephalon has four "thalami": thalamus, epi-, hypo-, and sub-. (3) The basal ganglia asks, "**C**an **P**utamen **G**et **S**mart?" = **C**audate nucleus, **P**utamen, **G**lobus pallidus, and **S**ubstantia nigra. (4) The cerebellum is formed by **3** lobes and attaches to brain stem by **3** cerebellar peduncles on each side (6 total) (5) The brain stem has **3** components. The mid*brain* is in the superior position because it is closest to the *brain*. The pons is in an intermediate position between the two "m's" (midbrain and medulla).

33) ***Lymph*** contains ***lymph*ocytes**

34) Elephantiasis is a parasitic disease caused by filarial worms that gain entrance and obstruct the lymphatic system, causing edema and massive tissue swelling.

35) **DUCT = LEFT = MOST:** Each word contains four letters. The *thoracic duct* is on the *left* and drains lymph from *most* of the body.

36) **Thoracic duct: CC right —AH→ left @ T5 to L. SC/IJ**

37) **CLINICAL CORRELATION: Transudate** is a fluid which has gone ***trans*membrane** or has crossed a membrane. **Exudate** is a fluid which crossed the membrane by the use of *ex*its in the membrane.

END OF CHAPTER TEST

Time for Exam = 60 minutes.
For questions 1-44, choose the single best answer.

_____1) What is the other name for the right innominate vein?
- a) superior vena cava
- b) azygos vein
- c) right brachiocephalic vein
- d) right subclavian vein
- e) none of the above

_____2) What tissue forms renal columns?
- a) minor calices
- b) renal medulla
- c) renal papilla
- d) renal cortex
- e) none of the above

_____3) Which vessels primarily carry deoxygenated blood?
- a) bronchial arteries
- b) pulmonary veins
- c) both a and b
- d) bronchial veins
- e) none of the above

_____4) The medulla oblongata contributes to the formation of the
- a) mesencephalon
- b) diencephalon
- c) mylencephalon
- d) metencephalon
- e) none of the above

_____5) Concerning the lungs, which of the following is true?
- a) The lingula is part of the right upper lobe.
- b) The left lung has two fissures.
- c) The right lung has three lobes.
- d) A bronchopulmonary segment is formed by a segmental bronchus and it corresponding bronchial artery and vein branches.
- e) None of the above

_____6) Which is the correct order of venous drainage of blood returning from the right (R.) external jugular vein?
- a) R. vertebral, R. internal jugular, R. subclavian
- b) R. internal jugular, R. brachio-cephalic, R. innominate
- c) R. brachiocephalic, R. subclavian, superior vena cava
- d) R. subclavian, R. azygos, superior vena cava
- e) None of the above

_____7) What constitutes most of the volume of semen?
- a) secretions from the seminal vesicles
- b) spermatozoa
- c) secretions from the prostate gland
- d) secretions from the bulbourethral glands
- e) secretions from the epididymis

_____8) What is the lingula?
- a) the downward extension of the right upper lobe of the lungs
- b) the downward extension of the left middle lobe of the lungs
- c) the upward extension of the left lower lobe of the lungs
- d) the upward extension of the right lower lobe of the lungs
- e) none of the above

_____9) The serous membrane lining the inner surface of the abdominal wall is known as
- a) the parietal pleura
- b) the visceral perineum
- c) the parietal perineum
- d) the dura mater
- e) none of the above

_____10) What is the correct sequence of heart valves through which blood must flow?
      a) tricuspid, mitral, aortic, pulmonary
      b) tricuspid, pulmonary, mitral, aortic
      c) mitral, tricuspid, pulmonary, aortic
      d) tricuspid, mitral, pulmonary, aortic
      e) none of the above

_____11) Which of the following could be classified as a transitional airway?
      a) alveolar ducts
      b) terminal bronchioles
      c) both a and b
      d) alveolar sacs
      e) none of the above

_____12) Which structure is immediately exterior to the external os of the cervix?
      a) uterine canal
      b) vaginal isthmus
      c) cervical canal
      d) vaginal fornices
      e) supravaginal segment of cervix

_____13) Which structures carry deoxygenated blood?
      a) left atrium
      b) left ventricle
      c) both a and b
      d) pulmonary vein
      e) none of the above

_____14) What is the first bronchopulmonary component that does not contain smooth muscle cells?
      a) alveolar sacs
      b) respiratory bronchioles
      c) alveolar ducts
      d) terminal bronchioles
      e) all of the above contain smooth muscle

_____15) The superior component of the brain stem is the
      a) cerebellum
      b) medulla
      c) pons
      d) midbrain
      e) none of the above

_____16) The serous membrane lining the inner surface of the chest wall is known as
      a) the parietal pleura
      b) the visceral pleura
      c) the visceral perineum
      d) the parietal perineum
      e) none of the above

_____17) What is the last bronchopulmonary component to contain cartilage?
      a) bronchi
      b) respiratory bronchioles
      c) terminal bronchioles
      d) alveolar ducts
      e) none of the above

_____18) What may be found in the epididymis?
      a) secretions rich in zinc
      b) rete testis
      c) secretions rich in sugars, proteins, enzymes, vitamins, and other chemicals
      d) mature spermatozoa
      e) none of the above

_____19) To reach the right (R.) internal carotid artery, which of the following structures represent the correct sequence of blood flow?
      a) ascending aorta, R. subclavian artery, R. innominate artery
      b) ascending aorta, innominate artery, R. common carotid artery
      c) aortic valve, ascending aorta, branches directly off aortic arch
      d) ascending aorta, R. subclavian artery, R. common carotid artery
      e) none of the above

_____20) Which lung lobe is the apical-posterior segmental bronchus located?
      a) left upper lobe
      b) right middle lobe
      c) right upper lobe
      d) left lower lobe
      e) none of the above

_____21) Which structures carry venous blood returning from tissues below (inferior to) the level of the heart?
    a) superior vena cava
    b) inferior vena cava
    c) azygos vein
    d) all of the above
    e) none of the above

_____22) What is the name of the opening of the hepatopancreatic duct into the lumen of the duodenum?
    a) ampulla of Vater
    b) sphincter of Oddi
    c) ductus deferens
    d) major duodenal papilla
    e) none of the above

_____23) Which lung lobe is the anterior-medial basal segmental bronchus located?
    a) right lower lobe
    b) left upper lobe
    c) left lower lobe
    d) right middle lobe
    e) none of the above

_____24) The serous membrane lining the outer surface of the thoracic organs is known as the
    a) parietal pleura
    b) visceral pleura
    c) parietal peritoneum
    d) visceral peritoneum
    e) none of the above

_____25) Which of the following is most likely to be associated with an infection of the right forearm?
    a) right axillary lymphadenopathy
    b) right cervical lymphadenopathy
    c) right inguinal lymphadenopathy
    d) mediastinal lymphadenopathy
    e) none of the above

_____26) Where may an anterior segmental bronchus be found?
    a) right upper lobe
    b) lingula
    c) right middle lobe
    d) left lower lobe
    e) none of the above

_____27) What may be found in the spermatic cord?
    a) scrotal artery
    b) ductus deferens
    c) scrotal vein
    d) all the above
    e) none of the above

_____28) What is the first bronchopulmonary component that does not contain cartilage?
    a) alveolar sacs
    b) alveolar ducts
    c) tertiary bronchi
    d) bronchioles
    e) none of the above

_____29) Which lung lobes does the oblique fissure immediately border?
    a) right upper and right lower lobes
    b) left upper and left lower lobes
    c) both a and b
    d) right upper and right middle lobes
    e) none of the above

_____30) Which organ can become inflamed and diseased as a result of gallstones?
    a) spleen
    b) duodenum
    c) cecum
    d) pancreas
    e) none of the above

_____31) Which heart valves are bi-leaflet (have two leaflets or cusps)?
    a) tricuspid
    b) aortic
    c) both a and b
    d) pulmonary
    e) none of the above

_____32) How many lobar bronchi are found in the right upper lobe?
    a) two
    b) three
    c) one
    d) numerous
    e) none of the above

_____33) The majority of blood flow to the liver is provided by the
       a) hepatic artery
       b) aorta
       c) portal vein
       d) hepatic vein
       e) vena cava

_____34) What is the direct order of structures through which venous blood returning from the left (L.) internal jugular vein must pass?
       a) L. vertebral, L. innominate, L. subclavian
       b) L. brachiocephalic, superior vena cava, L. atrium
       c) superior vena cava, R. ventricle, R. atrium
       d) L. brachiocephalic, azygos, superior vena cava
       e) None of the above

_____35) The name of the point of the bifurcation of the trachea into the right and left main bronchi is the
       a) root of the lung
       b) lingula
       c) acinus
       d) carina
       e) none of the above

_____36) Which structures carry oxygenated blood?
       a) left atrium
       b) pulmonary vein
       c) both a and b
       d) pulmonary artery
       e) none of the above

_____37) Which component of a fallopian tube is the most distal or farthest removed from the uterus?
       a) intramural portion
       b) infundibulum
       c) isthmus
       d) body
       e) ampulla

_____38) Which tissues may separate (be positioned between) an open and a closed cavity?
       a) the wall of a viscus
       b) a serous membrane
       c) a musous membrane
       d) all of the above
       e) none of the above

_____39) To reach the right (R.) subclavian artery, what is the correct sequence of structures through which blood must flow?
       a) aortic valve, ascending aorta, brachiocephalic artery
       b) aortic valve, brachiocephalic artery, R. common carotid artery
       c) vena cava, brachiocephalic artery, R. common carotid artery
       d) the right subclavian artery branches directly off the aorta
       e) none of the above

_____40) What is the last bronchopulmonary component to contain smooth muscle cells?
       a) terminal bronchioles
       b) respiratory bronchioles
       c) alveolar sacs
       d) bronchi
       e) none of the above

_____41) The serous membrane lining the outer surface of the abdominal organs is known as
       a) the visceral pleura
       b) the visceral peritoneum
       c) the parietal peritoneum
       d) the dura mater
       e) none of the above

_____42) Urine drains from renal pyramids at the
       a) renal sinus
       b) renal columns
       c) renal cortex
       d) renal papillae
       e) none of the above

_____43) What drains chyme?
       a) lacteals
       b) cisterna chyli
       c) both a and b
       d) the duodenum
       e) none of the above

_____44) Fimbriae extend from the
       a) isthmus
       b) papillae
       c) ampulla
       d) trabeculae
       e) none of the above

For questions 45-60, use the following directions:
 a.......1,2,3 are correct
 b.......1,3 are correct
 c.......2,4 are correct
 d.......only 4 is correct
 e.......all are correct

_____45) Which of the following are located in the right lower lobe of the lungs?
 1. the anterior basal segmental bronchus
 2. the lateral basal segmental bronchus
 3. the posterior basal segmental bronchus
 4. the superior segmental bronchus

_____46) The quadrate lobe of the liver is bordered by the
 1. fissure for ligamentum teres
 2. gallbladder
 3. porta hepatis
 4. fissure for ligamentum venosum

_____47) Which of the following serve as a membrane which surrounds a closed cavity?
 1. perineum
 2. mucosa
 3. myocardium
 4. dura mater

_____48) As compared to the left main bronchus, the right main bronchus
 1. is larger in diameter
 2. is longer
 3. departs from the trachea at a less acute angle
 4. is also a secondary bronchus

_____49) Which of the following contribute to the structure of the spleen?
 1. papillae
 2. trabeculae
 3. pyramids
 4. capsule

_____50) Which of the following is part of a portal triad?
 1. hepatic artery
 2. central vein
 3. bile duct
 4. vena cava

_____51) Through which structures do digested fatty acids pass to reach the systemic circulation?
 1. portal vein
 2. splenic vein
 3. superior mesenteric vein
 4. left subclavian vein

_____52) Which of the following are true?
 1. A superior segmental bronchus is located in the lingula.
 2. An anterior-medial segmental bronchus is located in the left upper lobe.
 3. A superior segmental bronchus is located in the left lower lobe.
 4. An inferior basal segmental bronchus is located in the right lower lobe.

_____53) Which structures are located in the scrotum?
 1. ductus deferens
 2. testis
 3. epididymis
 4. seminal vesicle

_____54) Which of the following could be classified as a respiratory airway?
 1. alveolar sacs
 2. alveolar ducts
 3. alveoli
 4. respiratory bronchioles

_____55) Which statements are true concerning membranes of closed cavities?
 1. The peritoneum is a serous membrane.
 2. The pleura is a mucous membrane.
 3. The peritoneum lines both the abdominal and the pelvic cavities.
 4. The dura mater lines the ventral cavity.

_____56) Where could a superior segmental bronchus be found?
 1. right lower lobe
 2. lingula
 3. left lower lobe
 4. right upper lobe

____57) Which of the following drain to the right lymph duct?
1. right subclavian duct
2. right bronchomediastinal duct
3. right jugular duct
4. right intercostal duct

____58) Components of an acinus include
1. alveolar sacs
2. alveolar ducts
3. alveoli
4. respiratory bronchioles

____59) Which organs may be divided into lobes?
1. spleen
2. kidney
3. pancreas
4. liver

____60) Which structures are found in the porta hepatis?
1. vena cava
2. hepatic artery
3. gallbladder
4. the hilum of the liver

END OF CHAPTER TEST: Answers and Explanations

1) c – The right innominate vein is also known as the right brachiocephalic vein. Because the heart is located slightly to the left side of the body and the venous system drains to the right side of the heart, the venous system is draining toward the midline of the body. This allows it to be relatively symmetrical with regard to right and left. Hence, there is both a right and left innominate (brachiocephalic) vein. This is in contrast to the arterial system which only has one innominate (brachiocephalic) artery. This artery "carries" the right common carotid and right subclavian artery from the left heart to the right side of the body.

2) d – Renal columns are formed by strands of cortex that extend toward the renal sinus from the periphery. They travel between isolated areas of renal medulla known as the renal pyramids.

3) d – Bronchial arteries carry oxygenated blood from the descending aorta (or aortic arch) to bronchial and connective tissues in the lungs. Bronchial veins drain deoxygenated blood from these tissues back to the heart. Pulmonary arteries carry deoxygenated blood from the right side of the heart to capillary beds surrounding respiratory epithelium in the lungs. The blood is oxygenated and returns to the left side of the heart in pulmonary veins.

4) c – The myelencephalon is formed by the medulla. The mesencephalon is formed by the midbrain. The diencephalon contributes to the formation of the cerebrum and contains the thalamus, epithalamus, hypothalamus, and subthalamus. The metencephalon is formed by the pons and cerebellum.

5) c – The right lung has three lobes and two fissures; the left lung has two lobes and one fissure. The lingula is the inferior extension of the left upper lobe. A bronchopulmonary segment is formed by a segmental bronchus and its corresponding *pulmonary* artery and vein branches.

6) e – Blood returning from the right (R.) external jugular vein flows into the right (R.) subclavian vein. The R. subclavian combines with the R. internal jugular vein to form the R. brachiocephalic (R. innominate) vein. The right and left brachiocephalic (innominate) veins then combine to form the superior vena cava, which drains into the right atrium.

7) a – Spermatozoa are mixed with zinc-rich secretions from the prostate and secretions from the seminal vesicles to create semen. Sixty percent of the volume of semen is obtained from the seminal vesicles and these secretions are rich in sugars, proteins, enzymes, vitamins, and other chemicals. During arousal and before ejaculation, bulbourethral glands secrete the pre-ejaculate, which lubricates the urethra and neutralizes urethral acidity caused by urine. The epididymis stores mature spermatozoa.

8) e – The lingula is the inferior extension of the left upper lobe. The right lung has three lobes and the left lung has two. There is no left middle lobe of the lungs.

9) e – The word *parietal* refers to an outer wall of a cavity. The parietal peritoneum lines the inner surface of the abdominal wall. Likewise, the parietal pleura lines the inner surface of the chest wall. The word *visceral* refers to the internal organs. The visceral peritoneum lines the outer surface of the abdominal organs. Likewise, the visceral pleura lines the outer surface of the thoracic organs (lungs). The perineum is not a serous membrane but an area of the body which forms the floor of the pelvis. The dura mater is the fibrous membrane lining the dorsal cavity.

10) b – There are four chambers of the heart. Each heart chamber must pump blood through a valve. Hence, there are four valves. The tricuspid valve is between the right atrium and right ventricle. The pulmonary valve is between the right ventricle and pulmonary artery. The mitral valve is between the left atrium and left ventricle. Finally, the aortic valve is between the left ventricle and ascending aorta.

11) a – Conducting airways carry (conduct) air and do not participate in gas exchange. They include

all airways from the trachea to the level of the terminal bronchiole. Terminal bronchioles are the last airways that do not function in gas exchange. Transitional airways have limited participation in gas exchange and include respiratory bronchioles, which originate from terminal bronchioles, and alveolar ducts. Respiratory airways primarily function in gas exchange and include alveolar sacs and alveoli.

12) d – The cervix has two openings separated by the narrow cervical canal. The external os opens into the vagina and appears as a crevice formed by anterior and posterior lips. The internal os opens into the uterine canal. The lumen of the vagina that borders the cervix is known as the fornices of the vagina. A fornix is a vault-like or arch-like space. The *vaginal portion* is the portion of the cervix that extends into the vagina; the *supravaginal cervix* does not. The supravaginal cervix and cervical canal are immediately *internal* to the external os.

13) e – Systemic veins return deoxygenated blood to the superior and inferior vena cava, both of which drain directly into the right atrium of the heart. From there, the deoxygenated blood travels through the right ventricle and pulmonary artery to reach the lungs and become oxygenated. The oxygenated blood returns to the left atrium via the pulmonary vein. From the left atrium, the oxygenated blood is pumped through the left ventricle and ascending aorta to reach the systemic arteries. Note that the pulmonary artery is the only artery which carries deoxygenated blood. Likewise, the pulmonary vein is the only vein which carries oxygenated blood.

14) c – Bronchioles contain smooth muscle cells, but no cartilage. Alveolar ducts branch from respiratory bronchioles and are the first bronchopulmonary structures that don't contain smooth muscle. They are described as alveolar *ducts*, not bronchioles.

15) d – The three components of the brain stem are the midbrain, pons, and medulla. The midbrain is in a superior position, the pons in an intermediate position, and the medulla in an inferior position.

16) a – See #9 answer explanation.

17) a – Bronchi are the last bronchopulmonary component to contain cartilage. Bronchioles contain smooth muscle cells, but no cartilage. Alveolar ducts branch from respiratory bronchioles and are the first bronchopulmonary structures that don't contain smooth muscle.

18) d – See #7 answer explanation. The epididymis stores mature spermatozoa which arrive via efferent ductules from the rete testes of the posterior border of a testis.

19) b – Because the heart is located on the left side of the thorax and the arterial system comes off the left side of the heart (left ventricle), the proximal arterial system is somewhat asymmetric. This is required to provide oxygenated blood to the symmetric body (with regards to right and left). The left common carotid and left subclavian arteries are able to simply branch off the arch of the aorta because they are already in the proper position in the left side of the body. The right common carotid and right subclavian arteries require the assistance of the brachiocephalic (innominate) artery, which "carries" them to the proper position on the right side of the symmetrical body. By contrast, the venous system drains to the right side of the heart, closer to the midline. Because of this, the venous system is more symmetrical as compared to the arterial system. Hence, there are two brachiocephalic (innominate) veins: a right and left one. There is only one brachiocephalic (innominate) artery.

20) a – The right upper lobe contains an apical, anterior, and posterior segmental bronchus. The apical and posterior bronchi are combined in the left upper lobe to form the apical-posterior segmental bronchus. This bronchus later divides into apical and posterior bronchi.

21) d – Deoxygenated blood from the chest wall, including areas below or inferior to the level of the heart, drains into the azygos vein. The azygos vein drains into the superior vena cava just before the superior vena cava enters the pericardium to empty into the right atrium of the heart. Deoxygenated blood from other areas of the lower body returns to the heart by way of the inferior vena cava.

22) d – A papilla is a nipple-shaped structure. The

hepatopancreatic duct dilates into the ampulla of Vater while approaching the posterior wall of the duodenum. It forms the major duodenal papilla as it opens into the internal lumen of the duodenum. The opening is surrounded by independent smooth muscle fibers that form the sphincter of Oddi and control release of duct contents into the duodenum.

23) c – The right lower lobe contains a superior segmental bronchus and four basal segmental bronchi: anterior basal, medial basal, posterior basal, and lateral basal bronchi. The left lower lobe contains a superior segmental bronchus and three basal segmental bronchi: anterior-medial basal, posterior basal, and lateral basal bronchi. The anterior-medial basal bronchus later divides into the anterior basal and medial basal segmental bronchi.

24) b – See #9 answer explanation.

25) a – Lymphadenopathy is characterized by inflammation and enlargement of lymph nodes and may represent infection or metastatic tumor in the area drained by the nodes. Axillary lymph nodes are located in the axilla (armpit) and receive lymph from the upper extremity and chest wall on their respective side. Cervical nodes drain the head and neck. Inguinal nodes receive lymph from the lower extremity and pelvic wall. Mediastinal nodes drain structures of the mediastinum and the lungs.

26) a – The right upper lobe contains an apical, anterior, and posterior segmental bronchus. The left lower lobe contains an anterior-medial basal segmental bronchus that later divides into anterior *basal* and medial basal bronchi.

27) b – The spermatic cord contains the ductus (vas) deferens, testicular artery, testicular vein, nerves, and lymph vessels. Although the *scrotal* artery and vein may seem like logical choices, correct names must be learned.

28) d – See #17 answer explanation

29) b – The right lung has three lobes and the left has two. An oblique fissure separates the right middle and right lower lobes and the left upper

and left lower lobes. The horizontal fissure separates the right upper and right middle lobes.

30) d – Although this was not formally discussed in the text, the answer may be deduced after a consideration of the anatomy of the hepato-pancreatic duct. The common bile duct is formed by the combination of the hepatic duct from the liver and the cystic duct from the gallbladder. The common bile duct is later joined by the pancreatic duct and the two dilate into the ampulla of Vater and empty into the duodenum. Gallstones can block the flow of bile at any point along the path of the cystic and common bile ducts. When this occurs, the gallbladder may spasm in an effort to clear the blockage and the person experiences a "gallbladder attack." The gallbladder can become inflamed, diseased, and, in severe cases, even rupture. This disease process is the reason many individuals require the surgical removal of the gallbladder (cholecystectomy). The gallstone occlusion can also occur in the portion of the hepatopancreatic duct that extends past the merger of the common bile and the pancreatic ducts. When this occurs, the flow of digestive enzymes from the pancreas is halted. The pancreas can become inflamed and "leak" digestive enzymes into the surrounding tissues. *Gallstone pancreatitis* can be a life-threatening event.

31) e – Of the four heart valves, the mitral valve is the only valve which is bicuspid, meaning it has only two cusps or leaflets. It is located between the left atrium and left ventricle. The other three valves, the tricuspid, pulmonary, and aortic valves, have three cusps each. The tricuspid valve is actually named for its three cusps. Both the pulmonary and aortic valves are named for the arteries they open into.

32) c – A *lobar* bronchus is also known as a secondary bronchus and supplies one lung *lobe*. Each lung lobe contains only one lobar bronchus and that bronchus is named for the lobe it supplies. The right upper bronchus is the lobar bronchus that supplies the right upper lobe.

33) c – The portal vein drains the intestines and trans-

ports recently-digested food, vitamins, toxins, and electrolytes for processing by the liver. Eighty-percent of blood arriving to the liver is by way of the portal vein, but portal blood provides only twenty-percent of the liver's oxygen requirement. Twenty-percent of blood arriving to the liver travels in the hepatic artery. This blood provides eighty-percent of the oxygen requirement. The hepatic artery is a branch of the celiac trunk of the aorta.

34) e – The left (L.) internal jugular vein combines with the left subclavian vein to form the left brachiocephalic (L. innominate) vein. The right and left brachiocephalic (innominate) veins subsequently combine to form the superior vena cava. The superior vena cava receives the azygos vein (which drains blood from below the level of the heart) prior to emptying into the *right* atrium of the heart.

35) d – The carina is formed by the inferior projection of the last tracheal ring and forms a ridge between the takeoff of the two primary bronchi. The root of the lung is formed by a primary bronchus, pulmonary artery, pulmonary vein, lymphatic tissue, nerves, and supporting structures. The lingula is the inferior extension of the left upper lobe. An acinus is the respiratory unit of the lungs. It branches from a terminal bronchus and contains respiratory bronchi, alveolar ducts, alveolar sacs, and alveoli.

36) c – See #13 answer explanation.

37) b – The intramural (uterine) portion of the fallopian tube extends from the uterine ostium. The isthmus is the narrow portion that continues away from the uterus. The tube dilates and becomes tortuous at the ampulla. The infundibulum is the terminal, funnel-shaped aspect of the tube found near the ovary. Although the uterus is composed of a *body*, the fallopian tube is not.

38) d – Each of the large closed cavities that form the ventral cavity is lined with a serous membrane. This membrane folds over on itself to cover the inner surface of the body wall (or, in the case of the pericardial cavity, the inner surface of the

membranous pericardium) and outer surface of visceral organs. Serous membranes secrete a watery substance that acts as a lubricant, preventing frictional tissue damage caused by moving organs. There is no direct communication between a closed cavity and the external environment. Open cavities are associated with an opening to the outside of the body and are formed by hollow visceral organs or bony cavities. Open cavities are lined with mucosal membranes, which secrete a layer of mucous that traps foreign substances and prevents their entry into the body. With visceral organs, the open cavity created by the organ may be positioned within the same body wall structures as a closed cavity. In this situation, the two cavities are separated by the serous membrane of the closed cavity, the tissue of the visceral organ, and the mucosal membrane of the open cavity.

39) a – See #19 answer explanation.

40) b – Bronchi are the last bronchopulmonary component to contain cartilage. Bronchioles contain smooth muscle cells, but no cartilage. Alveolar ducts branch from respiratory bronchioles and are the first bronchopulmonary structures that don't contain smooth muscle.

41) b – See #9 answer explanation.

42) d – The renal medulla is divided into renal pyramids by columns of cortex, the renal columns, which stretch from the periphery toward the renal sinus. The renal sinus is the center space formed by the bean-shaped curve of kidney tissue. Urine drains from collecting tubules and ducts of renal pyramids (medulla) into minor calices at renal papillae. The Latin word *papilla* describes a nipple-shaped structure.

43) d – Chyme is the partially-digested semifluid mixture that enters the duodenum from the stomach. Lacteals are lymphatic vessels that drain chyle from the intestines during digestion. Chyle contains lymph and fatty acids, which cannot penetrate the walls of the higher-pressure venous system. Chyle drains to the cisterna chyli and is transported to the left subclavian vein by way of the thoracic duct.

44) e – See # 37 answer explanation. Fimbriae are small, finger-like projections that extend from the infundibulum of a fallopian tube toward the ovary. The Latin word *fimbriae* describes a fringe.

45) e – The right lower lobe contains a superior segmental bronchus and four basal segmental bronchi: anterior basal, medial basal, posterior basal, and lateral basal bronchi.

46) a – On the visceral surface of the liver, the quadrate lobe is positioned between the fissure for ligamentum teres (round ligament) and the gallbladder, anterior to the porta hepatis. The caudate lobe is positioned between the fissure for ligamentum venosum and vena cava, posterior to the porta hepatis. The right lobe is right of these structures and the left lobe is left of them.

47) d – The dura mater lines the dorsal cavity, including both the cranial and spinal cavities. The perineum is not a membrane, but a region of the body between the anus and genitalia. It forms the floor of the pelvis. Mucosa is a mucous-producing type of membrane that lines open cavities. The mucous helps "trap" unwanted foreign substances and return them to the outside world. The myocardium is the thick layer of heart muscle. It is not a membrane.

48) b – Both the right and left main bronchi are primary bronchi; they are the first bronchi. Lobar bronchi form secondary bronchi. Although the right main bronchus has a larger diameter, it is shorter than the left. It also leaves the trachea at a less acute angle. All of these characteristics contribute to the fact that aspirated foreign material usually gets deposited in the right lung.

49) c – Splenic trabeculae project inward from the splenic capsule and form the framework for numerous sinusoids that are filled with red and white blood cells. A papilla is a nipple-shaped structure. Renal papillae extend from renal pyramids in the kidney. In addition, the major duodenal papilla is the opening of the hepatopancreatic duct into the duodenum.

50) b – A portal triad is formed by branches of the hepatic artery, portal vein, and bile duct (as well as lymph vessels). Portal triads are found around the periphery of a liver lobule. In the center of each lobule is a *central vein* that is oriented in the same direction as the portal triads. Blood leaves from the portal vein and hepatic artery of each triad, flows through the hepatocytes of the lobule, and eventually drains to the central vein. Portal blood contains substances obtained during the digestive process and delivers these substances to the hepatocytes for processing. Blood from the hepatic artery provides oxygen for the metabolic needs of the hepatocytes. Central veins drain to hepatic veins, which drain to the vena cava. Bile flows in the opposite direction in a liver lobule. Bile is produced by hepatocytes and flows in canaliculi to reach bile ducts in the portal triads at the periphery of the lobule. Bile drains to the hepatic duct and is subsequently stored in the gallbladder.

51) d – Because of their large molecular size, fatty acids cannot penetrate the walls of the higher-pressure venous system during digestive uptake. Carbohydrates and amino acids are smaller and are granted access. They are immediately taken up and transported to the liver for processing by the superior mesenteric and portal veins. Fatty acids must enter the thin walls of the low-pressure lymphatic system, combining with lymph and forming chyle. Lacteals are lymphatic vessels that drain the intestines and transport chyle to the cisterna chyli. The thoracic duct leaves from the upper portion of the cisterna chyli, travels superiorly, and drains into the left subclavian vein at the merger of the left subclavian and left internal jugular veins. It is by this circuitous route that fatty acids travel to enter the blood of the systemic circulation.

52) b – The lingula contains a superior segmental bronchus and an inferior segmental bronchus. The left lower lobe contains a superior segmental bronchus and three basal segmental bronchi: anterior-medial basal, posterior basal, and lateral basal bronchi. The left upper lobe contains an apical-posterior and anterior segmental bronchus. The right lower lobe contains

a superior segmental bronchus and four basal segmental bronchi: anterior basal, medial basal, posterior basal, and lateral basal bronchi.

53) a – The testis produces spermatozoa, which travel via efferent ductules to be stored in the nearby epididymis. The ductus (vas) deferens is the duct that emerges from the terminal aspect of the epididymis and leaves the scrotum to transport mature spermatozoa to the urethra. The seminal vesicles are located in the perineal cavity at the entry of the ductus deferens into the prostate.

54) b – Although respiratory bronchioles and alveolar ducts participate in gas exchange, they do so in a limited fashion. The primary function of both types of airway components is to conduct air to the respiratory airways (the alveolar sacs and alveoli) where gas exchange occurs. Respiratory bronchioles and alveolar ducts are therefore classified as *transitional* airways.

55) b – Like the peritoneum, the pleura is a serous membrane. The pleura lines a closed cavity, the thorax. Because the peritoneum lines both the abdominal and pelvic cavities, the two are often referred to as one closed cavity, the abdominopelvic cavity. Mucous membranes line open cavities. The mucous produced by these membranes helps to "trap" foreign substances and return them to the outside world. The dura mater is a fibrous membrane that lines the dorsal cavity, including both the cranial and spinal cavities.

56) a – The right lower lobe contains a superior segmental bronchus and four basal segmental bronchi: anterior basal, medial basal, posterior basal, and lateral basal bronchi. Similarly, the left lower lobe contains a superior segmental bronchus and three basal segmental bronchi: anterior-medial basal, posterior basal, and lateral basal bronchi. The anterior-medial basal bronchus later divides into anterior basal and medial basal bronchi. The lingula contains superior and inferior segmental bronchi. The right upper lobe contains apical, anterior, and posterior segmental bronchi.

57) a – The right lymph duct receives the right jugular trunk, right subclavian trunk, and right bronchomediastinal trunk. The right jugular trunk transports lymph from the right side of the head and neck. The right subclavian trunk drains the right upper extremity and right chest wall. The right bronchomediastinal trunk carries lymph from the mediastinum and right lung. After receiving these trunks, the right lymph duct empties into the right subclavian vein at the merger of the right subclavian and right internal jugular veins. The right duct can be considered the counterpart of the thoracic duct, except it is responsible for much less body area and does not drain chyle from the intestines. As compared to the right duct, the thoracic duct additionally transports lymph from the lower extremities, lymph from the abdomen, lymph from the lower thorax, and chyle from the intestines. The right intercostal duct empties into the cisterna chyli (along with its left-sided counterpart, lumbar ducts, and intestinal ducts) and carries lymph that is subsequently transported in the thoracic duct.

58) e – An acinus is the respiratory unit of the lungs. It branches from a terminal bronchus and contains respiratory bronchi, alveolar ducts, alveolar sacs, and alveoli. Respiratory bronchioles and alveolar ducts are classified as transitional airways. Alveolar sacs and alveoli are classified as respiratory airways.

59) c – The liver may be divided into four lobes: the right, left, caudate, and quadrate lobes. Each renal pyramid and the cortex that extends from its base to the capsule constitutes a renal lobe. Depending on the number of renal pyramids, a particular kidney may have 5-15 lobes.

60) c – The porta hepatis is a fissure on the visceral surface of the lung through which the hilum of the liver passes. The hepatic artery and portal vein enter the liver at the hilum and the hepatic duct leaves from it.

*"Imagination is more important than knowledge.
Knowledge is limited. Imagination encircles the world."*

– Albert Einstein

CHAPTER FIVE

INTRODUCTION TO NERVE ANATOMY AND PHYSIOLOGY

The basic component of the nervous system is the **neuron.** A neuron is simply a nerve cell. It consists of a cell body and at least one appendage or extension from the cell body. The **cell body** or **soma** is the "torso" of the neuron and the location of the cell nucleus.

Neurons having only one extension from the cell body are classified as **pseudounipolar neurons**. Peripheral pseudounipolar neurons are sensory neurons and their cell bodies are located in peripheral ganglia. This will be described in more detail later. The lone extension from the cell body is an axon. It travels out to divide into two branches. The longer branch travels to a peripheral sensory receptor. The shorter branch travels to the brain or spinal cord. When the sensory receptor is activated, the pseudounipolar neuron transmits a sensory signal to the central nervous system (CNS).

The majority of this discussion pertains to multipolar neurons. **Multipolar neurons**, such as motor neurons, possess more than one extension from the cell body. These extensions include one axon and multiple dendrites which originate from the cell body. **Dendrites** are numerous appendages which extend from the cell body to receive neurotransmission from other neurons by way of a synapse. A **synapse** is a point of association between an axon of one neuron and a dendrite or soma of another neuron. Alternatively, a synapse may occur between an axon and an effector organ. The majority of incoming synapses occur on dendrites, but some do occur on the cell body itself. The **axon** is the long extension from the cell body through which information is sent. This information travels to one of two structures, the next neuron in line or the effector organ. The **effector organ** is the end-organ or structure which is supplied by a particular chain of neurons. Although there is only one axon, this single axon may communicate with more than one other neuron. The dendrites are the information receivers; the axon is the information sender.

The space between the axon and dendrite is known as the **synaptic cleft**. Information is sent across the synaptic cleft by diffusion of a chemical **neurotransmitter**, which is released by the tip of the axon to bind receptors on the dendrite. This neurotransmitter quickly diffuses across the synaptic cleft and may either stimulate or inhibit the next neuron in line. If it stimulates the neuron, it increases the likelihood that the next neuron will pass the signal on. If it inhibits the neuron, it reduces the likelihood that nerve signal transmission will occur. Whether the neurotransmitter causes stimulation or inhibition depends on the neuron sending the information, the neuron receiving the information, and the type of neurotransmitter used. Some chemicals used as neurotransmitters include acetylcholine, epinephrine, norepinephrine, serotonin, dopamine, glycine, asparate, glutamate, and gamma-aminobutyric acid (GABA).

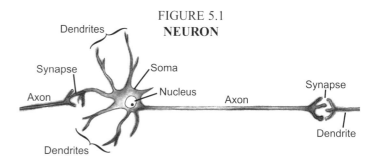

FIGURE 5.1
NEURON

How does a neuron send and receive information? Volumes are written on neurophysiology and still, much remains unknown. Some of the general processes and concepts of nerve transmission will be presented here.

Before neuronal signal conduction is discussed, a few generalities about human cell physiology should be considered. Electrolytes are charged ions. An **ion** is an atom or molecule which carries an **electrical charge**. This charge results from a change in the number of electrons. A **cation** is an ion which carries a positive charge. An **anion** carries a negative charge. Concentrations of various electrolytes must be maintained within a narrow range to ensure adequate function of body systems. The utilization of various ions during nerve transmission is an example of the importance of these electrolytes and their contribution to cellular functions.

In a resting state, all human cells have a **membrane potential** across their cell membrane. That is, there is a difference in electric charge on one side of the membrane as compared to the other side. In a resting state, the inside of the cell is more negative than the outside. Because there is a difference in charge across the membrane, the cell is said to be **polarized**.

This membrane potential is created by multiple conditions and processes. First, many intracellular proteins, organic molecules, and cellular compounds have a negative charge and are *trapped* in the intracellular space. They cannot penetrate the cell membrane, so their negative charges remain intracellular. The cell membrane may be permeable to some electrically-charged ions and not to others. This prevents certain positive-charged ions, or cations, from crossing the membrane in an effort to equalize the negative intracellular charge. In addition, there are membrane pumps which actively pump specific ions against their respective concentration gradients. This further prevents the entry of positive charges.

As a particular cation attempts to flow down its concentration gradient and enter the cell, it and its corresponding positive charge may be returned to the extracellular space by a membrane pump. Energy is required to *actively* pump these ions against a gradient. This form of membrane transport is therefore known as active transport. One of the more relevant membrane pumps is the **sodium-potassium (Na$^+$-K$^+$) pump**. Three (3) Na$^+$ ions are actively pumped out of the cell for every two (2) K$^+$ ions pumped into the cell. As will later be discussed, both ions are pumped against their respective concentration gradients. Because both Na$^+$ and K$^+$ are positive-charged cations, there is a net loss of one intracellular positive charge every time the Na$^+$-K$^+$ exchange occurs. With repeated use, the intracellular space becomes more negative compared to the extracellular space. This active transport requires metabolism of adenosine triphosphate (ATP) for energy substrate. Practically all cells of the body have these Na$^+$-K$^+$ membrane pumps. They are one of several contributors to the negative intracellular membrane potential of all resting cells.

FIGURE 5.2
Na$^+$-K$^+$ MEMBRANE PUMP

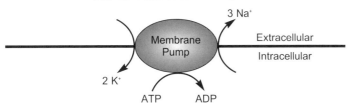

FIGURE 5.3
MORE NA$^+$ IS TRANSPORTED OUT OF CELL THAN K$^+$ IS TRANSPORTED INTO CELL.

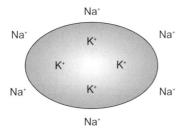

FIGURE 5.4
INTRACELLULAR ENVIRONMENT BECOMES MORE NEGATIVE

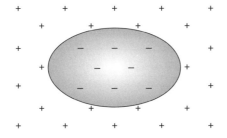

Since a membrane potential is present across a certain cell membrane, changes in the electric charge difference across the membrane may be used as a signal to initiate, alternate, or terminate various cellular processes. The specific processes depend on the type of cell in which this is occurring. Electricity plays a vital role in the adequate function of many varied and complicated body systems. Changes in membrane potentials are especially useful in regulating cellular processes required to pass a signal from one cell to another. This is particularly important with two cell types: muscle and nerve.

After receiving a signal, a contracting skeletal muscle cell must signal the next skeletal muscle cell to also contract. The same is true for cardiac or smooth muscle cells. Membrane potentials are used to initiate and coordinate a heartbeat. An electrocar-

diogram (ECG or EKG) is a measure of voltage changes occurring across the heart as it beats. Likewise, rhythmic contractions of smooth muscles cells within the walls of an organ or gland permit movement of its contents.

The principle function of nerve cells is signal transmission. During normal neuron function, alterations in membrane potentials are utilized in a repetitive and ongoing fashion to transmit signals. Further discussion in this section is specific for *neuron* membrane potentials, including their formation and use in nerve signal transmission.

The creation of a neuron resting membrane potential occurs in a manner similar to that of other cells of the body, only it is more pronounced and reoccurring than most. The potential must be reestablished every time the neuron fires, which could be hundreds of times a second. Before discussing the applications of neuron membrane potentials, some of the conditions and properties which contribute to their formation will be described. These include ion concentration gradients, electrical charge, selective cell membrane permeability, and membrane pumps.

The distribution of a hypothetical uncharged molecule on both sides of a permeable membrane will now be considered. If a certain number of these molecules is placed on one side of the membrane, the molecules would simply move down the **concentration gradient** until they were equally dispersed on both sides of the membrane. Again, this assumes that the membrane was completely permeable to the molecule.

FIGURE 5.5
CONCENTRATION GRADIENT
Before and After: random distribution of uncharged molecules

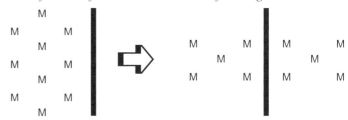

Distribution of molecules possessing an electrical charge will be further affected by the charge of the molecule and the charge of the surrounding environment. Positive charges repel positive charges and attract negative charges. Likewise, negative charges repel negative charges and attract positive charges. A particular area in which ions are distributed may contain preexisting electrical charges.

When a membrane potential exists across a cell membrane, each side of the membrane has a different charge. In a resting state, the intracellular contents are negatively-charged compared to the extracellular space. If all other processes and forces are ignored, this predisposes to an intracellular attraction of positive-charged cations and repulsion of negative-charged anions.

FIGURE 5.6
ELECTRICAL CHARGE
Before and After: intracellular attraction/repulsion of ions

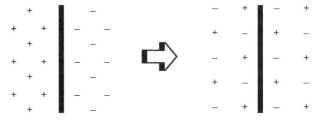

At this point, there are two principal forces working to establish the distribution of a charged ion across a permeable membrane. The charged ion will attempt to disperse randomly, down its concentration gradient. Due to the membrane potential, there will also be an intracellular attraction for positively-charged cations and an intracellular repulsion of negatively-charged anions. The amount of attraction or repulsion depends on the amount of charge present. These two forces interact to create a balance between them. Equilibrium in ion distribution across a membrane is established by and depends upon the concentration gradient of the ion, the electrical charge of the ion, and the electrical charge difference across the membrane (membrane potential).

Up to now, the described cell membrane has been completely permeable to the ion of question. A membrane which has **selective permeability** to different ions will now be considered. Ions of which the membrane is permeable will disperse across a membrane in the same fashion as recently described. Because they cannot freely cross the membrane, ions with limited permeability will attempt to disperse in the same manner but will not be able. A higher number of these ions are located on one side of the membrane than if ion distribution were based on concentration gradient and charge alone. A force is created for these ions to cross the membrane, if allowed. In other words, there is a potential energy for the ions to cross the membrane.

In addition to selective membrane permeability influencing ion concentrations across a membrane, **membrane pumps** may actively distribute certain ions against their gradient. As an ion passes to the intracellular space, it may be actively returned to the extracellular space by a membrane pump, even though the ion's concentration may be much greater in the extracellular space. Active transport requires energy, which is provided in the form of ATP. The active transport of ions against their concentration gradient further increases the force on the extracellular ions to cross the cell membrane and enter the intracellular space, if allowed. The potential energy for the ion to cross the cell membrane is therefore increased by membrane pumps.

If the membrane is impermeable to a certain ion, once that ion is placed on one side of the membrane, it cannot cross to the other side unless allowed to do so by the opening of a passage through the membrane. **Membrane channels** serve as those passageways. Membrane channels through the cell membrane are gated passages which are specific for certain ions. They usually remain in a closed state. Periodically they open and close in response to chemical mediators or changes in electrical charge. When stimulated by the presence of a certain chemical or voltage change, membrane channels open for a brief period to allow selective entry or exit of certain ions. Membrane channels do not require the utilization of energy (ATP) because the ions travel across the membrane in response to their electrical charge and/or concentration gradient. The preexisting potential energy provides the energy required for transport. Since these ions carry a charge, the selective opening and closing of membrane channels provide a regulatory mechanism to alternate intracellular charge, and hence, membrane potential.

Like other cells, the intracellular environment of a neuron contains proteins, organic molecules, and cellular compounds which cannot penetrate the cell membrane. Most possess a negative charge. This creates an intracellular attraction for positive charges and hence, positive ions. Three of the most freely abundant cations in the body are sodium (Na^+), potassium (K^+), and Calcium (Ca^{++}). Although Ca^{++} has important roles in nerve transmission, its cation properties are utilized more in muscle signal transmission.

The neuron cell membrane is significantly more permeable to K^+ than it is to Na^+. For this reason, it is mostly K^+ which crosses the membrane to counteract the preexisting negative intracellular charge. Na^+ cannot freely cross the membrane. Most Na^+ ions therefore remain outside the neuron in the extracellular space. This results in a high intracellular K^+ concentration and high extracellular Na^+ concentration.

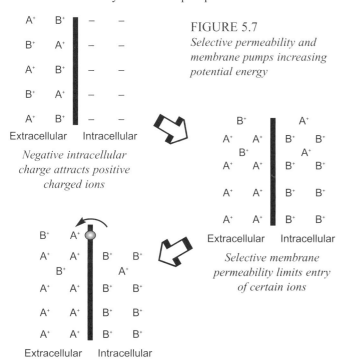

FIGURE 5.7

Selective permeability and membrane pumps increasing potential energy

Negative intracellular charge attracts positive charged ions

Selective membrane permeability limits entry of certain ions

Membrane pumps transfer certain ions against their concentration gradient

---

Coincidently, the intracellular concentration of K^+ and extracellular concentration of Na^+ are essentially the same…approximately **140 mEq/L**. The extracellular K^+ concentration is approximately 4 mEq/L. The intracellular Na^+ concentration is approximately 14 mEq/L. Once the blood chemistries are learned with future medical experience, a normal blood (extracellular) Na^+ concentration of 140 and K^+ of 4 will become very familiar levels. Simply remember that the intracellular K^+ concentration is approximately the same as the extracellular (blood) Na^+ concentration. The two cations "flip-flop":

K^+: *intracellular high (140) = extracellular low (4)*
Na^+: *extracellular high (140) = intracellular low (14)*

REMEMBER THE 4s : There are **4** values to remember (intracellular K^+, extracellular K^+, intracellular Na^+, extracellular Na^+). Each of these values contains a **4**.

These are only approximate electrolyte levels. In normal circumstances, actual levels may differ slightly.

In summary, there are several reasons the resting intracellular environment of a neuron remains negatively charged compared to the extracellular environment. Because the cell membrane is somewhat permeable to potassium, K^+ ions attempt to move intracellular to counteract the preexisting internal negative charge. They soon reach equilibrium against their intracellular concentration gradient and are insufficient to offset the overall negative charge. Na^+ ions are also attracted by this intracellular negative charge, but most remain extracellular because the neuron membrane has little permeability to Na^+. There are notable forces attempting to move Na^+ intracellular. Na^+ ions would flow down their concentration gradient as well as carry positive charges to a negative environment. Because of these forces, there is a relatively high potential energy for Na^+ to cross the membrane and move internally.

The negative intracellular charge is further enhanced by the action of the Na^+-K^+ membrane pumps. For every 3 Na^+ ions pumped out of the neuron, only 2 K^+ ions are pumped into it. This results in a net deficit of one intracellular positive charge for every round of Na^+-K^+ exchange. With repeated use of the membrane pump, this deficit contributes to the negative charge of the intracellular space and broadens the membrane potential of the neuron.

Not only does the Na^+-K^+ pump contribute to the membrane potential, it also increases the potential energy for each cation to cross the neuron membrane. It increases the forces for K^+ to move extracellular and Na^+ to move intracellular. Both cations are actively pumped against their respective concentration gradients. The intracellular K^+ concentration is comparatively high and is based mostly on the balance between electric charge and concentration gradient. Since K^+ can pass the neuron membrane relatively freely, it theoretically could easily leave the neuron if this balance changes and the intracellular charge becomes too positive or the ion's intracellular concentration becomes too great. The Na^+-K^+ pump returns "escaped" K^+ to the interior of the neuron, maintaining a constant pressure for K^+ to move extracellular. Na^+ is pumped out, also against its concentration gradient. This intensifies the tendency for Na^+ to cross the neuron membrane and move intracellular, if allowed. The Na^+-K^+ membrane pump contributes to the neuron's membrane potential and increases the potential energy for K^+ to leave the neuron and Na^+ to enter the neuron.

QUIZ 1
Nerve Anatomy and Physiology

Time for Quiz = 15 minutes.
For questions 1-11, choose the single best answer.

_____1) What is the approximate extracellular concentration of potassium?
  a) 4 mEq/L
  b) 140 mEq/L
  c) 14 mEq/L
  d) 110 mEq/L
  e) none of the above

_____2) What is the extension of a neuron through which information travels to the next neuron or effector organ?
  a) soma
  b) axon
  c) dendrite
  d) ganglion
  e) none of the above

_____3) Which of the following are present in virtually all cells of the human body?
  a) a resting polarization
  b) a negative intracellular charge
  c) Na^+-K^+ membrane pumps
  d) all the above
  e) none of the above

_____4) What forces or events favor movement of potassium ions to the intracellular space of a neuron?
  a) electric charge
  b) opening of potassium membrane channels
  c) concentration gradient
  d) all the above
  e) none of the above

_____5) Which of the following do not directly contribute to the generation of a neuron's resting membrane potential?
  a) active transport of Na^+
  b) active transport of K^+
  c) selective membrane permeability
  d) preexisting negative charge of organic molecules
  e) none of the above

_____6) What serves as the cell body or torso of a neuron?
  a) nucleus
  b) soma
  c) axon
  d) dendrite
  e) none of the above

_____7) What is the basic component of the nervous system?
  a) brain
  b) nerve
  c) neuron
  d) soma
  e) none of the above

_____8) Chemicals which function as neurotransmitters include all of the following except
  a) gamma-aminobutyric acid
  b) glycine
  c) gallamine
  d) acetylcholine
  e) both a and c

_____9) The resting membrane potential
  a) is caused by an influx of sodium (Na^+) ions
  b) is achieved at threshold
  c) is primarily created by passive diffusion of Na^+ and K^+ across the neuron cell membrane
  d) is due to an extracellular deficit of positive charges compared to the neuron's intracellular space
  e) none of the above

_____10) What forces or events would favor movement of sodium ions to the intracellular space of a neuron?
  a) electric charge
  b) concentration gradient
  c) opening of sodium membrane channels
  d) all the above
  e) none of the above

_____11) What is the approximate intracellular concentration of sodium?
  a) 140 mEq/L
  b) 110 mEq/L
  c) 14 mEq/L
  d) 4 mEq/L
  e) none of the above

For questions 12-15, use the following directions:
  a.......1,2,3 are correct
  b.......1,3 are correct
  c.......2,4 are correct
  d.......only 4 is correct
  e.......all are correct

_____12) Which of the following would theoretically decrease the membrane potential?
  1. increasing the intracellular concentration of potassium
  2. decreasing the action of sodium-potassium membrane pump
  3. increasing the intracellular concentration of sodium
  4. increasing the intracellular concentration of chloride

_____13) True statements about the resting membrane potential include which of the following?
  1. It is increased by the pumping of anions across the nerve membrane.
  2. It is the same for all neurons.
  3. Two (2) sodium (Na^+) ions are pumped out of the neuron for every three (3) potassium (K^+) ions pumped into it.
  4. The maintenance of the potential requires energy in the form of ATP.

_____14) Which of the approximate electrolyte levels are correct?
  1. intracellular Na^+ = 140 mEq/L
  2. intracellular Na^+ = 4 mEq/L
  3. extracellular K^+ = 140 mEq/L
  4. intracellular K^+ = 140 mE/L

_____15) Which of the following would theoretically increase the membrane potential?
  1. opening K^+ membrane channels
  2. removing intracellular proteins, phosphates, and organic molecules
  3. increasing the action of the Na^+-K^+ membrane pump
  4. opening Na^+ membrane channels

QUIZ 1: Nerve Anatomy and Physiology Answers and Explanations

1) a – The negative charge of cellular compounds, such as proteins, phosphates, and organic molecules, contributes to the negative charge of the intracellular space of a neuron. This negative charge attracts cations, positive-charged ions, such as Na^+ and K^+. The neuron cell membrane is significantly more permeable to K^+ than Na^+. K^+ moves intracellular in an attempt to offset the negative charge. Na^+ cannot freely cross the membrane and remains mostly in the extracellular space. This results in both a high intracellular K^+ and extracellular Na^+ concentration. Coincidently, the intracellular concentration of K^+ and extracellular concentration of Na^+ are virtually the same…approximately 140 mEq/L. The approximate extracellular K^+ concentration is 4 mEq/L. The approximate intracellular Na^+ concentration is 14 mEq/L. Conveniently, all values contain a 4. It is the extracellular Cl^- concentration which has an approximate value of 110 mEq/L.

2) b – The neuron is the basic component of the nervous system. It is composed of a soma, dendrites, and an axon. The soma is the cell body and houses the nucleus. Dendrites are extensions from the cell body which receive information from other neurons. The axon is an extension from the cell body which sends information to other neurons or the effector organ.

3) d – Virtually all cells of the body are polarized at rest. This means a difference in electrical charge exists across the cell membrane. The intracellular space has a negative charge compared to the extracellular space. Many intracellular compounds such as proteins, phosphates, and organic molecules, have a preexisting negative charge. The negative charge of the intracellular space is further supplemented by the action of Na^+-K^+ membrane pumps, which are present on practically all cells. These pumps transfer 3 Na^+ ions out of the cell and 2 K^+ ions into the cell. This creates a net deficit of one intracellular positive charge every time the exchange occurs.

4) a – The negative charge of cellular compounds, such as proteins, phosphates, and organic molecules, contributes to the negative charge of the intracellular space of a neuron. The negative charge attracts the positive-charged K^+ ions. The intracellular K^+ concentration becomes great enough to prevent further intracellular movement of K^+. In addition to these two forces (electrical charge attracting K^+ and concentration repelling K^+), The Na^+-K^+ membrane pumps pump Na^+ extracellular and K^+ intracellular. This increases the intracellular K^+ concentration to more than it would be if based on charge and concentration alone. Because of this, if K^+ membrane channels were opened, they would allow exit of K^+.

5) e – All contribute to the generation of a resting membrane potential. The resting membrane potential of a neuron is created by negative-charged intracellular organic molecules, selective membrane permeability to certain ions, and active transport of positive-charged cations across the nerve membrane. Selective membrane permeability allows diffusion of certain ions across the membrane. Positive-charged K^+ ions enter the negative-charged intracellular space of the neuron, but the high intracellular K^+ concentration prevents entrance of enough K^+ to adequately counteract the negative charge. Na^+ ions cannot freely cross the membrane to offset the negative charge. Most Na^+ ions remain in the extracellular space. The Na^+-K^+ membrane pump requires the utilization of ATP to actively pump the two cations against their respective concentration gradients. Three (3) sodium ions are pumped out of the neuron for every two (2) potassium ions pumped into it. A net deficit of positive charges is created and the intracellular space becomes more negative compared to the extracellular space.

6) b – See #2 answer explanation.

7) c – See #2 answer explanation.

8) c – Gallamine is a muscle-relaxing drug once used during surgery. The often-used abbreviation for gamma-aminobutyric acid is GABA.

9) e – See #5 answer explanation.

10) d – The negative charge of cellular compounds, such as proteins, phosphates and organic molecules, contributes to the negative charge of the intracellular space of a neuron. This negative charge attracts positive-charged cations. Na^+ and K^+ are two of the more readily available cations in the body and both are attracted by the negative intracellular charge. The neuron cell membrane is relatively permeable to K^+ and impermeable to Na^+. Because of this, both the intracellular concentration of K^+ and the extracellular concentration of Na^+ are high. Both attempt to move intracellular, but most of the Na^+ cannot. Opening of Na^+ membrane channels would allow Na^+ to enter the neuron, flowing down its concentration gradient and toward an opposite charge.

11) c – See #1 answer explanation.

12) a – The membrane potential is the charge difference across a cell membrane. Since the interior of the cell is negatively-charged compared to the exterior, anything that decreases the intracellular negative charge theoretically decreases the difference in charge across the membrane if all else remains equal. Hence, the membrane potential decreases. Both potassium and sodium are cations. Increasing their intracellular concentration would therefore decrease the intracellular negative charge. Sodium-potassium pumps transfer 3 Na^+ ions out of the cell and 2 K^+ ions into the cell. This creates a net deficit of one intracellular positive charge every time the exchange occurs. Increasing the activity of these pumps increases the intracellular negative charge. Likewise, decreasing their activity decreases the intracellular negative charge. Chloride is a negative-charged anion. Increasing its intracellular presence would increase the intracellular negative charge and increase the membrane potential.

13) d – The resting membrane potential of a neuron is created by negative-charged intracellular organic molecules, selective membrane permeability to certain ions, and active transport of positive-charged cations across the nerve membrane. Three (3) sodium ions are pumped out of the neuron for every two (2) potassium ions pumped into it. A net deficit of positive charges is created and the intracellular space becomes more negative compared to the extracellular space. The resting membrane potential varies among different types of neurons. It may be as high as $^-90$ mv for large nerve fibers and as low as $^-40$ mv for some CNS neurons. The active transport provided by the Na^+-K^+ pump requires energy, as both cations are pumped against their respective concentration gradients. This is provided by the conversion of ATP to ADP.

14) d – See #1 answer explanation.

15) b – See #12 answer explanation. The intracellular concentration of K^+ is high. Opening K^+ membrane channels would allow K^+ ions, and their positive charges, to leave the intracellular space. This increases the intracellular negative charge and membrane potential. The extracellular concentration of Na^+ is high. Opening Na^+ membrane channels would allow positive-charged Na^+ ions to enter the cell and decrease the negative intracellular charge, thereby decreasing the membrane potential. Closing Na^+ channels would increase the membrane potential. The negative charge of cellular compounds, such as proteins, phosphates, and organic molecules, contributes to the negative charge of the intracellular space of a cell. Decreasing their presence would decrease the intracellular negative charge and membrane potential.

NERVE SIGNAL TRANSMISSION

The difference in electric charge from inside the neuronal membrane to outside is the **resting membrane potential.** A neuron is said to be **polarized** due to the difference in charge across the neuronal membrane.

> Because there is a difference in charge from inside to outside the membrane, a resting membrane *potential* exists across the membrane. The membrane is said to be *"polarized"* because it has opposite charges on both sides of the membrane. There is a *"potential"* for charged ions to enter or exit the cell, causing a *depolarization* or equalization of charge.

The resting membrane potential may be as high as -90 millivolts (mV) for large nerve fibers or as low as -40 mV for some neurons in the central nervous system. The remainder of this discussion will use -70 mV as the hypothetical example of a resting membrane potential of a neuron. The inside of the neuron is charged -70 mV in relation to the outside. In other words, a membrane potential of -70 mV exists across the cell membrane.

The process of one neuron's stimulation of another neuron will now be considered. Because the axon of the stimulating neuron and dendrite of the stimulated neuron are separated by a synaptic cleft, the stimulating neuron is known as the **presynaptic neuron**. The stimulated neuron is the **postsynaptic neuron**. A chemical neurotransmitter is released from the tip of the presynaptic axon. This neurotransmitter quickly diffuses across the synaptic cleft to bind membrane receptors on the postsynaptic neuron. Once bound, the receptor initiates intracellular processes which may trigger various postsynaptic membrane channels to open. A signal is considered to be a stimulating signal when it promotes nerve transmission to the next neuron. An inhibitory signal is functioning to prevent transmission. In the case of a stimulating signal, a number of postsynaptic Na^+ membrane channels open in response to the neurotransmitter binding of the receptor. Na^+ rushes down its concentration gradient, bringing positive charges into the postsynaptic neuron. The membrane potential becomes less negative.

Every neuron has a **threshold potential**. This is the predetermined membrane potential at which additional membrane channels open, the neuron fully depolarizes, and a signal is transmitted. Most threshold potentials are about 20-30 mV less negative than the resting membrane potential. For the hypothetical resting membrane potential of -70 mV, the threshold potential will be said to be -45 mV. As Na^+ moves intracellular, the additional positive charges cause the resting membrane potential to become progressively less and less negative. It rises from -70 mV toward the threshold of -45 mV. If -45 mV is reached, then threshold is reached and Na^+ channels are triggered to open. Although some Na^+ channels had previously opened in response to the stimulating signal, the majority do not open until threshold is reached. Na^+ channels are open only briefly before they close. The immediate effect is a large intracellular influx of Na^+ into the intracellular environment. The accompanying positive charges cause the membrane potential to quickly approach zero and become slightly positive (approximately +20 mV). This is known as an **action potential**. After a slight delay following the onset of the action potential, K^+ channels open, allowing K^+ to move down its concentration gradient and leave the intracellular environment. The departure of the positive charges associated with these ions contributes to the restoration of the membrane potential.

> During the resting state, a neuron has a membrane potential of -70 mV. It is **"polarized"** with regard to charge. There is a negative charge on one side of the membrane and a positive charge on the other side. As the positive-charged sodium ions enter the cell, the membrane potential approaches zero and the neuron transiently becomes **"_d_epolarized."**

Neurons have an **"all or none"** response. If an action potential is created in a specific area of the neuron, it will spread across the entire neuron. This includes traveling down the axon to cause neurotransmitter release and signal transmission. If an action potential is not created, no signal transmission will occur. The creation of this action potential depends on whether or not threshold is reached. If reached, an action potential is formed which is propagated along the entire neuron and a signal is transmitted. If threshold is not reached, no action potential is formed, and no signal transmission occurs. For instance, if the membrane potential reaches -50 mV and not -45 mV, threshold is not reached. The neuron will attempt to repolarize to the resting membrane potential and no signal will be transmitted. The response of a neuron to incoming stimuli is therefore "all or none." If threshold is reached, an action potential is created, and a signal is transmitted. If threshold is not reached, an action potential is not created, and no signal transmission occurs.

FIGURE 5.8

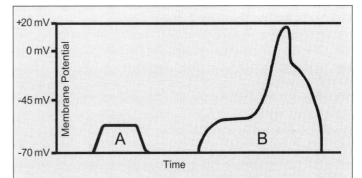

A – Stimulating impulses have caused an influx of Na^+. This brings in positive charges and makes the intracellular environment progressively less negative as compared to the extracellular environment. Threshold (-45 mV) is not reached and the membrane potential repolarizes, returning to the baseline of -70 mV. An action potential is not created.

B – Same scenario except the stimulating impulses are strong enough to depolarize the neuron to -45 mV. Hence, threshold is reached. Na^+ channels open, causing a rapid influx of Na^+ (positive charges). The membrane potential becomes less and less negative, resulting in the creation of an action potential.

Once an action potential is generated, its propagation across the neuron is made possible by several factors. When an action potential is formed in a specific area of the neuron, a number of Na^+ channels open in the immediately adjacent area. This is due to the positive intracellular charges from the action potential seeping into the adjacent intracellular area, causing the membrane potential to become progressively less negative in that area. The opening of these Na^+ channels allows entry of more positive charges. The membrane potential of the adjacent area becomes less and less negative, until threshold is reached and the area fully depolarizes. The same process reoccurs in the area immediately adjacent to this newly-depolarized area. In this fashion, the action potential is propagated along the entire length of the neuron. From the point of initiation, the action potential travels in all directions along the neuron. Not only is the action potential propagated by areas of depolarization causing adjacent Na^+ channels to open, but the intracellular contents of the neuron conduct electrical charge well. This promotes the progression of intracellular positive charges and propagation of the action potential. Again, once an action potential is formed, it travels across the entire neuron, resulting in release of neurotransmitter from the presynaptic membrane. The response of a neuron to incoming stimuli is "all or none." If it reaches threshold, it depolarizes and sends a signal. If it does not reach threshold, no signal is sent.

> An action potential may be considered as an intracellular wave of positive charges traveling through an intracellular sea of negative charges.

As the action potential travels past a specific area of the neuron, the area behind it attempts to repolarize to the resting membrane potential of -70 mV. As mentioned earlier, reaching the threshold triggers both the opening and, shortly thereafter, closing of Na^+ and K^+ channels. Both channels are stimulated to open at the same time, but it takes longer for the K^+ channels to open. The Na^+ channels open immediately, causing a depolarization and creation of an action potential. About the time the Na^+ channels close, limiting further intracellular entry of positive-charged Na^+ ions, the K^+ channels open. This allows K^+ ions (and their positive charges) to freely exit the neuron. Both the closing of Na^+ channels and opening of K^+ channels act to decrease the number of intracellular positive charges present and restore the membrane potential toward the resting state of -70 mV.

These actions work alongside other cellular processes to restore the resting membrane potential. Other repolarizing efforts include work of the Na^+-K^+ membrane pump and possible increased membrane permeability to certain negatively-charged anions. For instance, the extracellular concentration of Cl^- is greater than the intracellular concentration. Increased membrane permeability to Cl^- would allow the ion to flow down its concentration gradient and enter the depolarized neuron. This would increase the intracellular presence of negative charges and facilitate the reestablishment of the resting membrane potential.

Once the potential is repolarized, the neuron is able to propagate another depolarization, should a stimulating signal arrive. If another signal arrives before the neuron is repolarized, it will not be propagated. This period of time between an action potential and repolarization is known as the **refractory period**. A stimulus will not be transmitted if it arrives at a neuron during the neuron's refractory period.

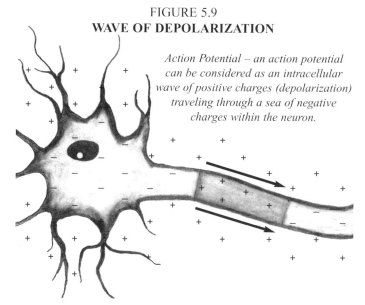

FIGURE 5.9
WAVE OF DEPOLARIZATION

Action Potential – an action potential can be considered as an intracellular wave of positive charges (depolarization) traveling through a sea of negative charges within the neuron.

Within the tip of the axon, numerous vesicles of neurotransmitter exist. As the action potential travels down the axon and reaches the tip, the depolarization triggers the opening of Ca^{++} channels on the presynaptic membrane. This is similar to the effect a depolarization has on other cation channels, such as Na^+ and K^+ channels. The result is an influx of Ca^{++} into the tip of the axon. The Ca^{++} promotes release of neurotransmitter into the synapse. The neurotransmitter-containing vesicles fuse with the presynaptic membrane, allowing release of the neurotransmitter into the synaptic cleft. The neurotransmitter quickly diffuses across the synaptic cleft to bind receptors on the next neuron or effector organ.

After binding postsynaptic membrane receptors, much of the chemical neurotransmitter is "recycled" by the presynaptic neuron. The neurotransmitter diffuses from the receptor and is chemically modified or metabolized into chemical precursors. It returns to the presynaptic axon terminal and crosses the cell membrane by **pinocytosis**. In this process, invaginations of the presynaptic cell membrane surround pockets of extracellular fluid which contain neurotransmitter or chemical precursors. Once these pockets are encircled by membrane, they separate from the rest of the membrane, forming intracellular fluid-filled vacuoles. These vacuoles contain neurotransmitter or its chemical precursors. Considering that a neuron may fire over a hundred times a second, the value of recycling neurotransmitter becomes evident. This saves time, resources, and energy.

As mentioned earlier, a particular neurotransmitter stimulus may have either an excitatory or inhibitory effect on a specific neuron. A neurotransmitter may cause opening of Na^+ channels, allowing entry of positive charges and causing the neuron membrane potential to become less negative. This stimulus would be considered excitatory on this particular neuron, as it predisposes to depolarization and creation of an action potential. Another stimulus may cause the neuron to hyperpolarize or become more negative. Since this would make the neuron more resistant to depolarization, the stimulus would be said to be inhibitory.

Similar to mechanisms employed during repolarization, possible inhibitory mechanisms include opening of K^+ channels and anion channels. Opening K^+ channels allows escape of intracellular positive K^+ ions, increasing the intracellular negative charge. Opening of anion channels, such as Cl^- channels, allows the intracellular influx of negative charges. Like Na^+, the concentration of

Cl^- is greater in the extracellular space. Depending on the amount of intracellular negative charge present, Cl^- would attempt to follow its concentration gradient and move to the intracellular space. Both the exit of K^+ and entry of anions increase the intracellular negative charge of the neuron, causing the neuron to become more polarized and resistant to depolarization and signal transmission.

A particular neuron receives stimuli from numerous other neurons, all at the same time. Some signals are excitatory and some are inhibitory. At any given time, if the sum of all the excitatory and inhibitory stimuli cause the membrane potential to reach threshold potential (-45 mV), the neuron will depolarize and an action potential is created. Once created, this action potential travels down the axon to either stimulate or inhibit the next neuron in line. Although it may receive numerous stimuli, a neuron will not pass a stimulus on to the next neuron unless its own threshold is reached. The transmission of nerve signals is a very dynamic process, involving numerous stimuli from different presynaptic neurons. Again, the sum of all excitatory and inhibitory signals determines if threshold is reached. If reached, a signal will be passed to the next neuron in line. This signal may be excitatory or inhibitory. If threshold is not reached, no signal is sent.

These action potentials, passing from neuron to neuron, may convey the sensation of pain, temperature, position, taste, sight, etc. They may be sending the stimulus to move certain voluntary or involuntary muscles. They also store memory and provide the ability to think. There are billions of synapses in the human nervous system. When one considers that some action potentials transmit excitatory stimuli while others convey inhibitory signals, one begins to form a distinct impression of the true complexity of our nervous system.

A peripheral nerve is formed by a collection of nerve fibers. A **nerve fiber** consists of one **neuron axon** surrounded by a series of **Schwann cells**, one following another along the length of the axon.

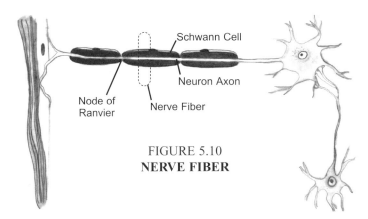

FIGURE 5.10
NERVE FIBER

Each Schwann cell is wrapped around the neuron axon many times. A cross-sectional view of a nerve fiber would reveal one centrally-located neuron axon which appears to be "rolled up" in a Schwann cell.

FIGURE 5.11
CROSS-SECTION OF NERVE FIBER

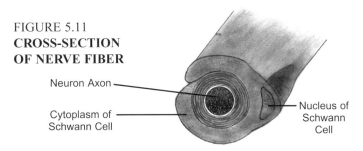

All nerve fibers contain Schwann cells. In some fibers, the Schwann cells produce a lipid chemical called myelin. Those fibers containing myelin are known as **myelinated fibers** and are said to be covered by a **myelin sheath**. In other fibers, the Schwann cells do not produce myelin and the nerve fibers are thereby known as **unmyelinated fibers**. Myelin is impermeable to Na^+. A myelin sheath prevents the intracellular entry of Na^+ during a depolarization. In myelinated fibers, the myelin sheath is interrupted by small unmyelinated distances located between successive Schwann cells. These unmyelinated areas are known as **nodes of Ranvier**.

FIGURE 5.12
MYELINATED FIBER

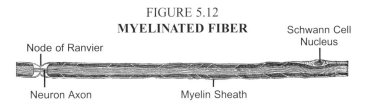

Nodes of Ranvier are the intermittent portals of entry for Na^+ and the accompanying positive charges which cause a depolarization. In an unmyelinated fiber, the action potential or wave of depolarization must travel down the entire length of the axon membrane to reach the tip and release neurotransmitter into the synaptic cleft. In a myelinated fiber, the action potential is able to "skip" from one node of Ranvier to the next. Much of the membrane is therefore bypassed and the speed of nerve signal transmission is significantly increased. This form of action potential conduction is known as **saltatory conduction**. The nerve impulse, action potential, or wave of depolarization can be considered to quickly "jump" down the nerve fiber from node of Ranvier to node of Ranvier. The presence of myelin thereby speeds nerve impulse conduction along the length of the axon. If two nerve fibers are otherwise identical, a myelinated fiber will have a faster conduction time than an unmyelinated fiber.

FIGURE 5.13
SALTATORY CONDUCTION

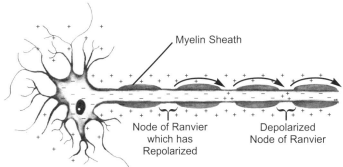

A **nerve** is simply a collection of nerve fibers. A particular nerve may contain both myelinated and unmyelinated fibers. In other words, within a nerve are numerous neuron axons and Schwann cells. Some of the Schwann cells produce myelin (myelinated fibers) and some do not (unmyelinated fibers). An axon is the only portion of a neuron found in peripheral nerves. The neuron cell bodies of these axons are either located within the central nervous system or a peripheral ganglion. Peripheral ganglia are discussed in the next section. The dendrites are located near the cell bodies.

QUIZ 2
Nerve Anatomy and Physiology

Time for Quiz = 20 minutes.
For questions 1-13, choose the single best answer.

_____1) Which of the following contributes to the repolarization of a neuron?
    a) opening Na^+ membrane channels
    b) opening K^+ membrane channels
    c) closing Cl^- membrane channels
    d) all the above
    e) none of the above

_____2) What does the phrase "all or none" refer to?
    a) Na^+ channels on a neuron membrane either completely open or they do not open at all.
    b) The neuron either completely depolarizes or it does not depolarize at all.
    c) Once an action potential reaches the tip of the axon either all of the available neurotransmitter is released into the synaptic cleft or none of it is.
    d) The U.S. tax code
    e) None of the above

_____3) An action potential may best be described as
    a) a wave of negative charges traveling through a sea of positive charges
    b) a wave of positive charges traveling through a sea of negative charges
    c) the membrane potential at which threshold occurs
    d) a polarization
    e) none of the above

_____4) Movement of which ion across the cell membrane is primarily responsible for generation of an action potential?
    a) Na^+
    b) K^+
    c) Both a and b
    d) Ca^{++}
    e) None of the above

_____5) Neurotransmitters enter the presynaptic neuron by way of
    a) pinocytosis
    b) active transport
    c) facilitated diffusion
    d) simple diffusion
    e) none of the above

_____6) A full depolarization of a neuron is the equivalent of a
    a) membrane potential
    b) action potential
    c) threshold potential
    d) repolarization
    e) none of the above

_____7) The threshold potential of a neuron is
    a) approximately 45 mV in most neurons
    b) the resting membrane potential of a neuron
    c) the membrane potential at which an action potential is created
    d) the membrane potential at which a hyperpolarization occurs.
    e) none of the above

_____8) How does most Na^+ enter the neuron during a depolarization?
    a) simple diffusion across the membrane
    b) membrane channels
    c) Na^+-K^+ membrane pumps
    d) Na^+ ions exit the neuron during a depolarization
    e) none of the above

_____9) An action potential is the equivalent of
    a) a polarization
    b) a repolarization
    c) a refractory period
    d) a depolarization
    e) none of the above

_____10) Which of the following structures make up a nerve fiber?
    a) axon
    b) Schwann cell
    c) both a and b
    d) dendrite
    e) none of the above

_____11) Which of the following is true concerning an unmyelinated nerve fiber?
    a) There is no Schwann cell.
    b) It is never located in the same nerve as myelinated fiber.
    c) It contains no nodes of Ranvier.
    d) Its conduction time is shorter as compared to myelinated fiber.
    e) None of the above

_____12) A specific neuron has a resting membrane potential of -70 mV. Its threshold potential is -55 mV. It received signals from both stimulating neurons and inhibitory neurons at the same time. The stimulating signals cause a depolarization of 30 mV from the resting membrane potential. The inhibitory signals cause a hyperpolarization of 18 mV from the resting membrane potential. What will happen?
    a) The signal will not be transmitted as threshold is not reached and an action potential is not created.
    b) An action potential would be created.
    c) The neuron would become hyperpolarized and more resistant to stimulation.
    d) Neurotransmitter would be released by the axon of the neuron.
    e) Both b and d

_____13) Which of the following occurs once threshold is reached?
    a) K^+ channels open
    b) Na^+ channels open
    c) Both a and b
    d) Ca^{++} channels open
    e) All the above

For questions 14-20, use the following directions:
a.......1,2,3 are correct
b.......1,3 are correct
c.......2,4 are correct
d.......only 4 is correct
e.......all are correct

_____14) The creation of an action potential requires the occurrence of which of the following?
    1. Na^+ channels must open.
    2. A depolarization must occur.
    3. Threshold must be reached.
    4. A preexisting membrane potential must be present.

_____15) Which of the following is true concerning myelin?
    1. It is produced by Schwann cells.
    2. Its presence speeds nerve conduction.
    3. It keeps Na^+ from crossing the axon membrane.
    4. It decreases conduction times.

_____16) When an action potential reaches the terminal end of an axon,
    1. The membrane potential approaches zero.
    2. Ca^{++} moves extracellular.
    3. Vesicles of neurotransmitter fuse with the outer membrane and release the neurotransmitter into the synaptic cleft.
    4. Na^+ moves extracellular.

_____17) Which of the following are true concerning Schwann cells?
    1. They are present in all nerve fibers.
    2. They produce myelin.
    3. They surround neuron axons.
    4. Some do not produce myelin.

_____18) Which of the following may be found in a nerve?
    1. neuron axon
    2. node of Ranvier
    3. Schwann cell
    4. myelin

_____19) True statements concerning nerve fibers include which of the following?
    1. All contain axons.
    2. All contain Schwann cells.
    3. They are the structures which form nerves.
    4. All contain myelin.

_____20) Which of the following is true concerning nodes of Ranvier?
    1. They occur only on myelinated nerve fibers.
    2. They are areas where Na^+ is allowed to move extracellular.
    3. They speed nerve signal conduction.
    4. They increase conduction times.

QUIZ 2: Nerve Anatomy and Physiology Answers and Explanations

1) b – After an action potential, any activity which increases the intracellular negative charge would theoretically promote repolarization of a neuron. As a neuron depolarizes, threshold triggers the opening of both Na^+ and K^+ membrane channels. The K^+ channels take longer to open, so the immediate effect is an influx of Na^+. The positive charges cause a complete depolarization. About the time the Na^+ channels close, the K^+ channels open. Both actions promote the repolarization of the neuron. Closing Na^+ channels prevents further entry of positive-charged Na^+ ions. Opening K^+ channels allows exit of positive-charged K^+ ions. In addition, opening of certain anion channels allows entry of negative-charged ions. For example, the extracellular concentration of Cl^- is much greater than the intracellular concentration. The opening of Cl^- channels would allow the anion to follow its concentration gradient and enter the neuron, thereby increasing the intracellular negative charge.

2) e – When a neuron reaches threshold, it fully depolarizes and an action potential is created. "All or none" refers to the fact that, once created, an action potential will be propagated along to the entire length of the neuron to transmit a signal to the next neuron. If threshold is not reached, no signal will be transmitted. The nerve may partially depolarize due to stimulation from other neurons. If threshold is not reached, the neuron will simply repolarize with the aid of membrane channels and Na^+-K^+ membrane pumps. No signal will thus be transmitted.

3) b – The resting membrane potential of a neuron, depending on the type and size of the neuron, is approximately -70 mV. This means the internal environment is charged -70 mV as compared to the external environment. Following a stimulus from another neuron, some Na^+ channels may open, allowing entry of positive charges. The membrane potential gradually becomes less negative. If threshold membrane potential is reached, a significantly larger number of Na^+ channels open and allow a large influx of Na^+ to occur. Because these ions carry positive charges, this causes a full depo-

larization or action potential. The area of depolarization (action potential) travels across the neuron and down the axon to potentially stimulate or inhibit the next neuron in line. As the action potential travels past a specific area of the neuron, the opening of membrane ion channels and the Na^+-K^+ membrane pumps act to repolarize the resting membrane potential to -70 mV. An action potential may thus be considered a moving wave of positive charges traveling through a sea of negative charges.

4) a – Because of limited neuron membrane permeability, the concentration of Na^+ ions is much greater in the extracellular space than in the intracellular space. When threshold is reached, Na^+ membrane channels open, allowing a large influx of Na^+. The Na^+ ions are accompanied by their positive charges, which cause a full depolarization and creation of an action potential.

5) a – After binding the postsynaptic membrane receptor, chemical neurotransmitter leaves the receptor and is often taken back and recycled by the presynaptic neuron for reuse. *Pinocytosis* is a process in which tiny invaginations are formed in a cell membrane. These invaginations eventually encircle an area of extracellular fluid which, in this case, contains chemical neurotransmitter or its chemical precursors. As these invaginations close, they break from the cell membrane to become intracellular vacuoles which contain neurotransmitter.

6) b – A resting neuron is "polarized" in that the intracellular contents are charged approximately -70 mV as compared to the extracellular environment. This is known as the resting membrane potential of the neuron. As the neuron is stimulated by other neurons, some Na^+ channels may open, allowing positively charged Na^+ ions to flow down the concentration gradient and enter the intracellular space. These positive charges cause the membrane potential to become less negative. If the potential reaches a certain predetermined level known as the threshold potential, significantly

more Na$^+$ channels open. This allows a relatively large influx of Na$^+$ cations and their accompanying positive charges, resulting in full depolarization of the membrane potential. **This full depolarization is known as an action potential**. It travels across the neuron like a wave of positive intracellular charges traveling through a sea of negative intracellular charges. When it reaches the end of the axon, it causes an influx of Ca^{++} and release of neurotransmitter into the synaptic cleft. This neurotransmitter may stimulate or inhibit the next neuron in line. As an action potential travels across a neuron, the area behind it is repolarized. Prior to its repolarization, the neuron is said to be in a refractory state. Should another stimulus arrive while the neuron is in the refractory state, it will not be transmitted.

7) c – See #6 answer explanation. Answer **a** is incorrect because *45 mV* is a positive number, hence the intracellular environment would be positive compared to the extracellular environment. *-45 mV* could be a correct answer.

8) b – The extracellular concentration of Na$^+$ is much greater than the intracellular concentration. Following a stimulus, some Na$^+$ membrane channels open, allowing positive charges into the neuron. The membrane potential gradually becomes less negative. If threshold membrane potential is reached, a significantly larger number of Na$^+$ channels open and allow a large influx of Na$^+$ to occur. Because these ions carry positive charges, this causes a full depolarization or action potential.

9) d – See #6 answer explanation.

10) c – A nerve is formed from nerve fibers. A nerve fiber is composed of a neuron axon which is surrounded by a series of Schwann cells, one following another down the length of the axon. Some Schwann cells produce a chemical called myelin. Some do not. The fibers with myelin-producing Schwann cells are thus surrounded by a myelin sheath and are said to be myelinated. Interruptions of the myelin sheath occur between successive Schwann cells at various distances down the length of

the axon. These interruptions are known as Nodes of Ranvier. They allow the action potential to "skip" down the axon from one Node of Ranvier to the next, and thereby speed nerve conduction velocity. A neuron is formed by a soma, dendrites, and an axon. Because peripheral nerves are formed by nerve fibers, the axon is the only part of a neuron that is present in peripheral nerves. The soma is the neuron cell body and is located either in the CNS or a peripheral autonomic ganglion. The neuron dendrites are located near the soma.

11) c – A nerve fiber is formed by a neuron axon which is surrounded by a series of Schwann cells, one behind another, down the length of the axon. Some Schwann cells produce a lipid compound called myelin. The nerve fiber is thereby said to be myelinated and contains a myelin sheath, which is impermeable to Na$^+$. Between two successive Schwann cells are interruptions in the myelin sheath. These intermittent interruptions are known as Nodes of Ranvier and serve as portals of entry for Na$^+$ into the neuron. Their presence speeds nerve conduction by allowing the action potential to skip down the axon, from node to node. Some Schwann cells do not produce myelin, and their fibers are therefore said to be unmyelinated. Because unmyelinated fibers have no myelin sheath, they cannot have functional Nodes of Ranvier. Any particular nerve may contain both myelinated and unmyelinated nerve fibers.

12) a – The sum of all stimulating and all inhibiting signals is what determines if threshold is reached and an action potential is subsequently created. In this case, the stimulating signal causes a depolarization of 30 mV (+30) and the inhibitory signal creates a hyperpolarization of 18 mV (-18 mV). The resting membrane potential is -70 mV, so -70 + 30 - 18 = -58. Since threshold is -55 mV, threshold will not be reached. The large number of Na$^+$ channels do not open, the neuron does not depolarize, and the action potential is not created. The only time a neuron is in a refractory period is during and immediately after a depolarization, before the neuron has a chance to repolarize.

13) e – Threshold triggers the opening of both Na^+ and K^+ membrane channels. The K^+ channels take longer to open, so the immediate effect is an influx of Na^+. The positive charges cause a full depolarization. About the time the Na^+ channels close, the K^+ channels open. Both actions promote the repolarization of the neuron. Closing Na^+ channels prevents further entry of positive-charged Na^+ ions. Opening K^+ channels allows exit of positive-charged K^+ ions. The membrane potential becomes more negative. As the action potential reaches the axon terminal, Ca^{++} membrane channels open. The influx of Ca^{++} promotes the fusion of neurotransmitter vesicles with the terminal cell membrane. The neurotransmitter is released into the synaptic cleft to bind receptors of the next neuron or effector organ.

14) e – In order for an action potential to occur, there must be a preexisting membrane potential present. This is a negative intracellular charge as compared to the extracellular charge. Upon stimulation from another neuron, some Na^+ channels open and Na^+ moves down the concentration gradient, traveling from the extracellular to intracellular space. This brings positive charges intracellular, making the membrane potential less negative or less "polarized." Hence, there is a partial depolarization. While becoming less and less negative, if the membrane potential reaches a certain predetermined level, called the threshold potential, more Na^+ channels open, more positive charges rush in, and the neuron completely depolarizes. The resultant complete depolarization following threshold is known as an action potential. If threshold is not reached, an action potential will not be created and processes occur within the neuron to repolarize it. The opening of certain membrane ion channels and activity of the Na^+-K^+ membrane pump function to reestablish the resting membrane potential. If threshold is reached and an action potential is created, it travels across the neuron and down its axon to potentially stimulate or inhibit the next neuron in line or supply the effector organ. Once the action potential travels past a certain area of the neuron, the resting membrane potential is reestablished by many of the same mechanisms as after a partial depolarization. When the resting membrane potential is reestablished, the neuron is said to be repolarized. The period of time from the onset of the action potential to the reestablishment of the membrane potential is known as the refractory period. Should a stimulus from another neuron occur during the refractory period, it would not be transmitted.

15) e – A nerve fiber is formed by a neuron axon and a sequence of accompanying Schwann cells, one following another along the length of the axon. Each Schwann cell wraps itself multiple times around the axon. A cross-section view of a nerve fiber would reveal a neuron axon near the center with one Schwann cell "wrapped" multiple times around it. Some Schwann cells produce a chemical called myelin. Some do not. Myelin is a lipid substance which is essentially impermeable to Na^+. The fibers with myelin are said to be myelinated fibers and are surrounded by a myelin sheath. The myelin sheath prevents the flow of Na^+ through membrane Na^+ channels into the axon during an action potential. At various intervals along the nerve fiber, there are interruptions in the myelin sheath between successive Schwann cells. These interruptions are known as nodes of Ranvier. They serve as the entry points for Na^+ into the axon. The presence of myelin allows the depolarization or action potential to skip from one node of Ranvier to the next. This speeds signal conduction and decreases nerve conduction times. In unmyelinated fibers, by contrast, the action potential must travel the entire length of the nerve fiber without the ability to bypass any areas of the membrane.

16) b – As an action potential arrives at the axon terminal, the membrane potential approaches zero and becomes positive. This is due to Na^+ entering the axon, not leaving it. The depolarization triggers an influx of Ca^{++} and fusion of the neurotransmitter vesicles with the nerve membrane. The neurotransmitter is released and diffuses across the synaptic cleft to reach the dendrite of the next neuron or the surface of the effector organ.

17) e – See #15 answer explanation. All nerve fibers have Schwann cells which accompany their particular neuron axon. In unmyelinated fibers, the Schwann cells do not produce myelin.

18) e – See #15 answer explanation. A nerve is simply a collection of nerve fibers. A nerve fiber is composed of a neuron axon which is surrounded by a sequence of Schwann cells, one following another. The soma is the neuron cell body and is located in either the CNS or a peripheral autonomic ganglion. The neuron dendrites are located near the soma.

19) a – See #15 answer explanation.

20) b – See #15 answer explanation. Nodes of Ranvier are areas where Na^+ is allowed to *enter* the axon. Na^+ therefore moves to the *intracellular* space. The presence of Nodes of Ranvier speeds nerve signal conduction. This *decreases* conduction times.

ORGANIZATION AND CLASSIFICATION OF THE PERIPHERAL NERVOUS SYSTEM

Now that the basic physiology of nerve transmission has been described, the primary subdivisions of the human nervous system will be covered. The general organizational structure of the peripheral nervous system and its clinical effect on the patient is much easier to learn, understand, and remember if details concerning the various nervous subdivisions are known. Basically, the human nervous system can be divided two ways: anatomically and functionally. Anatomically, the nervous system can be divided into the central nervous system (CNS) and the peripheral nervous system (PNS). Functionally, the nervous system can be divided into the somatic nervous system (SNS) and the autonomic nervous system (ANS). Regardless of the nervous system involved, there are some generalities that apply to all of the systems.

Depending on the function and location of a neuron, its axon may travel a very short or relatively long distance to synapse with the next neuron. Information may be sent from one area of the brain to another area which is very near the first. Alternatively, it may travel long distances along central and peripheral routes. In order to move an arm, nerve transmission may be sent from the brain down the spinal cord. From the spinal cord, the signal is transported by relatively long motor axons to innervate muscles that move the arm. These motor pathways are known as **descending pathways** because information travels from the brain downward. Nerve transmission may also travel in the opposite direction. Information from a cutaneous touch receptor may travel to the spinal cord to subsequently reach the brain. These sensory pathways are called **ascending pathways** because information is traveling up, toward the brain. If a neuron cell body were the size of a basketball, its net of dendrites could potentially fill a high school gym. Its axon could extend for several miles. With this in mind, it is possible to visualize a cell body in the brain sending its axon the entire length of the spinal cord. The information sent in these long axons travels at fractions of a millisecond.

As described in the second chapter, afferent structures transport an entity (i.e. blood, nerve transmission, fluid, etc.) to an object. Efferent structures transport the entity away from the object. Since the brain is the central command center of the nervous system, sensory pathways are said to be **afferent** because they carry nerve transmission to the brain. Motor pathways are **efferent**; they carry information away from the brain.

> Sensory pathways are **a**scending pathways which are **a**fferent.

Nerve transmission is constantly occurring along nerve pathways between the brain and periphery to maintain various unconscious functions of the body. Functions such as blood pressure control and digestion are maintained by the autonomic nervous system. In addition, communication occurs between the cerebellum of the brain and skeletal muscles to maintain balance and provide coordination. This enables us to perform complex muscular actions such as walking or riding a bike without having to consciously consider the exact movements required. These various pathways travel in tracts of the CNS and interact with one another in a very complex manner.

The nervous system can be anatomically divided into the central and peripheral nervous systems. The **central nervous system** is comprised of the brain and spinal cord. Both are surrounded by bone, the skull and vertebral column, respectively. The **peripheral nervous system** is the primary focus of this course. It is composed of both cranial and spinal systems. There are 12 pairs of cranial nerves which originate directly from the brain. There are 31 pairs of spinal nerves which branch from the spinal cord. Both the cranial and spinal nerves are extensively covered later in the reading.

The vast majority of neuron cell bodies are located within the CNS. Outside the CNS, neuron cell bodies are found in nerve structures called **ganglia**. Because dendrites do not extend far from the cell body, the location of cell bodies is also the location of synapses between two neurons. These synapses occur in three places: the brain, the spinal cord, and efferent autonomic ganglia of the peripheral nervous system. From these three places, the cell bodies send their axons to the next synapse and/or effector organ. The effector organ is the smooth, cardiac, or skeletal muscle fiber which a particular series of neurons is innervating.

Functionally, the human nervous system can be divided into the somatic and autonomic nervous systems. This division is based on the function of the tissue being innervated. The body is comprised of two general tissue types. *Somatic tissues* form the body wall and provide the structure of the body. *Visceral tissues* are the highly specialized structures which individually function to maintain a stable internal environment.

The **somatic nervous system** innervates somatic structures. Examples include bones, muscles, cartilage, tendons, ligaments, and fascia. These are the structures which form the body wall. The somatic nervous system participates in conscious functions such as motor movement. It also provides unconscious or involuntary functions such as muscular balance, coordination and pain sensation.

The **autonomic nervous system** innervates visceral structures of the body. These include glands, internal organs, and blood vessels. Visceral structures have highly individualized and specialized functions to provide a stable internal environment in the face of an ever-changing external environment. This includes maintenance of blood pressure, temperature, and electrolyte or chemical balance. The autonomic nervous system is responsible for involuntary functions such as heart rate, respiratory rate, and digestive activity. It receives sensory input from visceral structures. It also provides motor innervation to smooth muscle fibers responsible for the specific visceral action of each structure. With the heart, cardiac muscle fibers are innervated in the place of smooth muscle fibers.

The autonomic nervous system is further subdivided into the sympathetic and parasympathetic nervous systems. These two systems tend to oppose one another in function. The **sympathetic system** provides the excited "fight or flight" response. The parasympathetic system provides just the opposite. The **parasympathetic system** is associated with regular bodily functions that occur during normal, resting states. An example of one such function is digestion.

In addition to the difference of tissues supplied by the somatic and autonomic systems, the two systems also differ in the structure of peripheral neuron arrangement of their efferent or motor limb. The somatic system is a one-neuron system. The autonomic system is a two-neuron system.

In the somatic system, only one neuron that has structures outside the central nervous system participates in efferent signal transmission. This somatic neuron has its cell body located within the brain stem or ventral horn of the spinal cord. From the cell body, an axon leaves the central nervous system via a cranial or spinal nerve to eventually form a synapse with a voluntary muscle fiber. This synapse is known as a **motor end plate**. Because only one neuron is involved in nerve transmission outside the CNS, the **somatic nervous system is known as a one-neuron system**.

> The word *soma* refers to the body or tissues which form the body. The soma of a neuron is the "body" of the neuron. The word *somatic* is derived from the word *soma*. Somatic structures form the body wall, including the head and extremities. Just as there is only **one** body wall in an individual, the somatic nervous system has only **one** neuron outside the CNS which participates in efferent nerve signal transmission.

The autonomic nervous system has two neurons that participate in efferent nerve transmission outside the central nervous system. This includes the efferent limbs of both the sympathetic and parasympathetic systems. Like the neuron of the somatic system, the first neuron of the autonomic system has a cell body located in the brain or intermediolateral horn of the spinal cord.

From this cell body, an axon extends through a cranial or spinal nerve to reach and synapse with the second neuron of the autonomic system. This synapse occurs within an **autonomic ganglion** located outside the central nervous system. The first neuron of the autonomic system is known as the **preganglionic neuron**. The second neuron is known as the **postganglionic neuron**. From this postganglionic neuron, an axon travels out to terminate on the smooth or cardiac muscle fiber of the effector organ. The **autonomic nervous system is known as a two-neuron system**.

Because each cell body possesses multiple appendages, efferent neurons of both the somatic and autonomic systems are described as **multipolar.** One axon and numerous dendrites originate from each cell body.

FIGURE 5.14
CROSS-SECTION SPINAL CORD
SOMATIC VS. AUTONOMIC

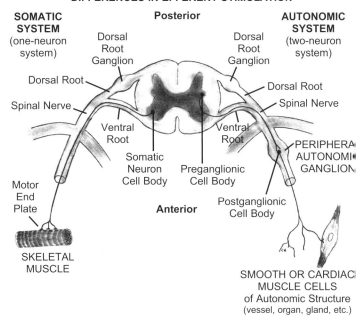

DIFFERENCES IN EFFERENT STIMULATION

This is a cross section of the spinal cord. On the left is the somatic nervous system. One neuron participates in efferent transmission outside the CNS. The cell body is shown residing in the spinal cord. It sends its axon out by way of a spinal nerve to stimulate a voluntary muscle via a motor end plate. On the right, the autonomic nervous system is shown with two neurons participating in efferent nerve conduction outside the CNS. The first neuron (preganglionic neuron) also has its body within the spinal cord. Its axon exits the spinal cord with a spinal nerve to synapse with a second autonomic neuron (postganglionic neuron) in an autonomic ganglion. The postganglionic neuron extends its axon to stimulate the smooth or cardiac muscle of the organ it innervates.

> Just as the autonomic nervous system is composed of **two** well-known systems, the sympathetic and parasympathetic systems, there are **two** autonomic neurons outside the CNS which participate in efferent nerve signal transmission.

The afferent (sensory) limbs of the somatic and autonomic systems are similar in structure in that each limb contains one afferent neuron housed in a sensory ganglion. Afferent neurons associated with spinal nerves and most cranial nerves are described as **pseudounipolar** in structure; only one appendage extends from the cell body and it soon divides in a T-shaped form into two axons. The longer branch extends to a peripheral sensory receptor and is analogous to a dendrite in that it receives information. The shorter branch courses to the brain stem or spinal cord. Once the sensory receptor is activated, a sensory signal is transmitted to the CNS. *Pseudounipolar* neurons form a subclass of unipolar neurons. Uniploar neurons are found in invertebrates and possess one axonal process that contains different areas that transmit (axonal) and receive (dendritic) information.

The structure of afferent neurons that are associated with certain special sensory cranial nerves are classified as **bipolar.** Two appendages or processes originate from the cell body. The peripheral process travels to a sensory receptor and the central process travels to the CNS. When the sensory receptor is activated, a signal is conducted to the CNS.

Peripheral Neuron Structure

Multipolar – Efferent neurons (somatic and autonomic) of spinal and cranial nerves

Pseudounipolar – Afferent neurons (somatic and autonomic) of spinal and most cranial nerves

Bipolar – Afferent neurons of certain special sensory cranial nerves

---

The afferent limbs of the somatic and autonomic systems are differentiated by the type of tissue innervated. The sensory receptor of the somatic system is located in a somatic tissue, such as skin, bone or muscle. Sensation of touch, pain, position, or balance

may be conveyed. With the autonomic system, the sensory receptor is located in a visceral structure, such as an internal organ, gland, or blood vessel. Sensory information concerning blood pressure, pain, or visceral organ function may be transmitted.

In overview, two general classifications exist for ganglia of both cranial and spinal nerves: autonomic efferent and sensory. A particular autonomic efferent ganglion contains postganglionic cell bodies of *either* the sympathetic or parasympathetic system. Autonomic ganglia are the location of the synapse between the preganglionic and postganglionic neurons. Postganglionic fibers leave the ganglion to innervate effector organs. Sensory ganglia contain afferent neuron cell bodies. The dorsal root ganglion is the sensory ganglion for a particular spinal nerve and contains both somatic and visceral pseudounipolar neurons. As will be described in Chapter Seven, various cranial nerves are also associated with sensory ganglia. Cranial nerve sensory ganglia may contain somatic cell bodies, visceral cell bodies, or a combination of both. Because the cell bodies are pseudounipolar in structure (or, in certain locations, bipolar) sensory ganglia do not contain synapses.

Ganglion are where neuron cell bodies are located outside the CNS.

Autonomic efferent ganglia are the only ganglia in which synapses occur.

The somatic efferent system is a "one-neuron" system and contains no ganglia. Sensory ganglia of both the visceral (autonomic) and somatic systems contain afferent cell bodies that are pseudounipolar; no synapse takes place.

Physically, ganglia often appear as knot-like beads on the string-like nerves.

FIGURE 5.15
PERIPHERAL NEURON STRUCTURE

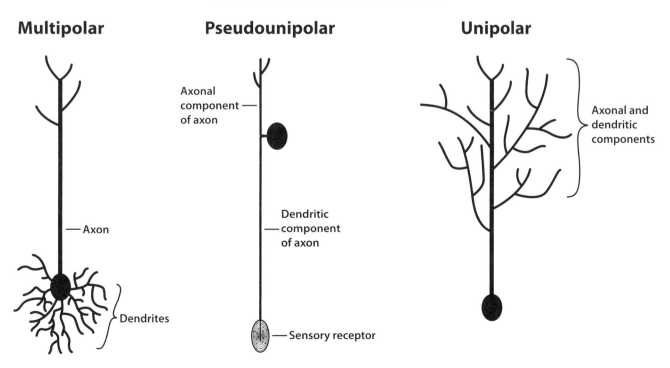

QUIZ 3
Nerve Anatomy and Physiology

Time for Quiz = 20 minutes.
For questions 1-13, choose the single best answer.

_____1) Motor pathways are
     a. descending
     b. efferent
     c. both a and b
     d. afferent
     e. none of the above

_____2) True statements about efferent somatic
ganglia include which of the following:
     a. They are where neuron cell bodies
        are located.
     b. They are where synapses between
        neurons occur.
     c. Both a and b
     d. They do not exist.
     e. None of the above

_____3) Synapses between two neurons occur in
which of the following structures?
     a. somatic sensory ganglia
     b. autonomic sensory ganglia
     c. spinal cord
     d. all of the above
     e. none of the above

_____4) Peripheral sensory neurons could be said to be
     a. descending
     b. pseudounipolar
     c. both a and b
     d. multipolar
     e. none of the above

_____5) The peripheral nervous system may be
anatomically divided into
     a. cranial and spinal systems
     b. somatic and parasympathetic
        systems
     c. sympathetic and parasympathetic
        systems
     d. somatic and autonomic systems
     e. none of the above

_____6) Where are neuron cell bodies located?
     a. brain
     b. spinal cord
     c. both a and b
     d. peripheral nerve
     e. none of the above

_____7) Motor pathways are
     a. ascending
     b. all myelinated
     c. efferent
     d. afferent
     e. none of the above

_____8) Which statements about a peripheral
pseudounipolar neuron are true?
     a. It could be an autonomic efferent
        neuron.
     b. It transmits ascending information.
     c. It has a membrane potential that
        does not change.
     d. It could be a motor neuron.
     e. None of the above

_____9) Which of the following structures is
supplied by the somatic nervous system?
     a. esophagus
     b. brachioradialis muscle
     c. sweat glands
     d. hair follicles
     e. none of the above

_____10) True statements about the autonomic
nervous system include which of the
following?
     a. It can be subdivided into the
        sympathetic and parasympathetic
        nervous systems.
     b. It includes peripheral ganglia.
     c. It has two neurons outside the CNS
        which participate in efferent nerve
        transmission.
     d. It provides the predominant
        innervation of the intestines.
     e. All are correct

_____11) The peripheral nervous system can functionally be divided into
    a. cranial and somatic systems
    b. sympathetic and somatic systems
    c. cranial and spinal systems
    d. somatic and autonomic systems
    e. none of the above

_____12) True statements about the somatic nervous system include which of the following?
    a. It relays information responsible for the "fight or flight" response.
    b. It is an anatomic division of the human nervous system.
    c. Two neurons outside the CNS participate in efferent nerve transmission.
    d. It provides the majority of innervation of the visceral organs of the body.
    e. None of the above

_____13) Where may a bipolar neuron be found?
    a. dorsal root ganglion of spinal nerve
    b. special sensory ganglion of cranial nerve
    c. autonomic efferent ganglion of cranial nerve
    d. all of the above
    e. none of the above

For questions 14-20, use the following directions:
  a.......1,2,3 are correct
  b.......1,3 are correct
  c.......2,4 are correct
  d.......only 4 is correct
  e.......all are correct

_____14) In what structures do synapses between neurons occur?
    1. brain
    2. autonomic efferent ganglion
    3. spinal cord
    4. peripheral nerve

_____15) Which of the following are true about motor and sensory pathways?
    1. Motor pathways are efferent.
    2. Sensory pathways are ascending.
    3. Efferent pathways are descending.
    4. Afferent pathways are ascending.

_____16) Which of the following are correct divisions of the human nervous system?
    1. autonomically, into sympathetic and parasympathetic systems
    2. functionally, into somatic and autonomic systems
    3. anatomically, into cranial and spinal systems
    4. realistically, into smart and well, not so smart

_____17) Which of the following is true concerning the somatic nervous system?
    1. It innervates parts of the body responsible for provision of structure.
    2. It is a functional division of the peripheral nervous system.
    3. Only one neuron participates in efferent nerve transmission outside the CNS.
    4. It contains no efferent ganglia.

_____18) Which of the following may be found in a particular peripheral nerve?
    1. neuron axons
    2. myelinated nerve fibers
    3. Schwann cells
    4. unmyelinated nerve fibers

_____19) Where may a neuron soma be found?
    1. brain
    2. sensory ganglion
    3. spinal cord
    4. peripheral nerve

_____20) What may be found in a dorsal root ganglion?
    1. somatic afferent neuron cell body
    2. bipolar neuron
    3. visceral afferent neuron cell body
    4. synapse

QUIZ 3: Nerve Anatomy and Physiology Answers and Explanations

1) c – Motor pathways travel from the brain to the skeletal muscles. This is by way of either a cranial nerve or the spinal cord and a spinal nerve. These pathways are said to be descending because nerve transmission is moving from the brain downward. These pathways are also efferent because the nerve transmission is being carried away from the brain.

2) d – Nerve cell bodies, or somas, may be found in three places in the body: the brain, the spinal cord, and peripheral ganglia. The somatic nervous system only has one neuron which participates in efferent nerve transmission outside the CNS. The cell body of this neuron is located in the brain or spinal cord, and its axon extends outward to supply a somatic structure such as a voluntary muscle fiber. Realize how relatively long this axon must be to supply somatic structures of the hands and feet! In the efferent limb of the somatic system, there are no ganglia because there is no second neuron to synapse with. By contrast, the autonomic system has two neurons that participate in efferent signal transmission outside the CNS. This necessitates the presence of ganglia in which to house the second neuron cell body and serve as the location for the synapse between the first (preganglionic) and second (postganglionic) autonomic neurons. Remember, there are no somatic efferent ganglia. Some texts fail to distinctly point this out.

3) c – Peripheral ganglia are the only location outside the CNS where neuron cell bodies are found. Because sensory ganglia contain cell bodies that are pseudounipolar (or, rarely, bipolar), peripheral autonomic efferent ganglia are the only ganglia in which synapses between two neurons occur. Preganglionic fibers synapse with dendrites of postganglionic neurons located in the autonomic efferent ganglia. Postganglionic fibers extend from the ganglia to supply end organs. There are no somatic efferent ganglia because the somatic efferent system is a "one neuron" system.

4) b – Most peripheral sensory neurons, both for the somatic and autonomic nervous systems, are *pseudounipolar*. This means that they have only one appendage or extension from the cell body. This appendage is an axon. There are no dendrites. The cell body is located in the dorsal root ganglion of a spinal nerve or sensory ganglion of a cranial nerve. The lone axon extends out and divides into two branches. One branch travels peripherally to a sensory receptor. The other branch travels to the spinal cord. When the sensory receptor is activated, a signal is transmitted to the central nervous system. Because the signal is traveling toward the brain, it is *afferent* in nature. The nerve transmission is also said to be *ascending*. The flow of transmission travels up, from the sensory receptor toward the brain.

5) a – There are several ways to subdivide the peripheral nervous system. This frequently serves as an area of confusion for the beginning student. Anatomically, the peripheral nervous system can be grossly divided into the cranial and spinal systems. This is because there are 12 pairs of cranial nerves originating directly from the brain and 31 pairs of spinal nerves originating from the spinal cord. Functionally, the peripheral nervous system may be divided into the somatic and autonomic systems. This classification is based on the general function of the tissue being innervated. The somatic system innervates somatic structures and the autonomic system innervates autonomic structures. Somatic structures are tissues which give the body structure. Examples include bones, skeletal muscles, tendons, ligaments, cartilage, and fascia. Conversely, autonomic (or visceral) structures are highly individualized and specialized structures which involuntarily function to maintain a stable internal environment. This includes maintenance of such things as fluid balance, electrolyte levels, and temperature. Autonomic structures are also responsible for adaptations needed to address the ever-changing external environment. Examples of autonomic structures include visceral organs, blood vessels, hair follicles, lymphatic vessels, and glands. Finally, the autonomic system may be subdivided into the sympathetic and parasympathetic systems.

6) c – See #2 answer explanation. Peripheral nerves are formed by nerve fibers. A nerve fiber is composed of a neuron axon and its accompanying schwann cells.

7) c – Motor pathways are efferent because they carry nerve transmission away from the brain. They are also said to be descending pathways because the signal "descends" from the brain. Both motor and sensory pathways are formed by nerve fibers. These fibers may or may not be myelinated.

8) b – See #4 answer explanation. *Efferent* neurons, both for the somatic and autonomic (sympathetic and parasympathetic) nervous systems, are *multipolar*. They have an axon and dendrites. Concerning answer *c,* all neuron membrane potentials change as the neuron depolarizes and repolarizes.

9) b – See #5 answer explanation.

10) e – All are true. The two (2) neurons that participate in efferent signal transmission outside the CNS are known as the preganglionic and postganglionic neurons. The preganglionic neuron's cell body is located within the CNS. Its axon travels peripherally to synapse with the postganglionic neuron within a peripheral autonomic ganglion. Since the autonomic nervous system is responsible for the "autonomic" functions of the body, it makes sense that the visceral organs would be richly innervated by autonomic fibers. This includes the intestines.

11) d – See #5 answer explanation.

12) e – The nervous system can be divided anatomically into the central and peripheral nervous systems. Functionally, the peripheral nervous system can be subdivided into the somatic and autonomic nervous systems. The somatic system has one neuron outside the CNS which participates in efferent nerve transmission. This neuron has its cell body located within the CNS and extends its axon to the effector organ it innervates. By contrast, the autonomic system has two neurons which participate in efferent nerve transmission outside the CNS. The preganglionic neuron cell body is located in the CNS and sends its axon periph-

erally to synapse with a postganglionic neuron within an autonomic ganglion. The postganglionic neuron axon then travels to the effector organ being innervated. The autonomic nervous system innervates visceral structures to provide for the "autonomic" functions of the body. The sympathetic nervous system is a subdivision of the autonomic nervous system that is responsible for the "fight or flight" response.

13) b – See #4 answer explanation. Bipolar neurons are found in sensory ganglia associated with certain cranial nerves that transmit special sensory information, such as sound and equilibrium. Two processes extend from a bipolar neuron. The peripheral process travels to a special sensory receptor. The central process courses to the CNS. When the sensory receptor is activated, a signal is transmitted to the CNS. Neurons with cell bodies located in automatic efferent ganglia are multipolar; one axon and numerous dendrites extend from each cell body.

14) a – See #3 and #6 answer explanations.

15) e – Motor pathways travel from the brain to the skeletal muscle. These pathways are therefore said to be descending. Because they are carrying nerve transmission away from the brain, they are also said to be efferent. By contrast, sensory pathways travel from sensory receptors to the brain. These pathways are therefore ascending. Because they are carrying nerve transmission to the brain, they are also afferent. Sensory pathways are **a**scending and **a**fferent.

16) a (or e!) – See #5 answer explanation.

17) e – The peripheral nervous system may be divided anatomically into the cranial and spinal nerve systems. It may be divided functionally into the somatic and autonomic systems. The somatic nervous system supplies somatic structures. These are structures which function to provide the structure of the body. Examples include bones, skeletal muscles, fascia, cartilage, tendons, and ligaments. The somatic system has only one neuron which participates in efferent signal transmission

outside the CNS (as opposed to the autonomic system, which has two). Because of this, there is no need for ganglia in which to house the second neuron. There are therefore no somatic efferent ganglia.

18) e – A nerve fiber is formed by a neuron axon surrounded by a series of Schwann cells, one following another along the length of the axon. Some Schwann cells produce a lipid compound called myelin, and the nerve fiber is said to be myelinated. Some Schwann cells do not produce myelin and their fibers are therefore unmyelinated. Myelin speeds nerve conduction by allowing the action potential to skip from one node of Ranvier to the next. Any particular nerve may contain both myelinated and unmyelinated nerve fibers.

19) a – See #3 answer explanation.

20) b – A dorsal root ganglion is *the* sensory ganglion for the particular spinal nerve it is associated with. Serving as the lone sensory ganglion for the nerve, it houses afferent cell bodies of both the somatic and visceral (autonomic) systems. Because these cell bodies are pseudounipolar, no synapses occur in dorsal root (or other sensory) ganglia.

"In theory, there is no difference between theory and practice. But in practice, there is."

– Yogi Berra

CLINICAL CORRELATION

Most people of the modern world have experienced an injection of local anesthetic to render an otherwise painful medical or dental procedure essentially painless. Such procedures might include surgical closure of a laceration, removal of a wart or mole, or filling of a dental cavity. How does the local anesthetic work to block the pain?

For thousands of years, natives of the Andes Mountains chewed leaves of the cocoa plant to increase energy and obtain a sense of fulfillment. The chemical source of these effects, cocaine, was advanced to modern medicine in 1884 as the first local anesthetic. It was used as a topical anesthetic for the eye. Later, it was learned that injection of cocaine into tissue could block conduction of pain impulses. Cocaine had several side effects which limited use as a local anesthetic. It produced a relatively weak blockade of pain when injected. It also carried significant abuse potential.

The first synthetic local anesthetic, procaine, was introduced in 1905. Although a significant improvement over cocaine, procaine was not the quintessential local anesthetic. It was relatively slow to work, did not last particularly long, and was ineffective topically.

In 1943, the second synthetic local anesthetic, lidocaine, was introduced. Lidocaine was effective topically. It had rapid onset and lasted almost twice as long as procaine. It also produced a more complete block of pain. It was not long before lidocaine was commonly found in medicine cabinets of hospitals and doctor's offices around the world.

Other local anesthetics continued to be developed. Each drug had certain qualities and characteristics which made it advantageous in certain circumstances. Nevertheless, because of its relatively inexpensive cost to manufacture, favorable properties, and broad spectrum of uses, lidocaine remains one of the most commonly used local anesthetics today.

Chemically, the molecule of each of the local anesthetics consists of a hydrophobic and hydrophilic section. These sections are connected by either an ester or amide bond. Depending on the structure of this bond, local anesthetics are classified as esters or amides. Cocaine and procaine are both ester local anesthetics. Lidocaine is an amide local anesthetic. Below is a list of currently available local anesthetics.

Esters	Amides	
Cocaine	Lidocaine	Etidocaine
Procaine	Mepivacaine	Prilocaine
Chloroprocaine	Bupivacaine	Ropivacaine
Tetracaine		

All local anesthetics have a "caine" in their generic name. The word *ami̲de* has one "i" in it. The names of all of the amide local anesthetics have one "i" which is located before the "caine" component of their name. None of the esters have an "i" prior to the "caine."

The names listed in the table are generic names of the local anesthetics. These are the names of the actual chemical compounds which form the drug. These and other medications are also known by additional commercial or trademark names. As if the practice of medicine is not complicated enough, several names for the same medication must be remembered! The trademark names are determined by the pharmaceutical company which develops, manufactures, and/or distributes the medication. For example, xylocaine is a commercial preparation of lidocaine. Carbocaine is a commercial preparation of mepivacaine. Nesacaine is a trademark name for chloroprocaine. Bupivacaine is marketed as both marcaine and sensorcaine by different companies.

Novocaine is a well-known local anesthetic which is actually a commercial preparation of procaine. Because procaine is the oldest of the commonly used local anesthetics, generations of people are familiar with it. It is not unusual to hear individuals mistakenly call any of the local anesthetics novocaine, even though novocaine is no longer used with any great frequency.

Each local anesthetic has a specific niche for which it is used. Some work topically. Some have rapid onset while others may last longer. Some are effective for epidural and/or spinal anesthesia. Some have less toxicity. Finally, some are simply less expensive. The common trait among them is temporary blockage of nerve signal conduction without damage to the nerve.

Local anesthetics bind sodium channels of nerve cell membranes and prevent the influx of sodium during a stimulating signal. Because a meaningful amount of sodium is not allowed to enter the neuron, threshold is not reached and an action potential is not created. The nerve signal is not propagated and the information being carried is not communicated. Local anesthetics do nothing to change the resting transmembrane potential or the threshold potential. They simply impede the intracellular flow of sodium and their accompanying positive charges, so that threshold is never reached.

Local anesthetics bind sodium channels in the inactivated closed state. This is the state the channels are in between nerve signals. Once bound, these channels remain in the closed state until the drugs diffuse from the site. During this period, if enough sodium channels are bound with anesthetic, an action potential cannot be created and the nerve fiber cannot conduct a signal. This includes signals conveying pain sensation.

The amount of time it takes for the drug to bind to, and diffuse from, the sodium channel depends on the amount of available drug (dose), characteristics of each specific drug, and characteristics of the patient. The time it takes to bind to the channel correlates with onset of action. This is how quickly the medicine works. The time it takes for the anesthetic to diffuse from the channel correlates with the duration of action. Relevant drug characteristics include properties such as pKa, lipid solubility, and protein binding. The physical condition of the patient is also important. Fluid and electrolyte levels, nutritional status, acid-base balance, and hemodynamic function can all potentially affect local anesthetic function and duration. When enough sodium channels become free of the drug so that an action potential can be created, the nerve fiber resumes signal communication. The medicine thereby "wears off."

Myelinated nerve fibers are more susceptible to local anesthetic blockade than nonmyelinated fibers. The presence of myelin speeds nerve conduction by allowing the action potential to jump down a nerve fiber, skipping from one Node of Ranvier to the next. The functioning sodium channels are only located at these nodes and the influx of positive charges occurs only at these sites. The same grouping of channels which speeds nerve signal conduction also causes myelinated fibers to be more susceptible to local anesthetic blockade. Phrased differently, not as much drug is needed to block a myelinated fiber because the sodium channels are located in isolated groupings. It is more likely that the same amount of local anesthetic will bind enough sodium channels to prevent the generation of an action potential in a myelinated fiber as compared to a nonmyelinated fiber. From a clinical standpoint, the susceptibility of myelinated fibers to blockade is of little significance. Local anesthetics are used in tissue containing both myelinated and nonmyelinated nerve fibers. Depending on the desired effect, the same dose will be used without regard to the myelination of nerve fibers.

Obviously, pain is not the only information nerves carry. Nerves transmit signals conveying other sensory modalities such as temperature and touch. Skeletal muscles contract in response to information received from motor nerves. Information concerning proprioception maintains balance and coordination. Autonomic nerves carry information related to the sympathetic and parasympathetic nervous systems. All of this nerve transmission can be blocked by local anesthetics.

There are varying susceptibilities to local anesthetic blockade among the different types of information carried by nerves. These variances are not caused by the information being transmitted, but rather, by the characteristics of the nerves which transmit the information. In addition to the presence or absence of myelin, the size of the nerve fiber also contributes to blockade susceptibility. Small diameter nerve fibers are more easily blocked. Large diameter nerve fibers, such as those present in motor nerves, are more difficult to block. For these reasons, temperature is the easiest modality to block. Next is touch. That is followed by pain. Finally, motor function is the most difficult entity to block.

This spectrum of susceptibility creates a predictable progression of blockade following the use of local anesthetic. This pro-

gression can be monitored to estimate the adequacy of anesthetic-induced pain relief prior to the onset of a painful stimulus. For example, consider a female patient who must have a cesarean section (c-section) for childbirth and desires a spinal anesthetic.

A spinal needle is placed in the lower back and local anesthetic is injected into the subarachnoid space, the fluid-filled space immediately surrounding the spinal cord. After removal of the needle, steps are taken to ensure that the spinal is working prior to surgical incision. Change in temperature sensation is one of the first indicators of a successful anesthetic block, as temperature fibers are easily blocked. A piece of metal may feel cold when touched to the patient's upper arm but neutral when contacting the patient's lower abdomen. Blockade of touch sensation is the next indicator of a functioning anesthetic. The edge of a piece of wood or plastic may feel sharp when scratched against the skin of the arm. Although she may feel contact of the object with the skin of the lower abdomen, it does not feel sharp. If these two sensory modalities are blocked, the spinal will likely be effective and preparation for the c-section continues. If not, considerations are made to give the spinal more time to work, repeat the spinal, or consider other anesthetic options such as an epidural or general anesthetic. If temperature and touch are indeed effectively blocked, the patient is prepped and draped for surgery while the spinal continues to intensify. The next sensory modality to be blocked is pain. To ensure a functioning spinal, the surgeon checks for pain blockade by pinching the skin prior to incision. If the patient experiences no discomfort, the surgical procedure is started.

Motor function is the most resistant entity to local anesthetic blockade. Despite this, a flaccid paralysis of the affected extremity often follows a regional anesthetic. Such regional anesthetics include spinals, epidurals, and nerve blocks. This motor blockade occurs because the administered dose of local anesthetic is often more than what is needed to block only the sensory fibers of a particular patient. Enough medicine must be given to prevent the experience of pain, regardless of the variable characteristics of the patient. In other words, it is preferable to give a little too much than not enough. Occasionally, there is preservation of motor function after a regional anesthetic, despite a complete sensory block. When this occurs, patients may become anxious. They can move an extremity and become concerned that the regional anesthetic is not working. In spite of verbal reassurances, it is not unusual that a surgical incision is required to convince the patient that he or she will indeed be comfortable during the procedure.

SUMMARY OF CHAPTER BOXES

1) Intracellular K^+ = Extracellular Na^+ = approx. 140 mEq/L. The 2 cations "flip-flop":
REMEMBER THE 4s (**4** Values to remember)
K^+ = intracellular high (1**4**0), extracellular low (**4**)
Na^+ = extracellular high (1**4**0), intracellular low (1**4**)

2) **Membrane potential** = the difference in charge across a cell membrane. When present, the membrane is **polarized**. There is a *potential* for charged ions to enter or exit the cell, causing a *depolarization* or equalization of charge.

3) A resting neuron with a resting membrane potential of -70 mV is "**polarized.**" There is a difference in charge from inside to outside the membrane. The intracellular space is charged 70 mv less than the extracellular space. As positive-charged Na^+ ions enter the cell, the membrane potential becomes less negative, approaching zero. The neuron is *depolarizing*.

4) **Graph: A** = Stimulating impulses cause an influx of Na^+, which causes the resting membrane potential to progressively become less negative. Threshold of -45 mV is not reached and the membrane repolarizes to the resting potential of -70 mV. **An action potential is not created**.

   B = Same scenario except threshold (-45 mV) is reached… Na^+ channels open, causing rapid influx of Na^+ (positive charges) and complete depolarization. **An action potential is created.**

5) **Action potential = intracellular wave** of positive charges (depolarization) traveling through an intracellular sea of negative charges.

6) Sensory pathways are **a**scending pathways which are **a**fferent.

7) **Soma = body**. *Soma*tic structures form the body wall, including head and extremities. They function to provide structure. Visceral structures have specialized functions to maintain a stable internal environment. They do not function to provide structure. Just as there is only *one* **body wall** in an individual, the **somatic system has only** *one* **neuron** outside the CNS that participates in efferent nerve signal transmission.

8) Just as the **autonomic nervous system** (visceral structures) **is subdivided into** *two* **systems** (sympathetic and parasympathetic), it **possesses** *two* **neurons** outside the CNS which participate in efferent nerve signal transmission.

9) **Peripheral Neuron Structure: Multipolar** = Efferent, **Pseudounipolar** = Afferent, **Bipolar** = Afferent (certain special sensory cranial nerves).

10) **Ganglion = location of cell bodies outside CNS.** Autonomic efferent ganglia are the only ganglia that contain synapses.

11) **CLINICAL CORRELATION:** All am**i**de local anesthetics have an "**i**" in their name prior to the "caine." Example: L**i**docaine. The only "i" in the names of esters is located in the "ca**i**ne." Example: Coca**i**ne

END OF CHAPTER TEST

Time for Exam = 55 minutes.

For questions 1-5, fill in the blank. Each blank may require more than one word.

1) In order to pass a signal on to the next neuron, the neurotransmitter must diffuse across the _____ to reach the dendrite of the neuron.

2) The synapse between a neuron axon and a voluntary (skeletal) muscle fiber is known as a _____.

3) Within the autonomic nervous system, the postganglionic neuron has its soma located within _____.

4) Functionally, the _____ nervous system is responsible for conscious movement.

5) The _____ is the membrane potential at which a neuron depolarizes and an action potential is created.

For questions 6-37, choose the single best answer.

_____6) Neurotransmitters enter the presynaptic neuron by way of
    a. phagocytosis
    b. pinocytosis
    c. active transport
    d. simple diffusion
    e. none of the above

_____7) A full depolarization of a neuron is the equivalent of
    a. an action potential
    b. hyperpolarization
    c. membrane potential
    d. threshold potential
    e. none of the above

_____8) What is the extension of a neuron through which information travels to the next neuron or effector organ?
    a. synapse
    b. soma
    c. dendrite
    d. axon
    e. none of the above

_____9) Which structure is supplied by the somatic nervous system?
    a. knee cartilage
    b. fibrous sheath of the palm
    c. both a and b
    d. thyroid gland
    e. none of the above

_____10) Sensory pathways are:
    a. descending
    b. efferent
    c. both a and b
    d. afferent
    e. none of the above

_____11) What is the basic component of the nervous system?
    a. axon
    b. nerve fiber
    c. nerve
    d. neuron
    e. none of the above

_____12) Which of the following conditions or processes do not directly contribute to the generation of a neuron's resting membrane potential?
   a. diffusion of ions
   b. active transport of ions
   c. pinocytosis
   d. preexisting negative charge of organic molecules
   e. none of the above

_____13) What does the phrase "all or none" refer to?
   a. The neuron either completely depolarizes or it does not depolarize at all.
   b. If an action potential is created, a signal will be sent to the next neuron. If an action potential is not created, no signal will be sent.
   c. Na^+ membrane channels either completely open or they do not open at all.
   d. Once an action potential reaches the distal tip of the axon, either all of the available neurotransmitter is released into the synaptic cleft or none of it is.
   e. None of the above

_____14) True statements about somatic efferent ganglia include which of the following?
   a. They do not exist.
   b. They are more numerous than peripheral autonomic ganglia.
   c. They contain somatic neuron cell bodies only.
   d. They contain both somatic and autonomic cell bodies.
   e. None of the above

_____15) A particular neuron has a resting membrane potential of -93 mV and a threshold of -50 mV. It received neurotransmission from both stimulating neurons and inhibiting neurons at the same time. The stimulating signals cause a cumulative depolarization of 52 mV from the resting membrane potential. The inhibitory signals cause a cumulative hyperpolarization of 13 mV from the resting membrane potential. What will happen?
   a. The signal will not be transmitted because threshold is not reached and an action potential is not created.
   b. An action potential is created and a signal is transmitted.
   c. The neuron would become hyperpolarized and more resistant to stimulation.
   d. A less intense signal would be transmitted to the next neuron.
   e. None of the above

_____16) The threshold potential of a neuron is
   a. the membrane potential at which an action potential is created
   b. the membrane potential at which a full polarization occurs
   c. both a and b
   d. the resting membrane potential of a neuron
   e. none of the above

_____17) Which of the following is true concerning an unmyelinated nerve fiber?
   a. It is never located in the same nerve as a myelinated fiber.
   b. It is not associated with a Schwann cell.
   c. Its conduction time is longer as compared to myelinated fibers.
   d. It contains nodes of Ranvier.
   e. None of the above

_____18) The peripheral nervous system can functionally be divided into
   a. sympathetic and spinal systems
   b. autonomic and somatic systems
   c. cranial and spinal systems
   d. somatic and parasympathetic systems
   e. none of the above

_____19) Synapses between two neurons occur in which of the following structures?
   a. sciatic nerve
   b. stellate ganglion
   c. facial nerve
   d. all of the above
   e. none of the above

_____20) What serves as the cell body or torso of a neuron?
   a. nucleus
   b. dendrite
   c. soma
   d. Schwann cell
   e. none of the above

_____21) An action potential is the equivalent of a
   a. hyperpolarization
   b. depolarization
   c. polarization
   d. membrane potential
   e. none of the above

_____22) Peripheral motor neurons could be said to be
   a. multipolar
   b. descending
   c. both a and b
   d. afferent
   e. none of the above

_____23) Where are neuron cell bodies located?
   a. brain
   b. peripheral ganglia
   c. both a and b
   d. peripheral nerve
   e. none of the above

_____24) Movement of which ion across the cell membrane is primarily responsible for generation of an action potential?
   a. Na^+
   b. K^+
   c. Cl^-
   d. Ca^{++}
   e. None of the above

_____25) An action potential may best be described as
   a. a polarization
   b. a hyperpolarization
   c. a wave of positive charges traveling through a sea of negative charges
   d. a wave of negative charges traveling through a sea of positive charges
   e. none of the above

_____26) Which of the following structures make up a nerve fiber?
   a. dendrite
   b. Schwann cell
   c. both a and b
   d. soma
   e. none of the above

_____27) The peripheral nervous system may be anatomically divided into
   a. cranial and somatic systems
   b. somatic and autonomic systems
   c. cranial and spinal systems
   d. sympathetic and parasympathetic systems
   e. none of the above

_____28) Chemicals that function as neurotransmitters include all of the following except
   a. gamma-aminobutyric acid
   b. glycine
   c. guanine
   d. acetylcholine
   e. both a and c

_____29) True statements about the somatic nervous system include which of the following?
   a. It relays information responsible for the "fight or flight" response.
   b. It is an anatomic division of the human nervous system.
   c. Two neurons outside the CNS participate in efferent nerve transmission.
   d. It provides the majority of innervation of the visceral organs of the body.
   e. None of the above

_____30) The resting membrane potential
  a. is caused by an influx of sodium
     (Na^+) ions
  b. is achieved at threshold
  c. is created by passive diffusion of
     Na^+ and K^+ across the neuron cell
     membrane
  d. is due to an intracellular deficit of
     positive charges compared to the
     extracellular space.
  e. none of the above

_____31) Which statements about a peripheral mul-
     tipolar neuron are true?
  a. It could be a sympathetic efferent
     neuron.
  b. It could be a somatic efferent neuron.
  c. It could be a parasympathetic
     efferent neuron.
  d. All of the above
  e. None of the above

_____32) A specific neuron has a resting membrane
     potential of -85 mV and a threshold of
     -60 mV. It received neurotransmission from
     both stimulating neurons and inhibitory
     neurons at the same time. The stimulating
     signals cause a cumulative depolarization of
     35 mV from the resting membrane poten-
     tial. The inhibitory signals cause a cumula-
     tive hyperpolarization of -15 mV from the
     resting membrane potential. What will
     happen?
  a. The signal will not be transmitted as
     threshold is not reached and an
     action potential is not created.
  b. If the neuron received more neuro-
     transmission at this time, it could
     not propagate a signal because it is
     in a refractory period.
  c. The neuron would become hyperpo-
     larized and more resistant to stimu-
     lation.
  d. An action potential would be created.
  e. Both a and b

_____33) True statements about the autonomic nerv-
     ous system include which of the following?
  a. It can be subdivided into the sympa-
     thetic and parasympathetic nervous
     systems.
  b. It includes peripheral ganglia.
  c. It has two neurons outside the CNS
     which participate in efferent nerve
     transmission.
  d. It provides the predominant
     innervation of the heart.
  e. All of the above

_____34) If two nerve fibers are the same type, size,
     and diameter,
  a. Schwann cells cannot be present
  b. they either both must be myelinated
     or they both must be unmyelinated
  c. the unmyelinated fiber will have a
     slower conduction rate
  d. the myelinated fiber will have a
     shorter conduction time
  e. both c and d

_____35) Which of the following is present in a
     peripheral nerve?
  a. synapses
  b. neuron cell bodies
  c. dendrites
  d. all the above
  e. none of the above

_____36) Concerning unmyelinated nerve fibers,
  a. conduction time is shorter than with
     myelinated nerve fibers
  b. there are no Schwann cells
  c. there are no nodes of Ranvier
  d. the action potential travels by
     saltatory conduction
  e. both b and c

_____37) What could be an effector organ for a
     somatic efferent neuron?
  a. a smooth muscle cell
  b. a cardiac muscle cell
  c. a skeletal muscle cell
  d. all the above
  e. none of the above

For questions 38-55, use the following directions:
   a.......**1,2,3 are correct**
   b.......**1,3 are correct**
   c.......**2,4 are correct**
   d.......**only 4 is correct**
   e.......**all are correct**

_____38) Which of the following is true concerning myelin?
   1. It is present in all nerve fibers.
   2. It is a lipid compound.
   3. It is produced by the axon cell membrane.
   4. It increases the speed of nerve conduction.

_____39) Which of the following could be a pseudounipolar neuron?
   1. visceral afferent neuron
   2. parasympathetic efferent neuron
   3. parasympathetic afferent neuron
   4. somatic efferent neuron

_____40) Which of the following are true about motor and sensory pathways?
   1. Efferent pathways are ascending.
   2. Motor pathways are ascending.
   3. Afferent pathways are descending.
   4. Sensory pathways are afferent.

_____41) Which of the following is true concerning the somatic nervous system?
   1. It innervates parts of the body responsible for provision of structure.
   2. It is a functional division of the peripheral nervous system.
   3. Only one neuron participates in efferent nerve signal transmission outside the CNS.
   4. It contains no efferent ganglia.

_____42) Which of the following may be found in a nerve?
   1. neuron soma
   2. myelin
   3. neuron dendrite
   4. node of Ranvier

_____43) In what structures do synapses between neurons occur?
   1. trigeminal nerve
   2. spinal cord
   3. sciatic nerve
   4. celiac ganglion

_____44) Which of the following must occur for an action potential to be created in a neuron?
   1. The refractory state must have ended.
   2. A membrane potential must be present.
   3. A depolarization must occur.
   4. The intracellular environment must become less positive.

_____45) Where may a neuron soma be found?
   1. sciatic nerve
   2. spinal cord
   3. facial nerve
   4. stellate ganglion

_____46) Which of the following are true concerning Schwann cells?
   1. Some, but not all, produce myelin.
   2. Their presence speeds nerve conduction.
   3. They are present in all nerve fibers.
   4. They are only found in somatic nerves.

_____47) Which of the following may be found in a particular peripheral nerve?
   1. neuron somas
   2. unmyelinated nerve fibers
   3. neuron dendrites
   4. myelinated nerve fibers

_____48) Which of the following is true concerning nodes of Ranvier?
   1. They require the presence of myelin.
   2. Their presence allows a depolarization to jump from one node to the next.
   3. They are the areas along an axon where Na^+ is allowed to move intracellularly.
   4. They increase nerve conduction times.

_____49) Which of the following are correct divisions of the human peripheral nervous system?
1. anatomically, into somatic and autonomic systems
2. anatomically, into neuron and Schwann systems
3. functionally, into cranial and spinal systems
4. autonomically, into sympathetic and parasympathetic systems

_____50) When an action potential reaches the terminal end of an axon,
1. the membrane potential approaches zero
2. Ca^{++} moves extracellularly
3. vesicles of neurotransmitter fuse with the outer membrane and release the neurotransmitter into the synaptic cleft
4. K^+ moves intracellularly

_____51) Which of the following may be found in a nerve fiber?
1. neuron axon
2. neuron dendrite
3. node of Ranvier
4. neuron soma

_____52) True statements about the resting membrane potential include which of the following?
1. It is increased by the pumping of anions across the nerve membrane.
2. It is the same for all neurons.
3. Two (2) sodium (Na^+) ions are pumped out of the neuron for every three (3) potassium (K^+) ions pumped into it.
4. Maintenance of the potential requires energy in the form of ATP.

_____53) True statements concerning nerve fibers include which of the following?
1. All have axons.
2. They are what forms nerves.
3. All have Schwann cells.
4. All have melanin.

_____54) Which pathway utilizes only one neuron which has structures located outside the CNS?
1. sympathetic afferent
2. somatic afferent
3. parasympathetic afferent
4. somatic efferent

_____55) What information may be transmitted by a pseudounipolar neuron?
1. stimulation causing a skeletal muscle to contract
2. stimulation causing the pancreas to secrete digestive enzymes
3. stimulation causing the bladder to empty
4. pain from an inflamed appendix

END OF CHAPTER TEST: Answers and Explanations

1) synaptic cleft

2) motor end plate

3) an autonomic efferent ganglion

4) somatic

5) threshold potential

6) b – After binding the postsynaptic membrane receptor, chemical neurotransmitter leaves the receptor and is often taken back and recycled by the presynaptic neuron for reuse. *Pinocytosis* is a process in which tiny invaginations are formed in a cell membrane. These invaginations eventually encircle an area of extracellular fluid which, in this case, contains chemical neurotransmitter or its chemical precursors. As these invaginations close, they break from the cell membrane to become intracellular vacuoles containing neurotransmitter.

7) a – A resting neuron is "polarized" in that the intracellular contents are charged approximately $^-70$ mv as compared to the extracellular environment. This is known as the resting membrane potential of the neuron. As the neuron is stimulated by other neurons, some Na^+ channels may open, allowing positively charged Na^+ ions to enter the intracellular space. These positive charges cause the membrane potential to become less negative. If the potential reaches a certain predetermined level, known as a threshold potential, more Na^+ channels open causing an influx of Na^+ and a full depolarization of the membrane potential. This full depolarization is known as an action potential. It travels across the neuron like an intracellular wave of positive charges traveling through an intracellular sea of negative charges. When it reaches the end of the axon, it causes an influx of Ca^{++} and release of neurotransmitter into the synaptic cleft. This neurotransmitter may stimulate or inhibit the next neuron in line. As an action potential travels across a neuron, the area behind it is repolarized. Prior to its repolarization to the membrane potential, the neuron is said to be in a refractory state. Should another stimulus arrive while the neuron is in the refractory state, it will not be transmitted.

8) d – The neuron is the basic component of the nervous system. It is composed of a soma, dendrites, and an axon. The soma is the cell body and houses the nucleus. Dendrites are extensions from the cell body and receive information from other neurons. The axon is an extension of the cell body that sends information to other neurons.

9) c – The human nervous system may be divided into the central and peripheral nervous systems. The peripheral system may be subdivided anatomically into the cranial and spinal nerve systems. It may also be subdivided functionally into the somatic and autonomic systems. The somatic nervous system supplies somatic structures. These are structures that function to provide structure to the body. Examples include bones, skeletal muscles, fascia, cartilage, tendons, and ligaments. The autonomic nervous system supplies autonomic structures. These are specialized structures that function to provide a stable internal environment. These include the visceral organs, blood vessels, sweat glands, hair follicles, salivary glands, lymphatic vessels, etc.

10) d – Sensory pathways travel from a sensory receptor to the brain. They are therefore said to be ascending pathways. Because they are carrying nerve transmission to the brain, they are also afferent. Sensory pathways are **a**scending and **a**fferent.

11) d – See #8 answer explanation.

12) c – The resting membrane potential of a neuron is created by negative-charged intracellular organic molecules, selective membrane permeability to certain ions, and active transport of positive-charged cations across the nerve membrane. Selective membrane permeability allows diffusion of certain ions across the membrane. No additional energy is required because the ions are flowing down their concentration gradients.

The Na^+-K^+ membrane pump, by contrast, requires the utilization of ATP to actively pump the two cations against their respective concentration gradients. Three (3) sodium ions are pumped out of the neuron for every two (2) potassium ions pumped into it. A net deficit of intracellular positive charges is created, and the intracellular space becomes more negative compared to the extracellular space. Pinocytosis is a process employed by the presynaptic neuron that returns a chemical neurotransmitter to be recycled. With pinocytosis, tiny invaginations are formed in a cell membrane. These invaginations eventually encircle an area of extracellular fluid which, in this case, contains chemical neurotransmitter or its chemical precursors. As these invaginations close, they break from the cell membrane to become intracellular vacuoles containing neurotransmitter.

13) b – When a neuron reaches threshold, it fully depolarizes and an action potential is created. "All or none" refers to the fact that, once created, an action potential will be propagated along to the entire length of the neuron to transmit a signal to the next neuron. If threshold is not reached, no signal will be transmitted. The nerve may partially depolarize due to stimulation from other neurons. If threshold is not reached, the neuron will simply repolarize by opening of certain ion membrane channels and the function of Na^+-K^+ membrane pumps. No signal will thus be transmitted.

14) a – Nerve cell bodies or somas may be found in three places in the body: the brain, the spinal cord, and peripheral ganglia. The somatic nervous system has only one neuron that participates in efferent nerve transmission outside the CNS. The cell body of this neuron is located in the brain or spinal cord, and its axon extends outward to supply a somatic structure, such as a voluntary muscle fiber. In the somatic system, there are no ganglia because there is no second neuron to synapse with. By contrast, the autonomic system has two neurons that participate in efferent signal transmission outside the CNS. This necessitates the presence of ganglia, which house the second neuron cell body. The synapse between the first (preganglionic) and second (postganglionic) autonomic neurons occurs in these

autonomic ganglia. Remember, there are no somatic efferent ganglia.

15) a – -93 + 52 – 13 = -54. Threshold is -50 mV and is therefore not reached. Neurons participate in signal transmission in an "all or none" fashion. They either fully depolarize and transmit a signal, or they do not transmit a signal at all.

16) a – See #7 answer explanation. Answer **b** is incorrect because it says a full *polarization*, which implies the presence of a resting membrane potential. It would be correct if it said *depolarization*.

17) c – A nerve fiber is formed by a neuron axon and a series of Schwann cells, one following another down the length of the axon. Some Schwann cells produce a lipid compound called myelin, and the nerve fiber is said to be myelinated. Some Schwann cells do not produce myelin, and their fibers are therefore unmyelinated. Myelin speeds nerve conduction by allowing the action potential to skip from one node of Ranvier to the next. Any particular nerve may contain both myelinated and unmyelinated nerve fibers.

18) b – There are several ways to subdivide the peripheral nervous system. This frequently serves as an area of confusion for the beginning student. Anatomically, the peripheral nervous system can be grossly divided into the cranial and spinal systems. This is because anatomically, there are 12 pairs of cranial nerves originating directly from the brain, and 31 pairs of spinal nerves originating from the spinal cord. Functionally, the peripheral nervous system may be divided into the somatic and autonomic systems. This classification is based on the general function of the tissue being innervated. Somatic structures are tissues that give the body structure. Examples include bones, skeletal muscles, tendons, ligaments, cartilage, and fascia. Alternatively, autonomic (or visceral) structures are highly individualized and specialized structures that involuntarily function to maintain a stable internal environment. This includes maintenance of such entities as fluid balance, electrolyte levels, and temperature. Autonomic structures are also responsible for adaptations

needed to address the ever-changing external environment. Examples of such structures include visceral organs, blood vessels, hair follicles, lymphatic vessels, and all glands. Finally, the autonomic system may be further subdivided into the sympathetic and parasympathetic systems.

19) b – A neuron cell body is also known as a soma. They are found in three locations: the brain, the spinal cord, and peripheral ganglia. Two of these, the brain and the spinal cord, comprise the central nervous system. This means that peripheral ganglia are the only location outside the CNS where a neuron cell body may be found. Because these three locations serve as the place where the cell bodies are located, they also serve as the only place where synapses between two neurons may occur. A peripheral nerve is simply a collection of nerve fibers. Each nerve fiber is composed of a neuron axon and its accompanying schwann cells.

20) c – See #8 answer explanation.

21) c – See #7 answer explanation.

22) c – Peripheral motor neurons are *multipolar*. This indicates that they have more than one appendage or extension from the cell body. A multipolar neuron has an axon and dendrites. This is in contrast to peripheral sensory nerves, which only have one axon and no dendrites. Thus, sensory neurons are said to be *pseudounipolar*. The pseudounipolar neuron cell body is located in the dorsal root ganglion of a spinal nerve or a sensory ganglion of a cranial nerve. The lone axon extends out and divides into two branches which travel to a sensory receptor and the CNS, respectively. With motor nerves, the signal is traveling away from the brain. The motor pathway is therefore said to be an *efferent* pathway. The nerve transmission is also said to be *descending*. The flow of transmission travels down from the brain toward smooth, cardiac, and skeletal muscle fibers.

23) c – See #19 answer explanation.

24) a – See #7 answer explanation.

25) c – See #7 answer explanation.

26) b – A nerve is formed solely from nerve fibers. A nerve fiber is composed of a neuron axon that is surrounded by a series of Schwann cells, one following another down the length of the axon. Some Schwann cells produce a chemical called myelin. Some do not. The fibers with myelin-producing Schwann cells are thus surrounded by a myelin sheath and are said to be myelinated. Between successive Schwann cells are interruptions of the myelin sheath at various distances down the length of the axon. These interruptions are known as nodes of Ranvier and they serve as the entry portals for Na^+ during a depolarization. The presence of myelin thus allows the action potential to "skip" down the axon from one node of Ranvier to the next. This is known as salutatory conduction and it speeds nerve conduction velocity. Again, a nerve is simply a collection of nerve fibers. The soma is the neuron cell body and is located in either the CNS or a peripheral ganglion. The neuron dendrites are located near the soma.

27) c – See #18 answer explanation.

28) c – Guanine is a purine base. The often-used abbreviation for gamma-aminobutyric acid is GABA.

29) e – The peripheral nervous system can be divided anatomically into the cranial and peripheral nervous systems. Functionally, it can be divided into the somatic and autonomic nervous systems. The somatic system has one neuron outside the CNS which participates in efferent nerve transmission. This neuron has its cell body located within the CNS and extends its axon to the effector organ that the neuron is innervating. By contrast, the autonomic system has two neurons, which participate in efferent nerve transmission outside the CNS. The preganglionic neuron cell body is located in the CNS and sends its axon peripherally to synapse with a postganglionic neuron within an autonomic ganglion. The postganglionic neuron axon then travels to the effector organ being innervated. The autonomic nervous system innervates visceral structures which provide the "autonomic" functions of the body.

The "fight or flight" response is the responsibility of a subdivision of the autonomic nervous system, the sympathetic nervous system.

30) d – The resting membrane potential of a neuron is created by negatively-charged intracellular organic molecules, selective membrane permeability to certain ions, and active transport of positive-charged cations across the nerve membrane. Selective membrane permeability allows diffusion of certain ions across the membrane. The membrane is relatively permeable to K^+, so this ion moves intracellular in an attempt to counteract the negative charge of intracellular organic molecules. Na^+ has limited membrane permeability, so it is mostly confined to the extracellular space. The Na^+-K^+ membrane pump requires the utilization of ATP to actively pump the two cations against their respective concentration gradients. Three (3) sodium ions are pumped out of the neuron for every two (2) potassium ions pumped into it. A net deficit of intracellular positive charges is created and the intracellular space becomes more negative compared to the extracellular space. The threshold potential is the membrane potential at which a full depolarization occurs and an action potential is created.

31) d – See #22 answer explanation.

32) a – The sum of all stimulating and all inhibiting signals is what determines if threshold is reached and a subsequent action potential is created. In this case, the stimulating signal causes a depolarization of 35 mV (+35) and the inhibitory signal creates a hyperpolarization of 15 mV (-15 mV). The resting membrane potential is -85 mV, so -85 + 35 - 15 = -65. Since threshold is -60 mV, threshold will not be reached. The large number of Na^+ channels does not open, the neuron does not depolarize, and an action potential is not created. The only time a neuron is in a refractory period is during and immediately after a depolarization, before the neuron has a chance to repolarize.

33) e – All are true. The two (2) neurons that participate in efferent signal transmission outside the CNS are known as the preganglionic and post-

ganglionic neurons. The preganglionic neuron's cell body is located within the CNS. Its axon travels peripherally to synapse with the postganglionic neuron within a peripheral autonomic ganglion. Since the autonomic nervous system is responsible for the "autonomic" functions of the body, it makes sense that the visceral organs would be richly innervated by autonomic fibers. This includes the heart.

34) e – Peripheral nerves are formed by the combination of numerous nerve fibers. A nerve fiber consists of a neuron axon and a Schwann cell which envelopes the axon. Some Schwann cells produce myelin and others do not. Those that produce myelin contribute a myelin sheath to their respective nerve fiber. Myelin speeds nerve conduction. The myelinated fibers have faster conduction rates and shorter conduction times than unmyelinated fibers.

35) e – Peripheral nerves are formed by nerve fibers. A nerve fiber is comprised of one neuron axon which is surrounded by a series of Schwann cells, one following another. Neuron cell bodies are found in one of three places: the brain, the spinal cord, and peripheral ganglia. Because of this, these three places are also the location of neuron dendrites and the location where synapses may occur.

36) c – All nerve fibers have Schwann cells. In myelinated fibers, the Schwann cells produce a myelin sheath. In unmyelinated fibers they do not. In myelinated fibers, the myelin sheath is interrupted at intervals along the axon by small unmyelinated areas between successive Schwann cells. These unmyelinated areas are known as nodes of Ranvier. As the action potential (wave of depolarization) travels down the axon, it "skips" from one node of Ranvier to the next. This is known as saltatory conduction and speeds nerve signal transmission. Since unmyelinated fibers have no myelin sheath, they have no nodes of Ranvier and the action potential cannot travel by saltatory conduction. This means that the rate of conduction is slowed and conduction time is longer than that of myelinated fibers.

37) c – An effector organ is the end-organ supplied by

a particular chain of neurons. The somatic nervous system supplies somatic structures. These are structures that form the body wall and provide structure. Such structures include muscles, bones, ligaments, and cartilage. Efferent pathways are those which are traveling in the direction away from the brain. Smooth or cardiac muscle cells which form the contracting mass of glands, organs, and the heart are innervated by the autonomic nervous system. They would therefore be supplied by visceral efferent neurons.

38) c – A nerve fiber is formed by a neuron axon and its accompanying series of Schwann cells, each of which wraps itself multiple times around the axon. Some Schwann cells produce a chemical called myelin. Some do not. The fibers with myelin are said to be myelinated fibers. The axons of these fibers are therefore said to be surrounded by a myelin sheath. Myelin is a lipid substance that is essentially impermeable to Na^+. There are interruptions in the myelin sheath between successive Schwann cells along the nerve fiber. These interruptions are known as nodes of Ranvier, and they serve as an entry point of Na^+. The presence of myelin allows the depolarization or action potential to skip from one node of Ranvier to the next. This speeds signal conduction and decreases nerve conduction times. In unmyelinated fibers, by contrast, the action potential must travel the entire length of the nerve fiber without the ability to bypass any areas of the membrane.

39) b – Peripheral afferent neurons are *pseudounipolar*. This includes afferent neurons of both the somatic and autonomic systems. Afferent signals are those which are traveling toward the brain. Somatic afferent pathways transmit sensory signals from somatic structures such as skin, muscles, and bones. Visceral afferent pathways transmit sensory signals from visceral structures such as internal organs, glands, and vessels. Visceral structures are innervated by the sympathetic and parasympathetic divisions of the autonomic nervous system. The word *pseudounipolar* denotes that a neuron only has one axon and no dendrites. The pseudounipolar neuron cell body is located in the dorsal root ganglion of a spinal nerve or

sensory ganglion of a cranial nerve. The lone axon travels out to divide into two branches. One branch travels peripherally to a sensory receptor. The other branch travels to the CNS. When the sensory receptor is activated, a sensory signal is transmitted to the central nervous system. Peripheral efferent neurons are *multipolar*. This includes efferent neurons of both the somatic and autonomic nervous systems. Multipolar neurons have more than one appendage or extension from the cell body. This includes one axon and numerous dendrites. Efferent signals are those which are traveling away from the brain. Somatic efferent pathways innervate striated muscle cells, causing contraction and/or relaxation. Visceral efferent pathways innervate smooth or cardiac muscle cells of visceral structures, which are supplied by the autonomic nervous system. The amount of internal organ contraction, glandular secretion, blood vessel constriction, and heart contractility are examples of actions directed by these visceral efferent pathways.

40) d – Motor pathways travel from the brain to the skeletal muscle. These pathways are therefore said to be descending. Because they are carrying nerve transmission away from the brain, they are also said to be efferent. By contrast, sensory pathways travel from sensory receptors to the brain. These pathways are therefore ascending. Because they are carrying nerve transmission to the brain, they are also afferent. Sensory pathways are **a**scending and **a**fferent.

41) e – The peripheral nervous system may be divided anatomically into the cranial and spinal nerve systems. It may be divided functionally into the somatic and autonomic systems. The somatic nervous system supplies somatic structures. These are structures that function to provide the structure of the body. Examples include bones, skeletal muscles, fascia, cartilage, tendons, and ligaments. The autonomic nervous system supplies autonomic structures. These are specialized structures that function to provide a stable internal environment. Autonomic structures include the visceral organs, blood vessels, sweat glands, hair follicles, salivary glands, lymphatic vessels, etc. Because only one neuron in the somatic

system participates in efferent signal transmission outside of the CNS, there are no somatic efferent ganglia.

42) c – See #26 answer explanation.

43) c – See #19 answer explanation.

44) a – In order for an action potential to occur, there must be a preexisting membrane potential present. This is a negative intracellular charge relative to the charge of the extracellular space. Upon stimulation from another neuron, some Na^+ channels open and Na^+ moves from the extracellular to intracellular space. This brings positive charges intracellular and makes the membrane potential less negative or less "polarized." Hence, there is a partial depolarization. If the membrane potential reaches a certain predetermined level, as it becomes less negative, more Na^+ channels open, more positive charges rush in, and the neuron completely depolarizes. This predetermined level of the membrane potential is called the threshold potential. The complete depolarization following threshold is known as an action potential. If threshold is not reached, an action potential will not be created. This action potential travels across the neuron and down its axon to potentially stimulate or inhibit the next neuron in line. Once the action potential travels past a certain area of the neuron, the resting membrane potential is reestablished by the opening of certain ion membrane channels and the action of the Na^+-K^+ pump. The period of time from the onset of the action potential to the reestablishment of the membrane potential is known as the refractory period. Should a stimulus from another neuron occur during the refractory period, it would not be transmitted.

45) c – See #19 answer explanation.

46) b – Although Schwann cells produce myelin, it is the presence of myelin and not Schwann cells, that speeds nerve signal conduction and decreases conduction times. After all, Schwann cells are present in all nerve fibers. Some simply do not produce myelin. This includes fibers of both the somatic and autonomic nervous systems.

47) c – Nerves are formed by nerve fibers. A nerve fiber is formed by a neuron axon and a series of Schwann cells, one following another. Some Schwann cells produce a lipid compound called myelin, and the nerve fiber is said to be myelinated. Some Schwann cells do not produce myelin, and their fibers are therefore unmyelinated. Myelin speeds nerve conduction by allowing the action potential to skip from one node of Ranvier to the next. Any particular nerve may contain both myelinated and unmyelinated nerve fibers. Neuron cell bodies or somas and their corresponding dendrites are confined to three locations: brain, spinal cord, and peripheral ganglia.

48) a – See #38 answer explanation.

49) d – See #18 answer explanation.

50) b – As an action potential arrives at the axon terminal, the membrane potential approaches zero. This is due to Na^+ (not K^+) entering the neuron. This triggers an influx of Ca^{++} and fusion of the neurotransmitter vesicles with the nerve membrane. The neurotransmitter is released and diffuses across the synaptic cleft to reach the dendrite of the next neuron or effector organ.

51) b – See #26 answer explanation.

52) d – See #30 answer explanation. The resting membrane potential varies among different types of neurons. It may be as great as -90 mV for large nerve fibers and as small as -40 mV for some CNS neurons. The active transport provided by the Na^+-K^+ pump requires energy, as both cations are pumped against their respective concentration gradients. This is provided by the conversion of ATP to ADP.

53) a – See #38 answer explanation.

54) e – Autonomic efferent pathways are the only peripheral nerve pathways to utilize two neurons with structures located outside the CNS. This includes efferent pathways of both the sympathetic and parasympathetic systems. Autonomic pathways are frequently referred to as *visceral* pathways because they innervate visceral structures. Such structures include

visceral organs, glands, and vessels. Efferent signals are those which are traveling away from the brain. Because they are the only pathways to employ two neurons located outside the CNS, visceral efferent pathways are also the only efferent pathways containing ganglia. Auto-nomic ganglia house the second or *postganglionic* neuron cell body. Somatic efferent pathways utilize only one neuron with structures extending outside the CNS. Somatic pathways innervate somatic structures, including skin, muscles, and bones. Both somatic and visceral *afferent* pathways utilize only one pseudounipolar neuron outside the CNS. Afferent signals are those which are traveling toward the brain. Somatic affer-

ent pathways transmit sensory signals from somatic structures. Visceral afferent pathways transmit sensory signals from visceral structures. The word *pseudounipolar* denotes that a neuron only has one axon and no dendrites. The pseudounipolar neuron cell body is located in the dorsal root ganglion of a spinal nerve or sensory ganglion of a cranial nerve. The lone axon travels out to divide into two branches. One branch travels peripherally to a sensory receptor. The other branch travels to the CNS. When the sensory receptor is activated, a sensory signal is transmitted to the central nervous system.

55) d – See #39 answer explanation.

ANATOMY OF THE
PERIPHERAL NERVOUS SYSTEM

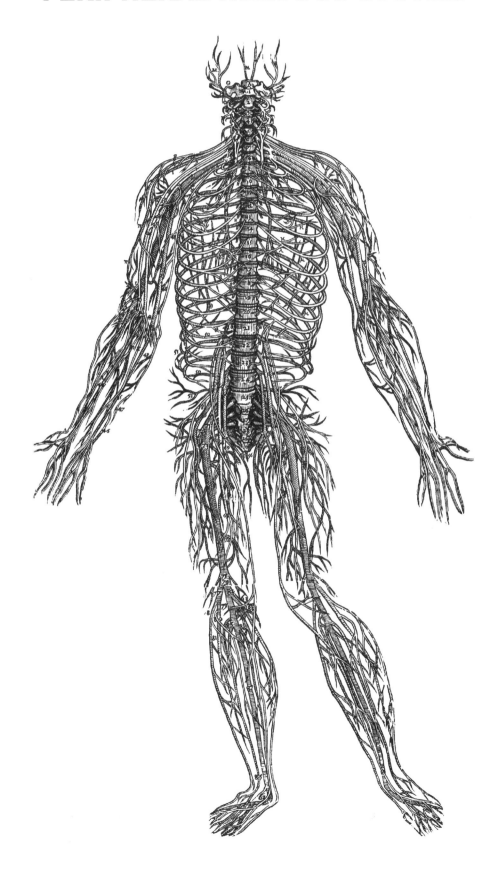

Image from previous page.
Reproduced from Versalius, A.: De Humani Corporis Fabrica (The Structure of the Human Body), Basel, 1543.

"The credit belongs…to the man who is actually in the arena, who strives valiantly;…who knows the great enthusiasms, and great devotions,…and spends himself in a worthy cause,…who at the best, knows the triumph of high achievement; and who, at the worst, if he fails, at least fails while daring greatly, so that his place shall never be with those cold and timid souls…who know neither victory nor defeat."

– Theodore Roosevelt

CHAPTER SIX

THE AUTONOMIC NERVOUS SYSTEM

The autonomic nervous system (ANS) is responsible for the maintenance of a stable internal environment in the face of an ever-changing external environment. This involves innervation of highly specialized and individualized organ systems and tissues. Each tissue has a specific function and these functions interact with one another in a very complex manner to provide the stable internal environment required for survival. The autonomic system provides involuntary innervation to visceral structures, including visceral organs, glands, and vessels. Visceral functions such as digestion, glandular secretion, heart rate, vascular tone, and sweating are modulated by the ANS.

The ANS consists of two subdivisions, the sympathetic and parasympathetic nervous systems. The effects of stimulation by each of the two systems tend to oppose one another. Sympathetic stimulation causes the heart rate to increase. Parasympathetic stimulation causes the heart rate to decrease.

As opposed to memorizing the specific sympathetic versus parasympathetic effect on each individual body system, learning the function of each system and WHY the system responds the way it does with sympathetic or parasympathetic stimulation creates a logical pattern that is easier to learn and remember. Each autonomic system can be associated with a basic theme or goal. The sympathetic systems functions in *fight or flight* situations; the parasympathetic system provides normal resting bodily functions. Every supplied tissue can be considered to respond in a manner that supports the overall goal of the ANS subdivision innervating it. As the effects of autonomic stimulation are described in this chapter, a reason for the reaction of each body system will be given. Many of these reasons are only theoretical; they segregate the effects of the two autonomic systems. The actual interplay between the sympathetic and parasympathetic systems and their effects on various body systems is much more dynamic and complex than what is presented here.

The interpretation of the reaction to sympathetic or parasympathetic stimulation by a particular organ system requires a familiarity with the organ system of question. This necessitates a brief explanation of the physiology involved with each of these systems. The only organ systems discussed are those with a well-established functional correlation with autonomic stimulation. Because of this, the reader will be presented with a rather fragmented compilation of human physiology.

EFFECTS OF SYMPATHETIC STIMULATION

The **sympathetic nervous system** provides the autonomic **"fight or flight"** response of the body. This is the response to sudden emotionally and physically stressful situations, some of which could be life-threatening. The purpose is to maximize the body's physical performance without requiring the individual to consciously think about it.

A **s**cared person activates the **s**ympathetic nervous system.

A hiker who is suddenly attacked by a large wild animal demonstrates the utility of the sympathetic nervous system. The hiker's sympathetic system is unconsciously activated and instantaneously becomes the dominant system in preparation for a potentially life-saving fight or flight response. The body is intuitively preparing for maximum physical performance without the hiker's having to think about it. It is an "automatic" response.

It is vital that the sympathetic response be both quick and intense. Not only will sympathetic nerve stimulation immediately induce a sympathetic response from certain organ and tissue systems, but the intensity of the response and overall sympathetic tone of the body will be greatly heightened by an increase in the systemic availability of sympathetic (adrenergic) neurotransmitters.

The adrenal gland is a secretory gland located just above the superior pole of each kidney. Sympathetic stimulation causes an increase in the secretion of epinephrine (adrenaline) and norepinephrine from the adrenal medulla, the inner aspect of the adrenal gland. The increased systemic availability of these two neurotransmitters increases heart rate, blood flow, and triggers and intensifies many sympathetic actions. In addition to adrenergic neurotransmitters from the adrenal medulla, sympathetic stimulation also causes secretion of steroid hormones from

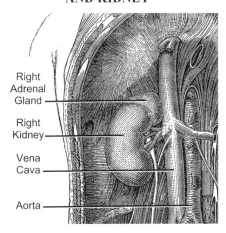

FIGURE 6.1
ADRENAL GLAND AND KIDNEY

Right Adrenal Gland

Right Kidney

Vena Cava

Aorta

the adrenal cortex, the outer aspect of the adrenal gland. Steroid hormones facilitate the body's stress response while promoting growth and healing.

> The *adren*al gland secretes *adren*ergic hormones. Adrenergic hormones include *adren*alin (epinephrine) and norepinephrine. These hormones form the *center* of the sympathetic response and are secreted from the *center* of the adrenal gland (adrenal medulla).
>
> The adrenal cortex is the outer portion of the adrenal gland. The adrenal *cort*ex secretes steroid hormones, including *cor*tisol.

Surviving emergency situations requires accurate thinking and optimal athletic performance. This necessitates a blood pressure high enough to provide the additional oxygen to the mind and body. Blood pressure regulation is an extremely complex mechanism involving numerous structures, organ systems, and reflexes. One mechanism, the **renin-angiotensin system,** directly raises blood pressure as a result of sympathetic stimulation. Renin is an enzyme secreted by the juxtaglomerular cells of the kidneys in response to hypotension (low blood pressure) or in this case, sympathetic stimulation. The juxtaglomerular cells are found on the inner surface of the afferent arterioles. These vessels supply blood to the glomeruli of the kidneys.

> The juxtaglomerular cells are just before the glomerulus.

In the systemic blood, renin converts angiotensinogen to angiotensin I. Angiotensin I then travels to the lungs where it is converted to angiotensin II by angiotensin converting enzyme (ACE). Angiotensin II is a very strong vasoconstrictor. The term *vasoconstriction* describes constriction or tightening of blood vessels. Vasoconstriction decreases the intravascular volume and hence, with all other variables remaining constant, increases the intravascular pressure. The blood pressure is thus increased.

> The renin-angiotensin system is an important mechanism for raising the blood pressure. The names of both renin and angiotensin provide clues which facilitate remembering their function. The kidneys have two different word combining forms which describe them. The first is **nephr-**. A **nephr**ologist is a physician who specializes in the treatment of kidney disorders. A **nephr**on is the basic structural unit of the kidney. The other word element describing the kidneys is **ren-**. **Ren**al is a word which pertains to the kidneys. The **ren**al arteries provide oxygenated blood to the kidneys whereas the **ren**al veins drain deoxygenated blood from them.
>
> **Ren**in is an enzyme secreted by the kidneys. Ren**in** increases blood pressure.
>
> **Angi-** is a combining form which means *vessel*. **Angi**ography is a process of obtaining radiologic images of blood vessels. **Angi**oplasty is reconstruction of a blood vessel. This is often done by flattening an arterial plaque against the wall of the artery by inflation of an intraluminal balloon.
>
> **Angi**otensin increases the blood pressure by "tensing" the blood vessels (it causes vasoconstriction).

With sympathetic stimulation, the brain, skeletal muscle, and heart become the three organ systems with the highest priority for distribution of oxygen and energy sources. During stressful periods of high sympathetic tone, blood vessels traveling to skeletal and cardiac muscles dilate to increase blood supply. By contrast, blood vessels to other areas of the body, especially the digestive tract, constrict in an effort to divert more blood and accompanying energy sources to areas where it is needed.

Because blood is shunted away from the digestive system, the organs must be able to endure less blood flow and hence, less oxygen and fuel. The digestive system must lower its energy demand. Gastrointestinal tone, secretory activity, and motility are all decreased as a result of sympathetic stimulation. This decreases the metabolic demand of digestive organs and permits the safe diversion blood to other areas of the body without suffering undue consequences. As will be discussed later, parasympathetic stimulation causes an increase in gastrointestinal tone, secretory activity, and motility.

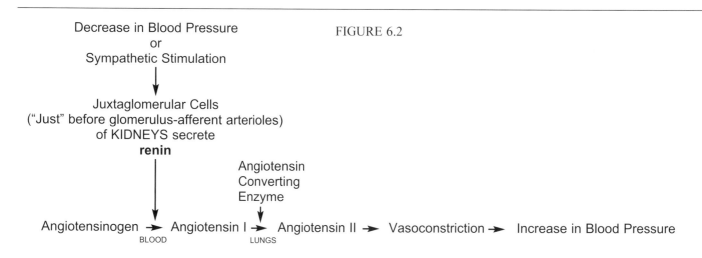

FIGURE 6.2

To further increase blood available to the brain and muscles, sympathetic stimulation causes contraction of the splenic capsule. The spleen is an abdominal organ which serves as a reservoir for blood cells. During normal resting states, the spleen acts as a storage container for extra blood which is not needed to support the relatively low basal metabolic rate. Splenic capsule contraction forces previously sequestered blood and its additional oxygen carrying capacity into the systemic circulation to be used by the harder-working muscles. There is no parasympathetic innervation of the splenic capsule.

FIGURE 6.3
TRANSVERSE SECTION OF SPLEEN
Sponge-like trabeculae form numerous venous structures

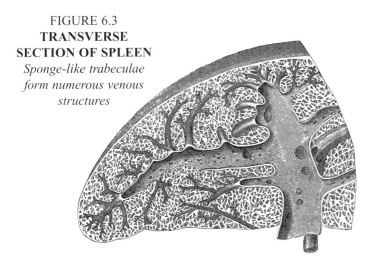

Because skeletal muscles are working harder, the heart must work harder to pump the needed blood. Sympathetic stimulation causes the conduction velocity of the heart's electrical activity, heart rate, and contractile force of each heartbeat to increase. Parasympathetic stimulation causes a decrease in conduction velocity and heart rate but has no effect on the contractile force of each heartbeat.

> The heart's electrical activity is measured by an electrocardiogram. Some wonder why "EKG" is the common abbreviation for an electrocardiogram. The abbreviation stems from the German word *elekrokardiogram*. The two abbreviations, EKG and ECG, are used interchangeably.

Sympathetic stimulation also causes the lungs to make adaptations. Not only is there a heightened need for oxygen, but the increased muscular activity produces an excessive amount of carbon dioxide that must be expelled. If the carbon dioxide levels are allowed to increase, the body becomes acidotic; acidosis diminishes cardiac function, skeletal muscle function, and vascular tone.

The trachea divides into a right and left main stem bronchus, each supplying one lung. These bronchi divide into progressively smaller bronchi until a sac-like alveolus is reached. It is at the alveolus that respiratory exchange occurs with the surrounding capillary beds. The walls of the bronchi are surrounded by smooth muscle. In a fashion similar to blood vessels, smooth muscle contraction and relaxation causes bronchial constriction and dilation, respectively. Sympathetic stimulation causes bronchial smooth muscle relaxation and hence, bronchial dilation. This increases airflow, which in turn increases oxygen provision and carbon

dioxide expulsion. Parasympathetic stimulation causes bronchial smooth muscle contraction.

In addition to physiologic changes that optimize physical performance, the sympathetic system is also responsible for metabolic changes that maximize fuel availability. A knowledge of basic metabolism is required for a true understanding of how and why these changes occur.

Adenosine triphosphate (ATP) is the basic substrate living cells utilize for energy. There are three primary dietary sources of energy that undergo metabolic processes to ultimately provide ATP. These three sources include carbohydrates, fats, and proteins. From their ingestion, these dietary sources go through three stages of catabolism to provide energy in the form of ATP.

> **3 dietary sources of energy go through 3 stages of catabolism**
> Catabolism is a process where complex compounds are broken down to simpler molecules for the production of energy. This is opposed to anabolism. Anabolism is a building process where simple molecules are transformed to more complex compounds which can be used in various cellular processes.
>
> Some athletes have been known to take anabolic steroids in an effort to "bulk up."
>
> All metabolic processes are either catabolic (break down, utilize) or anabolic (build up, create) in character.

The first stage of catabolism occurs with digestion. Here, all three dietary sources are broken down to simpler molecules which travel in the blood and are taken up by certain cells of the body. Carbohydrates (sugars) are broken down into glucose and other simple sugars. Lipids (fats) are broken down into fatty acids and glycerol. Proteins are broken down into amino acids.

In the second stage of catabolism, glucose, fatty acids, and amino acids go through individual metabolic routes and transformations to yield acetyl-CoA. Acetyl-CoA is the common precursor of all three dietary sources of energy to the citric acid (Krebs) cycle.

The third and final stage of catabolism is introduction of acetyl-CoA into the citric acid cycle and oxidative phosphorylation. The end products of this process are ATP, water, carbon dioxide, and ammonia.

Although all three dietary sources can be used as an energy substrate, each serves a different role in providing an adequate supply of energy for an ever-changing need. An ongoing basal energy requirement sustains life; during periods of stress, this requirement increases dramatically. Energy sources must be stored not only for these periods of stress, but also for periods of starvation.

Carbohydrates are composed of polysaccharides, which are multi-chain, complex sugars. During digestion, carbohydrates are broken down to **glucose** and other simple sugars. These sugars provide for the ongoing energy needs of the body. The brain has a very high metabolic requirement and is dependent on glucose as its sole energy source. In order to provide for this continual, yet fluctuating energy requirement, glucose must be readily available. This necessitates a storable and easily retrievable form of glucose.

Glycogen is the intracellular storage form of glucose. It is formed by the linkage of glucose molecules. The process of converting glucose to glycogen and glycogen back to glucose is very energy efficient. The mechanism provides for the basal energy requirement while maintaining ample stores for immediate, excessive energy needs which sporadically occur.

Because of the constant, high metabolic requirement of the brain, little glycogen is actually stored in brain cells; it is continually utilized for energy. This is in contrast to muscle cells. If muscles are in a resting state after a meal, a significant amount of intracellular glucose is not used immediately and is stored as glycogen. Resting muscle cells predominantly use fatty acids for energy. This utilization allows muscle cells to save the maximum amount of glycogen for sudden, tremendous energy requirements which may occur between meals. Glycogen can provide ATP quickly and efficiently. In addition, the preferential use of fatty acids as the energy source of resting muscle cells preserves total body glucose reserves for the brain, which is almost entirely dependent on glucose as its sole energy source.

Glycogen is also stored within the liver. Whereas, intracellular glycogen of the brain and muscle provides immediate energy substrate for each organ, glycogen storage within the liver acts predominantly as a reservoir for the rest of the body. **Glycogenolysis** is the process in which glycogen is broken down to glucose. As blood glucose levels fall, the liver releases glucose into the blood for the body to use. Glycogen stored within muscle cells is not allowed to reenter the circulation. It remains intracellular to be consumed by the muscle cell it originally entered. Glycogen stored within the brain is continually utilized. Because the brain is constantly using up its glycogen stores and skeletal muscle does not release glucose back to the circulation, the brain is very dependent on the liver as a reservoir for its predominant energy source, glucose. The process of glycogenolysis is increased by sympathetic stimulation. Parasympathetic stimulation has no effect on glycogenolysis.

Glycolysis is an anaerobic pathway that transforms glucose to pyruvate or lactate while producing ATP. The word *anaerobic* means *without oxygen*. In the presence of oxygen, most glucose is transformed to pyruvate. Pyruvate is subsequently converted to acetyl-CoA, which enters the citric acid (Krebs) cycle and oxidative phosphorylation resulting in significantly more ATP. Because glucose can also be converted to lactate, glycogen stores are a valuable source of energy during anaerobic periods of intense exercise. Instead of converting to acetyl-CoA and entering into the citric acid cycle and oxidative phosphorylation, glycogen can provide some ATP during anaerobic periods by undergoing glycogenolysis and the conversion of glucose to lactic acid.

Glycolysis can simply be thought of as the breakdown of glucose for energy. Specifically it involves:

glycogen → glucose ⟨ pyruvate → acetyl-CoA → citric acid (Krebs) cycle and oxidative phosphorylation / lactate → lactic acid

The suffix *-lysis* means *dissolution* or *breakdown*. Glycolysis can thus be considered the breakdown of glycogen (glucose) for energy.

The fight or flight responsibility of sympathetic stimulation increases glycolysis. This process increases the availability of energy substrate for the harder-working brain, heart, and skeletal muscles. Parasympathetic stimulation has no effect on glycolysis.

Fats (lipids) are broken down during digestion to fatty acids and glycerol. **Fatty acids** have two main functions in the body. First, they contribute to the formation of glycolipids and phospholipids. Both are used in the formation of cell membranes. The second function of fatty acids is to store energy. These energy storage molecules are also known as **triacylglycerols** or **triglycerides.** Triglycerides function well as storage molecules because of their hydrophobic state; they don't bind water. In addition, the molecules are also very non-polar as compared to carbohydrates and proteins. Because of these two properties, the molecules are relatively lighter and can be more tightly packed together. Triglycerides provide an efficient mechanism to store energy for a longer-term.

---

oil and water do not mix
Triglycerides are hydrophobic
(hydro = water; phobia = aversion)

Glycogen is hydrophilic; it binds more water, weighs more, and takes up more space. Because of the instant availability and efficiency of exchange between the metabolically active and storage form, the glucose/glycogen system serves as a better provider for the immediate, fluctuating requirement for energy. Triglycerides serve as a better provider of longer-term energy storage.

Lipolysis is a process involving the breakdown of triglycerides to fatty acids and their subsequent utilization as an energy source with the production of ATP. Lipolysis occurs normally during fasting. This provides energy for the body while preserving glycogen stores for the brain if needed. Lipolysis also occurs any time the energy demand exceeds energy supply. This includes periods of starvation, extreme exertion, and during certain disease states. As with glycolysis, sympathetic stimulation increases lipolysis in an effort to ensure enough energy substrate is available for the harder working body. Parasympathetic stimulation has no effect on lipolysis.

Lipolysis is the dissolution of lipids.

Proteins are broken down in the digestive process to 20 different amino acids. Under normal circumstances, these amino acids are then recombined and modified in anabolic pathways to form enzymes, hormones, and various cellular components. In times of glucose shortage, proteins can also serve as an energy source. **Gluconeogenesis** is a process during which certain amino acids function as building blocks in the formation of glucose. Glucose is therefore formed from non-carbohydrate sources. Gluconeogenesis is a valuable mechanism to provide glucose for the brain during periods of glucose shortage. Without dietary replenishment, there is approximately one day's worth of blood glucose and glycogen reserves in a normal person's body. Gluconeogenesis is an important source of glucose during periods of starvation or prolonged exertion, when normal glucose reserves are depleted. Gluconeogenesis occurs primarily in the liver, although a small amount occurs in the kidneys. As with glycolysis and lipolysis, sympathetic stimulation increases gluconeogenesis. This increases glucose availability during times of stress. Parasympathetic stimulation has no effect on gluconeogenesis.

All 3 metabolic pathways (glycolysis, lipolysis, and gluconeogenesis) increase fuel availability. They are therefore utilized in a sympathetic fight or flight response. All are increased with sympathetic stimulation and not affected by parasympathetic stimulation. The name of each pathway actually tells what the pathway is accomplishing. The suffix -*lysis* means dissolution. Glycolysis is the breakdown of glycogen to glucose and glucose to pyruvate. Lipolysis is the breakdown of lipid (fat) storage molecules, triglycerides, to fatty acids. Fatty acids are then used to eventually form acetyl-CoA. Gluconeogenesis is the creation of glucose from non-carbohydrate sources (amino acids from proteins). This glucose can then be converted to pyruvate and from pyruvate to acetyl-CoA. The acetyl-CoA (from all 3 pathways) is then available to enter the citric acid (Krebs) cycle and oxidative phosphorylation with the resultant generation of ATP. The word *gluconeogenesis* is especially helpful in describing what the pathway accomplishes. The combining form *gluco* refers to glucose. The combining form *ne(o)* means new (a neonate is a newborn, a neoplasm is a new growth, and a neocyte is a new cell). Finally, the word *genesis* means creation. Say this backwards and one has the creation of new glucose!

Insulin is a protein hormone secreted by the pancreas in response to elevated blood sugar. Its principal role is to determine which of the dietary sources of energy is used at any given time by different cell types of the body.

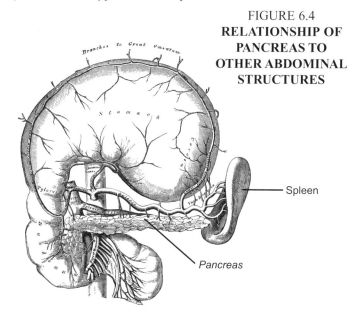

FIGURE 6.4
RELATIONSHIP OF PANCREAS TO OTHER ABDOMINAL STRUCTURES

Spleen

Pancreas

The pancreas has two broad, general functions: secretion of digestive enzymes into the duodenum of the small intestine and secretion of metabolic hormones into the blood. Histologically, there are two cell groupings which accomplish these two functions. The **acini** secrete digestive enzymes and thus have channels to the

duodenum. The **islets of Langerhans** have no such connections to the duodenum and must secrete their hormones straight into the blood. The islets are named for their histological appearance as tiny cell groupings or islands among the channel-bordering acini.

The islets of Langerhans are composed of several different cell types. **Alpha cells** secrete the hormone glucagon. **Beta cells** secrete insulin. **Delta cells** secrete somatostatin. There are also other, less plentiful cell types. More than 50% of all islet cells are beta cells.

After a meal, insulin secretion is increased instantaneously and almost exponentially as the blood glucose rises. Insulin binds a carrier protein on cell membranes and facilitates the intracellular passage of glucose. This mechanism of membrane transport is called **facilitated diffusion**. With most tissues, insulin must be present for glucose to move into the intracellular space. There are two notable exceptions: the brain and exercising muscle.

As mentioned earlier, the brain is totally reliant on glucose as its primary energy source. Because of this dependency, modifications of brain cell membranes allow glucose to pass without the requirement of insulin. The brain can continue its ever-present responsibilities, even in the absence of insulin.

Exercising muscle is also capable of transferring glucose to the intracellular space without insulin. Resting muscle requires insulin to transport glucose intracellularly. In the absence of insulin, resting muscle cells use fatty acids as the energy source of choice. This utilization maintains glycogen stores for potential future needs. Between meals, there is no glucose load to stimulate insulin release; thus, there is no mechanism to transport glucose into the resting muscle cell.

As blood glucose rises following a meal, insulin causes the intracellular movement of glucose into other tissues. This is especially important in the liver, where excess glucose is stored as glycogen. As the blood glucose falls, the insulin secretion falls and the liver releases glucose stores as needed for the rest of the body, especially the brain.

Excess glucose may also be stored as glycogen in resting muscle cells. There is no mechanism for glucose to cross the cell membrane and exit the muscle cell once it has entered. Glucose therefore cannot be released back to the circulation by muscle cells. It must be utilized by the muscle cell originally entered. If the muscle cell is engaged in activity, the glucose is immediately consumed; if the myocyte is dormant, the glucose is stored as glycogen.

Once the glycogen storage capacity of the liver and muscle is reached, additional glucose is converted to fatty acids. This takes place primarily in the liver, although the process also occurs in adipose or fat cells. Glucose is broken down to acetyl-CoA, the common precursor to the citric acid or Krebs cycle for all three dietary sources of energy. The acetyl-CoA is then transformed "backwards" into fatty acids. These fatty acids are used to form triglycerides by the liver. Most of the triglycerides are then released by the liver as lipoproteins. They travel in the blood to reach adipose cells and are broken down to fatty acids in order to cross the adipose cell membrane. Once in the adipose cell, the fatty acids are again transformed to triglycerides for long-term energy storage. It should be noted that insulin is required for this process. If insulin was not available, glucose could not be transported into liver and adipose cells for transformation into fatty acids.

In addition to its many other functions, the liver can metabolically be thought of as a "glucose factory." This factory makes and stores glucose for the rest of the body to use when needed.

First, it stores glucose as glycogen. Second, when the glycogen storage capacity is reached, the liver, along with adipose tissue, converts glucose to fatty acids. The fatty acids can subsequently be stored as triglycerides, providing long-term energy storage. Finally, during periods of glucose shortage, the liver, along with the kidney, can convert certain amino acids to glucose by the process of gluconeogenesis. This creates the brain's only energy substrate, glucose, during periods of shortage.

Insulin has a positive effect on protein production and protein sparing. The intracellular active transport of a great number of amino acids is facilitated by insulin. Once intracellular, the amino acids can then be modified to create the protein molecules that play a vital role in various structures and processes. Protein enzymes and hormones are created which may function in cellular functions of the host cell. Alternatively, these compounds may be released to the extracellular space for utilization by the body. Furthermore, insulin inhibits gluconeogenesis. This preserves proteins by preventing their breakdown to amino acids and subsequent conversion to glucose.

> Before going further, ask yourself "what effect should sympathetic stimulation have on insulin release and why?"

Sympathetic stimulation decreases insulin secretion. Insulin facilitates energy storage. In a sympathetic fight or flight state, energy availability is of the utmost importance. Storage matters not if people are unable to escape their dangerous situations.

If a recent carbohydrate meal has been consumed, glucose is present in abundant supply. Sympathetic inhibition of insulin secretion augments the energy sources available to the brain, heart, and exercising skeletal muscle. Less is available to the liver and adipose for storage. The brain and exercising muscle do not require insulin to transport glucose intracellularly; thus, they are unaffected by the acute lack of insulin. The optimal brain function and athletic performance required for a successful fight or flight response is still possible.

If a recent meal has not been consumed, the lack of insulin will facilitate glycolysis, lipolysis, and gluconeogenesis. All three pathways are functioning to provide energy substrate for the body. All three are also inhibited in the presence of insulin.

The body has truly developed an excellent system for efficiently utilizing the three dietary sources of energy in the presence of an ever-changing energy requirement. The presence of insulin is the switch which determines which dietary source is utilized. When insulin is present, carbohydrates are used as the preferential energy source. Any over-supply of glucose is stored in the liver as glycogen. The liver acts as a reservoir for later use by other tissues, including the brain. Glycogen is also stored in muscle cells. Once these two storage reservoirs are maximized, additional glucose is converted to fatty acids and stored as triglycerides. Fats are hydrophobic, so they do not bind water and hence weigh less. They are also non-polar, so more molecules can be tightly placed together. For these two reasons, lipids are a superior provider of long-term energy storage.

In the absence of insulin, lipids become the preferential energy source. This provides the slow "burn" of stored energy substrates. The use of fatty acids as the preferential energy source also preserves glycogen stores for the brain and muscle. Resting muscle utilizes fatty acids for energy. Exercising muscle utilizes any energy source available.

During periods of starvation or prolonged exertion, gluconeogenesis creates glucose from amino acids once glycogen stores are exhausted. This has a vital role in providing the energy substrate required by the brain, glucose.

Finally, it should be reiterated that during times of stress, sympathetic stimulation inhibits insulin release. In the absence of insulin, the catabolic or breakdown pathways are enhanced. Glycogenolysis, lipolysis, and gluconeogenesis become more active. These pathways increase blood glucose and maximize the availability of energy sources. Furthermore, the absence of insulin prevents the uptake of glucose by cells which are not vital in an emergency situation. The lack of glucose uptake by storage tissues amplifies the amount freely available to the brain and muscle. Finally, the lack of insulin has no effect on the utilization of glucose by the two tissues which need glucose the most in stressful situations: the brain and exercising skeletal muscle.

Maintaining its diametric relationship with sympathetic stimulation, parasympathetic stimulation increases insulin secretion. This will be described in greater detail in the discussion of parasympathetic effects.

In addition to increased heart and lung function, prioritization of blood flow, and increased energy substrate, there is another requirement for the body to sustain this heightened level of muscular performance, dissipation of heat. The increased metabolic rate raises the body temperature. Body temperature must be kept within a relatively narrow range or organ systems begin to fail. Sympathetic stimulation increases sweat gland secretion. Stimulation of sweat glands, if the individual is adequately hydrated, increases the amount of sweat produced. As sweat evaporates from the skin, it acts to cool the surface of the skin and thus dissipate heat.

Sympathetic innervation of piloerector muscles induces contraction. The word root *pilo* means hair and contraction of piloerector muscles causes the hair to stand *erect*. This effect has limited utility with humans, but plays a notable "fight or flight" role in the animal kingdom. An erect coat of hair or feathers creates the appearance of a larger, more fierce animal or bird. This may deter an attack from another creature and is utilized in the determination of feeding and courtship ranks.

> Scared people often describe their "hair standing up on the back of their neck." This is due to sympathetic stimulation.
>
> Another example is the hair sticking up on the back of an angry barking dog.

The eye also demonstrates autonomic effects. The pupillary aperture is the opening which determines how much light enters the eye. In dark environments, the pupil dilates. This allows more light to enter the aperture and improves vision in the dark. In bright environments, the pupil contracts and limits the amount of entering light. Sympathetic stimulation causes pupillary dilation or **mydriasis**. Theoretically, this ensures enough light is let into the eye to provide optimal vision in critical "fight of flight" situations. **Miosis** is contraction of the pupil and is caused by parasympathetic stimulation.

Accommodation is a mechanism in which alterations occur within the eye to enable structures at different distances to be seen clearly. In other words, accommodation is the ability to focus the eye. Positive accommodation involves contraction of the ciliary muscle to focus on objects which are near. Negative accommodation involves relaxation of the ciliary muscle; the focus is placed on objects located a greater distance away. Positive accommodation is due to parasympathetic innervation and is used for such activities as reading. Near vision is of little use in a "sympathetic" environment. Consequently, sympathetic stimulation has little influence on accommodation. For this reason, the process of accommodation is explained in more detail in the discussion of parasympathetic effects.

> A sympathetic-stimulated scared person has no time or chance to read.

Finally, the effects of sympathetic stimulation to the urinary bladder will be considered. The detrusor muscle is also known as the pubovesical muscle. The word *vesical* refers to the urinary bladder. The detrusor muscle is a smooth muscle running from the pubis to the bladder neck. Its contraction pulls the bladder in to facilitate emptying and hence urination. Sympathetic stimulation causes detrusor muscle relaxation.

The sphincter muscle of the urinary bladder is another smooth muscle. Its contraction tightens the sphincter around the bladder outlet. In contrast to the detrusor muscle, contraction of the sphincter muscle opposes bladder emptying and urination. Sympathetic stimulation causes contraction of the sphincter muscle of the bladder.

In summary, sympathetic stimulation to both bladder muscles inhibits or opposes urination. In true form, parasympathetic stimulation does just the opposite. Parasympathetic innervation causes contraction of the detrusor muscle and relaxation of the bladder trigone sphincter muscle. Both effects facilitate urination.

> Consider the example of our sympathetically stimulated hiker who is in a fight for life. There is no time to stop and urinate.

EFFECTS OF PARASYMPATHETIC STIMULATION

Many parasympathetic effects have already been mentioned in the discussion of the sympathetic nervous system. The common theme that binds parasympathetic effects is a calm environment with performance of normal bodily functions that maintain a homogenous internal environment.

> Sympathetics are "fight or flight."
> Parasympathetics are "calm and collected."

The responsibility of digestion is given to the parasympathetic nervous system. The digestive process starts in the mouth and extends to the anus. The parasympathetic system innervates the three pair of salivary glands: the sublingual, submaxillary, and parotid glands. Along with chewing, saliva initiates the digestive

breakdown process of consumed food. Parasympathetic stimulation increases gastrointestinal tone, secretory activity, and motility throughout the digestive tract.

While promoting the process of digestion, parasympathetic stimulation also increases insulin secretion. Insulin facilitates glucose and amino acid uptake by the cells of the body. Both energy sources are plentiful during digestion of a well-balanced meal. There is no need to mobilize stored energy sources from cells. Parasympathetic stimulation thus has no effect on glycolysis, lipolysis, or gluconeogenesis.

In the calm environment following a meal, the individual is frequently in a resting state. With the exception of the brain and digestive organs, the metabolic rate of much of the body is at a relative minimum. There is less of a requirement for blood flow, so the heart does not need to pump as much blood. Both the electrical conduction velocity of the heart and the heart rate decrease in response to parasympathetic stimulation. There is no parasympathetic effect on the contractile force of each heartbeat.

In a parasympathetically-dominant "calm" environment, there is no requirement to increase blood pressure and blood flow; the parasympathetic system therefore has no means to do so. There is no parasympathetic innervation of blood vessels. This includes both arteries and veins. There also is no parasympathetic innervation to the splenic capsule. In addition, there is no effect on renin secretion in response to parasympathetic stimulation.

Like the heart, the lungs also have less of a workload in a parasympathetic calm environment. There is less need for provision of oxygen and expulsion of carbon dioxide. Parasympathetic stimulation causes contraction of bronchial smooth muscle and bronchoconstriction.

> Asthma is a disease of bronchoconstriction. It is often treated with drugs which mimic or potentiate sympathetic stimulation. It is also treated with drugs which antagonize or block parasympathetic stimulation. The reverse is also true. Asthma may be made worse by drugs taken for unrelated reasons which block sympathetic or potentiate parasympathetic stimulation.

Parasympathetic effects on the eye were briefly described earlier. Parasympathetic stimulation causes miosis or contraction of the pupil. This limits the amount of light which enters the eye. Sympathetic stimulation causes mydriasis or dilation of the eye.

> Theoretically, not as much light is needed in "calm and collected" environments.

Accommodation is the process that allows the eye to focus on objects of varying distances away. The lens of the eye is elastic and tends to assume the shape of a sphere if associated with no other structure. When viewed from the front, the lens is in the center of the eye and has a circular shape. Around the periphery of the lens are numerous suspensory ligaments that attach the lens to the surrounding choroid. In a resting position, the ligaments pull the lens into a relatively flat position. Because the anterior and posterior walls of the lens are in a relatively parallel alignment, there is little bending of light rays as they travel through the lens. This is more conducive for focusing on objects at a distance (far-sighted vision).

> Cilia are hair-like appendages that extend from certain microorganisms and beat to provide locomotion. They are also found on certain mucous membranes and beat to move mucus across the surface. In any event, the ciliary muscle is named for its relationship to the suspensory ligaments of the lens, which appear as cilia.

The ciliary muscle encircles the periphery of the attachment points of the lens ligaments and the choroid. In response to parasympathetic stimulation, the muscle contracts, pulling the choroid in and loosening the tension on the lens ligaments. With less tension, the elastic lens attempts to assume a more spherical shape. The anterior and posterior walls become less and less parallel, causing the angle at which light strikes the lens to become greater and greater. As light rays pass through the lens, they curve at a greater angle and thus converge at a shorter distance. The focal distance is thereby shortened, favoring near-sighted vision. Although sympathetic stimulation causes some degree of ciliary muscle relaxation, it has little if any clinical effect on accommodation. In summary, parasympathetic stimulation causes positive accommodation. This process permits focusing on objects that are near. It is the lack of parasympathetic stimulation, as opposed to sympathetic stimulation, that is responsible for the negative accommodation of far-sighted focusing.

FIGURE 6.7
POSITIVE ACCOMMODATION

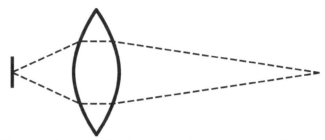

Ciliary muscle contraction loosens tension on suspensory ligaments, allowing the lens to assume a more spherical shape. Light rays bend at a more acute angle and converge at a shorter distance.

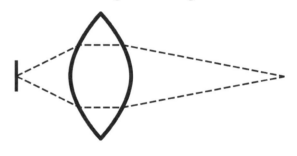

> Positive accommodation is used to read the newspaper while sipping on a cup of coffee in the parasympathetic "calm and collected" environment.

In addition to miosis and positive accommodation, there is another important parasympathetic responsibility concerning the eye. Parasympathetic innervation causes the lacrimal glands to secrete tears. Tears keep the eyes lubricated, prevent drying, and protect against foreign substances.

The effects of parasympathetic stimulation on the bladder were covered in the previous section. Parasympathetic stimulation causes contraction of the detrusor muscle and relaxation of the bladder trigone sphincter muscle. Both actions facilitate urination. This is consistent with the common parasympathetic theme: performance of normal bodily functions in a calm environment.

FIGURE 6.5
STRUCTURES OF EYE
Anterior View

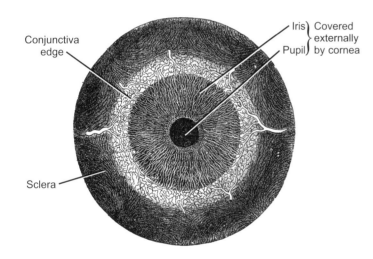

Conjunctiva edge

Iris — Covered externally by cornea
Pupil

Sclera

FIGURE 6.6
STRUCTURES OF EYE
Lateral View

Levator palpebrae superioris

Upper tarsus

Superior rectus muscle

Suspensory ligaments

Sclera
Choroid
Retina

Aqueous humor
Pupillary aperture

Vitreous body

Lens

Optic nerve

Cornea

Iris

Lower tarsus

Ciliary body (muscle)

Inferior rectus muscle

> Anyone who has had difficulty providing a urine sample in a doctor's office will remember that it is virtually impossible once the patient becomes frustrated, aggravated, and sympathetically-stimulated.

Although the sympathetic nervous system is the "fight or flight" system used in intense, potentially life-threatening situations, the parasympathetic system can become intensely activated in unexpected, startling events or excessively frightening periods. Acute lowering of the heart rate by a sudden parasympathetic outburst can make the heart "skip a beat." In some cases, the sudden decrease in heart rate may be severe enough to temporarily interrupt blood flow to the brain, causing syncopy or fainting. Sudden parasympathetic activation is also responsible for inadvertent emesis (regurgitation), urination, and defecation which can occur during these startling or frightening events. The parasympathetic activation is usually short-lived, only to be followed by a sympathetic predominance.

FIGURE 6.8

	Parasympathetic Stimulation	**Sympathetic Stimulation**
Adrenal gland	No innervation	Adrenal cortex – steroid hormone secretion Adrenal medulla – adrenergic hormone secretion: epinephrine (adrenaline) and norepinephrine
Arteries	No innervation	Constriction (also dilation of arteries to skeletal muscles and coronary arteries to heart)
Veins	No innervation	Constriction
Eye – pupil – accommodation	 Constriction (miosis) Positive accommodation for near vision	 Dilation (mydriasis) Limited effect
Renin secretion	No response	Increase
Glycogenolysis	No response	Increase
Glycolysis	No response	Increase
Lipolysis	No response	Increase
Gluconeogenesis	No response	Increase
Insulin secretion	Increase	Decrease
Heart – contractile force – rate – conduction velocity	 No effect Decrease Decrease	 Increase Increase Increase
Bronchial smooth muscle	Contraction	Relaxation
GI tract – tone – secretory activity – motility	 Increase Increase Increase	 Decrease Decrease Decrease
Urinary bladder – Trigone-sphincter muscle – detrusor muscle	 Relaxation Contraction	 Contraction Relaxation
Splenic capsule	No innervation	Contraction
Uterus	Contraction/relaxation	Contraction/relaxation
Piloerector muscles	No effect	Stimulation/contraction
Sweat glands	No effect	Stimulation/increase

QUIZ 1
Autonomic Nervous System

Time for Quiz = 27 minutes.
For questions 1-17, choose the single best answer.

_____1) Which statements about the pancreas are true?
    a) Cells of the acini secrete digestive enzymes.
    b) Cells of the islets of Langerhans secrete hormones.
    c) Beta cells secrete insulin.
    d) All of the above
    e) None of the above

_____2) Which biologic mechanism is increased by sympathetic stimulation?
    a) eye lens assuming a more spherical shape
    b) coronary artery dilation
    c) bronchial smooth muscle contraction
    d) gastrointestinal motility
    e) none of the above

_____3) Which substances are formed as a direct result of the third stage of catabolism of dietary sources of energy?
    a) ATP
    b) water
    c) carbon dioxide
    d) all of the above
    e) none of the above

_____4) What occurs during the process of glycolysis?
    a) Fats are transformed to fatty acids.
    b) Glucose is transformed to glycogen.
    c) Amino acids are transformed to glucose.
    d) Acetyl-CoA is transformed to pyruvate.
    e) None of the above

_____5) Which of the following occur during positive accommodation of the eye?
    a) ciliary muscle contraction
    b) pulling the lens into a flatter shape
    c) both a and b
    d) increased tension on the suspensory ligaments of the lens
    e) none of the above

_____6) Which statement concerning the renin-angiotensin system is true?
    a) Renin catalyzes the conversion of angiotensin I to angiotensin II.
    b) The conversion of angiotensinogen to angiotensin I occurs in the lungs.
    c) It is activated by parasympathetic stimulation.
    d) Angiotensin I is one of the most potent direct vasoconstrictors of the body.
    e) None of the above

_____7) Which statements are true concerning the detrusor muscle?
    a) Contraction causes emptying of the bladder.
    b) It is also known as the pubovesical muscle.
    c) Both a and b
    d) Contraction causes sphincter tightening and opposes bladder emptying.
    e) None of the above

_____8) Parasympathetic stimulation can increase which biologic mechanism?
    a) trigone-sphincter muscle (bladder) relaxation
    b) contractile force of the heart
    c) bronchial dilation
    d) vein constriction
    e) none of the above

_____9) Which statements about insulin are true?
    a) It is a protein hormone.
    b) Its secretion is stimulated by hyperglycemia.
    c) It is not required for intracellular transport of glucose into brain cells.
    d) All of the above
    e) None of the above

____10) What chemical compound is the common precursor to the Krebs cycle and oxidative phosphorylation for all three dietary sources of energy?
        a) adenosine triphosphate (ATP)
        b) adenosine diphosphate (ADP)
        c) glucose
        d) glycerol
        e) none of the above

____11) Which statement is true concerning autonomic innervation of the vasculature?
        a) Coronary arteries dilate in response to sympathetic stimulation.
        b) Veins dilate in response to parasympathetic stimulation.
        c) Veins dilate in response to sympathetic stimulation.
        d) Veins constrict in response to parasympathetic stimulation.
        e) None of the above

____12) What is the mechanism by which insulin exerts its effects on membrane transport?
        a) simple diffusion
        b) facilitated transport
        c) facilitated diffusion
        d) active transport
        e) none of the above

____13) Where does gluconeogenesis occur?
        a) skeletal muscle
        b) kidneys
        c) both a and b
        d) brain
        e) none of the above

____14) Which substances are formed as a result of the second stage of catabolism of dietary sources of energy?
        a) glucose
        b) glycerol
        c) fatty acids
        d) all of the above
        e) none of the above

____15) What occurs during the process of lipolysis?
        a) Triglycerides are converted to fatty acids.
        b) Triacylglycerols are converted to fatty acids.
        c) Both a and b
        d) Fatty acids are converted to triglycerides.
        e) None of the above

____16) Which biologic processes are decreased with sympathetic stimulation?
        a) insulin secretion
        b) glycolysis
        c) both a and b
        d) gluconeogenesis
        e) none of the above

____17) In addition to its effect on glucose membrane transport, what is another metabolic function of insulin?
        a) It promotes lipolysis.
        b) It promotes glycolysis.
        c) Both a and b
        d) It inhibits gluconeogenesis.
        e) None of the above

_____

For questions 18-27, use the following directions:
  a......1,2,3 are correct
  b......1,3 are correct
  c......2,4 are correct
  d......only 4 is correct
  e......all are correct

____18) Concerning cells of the islets of Langerhans, which of the following are true?
        1) Delta cells secrete glucagon.
        2) Greater than half of all islet cells are beta cells.
        3) Alpha cells secrete somatostatin.
        4) Insulin is secreted by beta cells.

____19) Which of the following serve as basic dietary sources of energy?
        1) carbohydrates
        2) sugars
        3) polysaccharides
        4) proteins

____20) Which biologic mechanisms are decreased in response to parasympathetic stimulation?
1) sweat gland secretion
2) piloerector muscle contraction
3) arterial constriction
4) conduction velocity of the heart

____21) Which statements about juxtaglomerular cells are true?
1) They are located in the kidneys.
2) They function in response to hypertension.
3) The enzyme they secrete catalyzes the conversion of angiotensinogen to angiotensin I.
4) They secrete angiotensin converting enzyme.

____22) Which substances are the direct result of the first stage of catabolism of dietary sources of energy?
1) glycogen
2) glycerol
3) triglycerides
4) fatty acids

____23) Which statements concerning accommodation of the eye are true?
1) Negative accommodation is the result of parasympathetic stimulation.
2) Positive accommodation involves ciliary muscle contraction.
3) Negative accommodation involves decreased tension on the suspensory ligaments of the eye.
4) Positive accommodation allows the lens to return to a more spherical shape.

____24) Which of the following occur during the process of lipolysis?
1) Fatty acids are transformed to triglycerides.
2) Triglycerides are transformed to glucose.
3) Glycerol is transformed to fatty acids.
4) Triglycerides are transformed to fatty acids.

____25) Which statements about the autonomic innervation of the urinary bladder are true?
1) Sympathetic stimulation causes detrusor muscle contraction.
2) Parasympathetic stimulation causes trigone sphincter muscle contraction.
3) Sympathetic stimulation causes trigone sphincter muscle relaxation.
4) Parasympathetic stimulation causes detrusor muscle contraction.

____26) Which biologic mechanisms are increased by sympathetic stimulation?
1) venous dilation
2) peripheral artery constriction
3) coronary artery constriction
4) bronchial smooth muscle relaxation

____27) Concerning dietary sources of energy, which of the following statements are true?
1) Polysaccharides are also known as carbohydrates.
2) Carbohydrates are also known as sugars.
3) Fats are also known as lipids.
4) Polysaccharides are also known as lipids.

QUIZ 1: Autonomic Nervous System

1) d – Insulin is a protein hormone secreted by the beta cells of the islets of Langerhans in the pancreas.

2) b – Sympathetic stimulation causes constriction of most arteries. An exception is the coronary arteries. The coronary arteries supply heart muscle and dilate in response to sympathetic stimulation. Parasympathetic stimulation causes ciliary muscle contraction. This decreases the tension on the suspensory ligaments of the lens and allows the lens to assume a more spherical shape, which provides for near-sighted vision. Sympathetic stimulation causes bronchial smooth muscle relaxation and hence, bronchial dilation. It also causes a decrease in gastrointestinal tone, secretory activity, and motility.

3) d – The third stage of catabolism of dietary sources of energy includes the citric acid (Krebs) cycle and oxidative phosphorylation.

4) e – The suffix *lysis* means *dissolution* or *breakdown*. Glycolysis involves the breakdown and transformation of glucose to pyruvate. Pyruvate is then converted to acetyl-CoA for entrance into the citric acid (Krebs) cycle and oxidative phosphorylation with the resultant production of energy (ATP). Gluconeogenesis is the pathway in which certain amino acids are converted to glucose.

5) a – Accommodation is a process of alterations within the eye which enable the eye to focus on structures at different distances away. Positive accommodation involves contraction of the ciliary muscle, which decreases the tension on the suspensory ligaments of the lens. This allows the lens to return to a more spherical shape, bend light rays at a greater angle, and provide for near-sighted vision. Positive accommodation is the result of parasympathetic stimulation.

6) e – In response to either sympathetic stimulation or low blood pressure (hypotension), the juxtaglomerular cells of the kidney secrete renin. The juxtaglomerular cells are located in the afferent arterioles of the glomerulus. In the blood, renin catalyzes the conversion of angiotensinogen to angiotensin I. Angiotensin I then travels to the lungs where it is converted to angiotensin II by angiotensin converting enzyme (ACE). Angiotensin II is one of the most potent vasoconstrictors of the body. Vasoconstriction acts to increase blood pressure.

7) c – The detrusor (pubovesical) muscle contracts in response to parasympathetic stimulation. Contraction of the trigone-sphincter muscle of the bladder occurs with sympathetic stimulation and opposes bladder emptying.

8) a – Parasympathetic stimulation relaxes the trigone-sphincter muscle of the bladder and facilitates bladder emptying. It also causes a decrease in heart rate and conduction velocity, but has no effect on the contractile force of each heart beat. Parasympathetic stimulation causes bronchial smooth muscle contraction and hence, bronchial constriction. There is no parasympathetic innervation of blood vessels. This includes both arteries and veins.

9) d – High blood sugar (hyperglycemia) as occurs after a carbohydrate-rich meal, is the stimulus for insulin secretion. Brain and exercising skeletal muscle cells do not require the presence of insulin for intracellular transport of glucose. All other cells require insulin.

10) e – The three dietary sources of energy include sugars (polysaccharides, carbohydrates), fats (lipids), and proteins. When used as energy, each is eventually broken down and transformed into acetyl-CoA, the common precursor to the citric acid (Krebs) cycle and oxidative phosphorylation. During this process, the universal energy source for all living cells, ATP, is created. When utilized for energy, ATP is transformed into ADP. Along with other simple sugars, glucose is a breakdown product of carbohydrates. Fatty acids and glycerol are the breakdown products of lipids.

11) a – Blood vessels, including both arteries and veins, are not innervated by the parasympathetic nervous system. Most arteries constrict in response to sympathetic stimulation. An

exception is the coronary arteries, which supply heart muscle. Coronary arteries dilate in response to sympathetic stimulation. Veins, like most arteries, constrict in response to sympathetic stimulation.

12) c – Insulin binds a cell membrane carrier protein, which facilitates the passage of glucose from the blood to the intracellular environment of the cell. This mechanism of membrane transport is called facilitated diffusion.

13) b – Gluconeogenesis is the production of glucose from non-carbohydrate sources. The word *gluconeogenesis* actually means "glucose new creation." It results from the breakdown of proteins to amino acids and the subsequent transformation of certain amino acids to glucose. The pathway serves as an important means of producing the brain's only energy source, glucose, in times of carbohydrate shortage. Gluconeogenesis occurs primarily in the liver, although a small amount also takes place in the kidneys.

14) e – There are three dietary sources of energy: sugars (carbohydrates, polysaccharides), fats (lipids), and proteins. Each goes through three stages of catabolism or breakdown in order to provide energy by the production of ATP. The first stage is digestion. During the first stage, sugars are broken down to glucose and simple sugars, fats to fatty acids and glycerol, and proteins to amino acids. Acetyl-CoA is the result of the second stage of catabolism for all three dietary sources of energy. It is the common precursor to the third stage of catabolism, the citric acid (Krebs) cycle and oxidative phosphorylation.

15) c – The suffix *lysis* means *dissolution* or *breakdown*. Lipolysis is breakdown of the storage form of lipids, triglycerides (triacylglycerols), into fatty acids. Fatty acids can then be transformed to acetyl-CoA, which can enter the citric acid (Krebs) cycle and oxidative phosphorylation for provision of energy (ATP).

16) a – Renin secretion, lipolysis, glycolysis, and gluconeogenesis are not affected by parasympathetic stimulation. All processes are increased

with sympathetic stimulation. Insulin secretion is increased with parasympathetic stimulation and decreased with sympathetic stimulation.

17) d – Insulin promotes the intracellular transport of glucose and the storage of glucose as glycogen. Because insulin is secreted in response to elevated blood sugar, there is no need for mobilization of other energy sources. Insulin therefore inhibits the catabolic pathways of lipolysis and glycolysis. In addition to its effect on carbohydrate metabolism, insulin also has significant effects on protein metabolism. The intracellular transport of a great number of amino acids is facilitated by insulin. Furthermore, insulin inhibits gluconeogenesis. This preserves proteins by preventing their breakdown to amino acids and subsequent transformation to glucose.

18) c – Alpha cells secrete glucagon. Beta cells secrete insulin. Delta cells secrete somatostatin. There are other, less common, cell types and chemicals secreted. More than half of all islet cell types are beta cells.

19) e – There are three basic dietary sources of energy. Sugars are also known as carbohydrates. Chemically, they are more specifically described as polysaccharides. Any of the three names can be used to describe them. Fats are also called lipids and make up the second dietary source of energy. Proteins make up the third energy source.

20) d – Parasympathetic stimulation causes a decrease in heart rate and conduction velocity, but has no effect on the contractile force of each heartbeat. Sympathetic stimulation, however, increases the heart rate, conduction velocity, and contractile force of each heartbeat. Although sweat gland secretion, piloerector muscle contraction, and peripheral artery constriction are all increased in response to sympathetic stimulation, all processes are unaffected by parasympathetic stimulation. In fact, there is no parasympathetic innervation to blood vessels, including both arteries and veins. In addition, there is no parasympathetic innervation to sweat glands or piloerector

muscles. Because these are the only visceral structures located in the extremities and body wall, **there is no parasympathetic innervation to the body wall or extremities.**

21) b – See #6 answer explanation.

22) c – See #14 answer explanation. Glycogen is an intracellular storage form of glucose. Triglycerides are a storage form of fatty acids (lipids).

23) c – See #5 answer explanation. Negative accommodation is the result of ciliary muscle relaxation. This increases the tension on the suspensory ligaments of the lens, which pulls the lens into a flatter shape. The flat shape of the lens bends light rays at less of an angle and provides for far-sighted vision.

24) d – See #15 answer explanation.

25) d – The detrusor muscle contracts in response to parasympathetic stimulation and pulls the bladder inward, facilitating bladder emptying. The detrusor muscle relaxes in response to sympathetic stimulation. The bladder trigone-sphincter muscle contracts when stimulated by the sympathetic nervous system. This closes the bladder outlet and opposes bladder emptying. The trigone-sphincter muscle relaxes with parasympathetic stimulation.

26) c – See #11 answer explanation. Sympathetic stimulation causes bronchial smooth muscle relaxation and hence, bronchial dilation.

27) a – See #19 answer explanation.

STRUCTURE OF THE AUTONOMIC NERVOUS SYSTEM

The previous chapter described the basic structure of the autonomic nervous system. With one exception, the efferent (motor) limb of the autonomic system is a *two-neuron* system. Two neurons participate in efferent transmission outside the central nervous system (CNS). Preganglionic cell bodies of both the sympathetic and parasympathetic systems are located in the CNS. Sympathetic preganglionic cell bodies are found in the spinal cord from the first thoracic (T1) to the second lumbar (L2) levels. Because of this origin, the sympathetic nervous system is also known as the **thoracolumbar system.** Those of the parasympathetic system are located in the brain and sacral spinal cord from the second sacral (S2) through fourth sacral (S4) levels. The parasympathetic system is therefore also known as the **craniosacral system**. Preganglionic axons from cell bodies of both systems leave the CNS to synapse with the second or postganglionic neuron in autonomic ganglia. Postganglionic neurons then extend axons to the innervated end organs, smooth or cardiac muscle fibers.

The one exception to the two-neuron structure of the autonomic efferent limb is the innervation of the adrenal gland. The adrenal gland is exclusively supplied by the sympathetic nervous system; there is no parasympathetic input. As discussed earlier, the adrenal gland is a neuroendocrine gland located at the superior pole of each kidney. The inner medulla secretes epinephrine (adrenaline) and norepinephrine. The outer cortex secretes steroid hormones. The neuroendocrine cells that secrete these hormones actually serve as the postganglionic neuron. In other words, the adrenal gland is innervated by preganglionic sympathetic fibers.

Only one neuron participates in afferent (sensory) signal transmission outside the CNS for both the sympathetic and parasympathetic systems. The cell bodies of both systems are located in dorsal root ganglia of spinal nerves and sensory ganglia associated with certain cranial nerves. Like most afferent neurons, autonomic afferent neurons are pseudounipolar; each contains only one axon and no dendrites. The lone axon extends outward and divides into two branches. The longer branch travels to a sensory receptor positioned within an autonomic (visceral) structure. The shorter branch courses to the CNS. When the sensory receptor is activated, a visceral afferent signal is conducted to the CNS.

In contrast to the autonomic system, the efferent limb of the somatic system is a *one-neuron* system. The cell body of this neuron is located in the brain or spinal cord. It extends an axon peripherally to synapse with the end organ, a skeletal muscle fiber. This synapse is known as a motor end plate. As opposed to the efferent limb, the structure of the somatic afferent limb is similar to that of the autonomic system. One pseudounipolar neuron participates in peripheral afferent signal transmission and its cell body is located in either a dorsal root ganglion or cranial nerve ganglion of the head. The somatic system transmits afferent information from somatic structures; the autonomic system conveys information from visceral structures.

The relative location of sympathetic efferent ganglia is distinct from that of parasympathetic ganglia. This accounts for the different nature of autonomic stimulation between the two systems. With the sympathetic system, the ganglia tend to be closer to the origin of preganglionic axons from the CNS. The preganglionic axon travels a relatively short distance to reach the ganglion as compared to the longer distance the postganglionic axon must travel to reach the effector organ. By contrast, the ganglia of the parasympathetic system are located closer to the effector organ. In fact, it is not unusual to find postganglionic cell bodies within the wall of the organ to be stimulated. The parasympa-

FIGURE 6.9
AUTONOMIC STRUCTURE

Types of neurons: Sensory neuron, with a cell body (perikaryon) and an axon with long peripheral and short central branches ("pseudounipolar" neuron). Interneuron with numerous dendrites, a cell body and one short axon ("multipolar" neuron). Motor neuron with a great many dendrites, a cell body, and a long peripheral axon ("multipolar" neuron). Two sympathetic neurons, one with a cell body in the spinal cord and the other with its cell body in the sympathetic chain, are also shown. Each has several dendrites and a medium length axon.

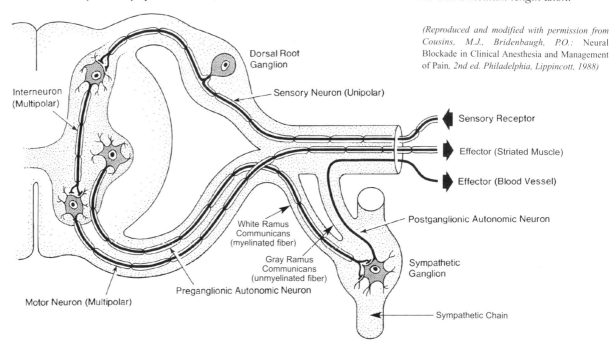

(Reproduced and modified with permission from Cousins, M.J., Bridenbaugh, P.O.: Neural Blockade in Clinical Anesthesia and Management of Pain, 2nd ed. Philadelphia, Lippincott, 1988)

thetic preganglionic axon is therefore much longer than the postganglionic axon. Because the sympathetic preganglionic fibers are relatively short and the postganglionic fibers are considerably longer in most instances, the postganglionic fibers that emanate from a particular sympathetic ganglion are widely distributed to the body's tissues; many different organs or structures may be supplied. A particular organ may receive sympathetic stimuli from numerous, far-removed sources. As opposed to the sympathetic system, ganglia of the parasympathetic system are located near the end organ. This allows more precise innervation of certain glands, organs, or organ groups. As a result, sympathetic responses tend to be more generalized, affecting the body as a whole. Parasympathetic responses may be more specific and localized to certain glands or organs.

SYMPATHETIC

○——◇◯—————————< END ORGAN

PARASYMPATHETIC

○—————————◇◯——< END ORGAN

Before proceeding, a brief overview of cranial and spinal nerves is required. Both nerve groups are described in greater detail in later chapters.

Twelve pairs of cranial nerves originate directly from the brain. Some of these nerves are motor, some are sensory, and some are mixed. The special sensory modalities of sight, smell, hearing, equilibrium, and taste are conveyed by several of the nerves. Many of the cranial nerves carry somatic fibers. More pertinent to this chapter is the fact that four pairs carry parasympathetic fibers. These four cranial nerves are the source of the *cranio-* portion of the *craniosacral* system.

There are 31 pairs of spinal nerves that originate directly from the spinal cord. Eight pairs of spinal nerves arise in the neck. Each is designated by the letter *C (cervical)* and a number which corresponds to the specific cervical spinal segment from which the nerve originates; thus, the eight cervical nerves are designated C1-C8. The twelve spinal nerves that originate from the thoracic spinal cord are designated T1-T12. Five nerves originate from the lumbar cord and are designated L1-L5. Five sacral spinal nerves are designated S1-S5. Finally, the coccygeal nerve represents the last pair of spinal nerves.

Each spinal cord segment is the origin of a right and left spinal nerve. Each spinal nerve is formed by the union of a ventral root from the ventral side of the spinal segment and a dorsal root from the dorsal side of the segment. Because two spinal nerves arise from a particular spinal cord segment, each segment contains two ventral roots and two dorsal roots. The right ventral root combines with the right dorsal root to form the right-sided spinal nerve. The left ventral root combines with the left dorsal root to form the left spinal nerve. Ventral roots primarily carry efferent fibers; dorsal roots carry afferent fibers. After formation, each spinal nerve continues distally to provide somatic innervation to the structures it supplies. As will be discussed, most spinal nerves also provide sympathetic innervation to supplied tissues. Spinal nerves arising from the S2-S4 segments provide parasympathetic input.

ANATOMY OF THE SYMPATHETIC (THORACOLUMBAR) SYSTEM

Preganglionic cell bodies of the sympathetic nervous system are located in the intermediolateral horn of the spinal cord at the level of T1 through L2. The preganglionic axon leaves the cord via the ventral root and enters a spinal nerve.

After traveling a short distance in the spinal nerve, the preganglionic fiber enters the sympathetic chain via a short nerve called a **white ramus communicans** (52). A *ramus* is simply a branch. *Communicans* denotes a communication between two structures. A white ramus communicans is a branch between a spinal nerve and the sympathetic chain. The **sympathetic chain** (65) is also known as the **sympathetic trunk** (see nerve 38); both names may be used interchangeably. The sympathetic chain is a large sympathetic nerve which runs parallel and in close proximity to the vertebral column. It is through this chain that *all* sympathetic stimulation is conveyed. There are two sympathetic chains, one on each side of the column. Each chain starts at the C1 vertebral level and ends at the coccyx. The sympathetic chain lies deep in the body, much closer to the vertebrae than can be clearly depicted on the poster. To indicate this position, the subject's right sympathetic chain appears as a dotted line in Figure 2 of the poster. The bead-like structures intermittently appearing on the chain represent enlargements known as **sympathetic chain ganglia** (36, 39, 42, 66, 69, 264, 266). These ganglia contain sympathetic postganglionic neuron cell bodies and are the location of synapses along the sympathetic chain. The **interganglionic sections** (65) of the chain are the sections found *between* the *ganglia* and are composed of nerve fibers (axons). The two sympathetic chains meet inferiorly at the coccyx forming the last ganglion, the **ganglion impar** (69). The left sympathetic chain and its branches are omitted from Figure 2 of the poster. Although variation occurs, its branches are similar to those of the right.

Based on location, there are two generalized classifications

FIGURE 6.10
ORIGINATION OF A SPINAL NERVE FROM A SPINAL CORD SEGMENT

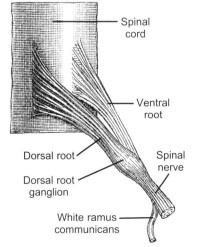

- Spinal cord
- Ventral root
- Dorsal root
- Dorsal root ganglion
- Spinal nerve
- White ramus communicans

FIGURE 6.11
SYMPATHETIC NERVES OF TRUNK

The left sympathetic chain is obscured by visceral structures.

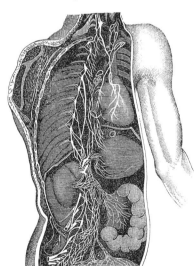

for sympathetic efferent ganglia. Those found in the sympathetic chain are known as **paravertebral ganglia** (36, 39, 42, 66, 69, 264, 266). The Greek word element *para-* means *beside*. The paravertebral ganglia are located in the sympathetic chain, which is immediately *beside* the *vertebrae*. Ganglia found outside the chain in more peripheral locations are known as **prevertebral ganglia** (261, 279, 282, 284). The Latin word element *pre-* means *before*. These ganglia are in more peripheral locations; they are *before* the *vertebrae* as opposed to beside them.

> The spine is part of the axial skeleton and thus forms a line (the long axis) along which the rest of the body may be rotated. Because of this, the spine can be considered the "center" of the body. The <u>pre</u>vertebral ganglia are in peripheral locations and are therefore *before* the *vertebrae* when moving from the periphery toward the "center."

Once the preganglionic axon enters the sympathetic chain by way of a white ramus communicans, it can travel to one of three destinations: it may enter the nearest paravertebral sympathetic chain ganglion and synapse with a postganglionic cell body, travel up or down the chain to synapse with a postganglionic cell body in a more distant paravertebral ganglion, or leave the sympathetic chain to synapse with a postganglionic cell body in a peripherally-located prevertebral sympathetic ganglion. In instances when the preganglionic fiber synapses with the postganglionic cell body in a paravertebral ganglion, the postganglionic fiber may then leave the sympathetic chain in a small nerve called a **gray ramus communicans** (53) to enter a spinal nerve. This spinal nerve may or may not be the original spinal nerve the preganglionic fiber previously traveled in. If either the preganglionic or postganglionic fiber travels up or down the chain, the postganglionic fiber will likely travel in a different spinal nerve.

Postganglionic axons that travel with spinal nerves provide sympathetic innervation to smooth muscle cells of piloerector muscles, sweat glands, and blood vessels. Instead of communicating with a spinal nerve, other postganglionic axons from paravertebral ganglia directly leave the sympathetic chain via small nerves that ultimately innervate smooth and cardiac muscle cells of visceral organs of the head, neck, and trunk. These nerves are described in more detail shortly.

The sympathetic chain runs from C1 to the coccyx. The sympathetic preganglionic cell bodies are only located at the T1-L2 levels of the spinal cord. After entering the sympathetic chain, the preganglionic axon may travel a variable distance up or down the

FIGURE 6.12
WHITE AND GRAY RAMI COMMUNICANS

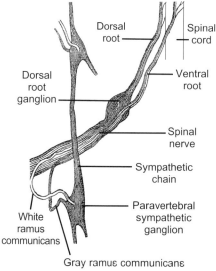

chain before synapsing in a paravertebral ganglion or leaving the chain. If a synapse occurs in the chain, the postganglionic fiber may also travel superiorly or inferiorly within the chain before leaving it in a gray ramus communicans or other nerve. The fact that preganglionic and postganglionic fibers can travel up or down the chain explains why the sympathetic chain is considerably longer than the area of spinal cord (T1-L2) from which the preganglionic input arises. All sympathetic transmission must travel through the sympathetic chain at some point.

> This is an important point to remember. **<u>ALL</u>** sympathetic innervation must travel through the sympathetic chain. Sympathetic innervation of the head, neck, perineum, and extremities travels through the sympathetic chain, even though the preganglionic cell bodies are only located at T1-L2.

FIGURE 6.13
SYMPATHETIC STRUCTURE

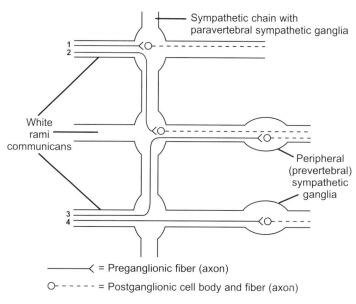

Sympathetic preganglionic fibers enter the sympathetic chain by way of white rami communicans. Once in the chain, a preganglionic fiber may (1) synapse with a sympathetic postganglionic neuron in the same paravertebral ganglion in which it entered, (2) travel up or down the chain to synapse with a sympathetic postganglionic neuron in a different paravertebral ganglion, (3) travel up or down the sympathetic chain to leave it and synapse with a postganglionic neuron at a peripheral (prevertebral) sympathetic ganglion, (4) leave the sympathetic chain at the same level in which it entered and synapse with a postganglionic neuron in a peripheral (prevertebral) ganglion.

Because the location of sympathetic preganglionic cell bodies is limited to the T1-L2 spinal levels, white rami communicans are only associated with paravertebral ganglia found at these levels. Within the sympathetic chain, axons may travel superiorly or inferiorly to either branch from the chain or enter a spinal nerve via a gray ramus communicans. Every paravertebral ganglion is associated with a gray ramus communicans. Only paravertebral ganglia at the T1-L2 levels are associated with white rami communicans. Phrased differently, each paravertebral ganglion is associated with a spinal nerve via a gray ramus communicans. All twelve thoracic and first two lumbar paravertebral ganglia also communicate via white rami communicans. The T4 and T7 paravertebral ganglia are shown in Figure 2 of the poster communicating with the T4 and T7 spinal nerves, respectively. This communication is by way of both a gray and white ramus communicans.

White – going into sympathetic chain (leaving spinal nerve)
Gray – leaving sympathetic chain (joining spinal nerve)

White comes before gray in the sequence of sympathetic transmission leaving the spinal cord. There is more gray than white. This is similar to an approaching storm on a clear day. The first clouds are white. As the storm approaches, the clouds become gray and there are more of them.

Consider the sympathetic chain as a recreational park. The white clouds of a clear day invite people to enter the park just as the white rami communicans carry fibers which are entering the sympathetic chain. The gray clouds of a storm cause people to leave the park. The gray rami communicans carry postganglionic fibers which are leaving the sympathetic chain. Again, once the storm arrives, there are more gray clouds than white clouds, just as there are more gray than white rami communicans.

The color is based on myelination. White rami communicans contain myelinated fibers; gray rami communicans contain unmyelinated fibers (see Figure 6.9). This is similar to white and gray matter of the brain. White matter contains various tracts; gray matter contains cell bodies.

Although each sympathetic chain ganglion is associated with a spinal nerve, not every spinal nerve is necessarily associated with a ganglion. More spinal nerves exist (31 pair). There are usually only three or four cervical ganglia, eleven thoracic ganglia, three or four lumbar ganglia, and four sacral ganglia.

The first cervical paravertebral sympathetic ganglion is located high in the neck and is known as the **superior cervical ganglion** (36). It is usually the largest paravertebral ganglion and is responsible for sympathetic innervation to visceral structures of the face and anterior head. Postganglionic fibers leave the superior cervical ganglion to form nerves that travel with blood vessels of the head. These fibers could otherwise form gray rami communicans except that no spinal nerves travel to this area. Other postganglionic fibers form the **superior cervical cardiac branch** (**38**, 243, 256) of the sympathetic trunk.

The **middle cervical ganglion** (39) is the origin of sympathetic postganglionic fibers that supply structures of the head, neck, and upper extremity. In addition, the middle cervical ganglion is the origin of the **middle cervical cardiac branch (40, 243, 256)** of the sympathetic trunk.

The **stellate ganglion** (42) is also known as the cervicothoracic ganglion. It is a large sympathetic ganglion formed by the combination of the last cervical and first thoracic sympathetic ganglia. The word *stellate* means *star-shaped*. The stellate ganglion provides sympathetic innervation to visceral structures of the neck and upper extremity. It is also the origin of the **inferior cervical cardiac branch (44,** 243, 256) of the sympathetic trunk. These three nerves,

the superior, middle, and inferior cervical cardiac branches, are formed by sympathetic postganglionic fibers. These fibers extend from postganglionic cell bodies housed the paravertebral ganglion from which each nerve originates. The three cervical cardiac branches (38, 40, 44) descend the neck to contribute sympathetic innervation to the **cardiac plexus** (253) and thus, the heart.

Other nerves formed by sympathetic postganglionic fibers originate from each of the upper thoracic paravertebral ganglia. These nerves provide additional sympathetic input to the heart and thoracic viscera.

The T11 and T12 paravertebral ganglia are usually also fused, explaining why there are eleven rather than twelve thoracic ganglia.

FIGURE 6.14
STRUCTURES OF THE POSTERIOR ABDOMINAL WALL
The great vessels and the autonomic nerves on the posterior abdominal wall. Around the celiac and superior mesenteric stems as they arise from the aorta are ganglia of the celiac plexus, and below these, the aortic plexus lies on the front of the aorta. The left lumbar sympathetic trunk is visible alongside the aorta; the right one is hidden by the inferior vena cava.

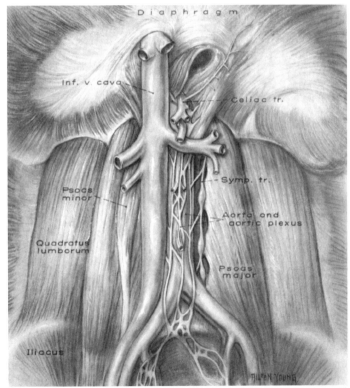

(Reproduced with permission from Hollinshead, W.H., Rosse, C.: Textbook of Anatomy, 4th ed. Philadelphia, Harper & Row, 1985)

There are four notable sympathetic ganglia of the abdomen. These prevertebral ganglia are the origin of postganglionic axons that provide sympathetic innervation to abdominal and pelvic viscera. Each ganglion is named for the aortic arterial branch near it. From superior to inferior, these include the celiac, aorticorenal, superior mesenteric, and inferior mesenteric ganglia. They are named for the celiac trunk, renal, superior mesenteric, and inferior mesenteric arteries, respectively. In addition to sympathetic structures, the first three ganglia usually also contain preganglionic parasympathetic fibers from the vagus nerve that are passing through en route to their synapse with postganglionic neurons near the effector organs.

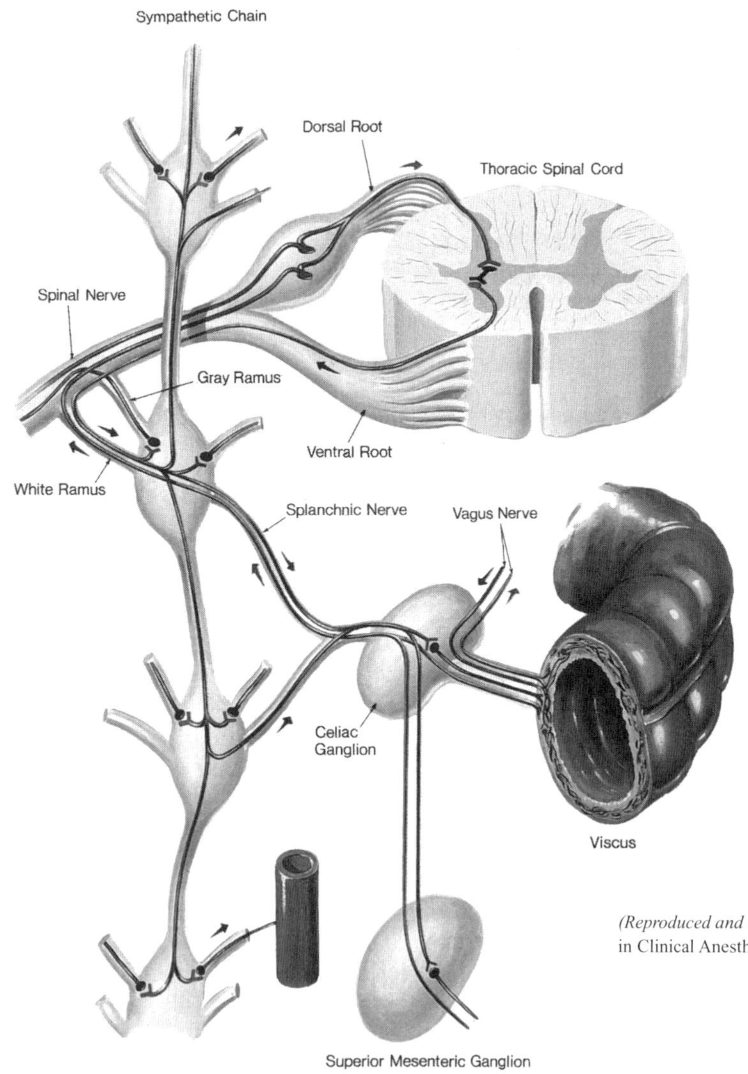

Sympathetic Chain

Dorsal Root

Thoracic Spinal Cord

Spinal Nerve

Gray Ramus

Ventral Root

White Ramus

Splanchnic Nerve

Vagus Nerve

Celiac
Ganglion

Viscus

Superior Mesenteric Ganglion

FIGURE 6.15
AUTONOMIC PATHWAYS

Peripheral sympathetic nervous system. Cell bodies are located in the intermediolateral cell column of T1-L2 spinal segments. Preganglionic efferent fibers (cholinergic) pass by way of the ventral root to a white ramus communicans and then to the paravertebral sympathetic ganglia or to more remotely located ganglia, such as the celiac ganglion. From each ganglion, they give rise to postganglionic fibers (adrenergic) to supply viscera (celiac ganglion) or to join spinal nerves (somatic nerves) to supply efferent fibers to the body wall and limbs (sudomotor and vasomotor effects). Postganglionic fibers (adrenergic) can swing backward by a gray ramus communicans to join the spinal nerve. Afferent fibers travel by way of ganglia, such as celiac and sympathetic paravertebral, without synapsing and reach spinal nerves and then their cell bodies in the dorsal root ganglia. They then pass to the dorsal root and synapse with interneurons in the intermediolateral area of the spinal cord. These afferent fibers convey pain impulses from the viscera.

(Reproduced and modified with permission from Cousins, M.D., Bridenbaugh, P.O.: Neural Blockade in Clinical Anesthesia and Management of Pain, *2nd ed. Philadelphia, Lippincott, 1988)*

The word *mesenteric* refers to the mesentery. This is the folded membrane that attaches the intestines to the body wall.

Sympathetic splanchnic nerves are formed by sympathetic preganglionic fibers. Each of the T5-T9 paravertebral ganglia gives a branch which combine to form the **greater splanchnic nerve** (**60,** 286). This nerve travels inferiorly through the diaphragm to the **celiac ganglion** (284). Branches of the T9 and T10 paravertebral ganglia form the **lesser splanchnic nerve** (**61,** 285) which also travels through the diaphragm to reach the celiac ganglion. The celiac ganglion is the origin of sympathetic postganglionic axons that supply the **celiac plexus** (260). The last thoracic ganglion, T11, is the origin of the **lowest splanchnic nerve** (**62,** 283). This nerve may also be known as the least splanchnic nerve. The lowest splanchnic nerve penetrates the diaphragm to end in the **aorticorenal ganglion** (282). Sympathetic postganglionic axons originate from the aorticorenal ganglion to supply the **aortic plexus** (280) and **renal plexus** (281). Other thoracic sympathetic ganglia may

FIGURE 6.16
AUTONOMIC NERVES OF THORAX
The splanchnic nerves are shown exiting the sympathetic chain. Vagus nerve branches are present on the esophagus.

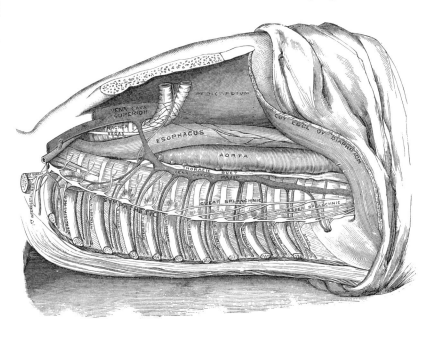

give off small **thoracoabdominal nerves** that provide sympathetic input to the body wall and abdominal viscera.

> The word *splanchnic* refers to the viscera. The splanchnic nerves provide sympathetic stimulation to the abdominal viscera.

> The greater, lesser, and lowest splanchnic nerves come off the sympathetic chain from top to bottom in alphabetical order.

The **upper lumbar paravertebral ganglia** (264) give off small **lumbar splanchnic nerves** (263). These nerves are formed by preganglionic sympathetic fibers that travel to the **superior mesenteric ganglion** (261) to synapse with postganglionic cell bodies. Postganglionic axons provide sympathetic input to the **superior mesenteric plexus** (262) and **aortic plexus** (280).

The **lower lumbar paravertebral ganglia** (266) are the origin of lower **lumbar splanchnic nerves** (265) that travel to the **inferior mesenteric ganglion** (279). From there, postganglionic axons extend to and innervate the **inferior mesenteric plexus** (278) and **superior hypogastric plexus** (277).

The **sacral splanchnic nerves** originate in the sacral sympathetic chain ganglia and course to the **inferior hypogastric plexus** (276). Both sympathetic chains continue down the length of the sacrum and meet at the coccyx, forming a knot-like ganglion, the **ganglion impar** (69).

In summary, the sympathetic nervous system supplies all areas of the body. All sympathetic transmission must travel through the sympathetic chain. Structures of the head, neck, and upper extremities are supplied by sympathetic postganglionic fibers from the superior cervical, middle cervical, and stellate ganglia. Other postganglionic fibers from each of these ganglia form nerves that supply the cardiac plexus and heart. Additional sympathetic input to thoracic viscera is provided by postganglionic fibers from the upper thoracic paravertebral ganglia.

Preganglionic fibers from paravertebral ganglia at T5 and below form splanchnic nerves. Splanchnic nerves supply abdominal and pelvic viscera by synapsing with sympathetic postganglionic cell bodies in prevertebral ganglia.

Each gray ramus communicans leaves the sympathetic chain and enters a spinal nerve to provide sympathetic innervation to the tissues supplied by the spinal nerve. Spinal nerve innervation is confined to the body wall and extremities. The body wall and extremities are formed by somatic structures. The only visceral structures present are blood vessels, piloerector muscles, and sweat glands; consequently, these three tissues are the only structures supplied by sympathetic postganglionic fibers of gray rami communicans. In other words, gray rami communicans are limited to vasomotor (blood vessel), pilomotor (hair), and sudomotor (sweat gland) innervations.

The sympathetic system is good example of variability in anatomy. Within a particular individual, there is limited symmetry between the two sympathetic chains with regard to the number and location of paravertebral ganglia. There are also inconsistencies in the number and sizes of sympathetic nerves which branch from the chains. Some individuals may have an absence of the lesser or lower splanchnic nerve. In turn, the greater splanchnic nerve may be larger to compensate for the omission. Furthermore, the ganglia to which the sympathetic nerves travel may also be somewhat diverse. The lesser splanchnic nerve, for instance, may travel to the aorticorenal ganglion as opposed to the celiac ganglion. The important point to remember is that variability does occur.

Half and Half

There are 6 named sympathetic nerves which branch from the sympathetic chain ganglia and are not associated with spinal nerves. The upper half (3) are cardiac (heart). The lower half (3) are splanchnic (viscera). From superior to inferior:

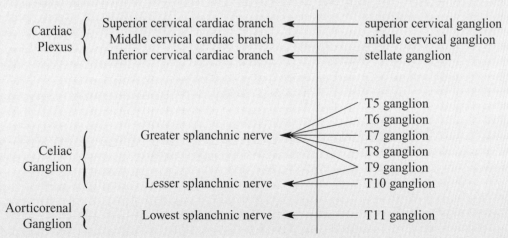

In addition to these 6 named nerves, thoracic sympathetic chain ganglia may also give off **thoracoabdominal nerves**. Lumbar sympathetic chain ganglia give off lumbar splanchnic nerves. The **upper lumbar splanchnic nerves** travel to the superior mesenteric ganglion. The **lower lumbar splanchnic nerves** travel to the inferior mesenteric ganglion. Sacral sympathetic chain ganglia give off **sacral splanchnic nerves**, which travel to the inferior hypogastric plexus.

FIGURE 6.17
PERIPHERAL SYMPATHETIC STRUCTURES

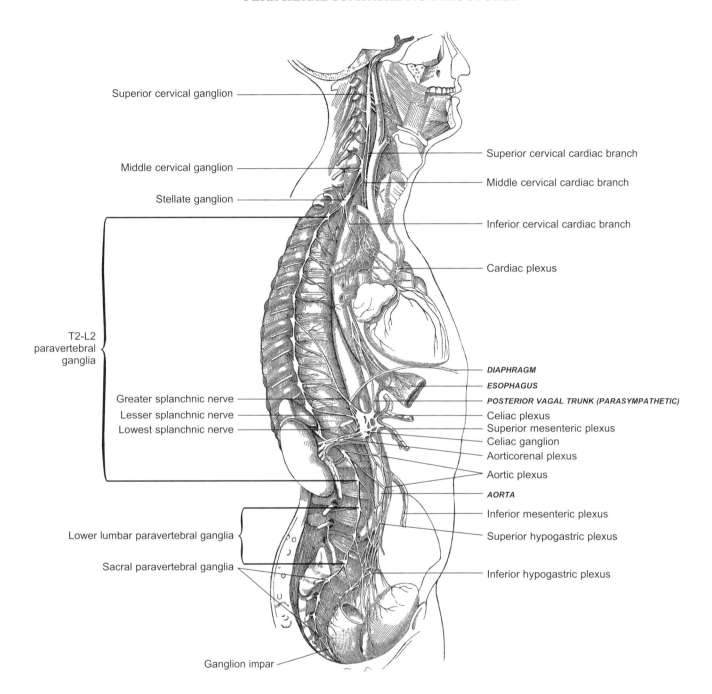

Superior cervical ganglion

Middle cervical ganglion

Stellate ganglion

T2-L2 paravertebral ganglia

Greater splanchnic nerve
Lesser splanchnic nerve
Lowest splanchnic nerve

Lower lumbar paravertebral ganglia

Sacral paravertebral ganglia

Ganglion impar

Superior cervical cardiac branch
Middle cervical cardiac branch
Inferior cervical cardiac branch
Cardiac plexus

DIAPHRAGM
ESOPHAGUS
POSTERIOR VAGAL TRUNK (PARASYMPATHETIC)
Celiac plexus
Superior mesenteric plexus
Celiac ganglion
Aorticorenal plexus
Aortic plexus
AORTA
Inferior mesenteric plexus
Superior hypogastric plexus
Inferior hypogastric plexus

QUIZ 2
Autonomic Nervous System

Time for Quiz = 20 minutes.
For questions 1-13, choose the single best answer.

_____1) What is the lowest spinal cord level where sympathetic preganglionic neuron cell bodies may typically be found?
   a) T6
   b) T12
   c) L2
   d) L5
   e) S2

_____2) Which of the following are true concerning the lesser splanchnic nerve?
   a) It is formed by branches of the T5-T8 paravertebral ganglia of the sympathetic chain.
   b) It travels to the celiac ganglion.
   c) Both a and b
   d) It travels to the superior mesenteric ganglion.
   e) None of the above

_____3) What is the predominant sympathetic ganglion of the upper extremity?
   a) superior cervical ganglion
   b) middle cervical ganglion
   c) stellate ganglion
   d) celiac ganglion
   e) none of the above

_____4) Which statement is true concerning a sympathetic preganglionic neuron?
   a) It forms a synapse with the effector organ.
   b) The cell body could be located in the sacral spinal cord.
   c) The axon is relatively longer than the parasympathetic preganglionic axon.
   d) It may synapse in either a paravertebral or prevertebral ganglion.
   e) None of the above

_____5) Which autonomic plexus is supplied by the sympathetic sacral splanchnic nerves?
   a) celiac plexus
   b) inferior hypogastric plexus
   c) renal plexus
   d) superior hypogastric plexus
   e) none of the above

_____6) Which of the following are true concerning gray rami communicans?
   a) They contain axons which are entering the sympathetic chain.
   b) They only contain sympathetic preganglionic axons.
   c) Both a and b
   d) They are more numerous than white rami communicans.
   e) None of the above

_____7) What is the ganglion impar?
   a) the first cervical paravertebral sympathetic ganglion
   b) an abdominal parasympathetic ganglion
   c) the most inferior sympathetic paravertebral ganglion
   d) the combination of the last cervical and first thoracic paravertebral sympathetic ganglia
   e) none of the above

_____8) Which statement about the sympathetic postganglionic neuron is true?
   a) The cell body may be located in the brain.
   b) The cell body may be located in the cervical spinal cord.
   c) The cell body may be located in the thoracic spinal cord.
   d) The cell body may be located in a prevertebral ganglion.
   e) None of the above

_____9) Which nerves carry sympathetic postganglionic fibers (axons)?
  a) sympathetic nerves to the heart
  b) greater splanchnic nerve
  c) sympathetic nerves to the adrenal gland
  d) upper lumbar splanchnic nerves
  e) none of the above

_____10) Which nerve is formed by a branch of the T11 paravertebral ganglion of the sympathetic chain?
  a) inferior cervical cardiac branch of the sympathetic chain
  b) greater splanchnic nerve
  c) lesser splanchnic nerve
  d) lowest splanchnic nerve
  e) none of the above

_____11) Which statements about the superior cervical cardiac branch of the sympathetic trunk are true?
  a) It is a branch of the stellate ganglion.
  b) It travels to the cardiac plexus.
  c) Both a and b
  d) It travels to the celiac trunk.
  e) None of the above

_____12) What may be found within interganglionic sections of the sympathetic chain?
  a) preganglionic neuron axons
  b) postganglionic neuron axons
  c) both a and b
  d) prevertebral ganglia
  e) none of the above

_____13) Which structure may be supplied by post-ganglionic sympathetic fibers that travel with a spinal nerve?
  a) coronary arteries
  b) gallbladder
  c) lungs
  d) deltoid muscle
  e) none of the above

For questions 14-20, use the following directions:
  a......1,2,3 are correct
  b......1,3 are correct
  c......2,4 are correct
  d......only 4 is correct
  e......all are correct

_____14) Which nerves carry sympathetic postganglionic fibers (axons)?
  1) white rami communicans
  2) inferior cervical cardiac branch of the sympathetic chain
  3) lowest splanchnic nerve
  4) sacral splanchnic nerves

_____15) Which of the following are sympathetic paravertebral ganglia?
  1) aorticorenal ganglion
  2) superior mesenteric ganglion
  3) celiac ganglion
  4) superior cervical ganglion

_____16) Which statements concerning direct sympathetic innervation to the heart are true?
  1) Postganglionic axons travel by way of the superior cervical cardiac branch of the sympathetic chain.
  2) Postganglionic axons travel by way of the middle cervical cardiac branch of the sympathetic chain.
  3) Postganglionic axons travel by way of the inferior cervical cardiac branch of the sympathetic chain.
  4) Preganglionic axons travel by way of nerves which branch from the T1-T5 paravertebral ganglia.

_____17) Which statements about the greater splanchnic nerve are true?
  1) It is formed by branches from the T5-T9 paravertebral ganglia.
  2) It carries postganglionic fibers.
  3) It travels to the celiac ganglion.
  4) It supplies the cardiac plexus.

_____18) Which statements are true concerning the anatomic relationship of paravertebral sympathetic ganglia?
1) Every spinal nerve is associated with a paravertebral ganglion.
2) Every paravertebral ganglion is associated with a gray ramus communicans.
3) Every paravertebral ganglion is associated with a white ramus communicans.
4) Every paravertebral ganglion is associated with a spinal nerve.

_____19) Which nerves carry sympathetic preganglionic fibers (axons)?
1) branches to the heart
2) branches to the lungs
3) branches to the intestines
4) branches to the adrenal gland

_____20) Which statements about white rami communicans are true?
1) They are more numerous than gray rami communicans.
2) They carry fibers which are entering the sympathetic chain.
3) They extend from the spinal nerve to the prevertebral sympathetic ganglia.
4) They are formed by sympathetic preganglionic neuron axons.

QUIZ 2: Autonomic Nervous System

1) c – The sympathetic nervous system is also known anatomically as the thoracolumbar system. This is because the cell bodies of the sympathetic preganglionic neurons are found in the intermediolateral horn of the spinal cord at the spinal levels of T1-L2.

2) b – The lesser splanchnic nerve is formed by branches from the T9 and T10 paravertebral sympathetic ganglia of the sympathetic chain. The greater splanchnic nerve is formed by branches from the T5-T9 paravertebral sympathetic ganglia. Like the greater splanchnic nerve, the lesser splanchnic nerve also travels to the celiac ganglion to synapse with postganglionic neurons. Postganglionic axons then extend from this ganglion in small nerves that supply abdominal viscera innervated by the celiac plexus. The superior mesenteric ganglion receives preganglionic fibers from upper lumbar sympathetic splanchnic nerves.

3) c – The stellate ganglion is the large paravertebral sympathetic ganglion formed by the combination of the last cervical and first thoracic paravertebral ganglia of the sympathetic chain. The celiac ganglion is the large prevertebral sympathetic ganglion located just below the diaphragm in close proximity to the celiac trunk artery. It is involved in sympathetic transmission to the abdominal viscera.

4) d – The peripheral network of the efferent limb of the autonomic nervous system, including both sympathetic and parasympathetic systems, is formed by two neurons with structures found outside the CNS (brain and spinal cord). Cell bodies of the first (preganglionic) neuron of the sympathetic or thoracolumbar system are located in the intermediolateral horn of the thoracic and lumbar spinal cord from T1 to L2. By contrast, the cell bodies of the preganglionic neuron of the parasympathetic or craniosacral system are located in the brain and sacral spinal cord. The sympathetic preganglionic fibers (axons) are usually shorter than the parasympathetic preganglionic axons. Accordingly, the sympathetic postganglionic fibers are relatively longer than their parasympathetic coun-

terparts. The sympathetic preganglionic axon synapses with a postganglionic neuron in an autonomic ganglion. This sympathetic ganglion may either be a paravertebral or prevertebral ganglion. The paravertebral ganglia are located in the sympathetic chain. The prevertebral ganglia are located outside and distal to the sympathetic chain. The axon of the postganglionic neuron extends to and innervates the effector organ (smooth or cardiac muscle). The preganglionic parasympathetic axon synapses with the postganglionic parasympathetic neuron very close to, and often *within*, the wall of the effector organ.

5) b – The inferior hypogastric plexus (pelvic plexus) is supplied by postganglionic axons in sacral splanchnic nerves. This plexus provides innervation to pelvic visceral organs.

6) d – Sympathetic preganglionic fibers exit the T1-L2 levels of the spinal cord by way of ventral roots, and, subsequently, spinal nerves. These axons then leave the spinal nerve by way of a white ramus communicans. A white ramus communicans is a small communicating nerve which extends from the spinal nerve to a paravertebral ganglion of the sympathetic chain. From here the preganglionic axon can go to one of three places: 1) synapse with the postganglionic neuron at the paravertebral ganglion of entry, 2) travel up or down the chain and synapse with the postganglionic neuron in a different paravertebral ganglion, 3) leave the sympathetic chain and synapse with the postganglionic neuron in a more distally-located prevertebral ganglion. The postganglionic neuron axon may also do one of three things: 1) reenter a spinal nerve by exiting the paravertebral ganglia by way of a gray ramus communicans, 2) leave the paravertebral or prevertebral ganglia directly, 3) travel up or down the sympathetic chain before exiting it. Because sympathetic preganglionic cell bodies are only located at the spinal levels of T1-L2, white rami communicans are only associated with paravertebral ganglia found at these levels. Since axons may travel up or down the sympathetic chain before reentering a spinal nerve via a gray ramus com-

municans, every paravertebral ganglion is associated with a gray ramus communicans. Only the T1-L2 paravertebral ganglia are associated with white rami communicans.

7) c – The ganglion impar is the last, or most inferior, of the paravertebral sympathetic ganglia. It is formed by the inferior fusion of the two sympathetic chains. The superior cervical ganglion is the most superior, or highest, paravertebral sympathetic ganglion of the sympathetic trunk. It may also be described as the first cervical ganglion. The stellate ganglion is the large paravertebral ganglion formed by the combination of the last cervical and first thoracic paravertebral ganglia.

8) d – Cell bodies of sympathetic preganglionic neurons are located in the thoracic and lumbar spinal cord from the levels of T1-L2. Because of this, the sympathetic nervous system is also known anatomically as the thoracolumbar nervous system. Cell bodies of the parasympathetic preganglionic neurons are located in the brain and sacral spinal cord. Hence, the parasympathetic system is also known anatomically as the craniosacral system. Sympathetic preganglionic neurons send their axons outward to synapse with sympathetic postganglionic neurons located in sympathetic ganglia. These synapses may occur in one of the two types of sympathetic ganglia. Paravertebral ganglia are sympathetic ganglia located along the sympathetic chain. Prevertebral ganglia are sympathetic ganglia that are more distal to the sympathetic chain. From sympathetic ganglia, sympathetic postganglionic neurons extend axons to innervate effector organs, including cardiac and smooth muscle fibers.

9) a – Because preganglionic sympathetic axons join the chain via white rami communicans at the T1-L2 levels, some of these preganglionic fibers are also able to leave the sympathetic chain at these levels. They travel out in nerves to synapse with postganglionic neurons in prevertebral sympathetic ganglia. These nerves, which carry preganglionic sympathetic fibers, include the greater splanchnic nerve (T5-T9), lesser splanchnic nerve (T9, T10), lowest splanchnic nerve (T11), and the upper lumbar splanchnic nerves. Nerves that come off the sympathetic chain above these levels (superior, middle, and inferior cervical cardiac branches of the sympathetic chain) and below these levels (lower lumbar splanchnic and sacral splanchnic nerves) may carry postganglionic axons from neurons that already synapsed in the sympathetic chain. Other sympathetic postganglionic axons may leave the sympathetic chain and reenter a spinal nerve via gray rami communicans. Virtually all thoracic and abdominal viscera receive direct sympathetic innervation from postganglionic fibers (axons). The adrenal gland is the exception. It only receives **pre**ganglionic sympathetic innervation. The neuroendocrine cells of the adrenal gland act as the postganglionic sympathetic neuron. The neuroendocrine cells of the adrenal medulla secrete epinephrine (adrenaline) and norepinephrine. The neuroendocrine cells of the adrenal cortex secrete steroid hormones.

10) d – The stellate ganglion is the origin of the inferior cervical cardiac branch. The greater splanchnic nerve is formed by branches from the T5-T9 paravertebral sympathetic ganglia of the sympathetic chain. The lesser splanchnic nerve is formed by branches from the T9 and T10 paravertebral ganglia.

11) b – The superior cervical ganglion is the origin of the superior cervical cardiac branch of the sympathetic chain. It is the most superior or highest paravertebral sympathetic ganglion and may also be described as the first cervical ganglion. The superior cervical cardiac branch provides sympathetic innervation to the cardiac plexus, and, subsequently, the heart. The stellate ganglion is the origin of the inferior cervical cardiac branch of the sympathetic chain.

12) c – See #6 answer explanation. The sympathetic chain is formed by paravertebral ganglia connected by interganglionic sections of the chain. The word element *inter-* means "between." Interganglionic sections are simply the sections of chain between the paravertebral ganglia.

13) e – Spinal nerve innervation is confined to the body wall and extremities. These body segments are formed by somatic structures. The

only visceral tissues present are blood vessels, piloerector muscles, and sweat glands. These structures are therefore the only structures supplied by sympathetic fibers that exit the sympathetic chain by way of gray rami communicans and travel with spinal nerves. There is no parasympathetic innervation to the body wall or extremities; hence, there is no parasympathetic innervation to blood vessels, piloerector muscles, and sweat glands. The coronary arteries of the heart are supplied by postganglionic fibers from the cardiac and coronary plexuses. Sympathetic supply to the gallbladder is by way of postganglionic fibers from abdominal sympathetic prevertebral ganglia. The lungs are sympathetically supplied by postganglionic fibers from the lower cervical and upper thoracic paravertebral ganglia. Finally, the deltoid is a skeletal muscle; it is supplied by the somatic nervous system.

14) c – See #9 answer explanation.

15) d – Prevertebral ganglia are those sympathetic ganglia that are distal to, and not immediately associated with, the sympathetic chain. This is opposed to paravertebral ganglia, which lie along the chain. The superior cervical ganglion is the most superior, or highest, paravertebral sympathetic ganglion of the sympathetic trunk. It may also be described as the first cervical ganglion.

16) a – All nerves that directly provide sympathetic innervation to the heart carry postganglionic fibers (axons). This includes the superior, middle, and inferior cardiac branches of the sympathetic chain. These nerves branch from the superior, middle, and stellate paravertebral ganglia, respectively. They carry postganglionic fibers that supply the heart. In addition, each of the T1-T5 paravertebral ganglia of the sympathetic chain can also provide nerves that carry postganglionic axons to the heart.

17) b – The greater splanchnic nerve is formed by branches from the T5-T9 paravertebral sympathetic ganglia of the sympathetic chain. It carries preganglionic sympathetic axons to the celiac ganglion. Sympathetic supply of the cardiac plexus occurs by way of postganglionic fibers from the C1-T5 paravertebral ganglia.

18) c – Paravertebral sympathetic ganglia occur along each sympathetic chain in a random and somewhat symmetric fashion. They communicate with spinal nerves via small nerves called white and gray rami communicans. There are more spinal nerves than paravertebral ganglia. Every paravertebral ganglion is associated with a spinal nerve, but not every spinal nerve is associated with a paravertebral ganglion. Sympathetic preganglionic cell bodies are located in the intermediolateral horn of the spinal cord at the T1-L2 levels. Preganglionic axons leave the spinal cord with a spinal nerve and enter the sympathetic chain via a white ramus communicans, which travels to a paravertebral ganglion. Because the preganglionic cell bodies are only located at the T1-L2 spinal levels, white rami communicans are only associated with paravertebral ganglia located at the T1-L2 spinal levels. Both preganglionic and postganglionic axons may travel a variable distance up or down the sympathetic chain before either synapsing with the postganglionic neuron or leaving the chain. The result is that the sympathetic chain is significantly longer than the length of the spinal cord in which the preganglionic cell bodies are located (T1-L2). Postganglionic axons leave the chain in gray rami communicans, which rejoin a spinal nerve. Again, *all* paravertebral ganglia associate with a spinal nerve, and they do this by way of a gray ramus communicans. The paravertebral ganglia which are located at the T1-L2 levels are the *only* ganglia that may also communicate with the spinal nerve by way of a white ramus communicans.

19) d – Virtually all thoracic and abdominal viscera receive sympathetic innervation from postganglionic fibers (axons). These axons come from postganglionic neurons located in either paravertebral or prevertebral sympathetic ganglia. The one exception to this structure is innervation to the adrenal gland. Neuroendocrine cells of the adrenal gland act as the postganglionic neuron. The adrenal gland therefore receives only sympathetic preganglionic innervation. The neuroendocrine cells of the adrenal medulla secrete epinephrine (adrenaline) and norepinephrine. The neuroendocrine cells of the adrenal cortex secrete steroid hormones. There is no parasympathetic innervation to the adrenal gland.

20) c – White rami communicans are small connecting nerves which extend from spinal nerves to the paravertebral ganglia of the sympathetic chain. They are formed by the axons of the sympathetic preganglionic neurons. These are axons (fibers) which are entering the sympathetic chain. The cell bodies of sympathetic preganglionic neurons are located in the intermediolateral horn of the spinal cord at the T1-L2 spinal levels. Because of this, white rami communicans are only present at paravertebral ganglia located at these spinal levels. This is in contrast to gray rami communicans, which are present at every paravertebral ganglion. Hence, gray rami communicans are more numerous than white rami communicans. Prevertebral ganglia are sympathetic ganglia distal to the sympathetic chain. They are not immediately associated with white or gray rami communicans.

ANATOMY OF THE PARASYMPATHETIC (CRANIOSACRAL) SYSTEM

Peripheral stimulation from the parasympathetic system comes from cell bodies located in the brain and sacral portion of the spinal cord. Hence, the parasympathetic system is also called the craniosacral system. Nerves can be grossly divided into those which branch directly off the brain, the cranial nerves, and those which branch off the spinal cord, the sacral spinal nerves.

There are twelve pairs of cranial nerves. Each cranial nerve has a name and a corresponding number which is often displayed in Roman numeral. The number correlates with the relative order the cranial nerve originates from the ventral surface of the brain. Cranial nerve I originates from the most anterior and superior position; cranial nerve XII is from the most posterior and inferior. Four cranial nerves carry parasympathetic fibers. Although these nerves also carry somatic fibers, they are classified as parasympathetic cranial nerves. The four parasympathetic cranial nerves include the oculomotor nerve (CN III), facial nerve (CN VII), glossopharyngeal nerve (CN IX), and vagus nerve (CN X). They provide parasympathetic stimulation to the head, neck, and viscera of the thorax and abdomen.

By far the most prominent parasympathetic contribution is by way of the vagus nerve. The name *vagus* is derived from a Latin word that means *wandering*. The course of the vagus nerve is extensive. It supplies structures of the head, muscles of the larynx and pharynx, and viscera of the thorax and abdomen. This includes most of the digestive tract. The vagus nerve innervates all digestive organs proximal to the level of the left (splenic) flexure of the large colon. Parasympathetic input from the other three parasympathetic cranial nerves is confined to the head and neck.

FIGURE 6.18
AUTONOMIC STRUCTURES OF ABDOMEN

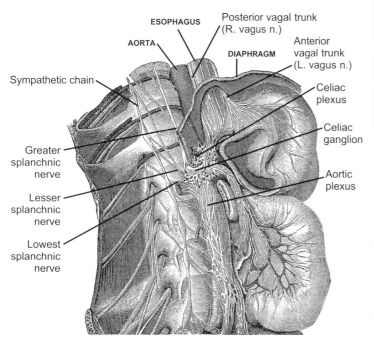

Parasympathetic innervation to pelvic viscera is provided by sacral spinal nerves. Supplied structures include the bladder, uterus, reproductive organs, and digestive organs distal to the left colon flexure.

There is no parasympathetic innervation to the body wall or extremities. These body components are formed with somatic tissues. The visceral structures that do exist in these segments are limited to blood vessels, sweat glands, and piloerector muscles of hair follicles. All three structures are supplied solely by the sympathetic system.

Consider the sympathetic and parasympathetic systems as opposites. Although rather simplistic, think of them as differing from each other in three basic ways: function, anatomy, and organization.

1. Functionally, "fight or flight" versus "calm and collected." e.g. Sympathetic stimulation increases heart rate while parasympathetic stimulation decreases it.

2. Anatomically, the sympathetic system = thoracolumbar system. Sympathetic preganglionic cell bodies lie in the spinal cord at the T1 through L2 levels. The parasympathetic system = craniosacral system. The parasympathetic preganglionic cell bodies lie in the ventral surface of the brain and brain stem (cranial) and the spinal cord at the S2 through S4 levels (sacral).

3. Structurally, the sympathetic preganglionic axon is relatively short compared to the postganglionic axon. This organizational structure can be remembered by the fact that paravertebral ganglia of the sympathetic chain lie very close to the spinal cord. By contrast, the parasympathetic preganglionic axon is relatively long compared to the postganglionic axon. The parasympathetic ganglion is located near the effector organ. The parasympathetic postganglionic cell body is often found within the wall of the structure which is to be stimulated.

The sympathetic and parasympathetic systems differ in many other ways (e.g. the neurotransmitter used).

CRANIAL NERVE PARASYMPATHETIC CONTRIBUTION

There are four parasympathetic cranial nerves. Each is a mixed nerve that carries other fiber types, including somatic fibers. The four nerves are described as parasympathetic nerves because they are the only cranial nerves to carry parasympathetic fibers. More focus is placed on the cranial nerves in the following chapter. The discussion here is limited to an overview of the general structure and function of the visceral efferent fibers of these four nerves.

→ **Oculomotor nerve (CN III)** – Preganglionic cell bodies of the oculomotor nerve are found in the **Edinger-Westphal nucleus** of the midbrain. Within the CNS, a nucleus is a collection of neurons that are associated with the fibers of a specific peripheral nerve. From the Edinger-Westphal nucleus, preganglionic axons leave the CNS and travel toward the eye to synapse with postganglionic cell bodies in the **ciliary ganglion**. Postganglionic axons then extend to the eye and innervate the ciliary muscle of the lens and muscles of the pupil. The oculomotor nerve is the route by which parasympathetic stimulation causes positive accommodation and pupillary contraction (miosis).

The Edinger-Westphal (E.W.) nucleus houses parasympathetic preganglionic neuron cell bodies of the oculomotor nerve (CN III). The Edinger-Westphal (E.W.) nucleus provides for EASY WATCHING (E.W.) because it causes pupillary contraction (miosis) in response to bright light and positive accommodation of the lens for near-sighted vision. Both of these responses occur automatically, without requiring the individual to consciously think about them.

Hence, it is EASY WATCHING (E.W.)

The *ciliary* ganglion sends postganglionic fibers to the *ciliary* muscle and pupil. The suspensory ligaments of the lens appear as *cilia*. Contraction of the encircling ciliary muscle loosens tension on the suspensory ligaments. The lens assumes a more natural, spherical shape which increases the bending of light rays. The focal point is thus moved closer, permitting parasympathetic-induced near-sighted vision. Parasympathetic postganglionic fibers from the ciliary ganglion are also responsible for miosis or pupillary contraction.

→ **Facial nerve (CN VII)** – Parasympathetic preganglionic cell bodies of the facial nerve are located in the **lacrimal nucleus** and **superior salivatory nucleus** of the brain stem. Each is named for the end organ which is eventually supplied. The lacrimal nucleus houses preganglionic cell bodies that ultimately supply the lacrimal gland, the gland that secretes tears. The superior salivatory nucleus is the location of preganglionic cell bodies responsible for the innervation of the submandibular and sublingual glands. These are two of the three pairs of salivary glands. The submandibular glands are also known as the submaxillary glands. The sublingual glands are named for their position under the tongue.

Because there is a *superior* salivatory nucleus, it may be inferred that there is also an *inferior* salivatory nucleus. Indeed, the inferior salivatory nucleus houses parasympathetic preganglionic cell bodies that send axons with the glossopharyngeal nerve (CN IX) to supply the parotid gland. The parotid gland is the largest of the three pairs of salivary glands and is located anterior and inferior to each ear. Digestion is a parasympathetic responsibility and secretion of saliva is the initiation of the autonomic process of digestion. In addition to the three paired salivary glands, there are numerous, small, unnamed secretory glands of the oral cavity that contribute to the formation of saliva.

From the lacrimal nucleus and superior salivatory nucleus of the brainstem, preganglionic parasympathetic axons travel out with the facial nerve to synapse in either the pterygopalatine or submandibular ganglion, respectively. The **pterygopalatine ganglion** is named for its location in the pterygopalatine fossa of the skull. It is also known as the **sphenopalatine ganglion** because of its relationship to the sphenoid and palatine bones. Of the four parasympathetic efferent ganglia of the head, the pterygopalatine is the largest. Postganglionic parasympathetic axons leave the ganglion to supply the lacrimal gland of the eye and glands of the nasal and oral cavities. Tears are secreted by the lacrimal gland and drain to the lacrimal sac.

FIGURE 6.19
LACRIMAL STRUCTURES

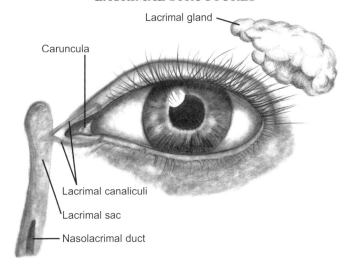

The name pterygopalatine ganglion is hard enough to remember, write, and spell. Add to that the fact that it is also known as the sphenopalatine ganglion…well, it is enough to make you want to cry.

The pterygopalatine (sphenopalatine) ganglion provides postganglionic parasympathetic axons which innervate the lacrimal glands of the eyes. The lacrimal glands secrete tears.

Other preganglionic parasympathetic axons of the facial nerve synapse with postganglionic cell bodies in the **submandibular ganglion**. Similar to the submandibular *gland*, the submandibular *ganglion* may also be known as the **submaxillary ganglion**. Postganglionic axons extend from the ganglion to innervate the sublingual and submandibular (submaxillary) glands.

The facial nerve (CN VII) provides parasympathetic innervation to all the "sub" salivary glands. This includes both the **sub**lingual and **sub**mandibular (**sub**maxillary) glands. Both are supplied via a "sub" ganglion, the **sub**mandibular (**sub**maxillary) ganglion.

By contrast, the glossopharyngeal nerve (CN IX) has the bigger name and appropriately innervates the biggest salivary gland, the parotid gland.

The "Two Faces" of the Facial Nerve

Preganglionic fibers extend from *two* brain stem nuclei, the lacrimal and superior salivatory nuclei.

The facial nerve is associated with *two* parasympathetic efferent ganglia of the head. Interestingly, each of these ganglia has *two* names:
- The pterygopalatine ganglion is also known as sphenopalatine ganglion.
- The submandibular ganglion is also known as the submaxillary ganglion.

The facial nerve provides parasympathetic input to *two* types of glands, lacrimal and salivary glands.

The facial nerve supplies *two* pairs of salivary glands, the submandibular (submaxillary) and sublingual glands.

→ **Glossopharyngeal nerve (CN IX)** (210) – Preganglionic parasympathetic fibers (axons) travel from the **inferior salivatory nucleus** of the brainstem to synapse with postganglionic cell bodies in the **otic ganglion**. From the otic ganglion, postganglionic nerve fibers travel to, and supply, the parotid gland. As mentioned before, the parotid is the largest salivary gland. It is located just anterior and inferior to each ear. The word root *-ot-* pertains to the ear. An otolaryngologist is an ear, nose, and throat specialist. The prefix *par (para)* means *beside*. The *parot*id gland is the salivary gland located *beside* the *ear*. It receives postganglionic fibers from the *ot*ic ganglion.

Remember, the **ot**ic ganglion provides **p**o**st**ganglionic axons to the par**ot**id gland. Both are named for their location relative to the ear. When you see parotid, think otic and vice-versa.

FIGURE 6.20
SALIVARY GLANDS

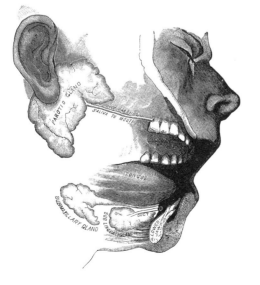

3 *Saliva*ry Glands Supplied by 2 *Saliva*tory Nuclei

The sublingual and submandibular (submaxillary) glands receive postganglionic fibers from the submandibular (submaxillary) ganglion. This is one of two parasympathetic efferent ganglia of the head associated with the facial nerve (CN VII). The submandibular ganglion receives preganglionic parasympathetic input from the **superior** salivatory nucleus.

The parotid gland receives postganglionic parasympathetic fibers from the otic ganglion. The otic ganglion is associated with the glossopharyngeal nerve (CN IX). Because the glossopharyngeal nerve is behind the facial nerve in cranial nerve sequence (CN IX comes after CN VII), it seems appropriate that the otic ganglion receives preganglionic parasympathetic input from the **inferior** salivatory nucleus.

→ **Vagus nerve (CN X)** (**29**, 49, 232, 236, 237, 241, 244, 255) – The vagus nerve is the dominant parasympathetic nerve of the body. In fact, seventy-five percent of all peripheral parasympathetic nerve fibers travel in the vagus nerves. Signals responsible for many of the parasympathetic functions discussed in this chapter are transmitted by cranial nerve X.

Preganglionic parasympathetic cell bodies located in the **dorsal vagal nucleus** send preganglionic fibers down the neck, thorax, and abdomen. These fibers end in various ganglia located near or within the walls of visceral structures. Postganglionic fibers then extend to and innervate the end organs. With the exception of the adrenal gland, capsule of the spleen, and pelvic structures, virtually all major organs are supplied by vagal fibers. The adrenal gland and splenic capsule are not supplied by the parasympathetic system. Reproductive organs and the digestive tract distal to the left (splenic) flexure of the colon obtain parasympathetic input from the S2-S4 levels of the spinal cord.

All cranial nerves are confined to the head and neck except the vagus nerve (CN X) and accessory nerve (CN XI). The accessory nerve is a motor nerve that is described in the next chapter. Parasympathetic actions of the head and neck are rather limited in number. Pupillary contraction and accommodation of the lens occur by way of the oculomotor nerve. Parasympathetic signals responsible for lacrimation (tears) and salivation are transmitted by the facial nerve. The glossopharyngeal nerve also relays efferent signals that induce salivation. Except for parasympathetic actions in the pelvis and lower abdomen, the vagus nerve is responsible for virtually all other parasympathetic functions.

3, 7, 9, 10

To remember the cranial nerve contribution to the parasympathetic system, one may simply memorize the sequence **3, 7, 9, 10** for CN III, CN VII, CN IX and CN X. It may be helpful to also think of the basic parasympathetic functions and which cranial nerves may be involved.

4 and 4

There are *four* cranial nerves that carry parasympathetic fibers. Coincidentally, there are *four* parasympathetic efferent ganglia of the head. Three of the parasympathetic cranial nerves (oculomotor (CN III), facial (CN VII), glossopharyngeal (CN IX)) remain confined to the head and neck. They are the ones associated with the four parasympathetic ganglia of the head. To provide for this structure, the facial nerve is associated with two parasympathetic ganglia, the pterygopalatine and submandibular ganglia. The vagus nerve (CN X), by contrast, is not affiliated with an efferent parasympathetic ganglion of the head.

The parasympathetic synapse between the preganglionic and postganglionic neuron occurs near the effector organ. The vagus is not responsible for the efferent innervation of any visceral structure of the head. The visceral structures it supplies are located in the neck, thorax and abdomen. The synapse between the vagal preganglionic and postganglionic neurons are also found in those areas, near the effector organs. The vagus carries 75% of all peripheral parasympathetic fibers; it leaves the supply of the parasympathetic efferent ganglia of the head to the other three parasympathetic cranial nerves.

SACRAL PARASYMPATHETIC CONTRIBUTION

Sacral parasympathetic input originates from preganglionic cell bodies located in the spinal cord at the S2-S4 levels. Preganglionic axons exit the cord as **pelvic splanchnic nerves** (267, 269). They travel to parasympathetic ganglia and synapse with postganglionic cell bodies. Postganglionic axons extend from these cell bodies to innervate viscera of the lower abdomen and pelvis. These structures include the distal part of the large colon, rectum, bladder, uterus, and genitals.

Parasympathetic innervation of the digestive tract involves three basic levels: (1) the facial nerve (CN VII) and glossopharyngeal nerve (CN IX) innervate salivary glands of the oral cavity; (2) the vagus nerve (CN X) innervates visceral structures of the digestive tract from the oral cavity to the left (splenic) flexure of the large bowel; (3) the sacral parasympathetics innervate distal to the left colic flexure.

FIGURE 6.21
PARASYMPATHETIC INNERVATION OF THE DIGESTIVE TRACT

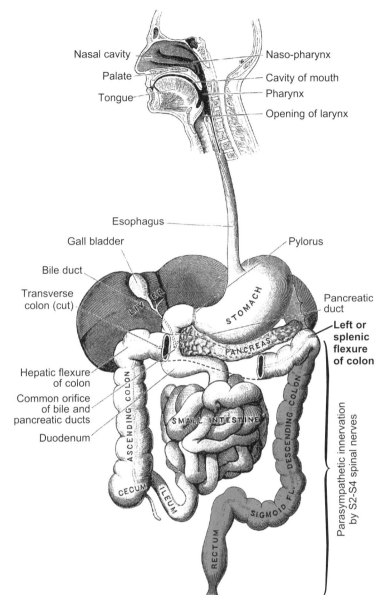

4 and 4 (again)

There are **four** notable parasympathetic efferent ganglia of the head. They include the ciliary, pterygopalatine (sphenopalatine), submandibular (submaxillary), and otic ganglia. Coincidentally, there are **four** notable sympathetic prevertebral ganglia of the abdomen. These include the celiac, aorticorenal, superior mesenteric, and inferior mesenteric ganglia.

$A_1U_2T_3O_4$ = autonomic system = **4**
1) **4** sympathetic paravertebral ganglia with names: superior cervical, middle cervical, stellate, ganglion impar
2) **4** sympathetic prevertebral ganglia of the abdomen
3) **4** parasympathetic cranial nerves
4) **4** parasympathetic efferent ganglia of the head

FIGURE 6.22
SYMPATHETIC NERVOUS SYSTEM

Sympathetic Nervous System
Thoracolumbar system

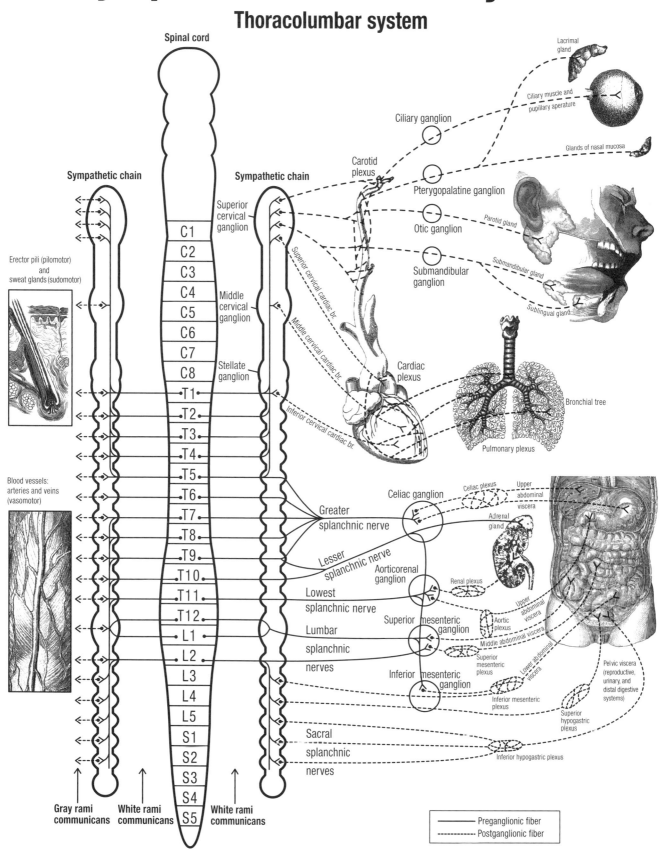

FIGURE 6.23
PARASYMPATHETIC NERVOUS SYSTEM

Parasympathetic Nervous System
Craniosacral system

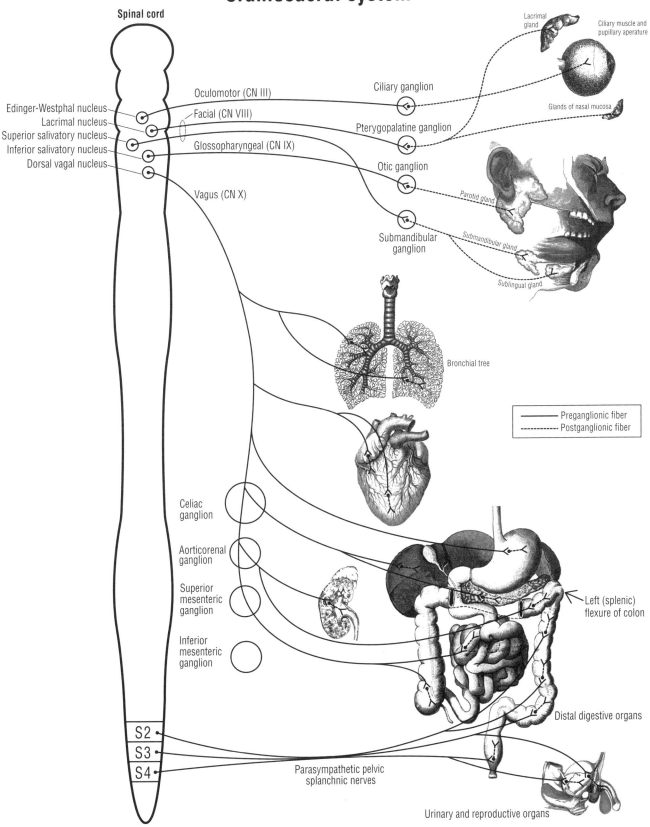

Spinal cord

Lacrimal gland

Ciliary muscle and pupillary aperature

Oculomotor (CN III)

Ciliary ganglion

Edinger-Westphal nucleus

Facial (CN VIII)

Glands of nasal mucosa

Lacrimal nucleus

Pterygopalatine ganglion

Superior salivatory nucleus

Inferior salivatory nucleus

Glossopharyngeal (CN IX)

Dorsal vagal nucleus

Otic ganglion

Parotid gland

Vagus (CN X)

Submandibular ganglion

Submandibular gland

Sublingual gland

Bronchial tree

Preganglionic fiber
Postganglionic fiber

Celiac ganglion

Aorticorenal ganglion

Left (splenic) flexure of colon

Superior mesenteric ganglion

Inferior mesenteric ganglion

Distal digestive organs

S2

S3

S4

Parasympathetic pelvic splanchnic nerves

Urinary and reproductive organs

QUIZ 3
Autonomic Nervous System

Time for Quiz = 16 minutes.
For questions 1-13, choose the single best answer.

_____1) What may be found in the ciliary ganglion?
    a) parasympathetic postganglionic cell bodies
    b) sympathetic postganglionic axons
    c) both a and b
    d) sympathetic preganglionic axons
    e) none of the above

_____2) Which statement about the parasympathetic postganglionic neuron is true?
    a) The cell bodies may be located in the brain.
    b) The cell bodies may be located in paravertebral ganglia.
    c) The cell bodies may be located in the thoracic spinal cord.
    d) The cell bodies may be located within the wall of the effector organ.
    e) None of the above

_____3) Postganglionic parasympathetic fibers travel from which ganglion to innervate the sublingual gland?
    a) otic
    b) submandibular
    c) sphenopalatine
    d) ciliary
    e) none of the above

_____4) Preganglionic fibers of the vagus nerve may synapse in which ganglion?
    a) otic ganglion
    b) inferior mesenteric ganglion
    c) ciliary ganglion
    d) sphenopalatine ganglion
    e) none of the above

_____5) Which nerve is associated with the submandibular ganglion?
    a) facial
    b) oculomotor
    c) glossopharyngeal
    d) vagus
    e) none of the above

_____6) Which of the following provide parasympathetic stimulation to the body wall?
    a) preganglionic fibers extending from the T1-L2 levels of the spinal cord
    b) postganglionic fibers extending from prevertebral ganglia
    c) postganglionic fibers extending from ganglia very near the effector organs
    d) postganglionic fibers traveling in the intercostal nerves
    e) none of the above

_____7) Preganglionic parasympathetic axons from the lacrimal nucleus of the brainstem travel to which autonomic ganglion to synapse?
    a) submandibular
    b) otic
    c) pterygopalatine
    d) ciliary
    e) none of the above

_____8) Which statement is true concerning the parasympathetic preganglionic neuron?
    a) It may synapse with an effector organ.
    b) The axon is relatively shorter than the sympathetic preganglionic axon.
    c) The cell body may be located in the cervical spinal cord.
    d) The cell body may be located in the thoracic spinal cord.
    e) None of the above

_____9) Preganglionic parasympathetic axons from the superior salivatory nucleus of the brainstem travel to which autonomic ganglion to synapse?
    a) otic
    b) submandibular
    c) ciliary
    d) stellate
    e) none of the above

_____10) Which cranial nerves carry parasympathetic fibers?
    a) the oculomotor nerve
    b) the abducens nerve
    c) the hypoglossal nerve
    d) the olfactory nerve
    e) none of the above

_____11) Which statement about the pterygopalatine (sphenopalatine) ganglion is true?
    a) It is a paravertebral sympathetic ganglion.
    b) It is a parasympathetic ganglion of the head associated with the glossopharyngeal nerve (CN IX).
    c) It is a prevertebral sympathetic ganglion.
    d) It is a parasympathetic ganglion of the head associated with the facial nerve (VII).
    e) None of the above

_____12) What is found in the parasympathetic pelvic splanchnic nerves?
    a) preganglionic vagus nerve fibers
    b) postganglionic vagus nerve fibers
    c) preganglionic fibers from the sacral spinal cord
    d) postganglionic fibers from the sacral spinal cord
    e) none of the above

_____13) Preganglionic parasympathetic axons from the inferior salivatory nucleus of the brainstem travel to which autonomic ganglion to synapse?
    a) otic
    b) sphenopalatine
    c) submandibular
    d) ciliary
    e) none of the above

For questions 14-16, use the following directions:
    a......1,2,3 are correct
    b......1,3 are correct
    c......2,4 are correct
    d......only 4 is correct
    e......all arc correct

_____14) Which statements about the vagus nerve are true?
    1) Preganglionic cell bodies may be found in the lacrimal nucleus of the brainstem.
    2) 75% of all peripheral parasympathetic fibers travel in the vagus nerve.
    3) Postganglionic cell bodies may be found in the submandibular (submaxillary) ganglion.
    4) Preganglionic fibers (axons) may travel in the aorticorenal ganglion.

_____15) What may be found in the submandibular (submaxillary) ganglion?
    1) parasympathetic postganglionic cell bodies
    2) parasympathetic preganglionic axons
    3) sympathetic postganglionic axons
    4) parasympathetic postganglionic axons

_____16) Which statements about the ciliary ganglion are true?
    1) It houses parasympathetic postganglionic neuron cell bodies.
    2) It receives preganglionic axons from the inferior salivatory nucleus.
    3) Postganglionic fibers travel to the muscles of the pupil and ciliary muscle of the eye.
    4) It is a prevertebral sympathetic ganglion located in the abdomen.

QUIZ 3: Autonomic Nervous System

1) c – Each of the four parasympathetic efferent ganglia of the head (ciliary, pterygopalatine, submandibular, and otic) is classified as a parasympathetic ganglion because it is the location of parasympathetic postganglionic cell bodies. These ganglia also have somatic and postganglionic sympathetic axons which are passing through en route to the tissues they innervate.

2) d – The parasympathetic nervous system is also known as the craniosacral system because preganglionic neuron cell bodies are found in the brain (cranium) and sacral spinal cord. Axons travel out to synapse with parasympathetic postganglionic neurons very near the effector organ. In fact, these synapses often occur *within* the wall of the effector organ. Because the synapse between the preganglionic and postganglionic neuron is so near the effector organ, the parasympathetic postganglionic axon is relatively short compared to the sympathetic postganglionic axon. Paravertebral and prevertebral ganglia are the location of sympathetic postganglionic neurons.

3) b – The submandibular (submaxillary) ganglion is one of two parasympathetic efferent ganglia associated with the facial nerve (CN VII). The submandibular ganglion receives preganglionic parasympathetic fibers (axons) from neuron cell bodies located in the superior salivatory nucleus of the brainstem. In turn, the ganglion sends postganglionic axons to provide efferent parasympathetic innervation to two salivary glands, the sublingual and submandibular (submaxillary) glands. The otic ganglion is a parasympathetic ganglion associated with the glossopharyngeal nerve (CN IX) and provides postganglionic fibers to the parotid gland, the largest of the salivary glands. The pterygopalatine (sphenopalatine) ganglion is the other parasympathetic efferent ganglion associated with the facial nerve (CN VII). It supplies postganglionic fibers to the lacrimal gland (tears) and glands of the nasal and oral cavities. The ciliary ganglion is a parasympathetic ganglion associated with the oculomotor nerve (CN III). It provides postganglionic axons to the pupillary muscles (miosis) and ciliary muscle (positive accommodation for near-sighted vision) of the eye.

4) e – There are four parasympathetic efferent ganglia of the head. They include the ciliary, pterygopalatine, submandibular, and otic ganglia. The vagus nerve is not associated with any of them. It already has enough of a parasympathetic responsibility, because it carries 75% of all peripheral parasympathetic fibers and provides parasympathetic innervation to structures of the neck, thorax, and abdomen. It leaves the responsibility of the four parasympathetic ganglia of the head to the other three parasympathetic cranial nerves. Abdominal preganglionic vagal fibers, en route to synapse with postganglionic neurons very near their effector organs, may pass through prevertebral sympathetic ganglia of the abdomen. These include the celiac, aorticorenal, and superior mesenteric ganglia. The fourth abdominal prevertebral sympathetic ganglion, the inferior mesenteric ganglion, is usually located so inferior that it does not contain vagal fibers. Parasympathetic innervation in this area is by way of parasympathetic pelvic splanchnic nerves. These nerves carry parasympathetic preganglionic fibers from cell bodies located at the S2-S4 spinal levels.

5) a – See #3 answer explanation.

6) e – There is no parasympathetic innervation to the extremities or body wall. The only visceral structures in these areas are sweat glands, piloerector muscles of hair follicles, and blood vessels. All are innervated solely by the sympathetic system. In addition to the upper extremities, lower extremities, and body wall, there is no parasympathetic innervation to the splenic capsule or adrenal gland.

7) c – The pterygopalatine (sphenopalatine) ganglion is one of the two parasympathetic efferent ganglia associated with the facial nerve (CN VII). The pterygopalatine ganglion receives preganglionic fibers (axons) from neuron cell bodies located in the lacrimal nucleus. In turn, it sends postganglionic fibers (axons) to innervate the lacrimal gland (tears) and glands of the nasal and oral cavities. The submandibular (submaxillary) ganglion is the other parasympathetic efferent ganglion associated with the facial

nerve (CN VII). It supplies postganglionic fibers to two salivary glands, the sublingual and submandibular (submaxillary) glands. The otic ganglion is a parasympathetic ganglion associated with the glossopharyngeal nerve (CN IX) and provides postganglionic fibers to the parotid gland, the largest of the salivary glands. The ciliary ganglion is a parasympathetic ganglion associated with the oculomotor nerve (CN III). It provides post-ganglionic axons to the pupillary muscles (miosis) and ciliary muscle (positive accommodation for near-sighted vision) of the eye.

8) e – The autonomic nervous system, including both the sympathetic and parasympathetic systems, has an anatomic structure with two neurons outside the CNS (brain and spinal cord) that participate in signal transmission. Cell bodies of the of the first (preganglionic) neurons of the sympathetic or thoracolumbar system are located in the intermediolateral horn of the thoracic and lumbar spinal cord from T1-L2. By contrast, cell bodies of the parasympathetic or craniosacral system are located in the brain and sacral spinal cord. Sympathetic preganglionic fibers (axons) are relatively shorter than parasympathetic pre-ganglionic axons. Sympathetic postganglionic fibers (axons) are therefore longer than their parasympathetic counterparts. The pregan-glionic parasympathetic axon synapses with the postganglionic neuron near the effector organ. This synapse often occurs within the actual wall of the effector organ. It is the axon of the postganglionic neuron which synapses with the effector organ.

9) b – See #3 answer explanation. The stellate gan-glion is a paravertebral sympathetic ganglion formed by the combination of the last cervical and first thoracic ganglion.

10) a – The parasympathetic nervous system is also known as the craniosacral nervous system because of its anatomic structure. Cell bodies located in the surface of the brain and brain stem extend preganglionic axons that leave with four parasympathetic cranial nerves. Additionally, cell bodies located in the spinal cord at the S2-S4 spinal levels extend fibers that ultimately supply the lower abdominal and pelvic viscera. The four parasympathetic cranial nerves are the oculomotor nerve (CN III), facial nerve (CN VII), glossopharyngeal nerve (CN IX), and the vagus nerve (CN X).

11) d – See #7 answer explanation.

12) c – The parasympathetic or craniosacral nervous system has preganglionic cell bodies located in the ventral surface of the brain and brain stem (*cranio-*) and spinal cord at the S2-S4 spinal levels (*-sacral*). The parasympathetic pelvic splanchnic nerves thereby carry pre-ganglionic parasympathetic fibers from the S2-S4 spinal cord. Remember, the parasym-pathetic preganglionic fibers synapse close to, often within, the wall of the effector organ. Due to this structure, parasympathetic nerves seldom carry postganglionic fibers. They almost always carry preganglionic fibers because the synapse with the postganglionic neuron does not occur until the effector organ is nearly reached.

13) a – See #7 answer explanation. The otic ganglion is one of the four efferent ganglia of the head which is associated with a parasympathetic cranial nerve. The otic ganglion is associated with the glossopharyngeal nerve (CN IX). The ganglion receives parasympathetic pre-ganglionic axons from the inferior salivatory nucleus of the brainstem. In turn, it sends out postganglionic axons to supply parasympa-thetic innervation to the parotid gland, the largest of the salivary glands.

14) c – The vagus nerve is the predominant parasym-pathetic peripheral nerve. In fact, 75% of all peripheral parasympathetic fibers travel in the vagus nerve. Preganglionic cell bodies of the nerve are found in the dorsal vagal nucleus of the brainstem. From here, preganglionic fibers travel out to reach effector organs of the neck, thorax, and abdomen. Vagus innervation of the digestive system extends to the level of the left colic flexure. Sacral parasympathetic splanchnic nerves from the S2-S4 levels of the spinal cord innervate everything distal to the left colic flexure. Because the parasympa-thetic synapse occurs very near the effector organ, preganglionic vagus fibers are what is seen coursing down the various nerve

plexuses. There are four significant prevertebral sympathetic ganglia of the abdomen. They include the celiac, aorticorenal, superior mesenteric, and inferior mesenteric ganglia. These are described as sympathetic ganglia because they are the location of postganglionic sympathetic cell bodies. It is important to realize that the ganglia may also contain preganglionic parasympathetic fibers (axons) that are traveling through, en route to synapse with the postganglionic neuron very near the effector organ. The three most superior prevertebral sympathetic ganglia (celiac, aorticorenal, and superior mesenteric) almost always have some preganglionic vagal fibers (axons) within them. The inferior mesenteric ganglion is located too inferior. Parasympathetic innervation to the area supplied by the inferior mesenteric ganglion is usually supplied by the parasympathetic pelvic splanchnic nerves (S2-S4). Because of its distal location, the inferior mesenteric ganglion rarely contains preganglionic vagal fibers. Preganglionic fibers from cell bodies found in the lacrimal nucleus travel in the facial nerve and synapse with postganglionic cell bodies in the pterygopalatine (sphenopalatine) ganglion. The submandibular (submaxillary) ganglion is another parasympathetic efferent ganglion of the head associated with the facial nerve (CN VII).

15) e – The submandibular (submaxillary) ganglion, along with the pterygopalatine (sphenopalatine) ganglion, is one of the two parasympathetic efferent ganglia associated with the facial nerve (CN VII). Postganglionic axons extend from the submandibular ganglion to innervate the sublingual and submandibular (submaxillary) salivary glands. This ganglion is said to be a parasympathetic ganglion simply because it houses parasympathetic postganglionic neuron cell bodies and is the location of the synapse between preganglionic and postganglionic parasympathetic neurons. Realize that sympathetic postganglionic and somatic fibers do travel in each of the four large parasympathetic ganglia of the head. Because the parasympathetic synapse occurs within the ganglion, any part of the ganglion may contain either preganglionic or postganglionic parasympathetic axons, depending on the location in the ganglion relative to the location of the synapse.

16) b – The oculomotor nerve (CN III) is one of the four cranial nerves that carry parasympathetic fibers. Preganglionic cell bodies are located n the Edinger-Westphal nucleus of the midbrain. From here, preganglionic axons travel out to synapse with postganglionic cell bodies located in the ciliary ganglion. Postganglionic axons then travel on to supply muscles of the pupil and ciliary muscles of the lens. Parasympathetic stimulation to the eye is by way of the oculomotor nerve. It causes miosis (pupillary contraction) and positive accommodation for near-sighted vision. The inferior salivatory nucleus houses preganglionic neurons that send axons to synapse in the otic ganglion. These parasympathetic fibers travel in the glossopharyngeal nerve (CN IX). Prevertebral sympathetic ganglia of the abdomen include the celiac, aorticorenal, superior mesenteric, and inferior mesenteric ganglia.

"Children today are tyrants. They contradict their parents, gobble their food, and tyrannize their teachers."

– Socrates

CLINICAL CORRELATION

Because basic metabolic mechanisms are described in this chapter, the metabolic disease, **diabetes mellitus**, is the topic of this clinical correlation. The function of the autonomic nervous system, like so many other tissues and systems, deteriorates as a result of the disease process of diabetes.

Diabetes mellitus exists in epidemic proportions. Its manifestations commonly contribute to atherosclerosis, heart attack, stroke, renal failure, dehydration, weakness, acidosis, and death. Any future health care provider should become very familiar with the pathophysiology and long-term effects of diabetes. Regardless of the health care specialty, patient care will involve treatment of diabetic patients. More money, time, and effort are spent treating the effects of diabetes than any other disease process.

The word *diabetes* actually describes a broad spectrum of diseases with the common effect of causing excessive excretion of urine. Diabetes insipidus, for instance, is due to an insufficient amount or response to antidiuretic hormone. Due to this deficiency, water is not reabsorbed by the renal tubules and a significant amount of urine is produced. Diabetes mellitus is a metabolic disease characterized by inadequate amount or response to insulin. For future discussion, whenever the single word *diabetes* is used, it is specifically referring to the disease process of diabetes mellitus.

There are two types of diabetes. **Type I diabetes** is also known as juvenile, juvenile-onset, ketosis-prone, acidosis-prone, or insulin-deficient diabetes. As may be inferred from the various names, type I diabetes is usually manifested in childhood. For some reason, there is inadequate insulin production. There are several possible reasons for the insufficiency. Many patients have a congenital deficit or genetic malformation of beta cells, the cells responsible for insulin production. It is thought that some patients develop autoimmune diseases with antibodies directed against beta cells. There is also evidence to suggest a viral cause. In all likelihood, these three possibilities, separate or in some combination, play a role in the disease onset. Regardless of the initial etiology, type I diabetes is due to a relative absence of insulin.

Type II diabetes is also known as adult-onset or latent diabetes. The onset is in adult life. Something changes during life to cause the disease. The patient may be born with a genetic predisposition that does not manifest until adult life. An autoimmune or viral phenomenon could occur that is directed against beta cells, insulin, or insulin receptors. Perhaps lifestyle and dietary habits over a lifetime cause the disease. As with type I diabetes, the true etiology may consist of some combination of any of these possibilities.

Unlike type I diabetes, where the disease is known to be due to a lack of insulin, the reasons for the development of type II diabetes are not as clear. There are four cellular levels where alterations could occur to contribute to the disease: the beta cell, the blood, the insulin receptor/cell membrane, and the intracellular environment of the target cell. Not only could something happen to the beta cell to affect the quantity of insulin produced, but the quality of insulin could just as easily be affected. Alterations in the chemical structure could affect function. Once insulin is released in the blood, chemical mediators could alter its structure or destroy it altogether. It may have to compete against chemical antagonists for binding the insulin receptor. Insulin receptors could be altered, transformed, or decreased in number. Finally, something could have changed within the intracellular environment to affect the action of insulin once it crosses the cell membrane.

Many type II patients actually have elevated basal levels of insulin. This implies **insulin resistance**. For some reason, the body has developed a resistance to insulin. Although the insulin is present, it could be subtly changed so the insulin receptor does not adequately respond to it. There may be changes to the quality or quantity of insulin receptors. Changes could occur within the target cell to diminish the response to insulin.

Insulin resistance is not the only contributing factor in type II diabetes. Despite an elevated basal insulin rate, the insulin response to a glucose challenge is markedly decreased in type II diabetics. Because the stimulus for insulin secretion is elevated blood glucose, the deficient insulin response represents a functional inability of beta cells. The actual cause of type II diabetes is unclear, but is thought to consist of some combination of decreased beta cell function and insulin resistance.

Type II diabetics are frequently overweight, and **obesity** is known to play a role in the development of type II diabetes. The exact role is uncertain. The obvious thought is that the individual simply outgrows the beta cell supply. In support of this, some patients are able to control their disease by merely losing weight. The true association of type II diabetes and obesity is actually much more complex than just supply and demand. Obese people secrete more insulin than non-obese people, regardless of whether or not they are diabetic. Over time, the increased insulin secretion may have its costs. Beta cell function could become exhausted. Insulin resistance could also develop. The response to insulin becomes less pronounced because there is more exposure to the hormone. The diminished insulin response could be due to a decrease in the number or function of insulin receptors in the face of chronically elevated insulin levels. **Down regulation of receptors** is a process by which the number of membrane receptors is decreased in response to a chronically elevated level of stimulating substance. This process has been shown to occur with numerous other substances and their accompanying cell membrane receptors. Down regulation is thought to be a major reason why some drugs have diminished effect with certain individuals after prolonged administration. In addition to membrane changes, the defect could occur within the intracellular environment of the target cell.

It is not known whether the elevated level of insulin in obese diabetics is a cause or a result of type II diabetes. The elevated basal insulin rate could be an attempt to recover from the poor response of a diabetic patient to a glucose challenge. Alternatively, the elevated basal rate could result from pre-existing obesity, genetic predisposition, or frequent high glucose meals and snacks. This chronically elevated insulin level could then trigger changes that make the beta cells, insulin receptors, or target cell intracellular environment less responsive to insulin. In other words, the frequent exposure to elevated insulin levels could predispose an individual to insulin resistance, and, subsequently, diabetes mellitus. Which came first, the chicken or the egg?

Obesity, in and of itself, is not the only factor contributing to the formation of type II diabetes. Dietary habits are certain to play a role, even in non-obese patients. Insulin is secreted in response to a carbohydrate meal; non-carbohydrate foods do not induce insulin secretion. Man has inhabited the earth for thousands of years. It was not until recently, that high carbohydrate food sources were readily available. Ancient man was a hunter/gatherer. He ate what he killed, caught, grew, or found. High fructose corn syrup was not an option. Today's environment provides a constant barrage of high carbohydrate foods which are conveniently packaged and available for ease of consumption. In the complexity of modern times, nearby soda and candy machines provide an ever-present means to obtain nourishment. The body is faced with frequent, very high carbohydrate bombardments which continually stimulate insulin release. Over time, the beta cells could simply burn out. As with the theories of the relationship of type II diabetics and obesity, it is also possible that the chronic over-secretion of insulin could lead to insulin resistance by the body. The period of time man has been exposed to frequent, carbohydrate-laden fast food, candy, sodas, and snacks is dwarfed by the period of time man has lived without such a diet. The human body has not had time to adjust.

Type I diabetics are frequently also called **insulin-dependent diabetics (IDDM)**. They produce little insulin and have to take insulin injections to survive. Because they can often treat their disease with diet, weight loss, or oral hypoglycemic medications, type II diabetics are often called **non-insulin-dependent diabetics (NIDDM)**. This description is somewhat confusing and should be discouraged. The cause of type I diabetes is different than that of type II diabetes. Furthermore, it is not uncommon to find an adult-onset diabetic who has progressed to requiring insulin shots to control blood glucose. With current therapy, all type I diabetics require insulin. A significant number of type II diabetics also eventually require insulin.

> How would one describe the above-mentioned individual? A non-insulin-dependent diabetic who takes insulin? How confusing?! A better description is an adult-onset diabetic or type II diabetic who takes insulin.

Disease manifestations are the same for the two types of diabetes with one notable exception. Because type I diabetics are unable to produce a significant amount of functional insulin, they can become extremely hyperglycemic, eventually leading to hyperosmolar coma and even death. The word *hyperglycemic* describes elevated blood glucose or elevated "blood sugar." Even though there is plenty of glucose in the blood, the cells (with the exception of the brain and exercising skeletal muscle) are unable to use it as energy because there is no available insulin to transport glucose intracellularly. The cells are therefore starving. In an effort to sustain life, the cells use fatty acids as the predominant energy supply. This over-usage of lipids by the citric acid (Krebs)

cycle produces acid byproducts known as ketone bodies. The over-abundance of ketone bodies can lead to an acidosis of the body. This acidosis is known as ketosis or, more commonly, ketoacidosis. Acidosis affects cellular function, leads to multiple organ system derangements, and can become life threatening. Although type II diabetics produce insufficient amounts of insulin for the body's overall need, they ordinarily produce enough to prevent ketoacidosis and hyperosmolar coma. The take-home point is that, under normal circumstances, type I diabetics are the only diabetic patients that are at risk for ketoacidosis and/or hyperosmolar coma. Because they make insulin, type II diabetics do not develop these life-threatening conditions.

Type I and type II diabetics otherwise share the same basic disease process. After a carbohydrate meal, the blood sugar of a diabetic rises. A normal patient would immediately secrete insulin and drive the sugar intracellularly. The diabetic's insulin response is inadequate. The blood sugar continues to rise, and the patient becomes **hyperglycemic**. This elevated blood glucose osmotically pulls fluid from the intracellular space. Cells become dehydrated. Furthermore, elevated blood glucose spills into the urine. This is known as **glycosuria**. The glucose in the urine osmotically pulls additional water with it. The patient excretes excessive amounts of urine, a condition known as **polyuria**. In fact, investigation of polyuria is a frequent reason the diagnosis of diabetes is initially made. This process of osmotically pulling water out of cells and subsequently excreting it in the urine leads to both intracellular and extracellular **dehydration,** both of which become severe. Because of the dehydration, the patient can become exceedingly thirsty. Tremendous amounts of water can be consumed. This excessive consumption is known as **polydipsia**.

In the absence of insulin, glucose is unable to move to the intracellular environment of all cells except brain cells and exercising muscles cells. Most cells of the body are therefore starving, even in the face of blood hyperglycemia. In an effort to provide energy and preserve life, these cells turn to lipids as the predominant energy source. This causes mobilization of fatty acids from triglyceride stores in adipose cells to be used by other cells as energy. As opposed to adipose cells, in which the lipid stores are depleted, liver cells have enzymes which convert fatty acids back to triglycerides for storage. Over time, this leads to a **fatty liver**. Excess lipids in the liver "spill over" into the blood. Surplus fatty acids favors the formation of cholesterol and phospholipids, which along with triglycerides, are released in the blood as lipoproteins.

The important consequence of the chronic utilization of fatty acids as an energy source is the overexposure of the intravascular environment to lipids. The excessive exposure predisposes all arteries to the premature development of **atherosclerosis**. Atherosclerosis leads to the development of heart attack, stroke, renal disease, peripheral vascular disease, and death.

> *Sclerosis* is a word which means hardening. It is used to describe structures undergoing an infective process. It also describes chronic conditions of the vascular and/or nervous system.
>
> *Arteriosclerosis* is a disease process meaning "hardening of the arteries."
>
> *Atherosclerosis* is a form of arteriosclerosis characterized by the formation of atheromas.

An ***atheroma*** is an intraluminal plaque of lipids, cholesterol, and thickened arterial intimal cells.

The words *atherosclerosis* and *arteriosclerosis* are often used interchangeably to describe this arterial disease process of diabetes. Atherosclerosis is a better choice because the word more specifically describes what is actually occurring within the arterial walls of diabetic patients. Atherosclerosis may also develop in non-diabetic patients. There are other disease processes which can cause arteriosclerosis (hardening of the arteries) and have nothing to do with diabetes or development of atheromas.

Atherosclerosis is the number one cause of morbidity and mortality among diabetic patients. Although hyperosmolar coma and/or ketoacidosis is a frequent cause of death in poorly controlled type I diabetic patients, the incidence of type I diabetes is significantly lower than type II. Furthermore, in the era of modern medicine, most type I diabetics are capable of controlling their disease so that they live long enough to die of other causes. Unfortunately, these other causes are frequently the result of atherosclerosis.

Atherosclerosis is a total body disease. Any artery can be affected and any tissue can have its blood supply adversely affected. Not only does decreased blood flow limit the amount of oxygen and fuel the tissue receives, but it also decreases the removal of metabolic by-products from the tissue. This predisposes to acidosis and toxicity. When blood supply to a coronary artery of the heart is stopped, a myocardial infarction, or heart attack, occurs. When blood supply to a cerebral artery of the brain is stopped, a cerebral infarction, or stroke, occurs. An **infarct** is an area of cell death in an organ or structure which is often due to inadequate supply of oxygen and/or energy sources. Although infarcts of the heart and brain get the most publicity, they can occur in any organ or structure that is dependent on blood flow. Infarcts occur in the lungs, bowel, kidneys, pancreas, etc. All can be life-threatening. Even if acute infarction does not occur, chronic decreased blood supply can lead to permanent organ dysfunction. In the extremities, atherosclerosis may require surgical vascular bypass procedures in an effort to preserve the limb. Amputations in long-term diabetic patients are not uncommon.

The microvascular effects of atherosclerosis also play a significant role in the pathogenesis of diabetes. Atherosclerosis of the arterioles supplying the retina, kidneys, and peripheral nerves negatively affects each of these tissues. In fact, the trio of retinopathy, nephropathy, and neuropathy is often present in long-term or severe diabetics. Most long-term diabetics have at least one of these conditions.

Retinopathy is a disease of the retina. Diabetic retinopathy is associated with arteriole atherosclerosis, microaneurysms, retinal hemorrhages, and neovascularization of the retina. Neovascularization is new blood vessel growth. In the retina, it is stimulated by the current arterial system's inability to adequately provide blood. Unfortunately, the new blood vessels occupy space previously occupied by retinal tissue. Vision is adversely affected.

Diabetic patients frequently have visual problems as a result of diabetic retinopathy. Poorly-controlled diabetics can become blind.

Nephropathy is simply a disease of the kidneys. Diabetes is only one of numerous diseases that can cause nephropathy. In diabetes, the functional unit of the kidney, the nephron, is particularly susceptible to atherosclerosis of the arterioles supplying the glomeruli. Renal function deteriorates throughout the course of the disease. The majority of patients who require hemodialysis carry the diagnosis of diabetes.

Neuropathy is any change of the peripheral nervous system which is caused by a disease process. As with other tissues, the microvasculature supplying peripheral nerves is negatively affected by atherosclerosis of diabetes. On a cellular level, there is demyelination of the nerves. The result is symmetrical sensory deficits which usually start at the feet. The feet are farthest from the heart and have the poorest circulation.

Because of the sensory deficits that develop in poorly-controlled diabetics, they become especially predisposed to foot injury. As unpleasant as it may be, pain serves a purpose. It notifies an individual as to the presence of a cut or sprain. Once the injury is known, it may be properly cared for. Pain provides negative reinforcement which motivates the individual to stay off the foot and let it heal. If nothing else, it forces the individual to inadvertently protect it by walking with a limp. Diabetics with significant neuropathy have no notification of injury. They cannot feel their feet. Wounds are not dressed and become infected. Injuries are chronically re-injured because the patients do not know to stay off their feet. To compound this, poor circulation of an atherosclerotic diabetic makes wound healing extremely difficult. All of these factors contribute to the formation of poorly healing foot ulcers. The **diabetic foot ulcer** is a well-known entity and a frequent cause of medical intervention in a diabetic patient.

Not only does neuropathy occur in peripheral nerves, but it also occurs in the autonomic nervous system. This autonomic neuropathy leads to **autonomic insufficiency**. Both the sympathetic and parasympathetic systems are affected. Diabetics frequently experience erratic changes in heart rate and blood pressure. Both ends of the spectrum, high and low, can be tested. All autonomic functions can be adversely affected. This leads to multiple tissue and organ system dysfunctions.

In addition to glucose, several amino acids also require the presence of insulin for intracellular transport. In the absence of insulin, these amino acids are not allowed to cross the cell membrane to form the various proteins required by the body. Amino acids are excreted in the urine as excessive amounts of urea. To compound the problem, existing proteins are broken down to increase the amount of amino acids available for conversion to glucose via gluconeogenesis. This process leads to **protein wasting**. Proteins are essential in a variety of cellular processes and are used to form hormones and enzymes. In their absence, there is **cellular and organ system dysfunction**. **Weakness** and **emaciation** are common occurrences in uncontrolled diabetics. Because of the loss of protein and overall lack of energy sources, patients can develop an insatiable hunger. **Polyphagia** is the excessive consumption of food and is often seen with poorly controlled diabetics.

The following, oversimplified summary may prove easy to remember:

There are three dietary sources of energy. Two of these, carbohydrates (glucose) and proteins (amino acids), require insulin for intracellular transport. In the absence of insulin, both are lost. The loss of each has its associated contributions to the disease process of diabetes. In an effort to provide vital energy, the body turns to the third dietary source of energy, fats (lipids). This excessive mobilization of lipids and their exposure to the intravascular environment predisposes to the development of atherosclerosis. Atherosclerosis is responsible for much of the severe pathology of diabetes.

SUMMARY OF CHAPTER BOXES

1) A **s**cared person activates the **s**ympathetic nervous system.

2) The *adren*al gland secretes *adren*ergic hormones, including *adren*alin (epinephrine) and norepinephrine. These hormones form the *center* of the sympathetic response and are secreted from the *center* of the adrenal gland (adrenal medulla).
   – The adrenal cortex is the outer portion of the adrenal gland. The adrenal *cor*tex secretes steroid hormones, including *cor*tisol.

3) The juxtaglomerular cells are just before the glomerulus.

4) The renin-angiotensin system is an important mechanism for raising blood pressure. The names of both renin and angiotensin provide clues that facilitate remembering their functions. The kidneys have two different word combining forms that describe them: **nephr-** and **ren-**. *Angi-* is a combining form which means *vessel*.
   Renin is an enzyme secreted by the kidneys. Ren**in** increases blood pressure.
   Angiotensin increases the blood pressure by "tensing" the blood vessels (it causes vasoconstriction).

5) *ECG* and *EKG* are used interchangeably. The German form of the word *electrocardiogram* is *elekrokardiogram*.

6) **3 dietary sources of energy go through 3 stages of catabolism** – compounds are broken down to simpler molecules for the production of energy. This is opposed to anabolism – a building process where simple molecules are transformed to more complex compounds. Anabolic steroids are taken in an effort to "bulk up." All metabolic processes are either catabolic (break down, utilize) or anabolic in character.

7) Glycolysis = breakdown of glucose for energy. Glucose can either be converted to pyruvate or lactate. The suffix **-lysis** means *dissolution* or *breakdown*.

8) Oil and water do not mix. Triglycerides are hydrophobic (hydro = water; phobia = aversion).

9) Lipolysis is the dissolution of lipids.

10) All 3 metabolic pathways (glycolysis, lipolysis, and gluconeogenesis) increase fuel availability. All are increased with sympathetic stimulation and not affected by parasympathetic stimulation. Glycolysis is the breakdown of glucose to pyruvate or lactate. Lipolysis is the breakdown of lipid (fat) storage molecules, triglycerides, to fatty acids. Fatty acids are then used to eventually form acetyl-CoA. Gluconeogenesis is the creation of glucose from non-carbohydrate sources (amino acids from proteins). The word element *gluco* refers to glucose, *neo* means new, and *genesis* means creation. This "new" glucose can then be converted to pyruvate and from pyruvate to acetyl-CoA. The acetyl-CoA (from all 3 pathways) is then available to enter the citric acid (Krebs) cycle and oxidative phosphorylation with the resultant generation of ATP.

11) What effect should sympathetic stimulation have on insulin release? Why?

12) Due to sympathetic stimulation, hair stands up on the back of the neck of scared people and the back of an angry barking dog.

13) A sympathetic-stimulated scared person has no time or chance to read.

14) A sympathetic-stimulated person who is in a "fight for life" state has no time to stop and urinate.

15) Sympathetics are "fight or flight." Parasympathetics are "calm and collected."

16) Asthma is a disease of bronchoconstriction. It is treated with drugs which mimic or potentiate sympathetic stimulation and/or antagonize or block parasympathetic stimulation. The reverse is also true. Asthma may be made worse by drugs taken for unrelated reasons that block sympathetic or potentiate parasympathetic stimulation.

17) Theoretically, not as much light is needed in "calm and collected" environments.

18) Cilia are hair-like appendages which extend from certain microorganisms and mucous membranes. The ciliary muscle is named for its relationship to the suspensory ligaments of the lens, which appear as cilia.

19) Accommodation is used to read the newspaper while sipping coffee in the parasympathetic "calm and collected" environment.

20) It is virtually impossible to provide a urine sample in a doctor's office once the patient becomes frustrated, aggravated, and sympathetically stimulated.

21) The spine is part of the axial skeleton and can be considered the "center" of the body. Prevertebral ganglia are located in the periphery. They are *before* the *vertebrae* when moving toward the "center."

22) **ALL** sympathetic innervation must travel through the sympathetic chain. Sympathetic innervation of the head, neck, perineum, and extremities travels through the sympathetic chain, even though the preganglionic cell bodies are only located at T1-L2.

23) **White – going into sympathetic chain (leaving spinal nerve)**

Gray – leaving sympathetic chain (joining spinal nerve)
Consider the sympathetic chain as a recreational park. The white clouds of a clear day invite people to enter the park. White rami communicans carry fibers which are entering the sympathetic chain. The gray clouds of a storm cause people to leave the park. Gray rami communicans carry postganglionic fibers which are leaving the sympathetic chain. Once the storm arrives, there are more gray clouds than white clouds, just as there are more gray than white rami communicans.

24) White rami communicans contain myelinated fibers; gray rami communican contain unmyelinated fibers.

25) The T11 and T12 paravertebral ganglia are usually fused, explaining why there are eleven, rather than twelve, thoracic ganglia.

26) The word *mesenteric* refers to the mesentery, the folded membrane that attaches the intestines to the body wall.

27) The word *splanchnic* refers to the viscera. The splanchnic nerves provide sympathetic stimulation to the abdominal viscera.

28) The greater, lesser, and lowest splanchnic nerves come off the sympathetic chain from top to bottom in alphabetical order.

29) **Half and Half:** 6 named sympathetic nerves branch from the sympathetic chain and are not associated with spinal nerves. The upper half (3) are cardiac (heart). The lower half (3) are splanchnic (viscera).

In addition to these 6 nerves, thoracic sympathetic chain ganglia may also give off **thoracoabdominal nerves**. Lumbar sympathetic chain ganglia give off **lumbar splanchnic nerves**. Sacral sympathetic chain ganglia give off **sacral splanchnic nerves**.

30) Consider the **sympathetic and parasympathetic systems as opposites in three** basic ways: function, anatomy, and organization. (1) Functionally, "fight or flight" versus "calm and collected." (2) Anatomically, sympathetic system = thoracolumbar system, parasympathetic system = craniosacral system. (3) Structurally, the sympathetic preganglionic axon is relatively short compared to the postganglionic axon. The parasympathetic preganglionic axon is relatively long compared to the postganglionic axon.

31) The **Edinger-Westphal (E.W.)** nucleus houses parasympathetic preganglionic neuron cell bodies of the oculomotor nerve (CN III) which synapse with postganglionic cell bodies in the ciliary ganglion. The Edinger-Westphal (E.W.) nucleus provides for **EASY WATCHING (E.W.)** because it causes pupillary contraction (miosis) in darker environments and positive accommodation of the lens for near-sighted vision.

32) The name **pterygopalatine** ganglion is hard enough to learn. Add to that the fact that it is also known as the **sphenopalatine** ganglion…well, it is enough to make you want to cry. This ganglion provides postganglionic parasympathetic axons that innervate the **lacrimal glands** of the eyes. The lacrimal glands secrete tears.

33) The facial nerve (CN VII) provides parasympathetic innervation to all the "sub" salivary glands: the **sub**lingual and **sub**mandibular (**sub**maxillary) glands. Both are supplied via a "sub" ganglion, the **sub**mandibular (**sub**maxillary) ganglion. The glossopharyngeal nerve (CN IX) has the bigger name and appropriately innervates the biggest salivary gland, the parotid gland.

34) **The "Two Faces" of the Facial Nerve:** Preganglionic fibers extend from *two* brainstem nuclei, the lacrimal and superior salivatory nuclei. The facial nerve is associated with *two* parasympathetic efferent ganglia of the head, each of these ganglia has *two* names: pterygopalatine ganglion = sphenopalatine ganglion, submandibular ganglion = submaxillary ganglion. The facial nerve provides parasympathetic input to *two* types of glands, lacrimal and salivary glands. The facial nerve supplies *two* pairs of salivary glands, the submandibular (submaxillary) and sublingual glands.

35) The **ot**ic ganglion provides **post**ganglionic axons to the par**ot**id gland. Both are named for their location relative to the ear. When you see parotid, think otic and vice-versa.

36) **3 *Saliva*ry Glands Supplied by 2 *Saliva*tory Nuclei:** The sublingual and submandibular (submaxillary) glands receive postganglionic fibers from the submandibular (submaxillary) ganglion. This ganglion receives preganglionic parasympathetic input from the ***superior*** salivatory nucleus (all via facial n. (CN VII)). The parotid gland receives postganglionic parasympathetic fibers from the otic ganglion. This ganglion receives preganglionic parasympathetic input from the ***inferior*** salivatory nucleus (all via glossopharyngeal n. (CN IX)).

37) **3, 7, 9, 10 = parasympathetic cranial nerves**

38) **4 and 4: 4** cranial nerves carry parasympathetic fibers. Coincidentally, there are **4** parasympathetic efferent ganglia of the head. Three of the parasympathetic cranial nerves (oculomotor (CN III), facial (CN VII), glossopharyngeal (CN IX)) remain confined to the head and neck. They are the ones associated with these ganglia. The facial nerve is associated with two. The vagus nerve (CN X), by contrast, has the huge responsibility of carrying 75% of all peripheral parasympathetic fibers. It leaves the supply of the parasympathetic ganglia of the head to the other three parasympathetic cranial nerves.

39) **3 levels of parasympathetic innervation of the digestive tract:** (1) the facial nerve (CN VII) and glossopharyngeal nerve (CN IX) innervate salivary glands of the oral cavity; (2) the vagus nerve (CN X) innervates visceral structures of the digestive tract from the oral cavity to the left (splenic) flexure of the large bowel; (3) the sacral parasympathetics innervate distal to the left colic flexure.

40) **4 and 4 (again): 4** notable parasympathetic efferent ganglia of the head (ciliary, pterygopalatine (sphenopalatine), submandibular (submaxillary), and otic ganglia). Coincidentally, there are **4** notable sympathetic prevertebral ganglia of the abdomen (celiac, aorticorenal, superior mesenteric and inferior mesenteric ganglia).

41) $A_1U_2T_3O_4$ = autonomic system = **4**
   1) **4** sympathetic paravertebral ganglia with names: superior cervical, middle cervical, stellate, ganglion impar
   2) **4** sympathetic prevertebral ganglia of the abdomen
   3) **4** parasympathetic cranial nerves
   4) **4** parasympathetic efferent ganglia of the head

42) The best way to describe a non-insulin-dependent diabetic who takes insulin is as an "adult-onset diabetic" or "type II diabetic who takes insulin."

43) ***Sclerosis*** = hardening
   Arteriosclerosis = hardening of the arteries.
   Atherosclerosis = a form of arteriosclerosis characterized by the formation of atheromas.
   Atheroma = intraluminal plaque of lipids, cholesterol, and thickened arterial intimal cells.

44) There are three dietary sources of energy. Two of these, carbohydrates (glucose) and proteins (amino acids), require insulin for intracellular transport. In the absence of insulin, both are lost. The loss of each has its associated contributions to the disease process of diabetes. In an effort to provide energy, the body turns to the third dietary source of energy, fats (lipids). This excessive mobilization of lipids and their exposure to the intravascular environment predisposes to the development of atherosclerosis. Atherosclerosis is responsible for much of the severe pathology of diabetes.

END OF CHAPTER TEST

Time for Exam = 65 minutes.
For questions 1-46, choose the single best answer.

_____1) Which statements concerning the otic
      ganglion are true?
        a) It receives preganglionic fibers
           (axons) from the inferior salivatory
           nucleus of the brainstem.
        b) It is associated with the
           glossopharyngeal nerve (CN IX).
        c) Both a and b
        d) It provides postganglionic fibers
           which innervate the sublingual
           gland.
        e) None of the above

_____2) Which biologic mechanisms are decreased
      by parasympathetic stimulation?
        a) heart rate
        b) contractile force of the heart
        c) both a and b
        d) bronchial constriction
        e) none of the above

_____3) Which substances are formed as a result of
      the second stage of catabolism of dietary
      sources of energy?
        a) acetyl-CoA
        b) glycerol
        c) both a and b
        d) glucose
        e) none of the above

_____4) Which statement is true concerning autonomic
      innervation of the vasculature?
        a) Veins constrict in response to
           parasympathetic stimulation.
        b) Veins constrict in response to
           sympathetic stimulation.
        c) Veins dilate in response to
           parasympathetic stimulation.
        d) Coronary arteries constrict in
           response to sympathetic stimulation.
        e) None of the above

_____5) What may be found within the celiac
      ganglion?
        a) sympathetic postganglionic cell
           bodies
        b) parasympathetic preganglionic
           axons
        c) both a and b
        d) parasympathetic postganglionic
           axons
        e) none of the above

_____6) Which biologic mechanisms are increased
      by sympathetic stimulation?
        a) insulin secretion
        b) detrusor muscle (bladder) contraction
        c) coronary artery constriction
        d) glycolysis
        e) none of the above

_____7) Which statements are true concerning the
      lowest splanchnic nerve?
        a) It carries sympathetic preganglionic
           axons.
        b) It travels to the celiac ganglion.
        c) Both a and b
        d) It provides sympathetic innervation
           to the inferior hypogastric plexus.
        e) None of the above

_____8) In an overabundance of carbohydrates,
      which of the following mechanisms occur in
      the liver?
        a) Glucose is transformed to glycogen,
           which is stored for the rest of the
           body to use.
        b) Glucose is transformed to fatty
           acids, which are stored for the rest
           of the body to use.
        c) Both a and b
        d) Insulin secretion is inhibited.
        e) None of the above

_____9) Postganglionic parasympathetic fibers travel from which ganglion to innervate the lacrimal gland?
    a) otic
    b) pterygopalatine
    c) submandibular
    d) celiac
    e) none of the above

_____10) What occurs during the process of lipolysis?
    a) Glucose is converted to pyruvate.
    b) Triglycerides are converted to fatty acids.
    c) Fatty acids are converted to triglycerides.
    d) Fatty acids are converted to glucose.
    e) None of the above

_____11) Which statements about the inferior cervical cardiac branch of the sympathetic trunk are true?
    a) It is a branch of the stellate ganglion.
    b) It travels to the cardiac plexus.
    c) Both a and b
    d) It is a branch of the middle cervical ganglion.
    e) None of the above

_____12) Which of the following occur during negative accommodation of the eye?
    a) increased tension on the suspensory ligaments of the lens
    b) the lens returns to a more spherical shape
    c) ciliary muscle contraction
    d) all of the above
    e) none of the above

_____13) Which statements are true concerning the parasympathetic preganglionic neuron?
    a) Its axon may synapse in a paravertebral ganglion.
    b) Its axon may synapse in a prevertebral ganglion.
    c) Its cell body may be found in the brain.
    d) All of the above
    e) None of the above

_____14) Where does innervation of the digestive tract by the vagus nerve end?
    a) right flexure of the small bowel
    b) right flexure of the large bowel
    c) left flexure of the small bowel
    d) left flexure of the large bowel
    e) none of the above

_____15) Which statement is false concerning the ganglion impar?
    a) It is the lowest paravertebral ganglia.
    b) It houses postganglionic sympathetic cell bodies.
    c) It is formed by the inferior fusion of the two sympathetic chains.
    d) There are two, a right and a left ganglion impar.
    e) All are true.

_____16) What chemical compound is the common precursor to the Krebs cycle and oxidative phosphorylation for all three dietary sources of energy?
    a) adenosine triphosphate (ATP)
    b) glycerol
    c) acetyl-CoA
    d) glucose
    e) none of the above

_____17) Which statements are true concerning white rami communicans?
    a) They are fewer in number than gray rami communicans.
    b) Every paravertebral ganglion is associated with one.
    c) Both a and b
    d) They extend from a spinal nerve to a prevertebral ganglion.
    e) None of the above

_____18) Which ganglion is associated with the facial nerve?
    a) ciliary
    b) otic
    c) pterygopalatine
    d) celiac
    e) none of the above

_____19) What is found in the parasympathetic pelvic splanchnic nerves?
    a) preganglionic fibers from the L2-L4 spinal cord
    b) preganglionic fibers from the vagus nerve
    c) preganglionic fibers from the S2-S4 spinal cord
    d) postganglionic fibers from the S2-S4 spinal cord
    e) none of the above

_____20) Which statements are true concerning the sympathetic preganglionic neuron?
    a) The axon is relatively longer than the parasympathetic preganglionic axon.
    b) The cell body could be located in the lumbar spinal cord.
    c) It synapses with the effector organ.
    d) It may synapse with the postganglionic neuron in a postvertebral ganglion.
    e) None of the above

_____21) Which substances are formed as a direct result of the first stage of catabolism of dietary sources of energy?
    a) triglycerides
    b) glycogen
    c) fatty acids
    d) lipoproteins
    e) none of the above

_____22) Which statement is true concerning the detrusor muscle?
    a) It contracts in response to sympathetic stimulation.
    b) Contraction causes sphincter tightening and opposes bladder emptying.
    c) Contraction loosens tension on the suspensory ligaments of the lens.
    d) Contraction causes bladder emptying.
    e) None of the above

_____23) What may be found in the pterygopalatine (sphenopalatine) ganglion?
    a) parasympathetic preganglionic cell bodies
    b) sympathetic postganglionic axons
    c) both a and b
    d) sympathetic preganglionic axons
    e) none of the above

_____24) Preganglionic parasympathetic axons from the Edinger-Westphal nucleus of the midbrain travel to which autonomic ganglion to synapse?
    a) ciliary ganglion
    b) pterygopalatine ganglion
    c) otic ganglion
    d) celiac ganglion
    e) none of the above

_____25) Which statements are true concerning accommodation of the eye?
    a) Positive accommodation is the result of parasympathetic stimulation.
    b) Negative accommodation is the result of sympathetic stimulation.
    c) Both a and b
    d) Positive accommodation is the result of sympathetic stimulation.
    e) None of the above

_____26) What occurs during the process of glycolysis?
    a) Glucose is transformed to pyruvate.
    b) Glycogen is transformed to glucose.
    c) Both a and b
    d) Glucose is transformed to glycogen.
    e) None of the above

_____27) Which statements about paravertebral sympathetic ganglia are true?
    a) Every paravertebral ganglion is associated with a spinal nerve.
    b) Every paravertebral ganglion is associated with a gray ramus communicans.
    c) Both a and b
    d) Every spinal nerve is associated with a paravertebral ganglion.
    e) None of the above

_____28) Postganglionic parasympathetic fibers travel from which ganglion in order to innervate the parotid gland?
- a) stellate
- b) otic
- c) submandibular
- d) sphenopalatine
- e) none of the above

_____29) Which statement about the parasympathetic postganglionic neuron is true?
- a) The axon is relatively shorter compared to the sympathetic postganglionic axon.
- b) The cell body may be located in the brain.
- c) The cell body may be located in a prevertebral ganglion.
- d) The cell body may be located in the thoracic spinal cord.
- e) None of the above

_____30) Which nerve is associated with the ciliary ganglion?
- a) oculomotor
- b) abducens
- c) trochlear
- d) facial
- e) none of the above

_____31) Where does gluconeogenesis occur in the body?
- a) liver
- b) kidneys
- c) both a and b
- d) skeletal muscle
- e) none of the above

_____32) Which of the following autonomic effects on the eye is correct?
- a) Parasympathetic stimulation causes mydriasis.
- b) Sympathetic stimulation causes ciliary muscle contraction.
- c) Sympathetic stimulation causes positive accommodation of the eye.
- d) Sympathetic stimulation causes miosis.
- e) None of the above

_____33) Which nerve is formed by branches of the T9 and T10 paravertebral ganglia of the sympathetic chain?
- a) inferior cervical cardiac branch of the sympathetic chain
- b) greater splanchnic nerve
- c) lowest splanchnic nerve
- d) lesser splanchnic nerve
- e) none of the above

_____34) Where do preganglionic fibers of the vagus nerve synapse with postganglionic cell bodies?
- a) pterygopalatine ganglion
- b) otic ganglion
- c) ciliary ganglion
- d) submandibular ganglion
- e) none of the above

_____35) Which of the following statements about insulin are true?
- a) It is secreted by the kidneys.
- b) It is secreted by beta cells of the acini.
- c) It works by promoting active transport of glucose across cell membranes.
- d) All of the above
- e) None of the above

_____36) Which autonomic plexuses are supplied via the inferior mesenteric ganglion?
- a) superior hypogastric plexus
- b) inferior hypogastric plexus
- c) both a and b
- d) renal plexus
- e) none of the above

_____37) Which statements concerning the stellate ganglion are true?
- a) It is the origin of the superior cervical cardiac branch of the sympathetic trunk.
- b) It is the most superior cervical paravertebral sympathetic ganglion.
- c) Both a and b
- d) It serves as the origin of the greater splanchnic nerve.
- e) None of the above

_____38) Which biologic processes are increased with sympathetic stimulation?
    a) gluconeogenesis
    b) renin secretion
    c) lipolysis
    d) all of the above
    e) none of the above

_____39) The word *splanchnic* refers to
    a) the thoracic cavity
    b) the abdomen
    c) the viscera
    d) the body wall
    e) the pelvic floor

_____40) Which statements about the sympathetic postganglionic neuron are true?
    a) The cell body may be located in the thoracic spinal cord.
    b) The cell body may be located in the lumbar spinal cord.
    c) Both a and b
    d) It synapses with the effector organ.
    e) None of the above

_____41) What is the highest spinal cord level where sympathetic preganglionic neuron cell bodies typically may be found?
    a) C1
    b) C3
    c) C6
    d) T1
    e) T4

_____42) Which structures are located within the interganglionic sections of the sympathetic chain?
    a) postganglionic neuron axons
    b) preganglionic neuron axons
    c) both a and b
    d) paravertebral ganglia
    e) none of the above

_____43) Parasympathetic stimulation of the lower extremity is provided by
    a) preganglionic fibers traveling in nerves of the lumbosacral plexus
    b) postganglionic fibers traveling in nerves of the lumbosacral plexus
    c) postganglionic fibers extending from prevertebral ganglia
    d) postganglionic fibers extending from ganglia very near the effector organs
    e) none of the above

_____44) Which nerves carry sympathetic preganglionic axons?
    a) sympathetic nerves to the kidney
    b) sympathetic nerves to the heart
    c) sympathetic nerves to the adrenal gland
    d) sympathetic nerves to the small intestine
    e) none of the above

_____45) What may be found within the inferior mesenteric ganglion?
    a) sympathetic postganglionic cell bodies
    b) parasympathetic postganglionic axons
    c) both a and b
    d) sympathetic preganglionic cell bodies
    e) none of the above

_____46) Which of the following are true concerning the greater splanchnic nerve?
    a) It is a branch of the stellate ganglion.
    b) It travels to the aorticorenal ganglion.
    c) Both a and b
    d) It travels to the celiac ganglion.
    e) None of the above

For questions 47-65, use the following directions:
   a.......1,2,3 are correct
   b.......1,3 are correct
   c.......2,4 are correct
   d.......only 4 is correct
   e.......all are correct

_____47) Which structures may be supplied by sympathetic fibers that travel in gray rami communicans?
   1. blood vessels
   2. heart
   3. piloerector muscles
   4. stomach

_____48) Which of the following could be said to occur in the process of glycolysis?
   1. Proteins are transformed to amino acids.
   2. Glycerol is transformed to glucose.
   3. Amino acids are transformed to glucose.
   4. Glucose is transformed to pyruvate.

_____49) Which statements about the trigone sphincter muscle of the bladder are true?
   1. Contraction facilitates bladder emptying.
   2. It contracts in response to sympathetic stimulation.
   3. It contracts in response to parasympathetic stimulation.
   4. It relaxes in response to parasympathetic stimulation.

_____50) Which of the following are true concerning the otic ganglion?
   1. It receives postganglionic parasympathetic fibers (axons) from the inferior salivatory nucleus of the brainstem.
   2. It is associated with the facial nerve (CN VII).
   3. It serves as the location of parasympathetic preganglionic cell bodies.
   4. It supplies parasympathetic innervation to the largest of the salivatory glands.

_____51) Which of the following are sympathetic prevertebral ganglia?
   1. inferior mesenteric ganglion
   2. stellate ganglion
   3. celiac ganglion
   4. superior cervical ganglion

_____52) Which statements about a parasympathetic preganglionic neuron are true?
   1. The cell body may be located in the sacral spinal cord.
   2. The axon is relatively shorter than the axon of a sympathetic preganglionic neuron.
   3. It may synapse with the postganglionic neuron in the wall of the effector organ.
   4. It may synapse with the postganglionic neuron in a paravertebral ganglion.

_____53) Which of the following serve as metabolic functions of insulin?
   1. inhibition of glycolysis
   2. promotion of gluconeogenesis
   3. inhibition of lipolysis
   4. inhibition of intracellular transport of amino acids

_____54) Which statements about the renin-angiotensin system are true?
   1. Angiotensin converting enzyme catalyzes the conversion of angiotensin I to angiotensin II.
   2. Renin is secreted by the juxtaglomerular cells of the kidney.
   3. The conversion of angiotensinogen to angiotensin I occurs in the blood.
   4. The conversion of angiotensin I to angiotensin II occurs in the lungs.

_____55) Which biologic mechanisms are decreased in response to sympathetic stimulation?
   1. glycolysis
   2. renin secretion
   3. lipolysis
   4. insulin secretion

_____56) Which of the following are true concerning the submandibular (submaxillary) ganglion?
1. It receives preganglionic axons from the superior salivatory nucleus of the brainstem.
2. It extends postganglionic axons to supply parasympathetic innervation to the submandibular (submaxillary) gland.
3. It is associated with the facial nerve (CN VII).
4. It extends postganglionic axons to supply parasympathetic innervation to the sublingual gland.

_____57) Which nerves carry sympathetic preganglionic fibers (axons)?
1. inferior cervical cardiac branch of sympathetic trunk
2. white rami communicans
3. sacral splanchnic nerves
4. lesser splanchnic nerve

_____58) Which statements about the vagus nerve are true?
1. Preganglionic cell bodies may be found in the inferior salivatory nucleus of the brainstem.
2. Preganglionic fibers (axons) may be found in the inferior mesenteric ganglion.
3. Postganglionic cell bodies may be found in the otic ganglion.
4. Of all peripheral parasympathetic fibers, 75% travel in the vagus nerve.

_____59) Which metabolic functions occur in the liver?
1. conversion of glucose into glycogen
2. gluconeogenesis
3. release of glucose into the blood during periods of hypoglycemia
4. conversion of glucose to fatty acids

_____60) Which statements about gray rami communicans are true?
1. They are associated with every paravertebral sympathetic ganglion.
2. They carry fibers which are exiting the sympathetic chain.
3. They carry fibers which are entering a spinal nerve.
4. They are more numerous than white rami communicans.

_____61) Which substances are a direct result of the third stage of catabolism of dietary sources of energy?
1. water
2. fatty acids
3. ATP
4. acetyl-CoA

_____62) Which statements concerning insulin are true?
1. It is a lipid hormone.
2. Its effect on membrane transport is by active transport.
3. It is secreted in response to hypoglycemia.
4. It has little, if any, effect on brain cells.

_____63) Which structures are not innervated by the parasympathetic nervous system?
1. the splenic capsule
2. the adrenal gland
3. blood vessels
4. the body wall

_____64) Which of the following are true concerning the celiac ganglion?
1. It is a parasympathetic ganglion of the oculomotor nerve.
2. It receives preganglionic fibers from the Edinger-Westphal nucleus of the midbrain.
3. It sends postganglionic axons to innervate the pupil and ciliary muscle of the eye.
4. It is a prevertebral sympathetic ganglion of the abdomen.

_____65) Which of the following are associated with the process of gluconeogenesis?
1. Proteins are transformed to amino acids.
2. Glucose is transformed to pyruvate.
3. Amino acids are transformed to glucose.
4. Acetyl-CoA enters the citric acid (Krebs) cycle and oxidative phosphorylation.

END OF CHAPTER TEST: Answers and Explanations

1) c – The otic ganglion is a parasympathetic efferent ganglion of the head that is associated with the glossopharyngeal nerve (CN IX). It receives preganglionic fibers (axons) from the inferior salivatory nucleus of the brainstem. Postganglionic axons extend from the otic ganglion to supply parasympathetic innervation to the parotid gland, the largest of the salivary glands. The sublingual gland, along with the submandibular (submaxillary) gland, receives postganglionic parasympathetic axons from the submandibular (submaxillary) ganglion. The submandibular ganglion is one of the two parasympathetic efferent ganglia which are associated with the facial nerve (CN VII).

2) a – Parasympathetic stimulation causes a decrease in heart rate and conduction velocity, but has no effect on the contractile force of each heart beat. Sympathetic stimulation increases the heart rate, conduction velocity, and contractile force of each heart beat. Parasympathetic stimulation also causes bronchial smooth muscle contraction and hence, bronchial constriction.

3) a – There are three dietary sources of energy: sugars (carbohydrates, polysaccharides), fats (lipids), and proteins. Each goes through three stages of catabolism or breakdown in order to provide energy by the production of ATP. The first stage is digestion. During the first stage, sugars are broken down to glucose and simple sugars, fats to fatty acids and glycerol, and proteins to amino acids. Acetyl-CoA is the result of the second stage of catabolism for all three dietary sources of energy. It is the common precursor to the third stage of catabolism, the citric acid (Krebs) cycle and oxidative phosphorylation.

4) b – Blood vessels, including both arteries and veins, are not innervated by the parasympathetic nervous system. Most arteries constrict in response to sympathetic stimulation. Exceptions include arteries to skeletal muscles and the coronary arteries, which supply heart muscle. Both groups of arteries dilate with sympathetic stimulation. Veins, like most arteries, constrict in response to sympathetic stimulation.

5) c – The four named prevertebral sympathetic ganglia of the abdomen (celiac, aorticorenal, superior mesenteric, and inferior mesenteric ganglia) are referred to as sympathetic ganglia because they are the location of sympathetic postganglionic cell bodies. It is important to realize that preganglionic parasympathetic fibers may also travel through the top three ganglia with vagal nerve branches. They are simply passing through en route to their synapse with postganglionic neurons near the effector organ. The lowest of these four ganglia, the inferior mesenteric ganglion, may contain preganglionic parasympathetic fibers traveling from parasympathetic sacral splanchnic nerves.

6) d – Glycolysis increases in response to sympathetic stimulation. Insulin secretion decreases in response to sympathetic stimulation. Sympathetic stimulation relaxes the detrusor muscle, which opposes bladder emptying. Finally, sympathetic stimulation causes constriction of most arteries. Exceptions include arteries to skeletal muscles and the coronary arteries. Both groups of arteries dilate in response to sympathetic stimulation.

7) a – The lowest splanchnic nerve originates from the last thoracic paravertebral ganglion (T11) of the sympathetic chain. It travels to the aorticorenal ganglion. From there, postganglionic axons travel in small nerves which contribute to the aortic and renal plexuses. They eventually provide sympathetic innervation to the upper abdominal viscera. Sympathetic input to the inferior hypogastric plexus is provided by the sacral splanchnic nerves.

8) c – In addition to its many other functions, the liver can metabolically be considered as a "glucose factory." This factory makes and stores glucose for the rest of the body to use when needed. First, it stores glucose as glycogen. Second, when the glycogen storage capacity is reached, the liver, along with adipose tissue, converts glucose to fatty acids. The fatty acids can subsequently be stored as triglycerides providing long term energy storage. Finally, during periods of glucose shortage, the liver (along with

the kidney) can convert certain amino acids to glucose by the process of gluconeogenesis. This creates the brain's only energy substrate, glucose, during periods of shortage.

9) b – The pterygopalatine (sphenopalatine) ganglion is one of the two parasympathetic efferent ganglia of the head which are associated with the facial nerve (CN VII). The pterygopalatine ganglion receives preganglionic fibers (axons) from neuron cell bodies located in the lacrimal nucleus. In turn, it sends postganglionic fibers (axons) to innervate the lacrimal gland (tears) and glands of the nasal and oral cavities. The otic ganglion is a parasympathetic ganglion of the head which is associated with the glossopharyngeal nerve (CN IX) and provides postganglionic fibers to the parotid gland, the largest of the salivary glands. The submandibular (submaxillary) ganglion is the other parasympathetic efferent ganglion associated with the facial nerve (CN VII). It supplies postganglionic fibers to two salivary glands, the sublingual and submandibular (submaxillary) glands. The celiac ganglion is a sympathetic prevertebral ganglion located in the upper abdomen.

10) b – The word element *lysis* means *dissolution* or *breakdown*. Lipolysis is breakdown of the storage form of lipids, triglycerides (triacylglycerols), into fatty acids. Fatty acids can then be transformed to acetyl-CoA, which can enter the citric acid (Krebs) cycle and oxidative phosphorylation for provision of energy (ATP). Glycolysis involves the transformation of glucose to pyruvate and subsequently, pyruvate to acetyl-CoA.

11) c – The stellate ganglion is the origin of the inferior cardiac branch of the sympathetic chain. It is the large paravertebral sympathetic ganglion formed by the combination of the last cervical and first thoracic paravertebral ganglia of the sympathetic chain. The inferior cervical cardiac branch, along with the middle and superior cervical cardiac branches, provides sympathetic innervation to the cardiac plexus, the autonomic plexus that supplies the heart. The middle cervical ganglion is the origin of the middle cervical cardiac branch of the sympathetic chain.

12) a – Accommodation is a process of alterations within the eye which enable the eye to focus on structures at different distances away. Negative accommodation is the result of ciliary muscle relaxation. This increases the tension on the suspensory ligaments of the lens, which pulls the lens into a flatter shape. The flat shape of the lens bends light rays at less of an angle and provides for far-sighted vision.

13) c – The cell bodies of the preganglionic parasympathetic neurons are located in the brain and sacral spinal cord. Hence, the parasympathetic nervous system is also known as the craniosacral system. The sympathetic nervous system is also known as the thoracolumbar system because the cell bodies of its preganglionic neurons are located in the thoracic and lumbar spinal cord (T1-L2). The sympathetic preganglionic neuron may synapse with the postganglionic neuron in either a paravertebral ganglia (located in the sympathetic chain) or a prevertebral ganglia (located distal to the sympathetic chain).

14) d – The vagus nerve provides parasympathetic innervation to the digestive tract to the level of the left (splenic) flexure of the large bowel or colon. Distal to this, parasympathetic innervation is provided by cell bodies located in the spinal cord at the S2-S4 spinal levels (remember, cranio<u>sacral</u> system). From these cell bodies, parasympathetic preganglionic fibers leave the spinal cord and synapse with postganglionic neurons very near their lower abdominal and pelvic effector organs.

15) d – The ganglion impar is the last or most inferior of the paravertebral sympathetic ganglia. It is formed by the inferior fusion of the two sympathetic chains. Along with prevertebral sympathetic ganglia of the abdomen, the ganglion impar is a rare exception to the rule that every peripheral nerve structure includes both a right and left member.

16) c – The three dietary sources of energy include sugars (polysaccharides, carbohydrates), fats (lipids), and proteins. When used as energy, each is eventually broken down and transformed into acetyl-CoA, the common precursor to the citric acid (Krebs) cycle and oxidative phosphorylation. During this process, the universal energy source for all living cells,

ATP, is created. When utilized for energy, ATP is transformed into ADP. Along with other simple sugars, glucose is a breakdown product of carbohydrates. Fatty acids and glycerol are the breakdown products of lipids.

17) a – Sympathetic preganglionic neuron cell bodies are located in the intermediolateral horn of the spinal cord at the T1-L2 levels. From here they extend axons that leave the spinal cord by way of a ventral root and enter a spinal nerve. These axons travel a short distance before leaving the spinal nerve by way of a white ramus communicans. A white ramus communicans is a small communicating nerve which extends from the spinal nerve to a paravertebral ganglion of the sympathetic chain. From here the preganglionic axon can go to one of three places: 1) synapse with the postganglionic neuron at that paravertebral ganglion, 2) travel up or down the chain and synapse with the postganglionic neuron in a different paravertebral ganglion, or 3) leave the sympathetic chain and synapse with the postganglionic neuron in a more distally-located prevertebral ganglion. The postganglionic neuron axon may also do one of three things: 1) reenter a spinal nerve by exiting the paravertebral ganglia by way of a gray ramus communicans, 2) leave the paravertebral or prevertebral ganglia directly, 3) travel up or down the sympathetic chain a variable distance before exiting it. Because the sympathetic cell bodies are only located at the spinal levels of T1-L2, white rami communicans are only located at the paravertebral ganglia located at these levels. Remember, axons may travel up or down the sympathetic chain to reenter a spinal nerve via a gray ramus communicans. Because of this, every paravertebral ganglion is associated with a gray ramus communicans. Only the paravertebral ganglia at T1-L2 are associated with white rami communicans.

18) c – See #9 answer explanation. The ciliary ganglion is a parasympathetic efferent ganglion of the head that is associated with the oculomotor nerve (CN III). It provides postganglionic axons to the pupillary muscles (miosis) and ciliary muscle (positive accommodation for near-sighted vision) of the eye. The otic ganglion is a parasympathetic ganglion of the head that is associated with the glossopharyngeal nerve (CN IX) and provides postganglionic fibers to the parotid gland, the largest of the salivary glands. The celiac ganglion is a sympathetic prevertebral ganglion located in the upper abdomen.

19) c – The parasympathetic or *craniosacral* nervous system has preganglionic cell bodies located in the ventral surface of the brain and brainstem (*cranio-*) and spinal cord at the S2-S4 spinal levels (*-sacral*). The parasympathetic pelvic splanchnic nerves carry preganglionic parasympathetic fibers from the S2-S4 spinal cord. Remember, the parasympathetic preganglionic fibers synapse close to, often within, the wall of the effector organ. Parasympathetic nerves therefore seldom carry postganglionic fibers. They almost always carry preganglionic fibers because the synapse with the postganglionic neuron does not occur until the effector organ is nearly reached.

20) b – The autonomic nervous system, comprised of both the sympathetic and parasympathetic nervous systems, has an anatomic structure with two neurons outside the CNS (brain and spinal cord). Cell bodies of the of the first (preganglionic) neuron of the sympathetic (or thoracolumbar) system are located in the intermediolateral horn of the thoracic and lumbar spinal cord from T1 to L2. By contrast, the cell bodies of the preganglionic neuron of the parasympathetic (or craniosacral) system are located in the brain and sacral spinal cord. Sympathetic preganglionic fibers (axons) are usually shorter than parasympathetic preganglionic axons. Sympathetic postganglionic fibers are therefore relatively longer than their parasympathetic counterparts. The sympathetic preganglionic axon synapses with a postganglionic neuron in an autonomic ganglion. This sympathetic efferent ganglion may either be a paravertebral or prevertebral ganglion. The paravertebral ganglia are located in the sympathetic chain. The prevertebral ganglia are located outside and distal to the sympathetic chain. There is no sympathetic postvertebral ganglion. The axon of the postganglionic neuron extends to and innervates the effector organ (smooth or cardiac muscle).

21) c – See #3 answer explanation. Triglycerides are a

storage form of fatty acids (lipids). Glycogen is the intracellular storage form of glucose (carbohydrates). Lipoproteins are molecules formed by the combination of lipids and proteins.

22) d – The detrusor (pubovesical) muscle contracts in response to parasympathetic stimulation and empties the bladder. Contraction of the trigone-sphincter muscle occurs with sympathetic stimulation and opposes bladder emptying. Contraction of the ciliary muscle loosens the tension on the suspensory ligaments of the lens of the eye.

23) b – Each of the four parasympathetic efferent ganglia of the head (ciliary, pterygopalatine, submandibular, and otic) is classified as a parasympathetic ganglion because each is the location of parasympathetic postganglionic cell bodies. These ganglia also have postganglionic sympathetic and somatic axons that are passing through, en route to their respective effector organs.

24) a – The oculomotor nerve (CN III) is one of the four cranial nerves that carry parasympathetic fibers. Preganglionic cell bodies are located n the Edinger-Westphal nucleus of the midbrain. From here, preganglionic axons travel to synapse with postganglionic cell bodies located in the ciliary ganglion. Postganglionic axons then travel to supply muscles of the pupil and the ciliary muscle of the lens. Parasympathetic stimulation to the eye is conveyed by the oculomotor nerve. It causes miosis (pupillary contraction) and positive accommodation for near-sighted vision. The pterygopalatine ganglion is also known as the sphenopalatine ganglion and is a parasympathetic efferent ganglion associated with the facial nerve (CN VII). The otic ganglion is the parasympathetic efferent ganglion associated with the glossopharyngeal nerve (CN IX). The celiac ganglion is a sympathetic prevertebral ganglion located just beneath the diaphragm and supplied by the greater and lesser splanchnic nerves.

25) a – Accommodation is a process of alterations within the eye which enable the eye to focus on structures at different distances away. Positive accommodation involves contraction of the ciliary muscle, which decreases the tension on the

suspensory ligaments of the lens. This allows the lens to return to a more spherical shape, bend light rays at a greater angle, and provide for near-sighted vision. Positive accommodation is the result of parasympathetic stimulation. Negative accommodation is the result of ciliary muscle relaxation. This increases the tension on the suspensory ligaments of the lens, which pulls the lens into a flatter shape. The flat shape of the lens bends light rays at less of an angle and provides for far-sighted vision. Although sympathetic stimulation causes ciliary muscle relaxation, this is thought to have little, if any, clinical significance in the process of accommodation. It is thought that the lack of parasympathetic stimulation, as opposed to sympathetic stimulation, is the main driving force causing negative accommodation for far-sighted vision.

26) a – The suffix *lysis* means *dissolution* or *breakdown*. Glycolysis involves the breakdown and transformation of glucose to pyruvate. Pyruvate is then converted to acetyl-CoA for entrance into the citric acid (Krebs) cycle and oxidative phosphorylation with the resultant production of energy (ATP). Glycogenolysis is the breakdown and transformation of glycogen to glucose.

27) c – Paravertebral sympathetic ganglia occur along each sympathetic chain in a random and somewhat symmetric fashion. They communicate with spinal nerves via small nerves called white and gray rami communicans. There are more spinal nerves than paravertebral ganglia. Every paravertebral ganglion is associated with a spinal nerve, but not every spinal nerve is associated with a paravertebral ganglion. Sympathetic preganglionic cell bodies are located in the intermediolateral horn of the spinal cord at the T1-L2 levels. Each preganglionic axon leaves the spinal cord with a spinal nerve and enters the sympathetic chain via a white ramus communicans. Because the preganglionic cell bodies are only located at the T1-L2 spinal levels, white rami communicans are only associated with paravertebral ganglia located at the T1-L2 spinal levels. Both preganglionic and postganglionic axons may travel a variable distance up or down the sympathetic chain before either synapsing with the postganglionic neuron (preganglionic fibers) or leaving

the chain (preganglionic or postganglionic fibers). This results in a sympathetic chain which is significantly longer than the length of spinal cord in which the preganglionic cell bodies are located (T1-L2). Postganglionic axons leave the chain in small nerves called gray rami communicans, which rejoin a spinal nerve. In summary, *every* paravertebral ganglion associates with a spinal nerve, and it does this by way of a gray ramus communicans. Paravertebral ganglia located at the T1-L2 levels are the *only* ganglia that also communicate with spinal nerves by way of white rami communicans.

28) b – See #1 answer explanation. The otic ganglion is one of the four efferent ganglia of the head that is associated with a parasympathetic cranial nerve.

29) a – The parasympathetic nervous system is also known anatomically as the craniosacral system because the preganglionic neuron cell bodies are found in the brain (cranium) and sacral spinal cord. From here they extend axons outward to synapse with parasympathetic postganglionic neurons very near the effector organ. In fact, these synapses often occur within the wall of the effector organ. Because the ganglia (or synapse with the preganglionic neuron) is so near the effector organ, the parasympathetic postganglionic axon is almost always shorter relative to the sympathetic postganglionic axon. Paravertebral and prevertebral ganglia are the location of sympathetic postganglionic neurons.

30) a – The ciliary ganglion is a parasympathetic efferent ganglion of the head that is associated with the oculomotor nerve (CN III). It receives preganglionic fibers (axons) from neuron cell bodies located in the Edinger-Westphal nucleus of the brainstem. Postganglionic axons leave the ciliary ganglion and travel to the eye to cause constriction of the pupil (miosis) and contraction of the ciliary muscle (positive accommodation for near-sighted vision).

31) c – Gluconeogenesis is the production of glucose from non-carbohydrate sources. The word *gluconeogenesis* actually means "glucose new creation." It results from breakdown of proteins to

amino acids and the subsequent transformation of certain amino acids to glucose. The pathway serves as an important means of producing the brain's only energy source, glucose, in times of carbohydrate shortage. Gluconeogenesis occurs primarily in the liver, although a small amount also takes place in the kidneys.

32) e – Parasympathetic stimulation causes positive accommodation for near-sighted vision. Specifically, parasympathetic stimulation causes ciliary muscle contraction, which lessens the tension on the suspensory ligaments of the lens. The lens is able to assume a more spherical shape. This shape bends light rays at a more acute angle and shortens the distance to the focal point. Parasympathetic stimulation causes pupillary constriction, or miosis. This limits the amount of light that enters the eye and is useful in bright environments. Sympathetic stimulation causes pupillary dilation, or mydriasis. This increases the amount of light which enters the eye and is useful in dark environments.

33) d – The stellate ganglion is the origin of the inferior cervical cardiac branch. The greater splanchnic nerve is formed by branches from the T5-T9 paravertebral sympathetic ganglia of the sympathetic chain. The lowest splanchnic nerve originates from the last thoracic paravertebral ganglion (T11).

34) e – Preganglionic parasympathetic cell bodies of the vagus nerve are located in the dorsal vagal nucleus of the spinal cord. From there, preganglionic axons travel down to synapse with postganglionic neuron cell bodies located very near the effector organs of the neck, thorax, and abdomen. The vagus nerve carries 75% of all peripheral parasympathetic fibers. The pterygopalatine (sphenopalatine) ganglion is one of two parasympathetic efferent ganglia of the head associated with the facial nerve (CN VII). It supplies postganglionic fibers to the lacrimal gland (tears) and glands of the nasal and oral cavities. The otic ganglion is a parasympathetic ganglion of the head associated with the glossopharyngeal nerve (CN IX) and provides postganglionic fibers to the parotid gland, the largest of the salivary glands. The ciliary ganglion is a

parasympathetic ganglion of the head associated with the oculomotor nerve (CN III). It provides postganglionic axons to the pupillary muscles (miosis) and ciliary muscle (positive accommodation for near-sighted vision) of the eye. The submandibular (submaxillary) ganglion is the other parasympathetic efferent ganglion associated with the facial nerve (CN VII). It supplies postganglionic fibers to two salivary glands, the sublingual and submandibular (submaxillary) glands.

35) e – Insulin is a protein hormone secreted by the beta cells of the islets of Langerhans in the pancreas. Insulin binds a cell membrane carrier protein that facilitates the passage of glucose from the blood to the intracellular environment of the cell. This mechanism of membrane transport is called facilitated diffusion.

36) c – Postganglionic sympathetic axons leave the inferior mesenteric ganglion in small nerves that travel to the superior and inferior hypogastric plexuses to innervate viscera of the lower abdomen and pelvis.

37) e – The stellate ganglion is the origin of the inferior cardiac branch of the sympathetic chain. The stellate is the large paravertebral sympathetic ganglion formed by the combination of the last cervical and first thoracic paravertebral ganglia of the sympathetic chain. The superior cervical ganglion is the most superior or highest paravertebral ganglion and may also be described as the first cervical ganglion. It is the origin of the superior cervical cardiac branch of the sympathetic chain. The greater splanchnic nerve is formed by branches from the T5-T9 paravertebral sympathetic ganglia.

38) d – Renin secretion, lipolysis, glycolysis, and gluconeogenesis are increased with sympathetic stimulation. Insulin secretion is increased with parasympathetic stimulation and decreased with sympathetic stimulation.

39) c – *Splanchnic* describes the viscera. It refers to structures associated with viscera. The greater, lesser, and lowest splanchnic nerves provide sympathetic innervation to abdominal viscera.

40) d – Cell bodies of sympathetic preganglionic neurons are located in the thoracic and lumbar spinal cord from the levels of T1-L2. Because of this, the sympathetic nervous system is also known as the thoracolumbar nervous system. Sympathetic preganglionic axons travel out to synapse with sympathetic postganglionic neurons located in sympathetic ganglia. These synapses may occur in one of the two types of sympathetic efferent ganglia. Paravertebral ganglia are sympathetic ganglia located along the sympathetic chain. Prevertebral ganglia are sympathetic ganglia that are more distal to the sympathetic chain. From the sympathetic ganglia, the sympathetic postganglionic neuron extends its axon to synapse with and innervate the effector organ, a cardiac or smooth muscle fiber.

41) d – See #40 answer explanation.

42) c – See #17 answer explanation. The sympathetic chain is formed by paravertebral ganglia connected by interganglionic sections of the chain. The prefix *inter-* means *between*. The interganglionic sections are simply the sections of chain which are between paravertebral ganglia. An interganglionic section of the sympathetic chain may contain both sympathetic preganglionic axons and sympathetic postganglionic axons.

43) e – There is no parasympathetic innervation to the extremities or body wall. The only visceral structures in these areas are sweat glands, piloerector muscles of hair follicles, and blood vessels. All are innervated solely by the sympathetic system. In addition to the upper extremities, lower extremities, and body wall, there is no parasympathetic innervation to the splenic capsule or adrenal gland.

44) c – Virtually all thoracic and abdominal viscera receive direct sympathetic innervation from postganglionic fibers (axons). These axons come from postganglionic neurons located in either paravertebral or prevertebral sympathetic ganglia. The one exception to this structure is innervation to the adrenal gland. Neuroendocrine cells of the adrenal gland act as the sympathetic postganglionic neuron. The adrenal gland therefore receives only sympathetic

preganglionic innervation. Neuroendocrine cells of the adrenal medulla secrete epinephrine (adrenaline) and norepinephrine. Neuroendocrine cells of the adrenal cortex secrete steroid hormones. There is no parasympathetic innervation to the adrenal gland.

45) a – See #5 answer explanation.

46) d – The greater splanchnic nerve is formed by branches from the T5-T9 paravertebral sympathetic ganglia of the sympathetic chain. The celiac ganglion is the large prevertebral sympathetic ganglion located just below the diaphragm in close proximity to the celiac trunk artery. It is involved in sympathetic transmission to the abdominal viscera. The stellate ganglion is the large paravertebral sympathetic ganglion formed by the combination of the last cervical and first thoracic paravertebral ganglia. The lowest splanchnic nerve travels to the aorticorenal ganglion.

47) b – Spinal nerve innervation is confined to the body wall and extremities. These body segments are formed by somatic structures. The only visceral tissues present are blood vessels, piloerector muscles, and sweat glands. These structures are therefore the only structures supplied by sympathetic fibers that exit the sympathetic chain by way of gray rami communicans to travel with spinal nerves. There is no parasympathetic innervation of blood vessels, piloerector muscles, or sweat glands; hence, there is no parasympathetic innervation to the body wall or extremities. The heart is supplied by postganglionic sympathetic fibers from the C1-T5 paravertebral ganglia. Sympathetic supply to the stomach is by way of postganglionic fibers from upper abdominal sympathetic prevertebral ganglia. These prevertebral ganglia receive preganglionic fibers from the splanchnic nerves.

48) d – The word element *lysis* means *dissolution* or *breakdown.* Glycolysis involves the breakdown and transformation of glucose to pyruvate. Pyruvate is then converted to acetyl-CoA for entrance into the citric acid (Krebs) cycle and oxidative phosphorylation with the resultant production of energy (ATP). Gluconeogenesis is the process by which certain amino acids are transformed to glucose. During the first stage of lipid catabolism (digestion), lipids are broken down to fatty acids and glycerol. Glycogen should not be confused with glycerol.

49) c – The bladder trigone-sphincter muscle contracts when stimulated by the sympathetic nervous system. This closes the bladder outlet and opposes bladder emptying. The trigone-sphincter muscle relaxes with parasympathetic stimulation.

50) d – The otic ganglion serves as the parasympathetic efferent ganglion of the glossopharyngeal nerve (CN IX). It receives preganglionic fibers (axons) from the inferior salivatory nucleus of the brainstem. Postganglionic parasympathetic cell bodies that are located in the otic ganglion extend postganglionic axons to supply parasympathetic innervation to the largest of the salivary glands, the parotid gland.

51) b – Prevertebral ganglia are those sympathetic efferent ganglia which are distal to, and not immediately associated with, the sympathetic chain. This is opposed to paravertebral ganglia which lie along the chain. The stellate ganglion is the large paravertebral ganglion formed by the combination of the last cervical and first thoracic paravertebral ganglia. The superior cervical ganglion is the most superior or highest paravertebral sympathetic ganglion. It may also be described as the first cervical ganglion.

52) b – The preganglionic neuron of the sympathetic nervous system may synapse with the postganglionic neuron in either paravertebral ganglia (located in the sympathetic chain) or a prevertebral ganglion (located distal to the sympathetic chain). The preganglionic neuron of the parasympathetic nervous system synapses with the postganglionic neuron very near, often within the wall of the effector organ. The axons of the parasympathetic preganglionic neurons are relatively longer than the axons of their sympathetic counterparts. The cell bodies of the preganglionic parasympathetic neurons are located in the brain and sacral spinal cord. Hence, the parasympathetic nervous system is also known as the

craniosacral system. The sympathetic nervous system is also known as the thoracolumbar system because the cell bodies of its preganglionic neurons are located in the thoracic and lumbar spinal cord (T1-L2).

53) b – Insulin promotes the intracellular transport of glucose and the storage of glucose as glycogen. Because insulin is secreted in response to elevated blood sugar, there is no need for mobilization of other energy sources. Insulin therefore inhibits the catabolic pathways of lipolysis and glycolysis. In addition to its effect on carbohydrate metabolism, insulin also has significant effects on protein metabolism. The intracellular transport of a great number of amino acids is facilitated by insulin. Furthermore, insulin inhibits gluconeogenesis. This preserves proteins by preventing their breakdown to amino acids and subsequent transformation to glucose.

54) e – In response to either sympathetic stimulation or low blood pressure (hypotension), the juxtaglomerular cells of the kidney secrete renin. The juxtaglomerular cells are located in the afferent arterioles of the glomerulus. In the blood, renin catalyzes the conversion of angiotensinogen to angiotensin I. Angiotensin I then travels to the lungs where it is converted to angiotensin II by angiotensin converting enzyme (ACE). Angiotensin II is one of the most potent vasoconstrictors of the body. Vasoconstriction acts to increase blood pressure.

55) d – Insulin secretion decreases in response to sympathetic stimulation. Glycolysis, lipolysis, and renin secretion increase in response to insulin secretion.

56) e – Along with the pterygopalatine (sphenopalatine) ganglion, the submandibular (submaxillary) ganglion is a parasympathetic efferent ganglion associated with the facial nerve (CN VII). From the superior salivatory nucleus of the brainstem, preganglionic axons travel to the submandibular ganglion to synapse with postganglionic neurons. From there, postganglionic axons extend to provide parasympathetic innervation to two salivary glands, the submandibular (submaxillary) and sublingual glands.

57) c – Because preganglionic sympathetic axons join the chain via white rami communicans at the T1-L2 levels, some of these preganglionic fibers are also able to leave the sympathetic chain at these levels. They travel out in nerves to synapse with postganglionic neurons in prevertebral sympathetic ganglia. These nerves, which carry preganglionic sympathetic fibers, include the greater splanchnic nerve (T5-T9), lesser splanchnic nerve (T9, T10), lowest splanchnic nerve (T11), and the upper lumbar splanchnic nerves. Nerves that come off the sympathetic chain above these levels (superior, middle, and inferior cervical cardiac branches of the sympathetic chain) and below these levels (lower lumbar splanchnic and sacral splanchnic nerves) carry postganglionic axons from neurons which already synapsed in the sympathetic chain. Other sympathetic postganglionic axons leave the sympathetic chain to reenter a spinal nerve via a gray ramus communicans.

58) d – The vagus nerve is the predominant parasympathetic peripheral nerve. In fact, 75% of all peripheral parasympathetic fibers travel in the vagus nerve. Preganglionic cell bodies of the vagus nerve are found in the dorsal vagal nucleus of the brainstem. From here, preganglionic fibers travel out to reach effector organs of the neck, thorax, and abdomen. The vagus supplies the digestive system from the mouth to the level of the left (splenic) flexure of the large colon. Sacral parasympathetic splanchnic nerves from the S2-S4 levels of the spinal cord innervate everything distal to the left colic flexure. Because the parasympathetic synapse occurs very near the effector organ, preganglionic vagal fibers are what is seen coursing down the various nerve plexuses. There are four significant prevertebral sympathetic ganglia of the abdomen. They include the celiac, aorticorenal, superior mesenteric, and inferior mesenteric ganglia. These are described as sympathetic ganglia because they are the location of postganglionic sympathetic cell bodies. It is important to realize that the ganglia may also contain preganglionic parasympathetic fibers (axons). These parasympathetic fibers are passing through, en route to their synapse with the postganglionic neuron near the effec-

tor organ. The three most superior prevertebral sympathetic ganglia (celiac, aorticorenal, and superior mesenteric) almost always have some preganglionic vagal fibers (axons) within them. The inferior mesenteric ganglion is located too inferior. Parasympathetic innervation of the area supplied by the inferior mesenteric ganglion is usually supplied by the parasympathetic pelvic splanchnic nerves (S2-S4). The inferior salivatory nucleus is the location of parasympathetic preganglionic cell bodies that extend axons that travel with the glossopharyngeal nerve (CN IX) to reach postganglionic neurons in the otic ganglion.

59) e – In addition to its many other functions, the liver can metabolically be thought of as a "glucose factory." This factory makes and stores glucose for the rest of the body to use when needed. First, it stores glucose as glycogen. Second, when the glycogen storage capacity is reached, the liver, along with adipose tissue, converts glucose to fatty acids. The fatty acids can subsequently be stored as triglycerides providing long term energy storage. Finally, during periods of glucose shortage, the liver (along with the kidney) can convert certain amino acids to glucose by the process of gluconeogenesis. This creates the brain's only energy substrate, glucose, during periods of shortage.

60) e – Preganglionic sympathetic cell bodies are located in the intermediolateral horn of the spinal cord at the T1-L2 spinal levels. Their axons leave the cord with a spinal nerve to enter the sympathetic chain by way of a white ramus communicans. This small nerve serves as a branch of communication between the spinal nerve and a paravertebral sympathetic ganglion. White rami communicans are only located at the paravertebral sympathetic ganglia which are located at the T1-L2 spinal levels. Once in the sympathetic chain, the preganglionic axon may synapse with a postganglionic neuron in a paravertebral ganglion. Alternatively, the preganglionic axon may leave the sympathetic chain to synapse with the postganglionic neuron in a prevertebral sympathetic ganglion. Prevertebral ganglia are sympathetic ganglia that are distal to and not immediately associated with the sympathetic chain.

The axons of some sympathetic postganglionic neurons located in the paravertebral ganglia exit the sympathetic chain to reenter a spinal nerve by way of gray rami communicans. These axons may exit at the same paravertebral ganglion in which the postganglionic neuron cell body is located. Alternatively, these postganglionic axons may travel a variable distance up or down the sympathetic chain to exit via a gray ramus communicans at a different paravertebral ganglion. For this reason, every paravertebral ganglion is associated with a gray ramus communicans. Only paravertebral ganglia at the T1-L2 spinal levels are associated with white rami communicans.

61) b – In the first stage of catabolism (breakdown), carbohydrates are broken down to glucose, lipids to fatty acids and glycerol, and proteins to amino acids. In the second stage, glucose, fatty acids, and amino acids each undergo its separate metabolic pathway to yield acetyl-CoA. Acetyl-CoA is the common precursor to the third stage of catabolism, the citric acid (Krebs) cycle and oxidative phosphorylation. The end products of the third stage include ATP, water, carbon dioxide, and ammonia.

62) d – See #35 answer explanation. Hypoglycemia is low blood sugar. Brain and exercising skeletal muscle cells do not require the presence of insulin for intracellular transport of glucose.

63) e – See #43 answer explanation.

64) d – The first three answers describe the ciliary ganglion.

65) e – Gluconeogenesis is the production of glucose from non-carbohydrate sources. The word *gluconeogenesis* actually means "glucose new creation." It results from breakdown of proteins to amino acids and the subsequent transformation of certain amino acids to glucose. The pathway serves as an important means of producing the brain's only energy source, glucose, in times of carbohydrate shortage. The glucose can be transformed to pyruvate. Pyruvate is subsequently converted to acetyl-CoA, which can enter the citric acid (Krebs) cycle and oxidative phosphorylation with the resultant production of energy (ATP).

"A ship in harbor is safe…but that is not what ships are built for."

– John Shedd

CHAPTER SEVEN

THE CRANIAL NERVES

Twelve pairs of cranial nerves originate directly from the brain and brain stem. Each pair includes a right and left nerve. The right nerve supplies right-sided structures and the left nerve supplies left-sided structures. Most cranial nerves remain confined to the head. Five also supply tissues of the neck. Of these five, two nerves continue their descent to innervate structures of the torso. The cranial nerves are introduced in this chapter to familiarize the reader with their names and basic functions. Their branches and specific innervations are more thoroughly covered in a separate *Medtutor* book, *The Cranial Nerves.*

Not only does each cranial nerve differ in the specific tissues supplied, but the information conveyed by each nerve also varies. Some cranial nerves are purely motor; striated muscles are the only tissues supplied. Others convey sensory information only. Still others are mixed, having both motor and sensory functions. In addition, four cranial nerves carry parasympathetic fibers. Finally, seven cranial nerves include fibers that convey the special sensory modalities: smell, sight, hearing, taste, and touch.

The cranial nerves are numbered with Roman numerals. Many times only the numeral is referred to when discussing a cranial nerve. The names of all twelve cranial nerves, along with their corresponding nerve numbers and functions, must be mastered.

I.	Olfactory nerve	VII.	Facial nerve
II.	Optic nerve	VIII.	Vestibulocochlear nerve
III.	Oculomotor nerve	IX.	Glossopharyngeal nerve
IV.	Trochlear nerve	X.	Vagus nerve
V.	Trigeminal nerve	XI.	Accessory nerve
VI.	Abducens nerve	XII.	Hypoglossal nerve

As seen in Figure 7.1, the nerves are numbered in the order in which they originate from the anterior side of the base of the brain. The numbering starts at the more anterior and superior aspect of the brain and proceeds in a posterior and inferior direction. Like other anatomic structures, many of the nerves are named with reference to the function of the nerve.

AUTONOMIC AND SENSORY GANGLIA OF THE HEAD

In the previous chapter the ciliary, submandibular, pterygopalatine and otic ganglia were identified as parasympathetic efferent ganglia. They are classified as such because each ganglion houses parasympathetic postganglionic cell bodies. These cell bodies receive preganglionic fibers via one of the four parasympathetic cranial nerves. Postganglionic fibers travel out to supply smooth muscles of the eye and various glands. In addition to parasympathetic cell bodies, these ganglia may also contain somatic and/or postganglionic sympathetic fibers which are passing through en route to the tissues they innervate. This structure necessitates communication between each of the four "parasympathetic" ganglia and nerve branches that carry somatic or sympathetic fibers. In other words, although these ganglia are parasympathetic ganglia, they also communicate with cranial nerve and sympathetic branches which are not part of the parasympathetic system.

Sympathetic innervation to structures of the anterior head is provided by postganglionic fibers from the superior cervical ganglion of the sympathetic chain. Although these fibers eventually travel with numerous cranial nerve branches, no sympathetic transmission originates with any of the cranial nerves. The fact that each sympathetic fiber is postganglionic signifies that no other synapse occurs except with the end organ. Even though sympathetic fibers may pass through parasympathetic or sensory ganglia, no synapse occurs at these locations.

Similar to the communication between parasympathetic cranial nerves and parasympathetic ganglia, cranial nerves that carry sensory fibers must communicate with sensory ganglia. The axons that form these fibers originate from afferent cell bodies located in the sensory ganglia. In most cranial nerves containing sensory fibers, the cell bodies are pseudounipolar in structure. One axon is the only appendage that extends from the cell body and it soon divides into two branches. One branch travels distally with the cranial nerve to reach a peripheral sensory receptor. The

---

There are numerous mnemonics out there that may prove helpful to the beginning student.
Here are a few. Take your pick, but learn only one.

I.	II.	III.	IV.	V.	VI.	VII.	VIII.	IX.	X.	XI.	XII.
Oh,	**O**h,	**O**h,	**T**he	**T**wins	**A**re	**F**acing	**V**ery	**G**ood	**V**acations	**A**nd	**H**olidays
Oh,	**O**h,	**O**h,	**T**he	**T**rail	**A**way	**F**rom	**V**irginia	**G**ets	**V**igorous	**A**nd	**H**ot
On	**O**ld	**O**lympus	**T**owering	**T**ops	**A**	**F**in	**A**nd	**G**erman	**V**iewed	**S**ome	**H**ops

The last one is probably the most well-known, but substitutes the name
Acoustic for **V**estibulocochlear (CN VIII) and **S**pinal **A**ccessory for **A**ccessory (CN XI).

FIGURE 7.1
CRANIAL NERVE ORIGINATION FROM BRAIN AND BRAIN STEM

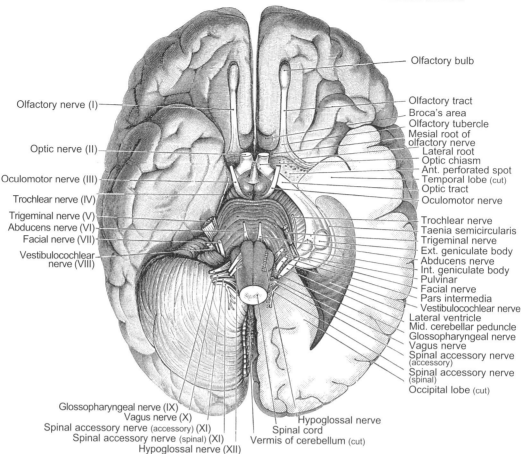

other branch courses with the proximal portion of the cranial nerve back to the brain stem. When the sensory receptor is activated, an afferent signal is transmitted to the CNS. Special sensory neurons of the olfactory (CN I), optic (CN II), and vestibulocochlear (CN VIII) nerves are bipolar in structure. Two processes extend from the cell body. The peripheral process travels to a sensory receptor and the central process travels to the brain.

Cranial nerve sensory ganglia can be compared to dorsal root ganglia of spinal nerves. With the exception of bipolar neurons contained in ganglia of the vestibulocochlear nerve (CN VIII), both subgroups of sensory ganglia contain afferent neuron cell bodies that are pseudounipolar in structure. Each dorsal root ganglion serves as *the* sensory ganglion of its affiliated spinal nerve. As such, it contains both somatic and visceral afferent cell bodies. A particular cranial nerve sensory ganglion, on the other hand, may contain somatic cell bodies, visceral cell bodies, or a combination of both.

CRANIAL NERVES I - VI

CN I = olfactory nerve. The olfactory nerve transmits information related to the sense of smell. It is composed of a tract and a bulb. The **olfactory tract** travels forward from the brain and ends in a dilated terminal portion, the **olfactory bulb**. Olfactory cells are sensory cells located in the mucous membrane of the upper nasal cavity. This includes membranes overlying the roof of the cavity, superior nasal concha, and upper nasal septum. Olfactory cells are bipolar; each cell has one peripheral and one central process. Peripheral processes travel to the mucosal surface to proj-

ect small **olfactory hairs** into the cavity. Olfactory hairs are the sensory receptors for the sense of smell. Central processes of olfactory cells travel away from the mucosal surface, joining together to form numerous small *olfactory* nerves. These nerves pierce the cribriform plate of the ethmoid bone to end in the olfactory bulb. The central processes of olfactory cells synapse in the bulb with cells that extend fibers centrally. Collectively, these fibers form the olfactory tract. Once stimulated, a signal is transmitted from the olfactory hair to the synapse in the bulb. From the bulb, the signal is relayed to the brain by way of the olfactory tract.

FIGURE 7.2
STRUCTURES OF THE OLFACTORY NERVE

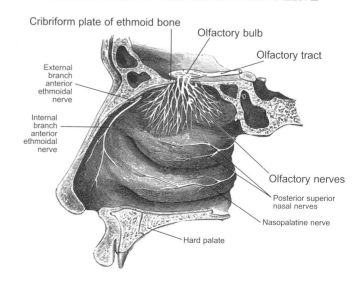

CN II = optic nerve. The optic nerve transmits information related to the sense of sight and travels from the back of the globe of the eye to the optic chiasm. The nerve is formed by central fibers of special sensory neuron cell bodies located in the retina. These multipolar neurons are known as ganglion cells. Multiple dendrites extend toward the pigmented layer of the retina to synapse with other neurons relaying visual signals from rods and cones. Central fibers leave the ganglion cells to travel toward the back of the eye and coalesce at the optic disc, forming the optic nerve. Each optic nerve exits its respective orbit via the optic canal and travels posteriorly and medially. After a short trek, the two optic nerves join, forming the x-shaped **optic chiasm**. In fact, the *chi*asm is named for its resemblance to the Greek letter for X, *chi*. The top of the "X" is formed by the convergence of the two optic nerves. The bottom of the "X" is formed by the parting of the two optic tracts. Each **optic tract** originates from one side of the chiasm and travels to an area of brain on the same side. Within the optic chiasm, fibers transmitting information from the medial or nasal half of each eye cross the chiasm to travel in the opposite optic tract and arrive at the opposite side of the brain. Fibers transmitting visual information from the lateral half of each eye do not cross at the chiasm and travel in the ipsilateral optic tract. They arrive at the same side of the brain as the optic nerve in which they traveled.

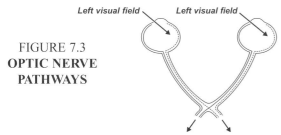

FIGURE 7.3
OPTIC NERVE PATHWAYS

*Light rays traveling from the left visual field stimulate the right half of each eye. This includes the medial or nasal half of the left eye and the lateral half of the right eye. Because fibers of the medial half of each eye cross at the chiasm, fibers from the **right** half of each eye travel in the **right** optic tract and are delivered to the **right** brain. These fibers carry information related to the **left** visual field. Fibers from the **left** half of each eye travel in the **left** tract and arrive at the **left** brain. They transmit visual signals for the **right** visual field.*

Left to Left	Right to Right
• Fibers of the *left* eye travel in the *left* optic nerve.	• Fibers of the *right* eye travel in the *right* optic nerve.
• Fibers of the *left* half of the left eye and *left* half of the right eye travel in the *left* optic tract.	• Fibers of the *right* half of the right eye and *right* half of the left eye travel in the *right* optic tract.

Olfactory (CN I) comes before optic (CN II) in alphabetic order.

The optic nerve is often mistakenly thought to be CN I. After all, the eyes are above the nose. The olfactory nerve must originate from a higher location in order to provide branches that *descend* into the very *top* of the nasal cavity.

THERE IS ONE NOSE AND TWO EYES.
The olfactory nerve is CN **I** and optic nerve is CN **II**.

FIGURE 7.4
OPTIC NERVES AND ASSOCIATED STRUCTURES

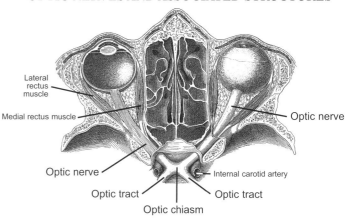

CN III = oculomotor nerve. This nerve is named for its innervation of four of the six extraocular muscles. Extraocular muscles are striated muscles which function in eye movement. Their contraction provides the ability to look up, down, in, or out without having to move the head. The four extraocular muscles include the superior rectus, medial rectus, inferior rectus, and inferior oblique muscles. Upon contraction, each rectus muscle causes the eye to rotate toward the direction of the muscle. The superior rectus causes the eye to look up. The medial rectus causes the eye to rotate in (adduction). The inferior rectus causes the eye to look down. The inferior oblique causes the eye to rotate in an *oblique* direction, upward and inward (adduction). The oculomotor nerve also innervates the levator palpebrae superioris muscle, which raises the eyelid.

In addition to motor fibers, the nerve also carries parasympathetic fibers responsible for pupillary constriction (miosis) and positive accommodation (near vision). Preganglionic cell bodies are located in the Edinger-Westphal nucleus of the midbrain. Preganglionic fibers synapse with postganglionic cell bodies in the ciliary ganglion. From there, parasympathetic postganglionic fibers extend to visceral structures of the eye.

FIGURE 7.5
MUSCLES SUPPLIED BY RIGHT OCULOMOTOR NERVE

Levator palpebrae superioris
Superior rectus
Medial rectus
Inferior rectus   Inferior oblique

CN IV = trochlear nerve. The trochlear nerve is the smallest cranial nerve. It is a motor nerve that innervates one striated muscle, the superior oblique muscle. A *trochlea* is a pulley-like structure. The superior oblique muscle is an extraocular muscle which is associated with a pulley-like apparatus or trochlea at the upper inner corner of the orbit. This trochlea is formed by cartilage and dense connective tissue attached to the frontal bone. The tissue forms a ring through which the tendon of the superior oblique passes. The presence of the trochlea permits rotation of the eyeball downward and outward (abduction) upon contraction of the superior oblique muscle.

So For Nose

Remember it as an election campaign slogan. For example, "Taylor For President." The superior oblique (So) is supplied by CN IV (four → "for"). To clinically test the function of the muscle, the patient is asked to look down and in, toward the nose.

Because the inferior rectus also depresses the eye (look down), the lateral rectus also abducts the eye (look out, laterally), and the depressing action of the superior oblique is optimized from an adducted position, superior oblique function is clinically tested by having the patient look toward the nose, down (depression) and in (adduction). This is a frequent cause of confusion because the muscles action is to rotate the eye down and out (abduction).

FIGURE 7.6
EXTRAOCULAR MUSCLES
Left Eye

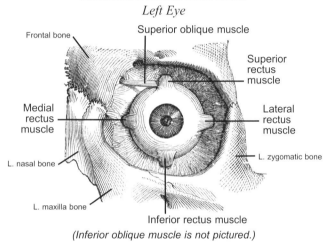

(Inferior oblique muscle is not pictured.)

A pulley (trochlea) is usually *above* the object it is moving. Thus, the trochlear nerve supplies the *superior* oblique muscle. The oculomotor nerve supplies the inferior oblique muscle.

CN V = **trigeminal nerve**. The trigeminal nerve is the largest cranial nerve. The nerve is named for its three divisions; *tri* equals three. Each division forms a large nerve which originates from the trigeminal ganglion and branches into other nerves. From superior to inferior, the three divisions include the ophthalmic nerve (V1 division), maxillary nerve (V2 division), and mandibular nerve (V3 division). The **ophthalmic nerve** travels toward the eye. The **maxillary nerve** is in an intermediate position and is named for its course within the maxilla bone. The **mandibular nerve** travels in the mandible.

SMALLEST AND LARGEST CRANIAL NERVES ARE NEXT TO ONE ANOTHER AND BOTH NAMES START WITH A "T."

The trochlear nerve (CN IV) is the smallest and the trigeminal nerve (CN V) is the largest.

The *tri*geminal nerve must be large; only a large nerve is capable of being named for its *three* divisions.

FIGURE 7.7
MAJOR BRANCHES OF THE TRIGEMINAL NERVE

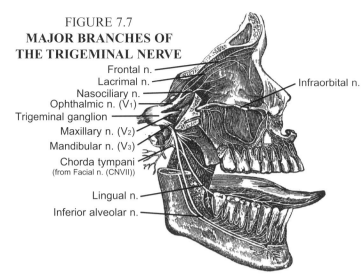

The trigeminal nerve has two primary functions: transmission of sensory information from somatic structures of the head and innervation of the muscles of mastication (chewing). The nerve is therefore formed by two roots, a sensory root and a motor root. The sensory root ends at the trigeminal ganglion. The motor root joins the mandibular nerve (V3). Of the three trigeminal divisions, the mandibular nerve is the only division that carries motor fibers. All three divisions carry somatic sensory fibers.

It only makes sense that the mandibular nerve is *the* trigeminal branch that carries motor fibers. After all, the trigeminal nerve supplies the muscles of mastication or chewing. What other nerve could be more appropriate than the *mandibular* or "lower jaw" nerve?

The **trigeminal ganglion** is also known as the semilunar ganglion because it is somewhat crescent-shaped. The gasserian ganglion is yet another name for the structure. The trigeminal ganglion is a somatic afferent or sensory ganglion. It houses pseudounipolar cell bodies that transmit sensory information from somatic structures. The trigeminal nerve is the first described cranial nerve that carries somatic afferent fibers. Coincidently, it is also the cranial nerve with the largest responsibility for transmission of somatic afferent information. It relays signals related to touch, pain, and proprioception from skin of the anterior face, subcutaneous tissues, temporomandibular joint, mucous membranes of the mouth, anterior 2/3 of tongue, gums and teeth. Due to the extensive area of sensory innervation, the trigeminal ganglion must be large. Significant space is required to house the multitudes of pseudounipolar cell bodies required to provide such innervation.

Three other cranial nerves carry somatic afferent fibers, but the area of innervation is relatively small for each nerve. The three cranial nerves include the facial nerve (CN VII), glossopharyngeal nerve (CN IX), and vagus nerve (CN X). Because each of these three nerves carries somatic afferent fibers, each is associated with at least one somatic sensory ganglion.

The trigeminal nerve innervates eight muscles, including four muscles of mastication and four other muscles. All motor fibers of CN V are located in the mandibular nerve (V3 division). The mandibular nerve is therefore responsible for innervating all trigeminal-supplied muscles. The ophthalmic nerve (V1 division) and maxillary nerve (V2 division) are purely sensory nerves. The four

FIGURE 7.8
CUTANEOUS INNERVATION OF TRIGEMINAL NERVE DIVISIONS AND CERVICAL PLEXUS

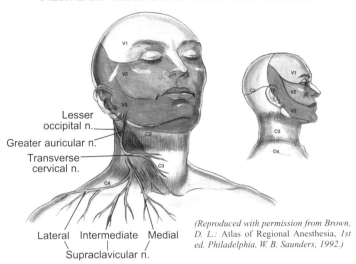

Lesser occipital n.
Greater auricular n.
Transverse cervical n.
Lateral Intermediate Medial
Supraclavicular n.

(Reproduced with permission from Brown, D. L.: Atlas of Regional Anesthesia, 1st ed. Philadelphia, W. B. Saunders, 1992.)

muscles of mastication include the masseter, temporalis, medial pterygoid, and lateral pterygoid muscles. The other four muscles consist of the tensor tympani, tensor veli palatini, anterior belly of digastric, and mylohyoid muscles.

HALF AND HALF
Half the striated muscles supplied by the trigeminal nerve (4) are muscles of mastication:
• masseter, temporalis, medial pterygoid, and lateral pterygoid
Half (4) are not:
• tensor tympani, tensor veli palatini, anterior belly of digastric, and mylohyoid

The *origin* of a muscle is its fixed point of attachment. The *insertion* is the attachment to the bone or other structure the muscle moves upon contraction. The masseter muscle originates from bones forming the zygomatic arch and inserts on the ramus and angle of the mandible. The muscle functions to close the jaw and lift the mandible. The temporalis originates from the temporal

FIGURE 7.9
STRUCTURES OF THE LATERAL HEAD
Superficial Layer

Epicranial aponeurosis
Temporalis fascia
Temporalis fascia (deep layer)
Occipito-frontalis
Temporalis muscle
Auriculotemporal nerve
Superficial temporal artery
Masseter (deep fibres)
Parotid gland (drawn backwards and downwards)
Orbicularis oculi
Zygomaticus major
Masseter (superficial fibres)
Stenson's duct
Buccinator
Depressor anguli oris
Facial artery

fossa of the side of the anterior skull and inserts on the coronoid process of it mandible. It closes the jaw upon contraction. The medial pterygoid muscle originates from the medial side of the lateral pterygoid plate of the sphenoid bone and underside of the maxilla. It inserts on the medial side of the mandible and also functions to close the jaw. The lateral pterygoid has two heads. Each originates from a different area of the lower surface of the sphenoid bone. Both heads insert on the neck of the mandible. As opposed to the other three muscles of mastication, the lateral pterygoid muscle opens the jaw. In addition, it advances the mandible forward and shifts it side to side.

To subdue an alligator or crocodile with bare hands, one must place the arms around each side of the ***lateral*** aspect of its mouth and hold its jaws shut. The muscles that open the jaws are not nearly as strong as those that shut them. The ***lateral*** pterygoid is the human muscle of mastication that opens the lower jaw.

FIGURE 7.10
STRUCTURES OF THE LATERAL HEAD
Deeper Layer

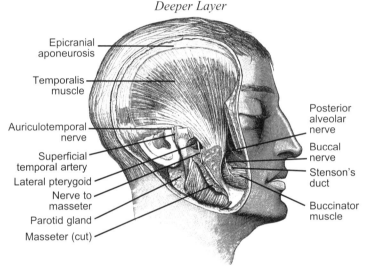

Epicranial aponeurosis
Temporalis muscle
Auriculotemporal nerve
Superficial temporal artery
Lateral pterygoid
Nerve to masseter
Parotid gland
Masseter (cut)
Posterior alveolar nerve
Buccal nerve
Stenson's duct
Buccinator muscle

The tensor veli palatini muscle originates from the scaphoid fossa and spine of the sphenoid bone and inserts on the wall of the auditory (eustachian) tube and aponeurosis of the soft palate. Upon contraction, it tenses the soft palate and opens the auditory tube, thereby allowing equalization of middle ear pressure with that of the external environment.

Tensor = tense *veli* = veil (soft) *palatini* = palate
It is contraction of the tensor veli palatini that opens the auditory tube and "clears the ears" following changes in outside pressure, as occurs with rapid changes in altitude or swimming deep underwater. Swallowing and yawning are associated with muscle contraction. These actions therefore promote opening the auditory tube, allowing equalization of pressure between the middle ear and external environment.

The tensor tympani muscle is a small muscle of the middle ear. The *tympanum* is the middle ear cavity of the temporal bone of the skull. The tensor tympani originates from cartilage of the auditory tube and greater wing of the sphenoid bone. It inserts on the manubrium of the malleus bone, the ear ossicle that contacts the tympanic membrane. Contraction of the tensor tympani pulls the tympanic membrane in a medial direction, increasing the tension on it. This dampens membrane movement in an effort to prevent damage to middle ear structures during particularly loud, repetitive noises.

> The *tensor tympani tenses* the *tympanic* membrane.

Point of Interest
The tensor tympani contracts when you talk, dampening tympanic membrane movement. This is the reason the perception of your own voice sounds different from an audio recording of it.

> The **t**rigeminal nerve innervates the **t**wo **t**ensors, the **t**ensor veli palatini and **t**ensor tympani.

CN VI = Abducens nerve. The abducens nerve innervates one extraocular muscle and is named for the action resulting from its contraction. The *abducens* nerve supplies the lateral rectus muscle, which *abducts* the eye. Upon contraction, the lateral rectus causes the eye to turn out laterally.

> The *abduc*ens nerve *abduc*ts the eye.
> It innervates the lateral rectus muscle.

The abducens nerve is the third and final cranial nerve that innervates muscles of eye movement. The three nerves include CN III, CN IV, and CN VI. Of these, only CN III has other functions: innervation of the levator palpebrae superioris and parasympathetic innervation causing miosis and positive accommodation.

LR₆SO₄3

The lateral rectus (LR) is supplied by CN VI (abducens n.). The superior oblique (SO) is supplied by CN IV (trochlear n.). The other 3 extraocular muscles are supplied by CN III (oculomotor n.).

FIGURE 7.11
**CRANIAL NERVE INNERVATION
OF EXTRAOCULAR MUSCLES**
Right Eye

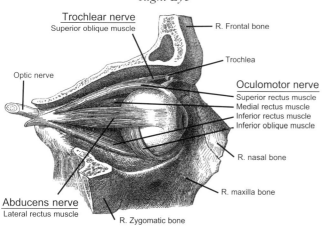

E₁Y₂E₃ : 3 cranial nerves supply extraocular muscles

***Rectus* is a Latin word for *straight*.**
Describing their "straight" course, the word is commonly found in the names of certain muscles. For instance, there is a rectus femoris muscle and rectus abdominis muscle.

The superior, medial, inferior, and lateral rectus muscles all run *straight* back from the globe of the eye. Because of this, there action upon contraction is easily estimated. The superior and inferior oblique muscles take an *oblique* course.

CN II - VI are associated with the eye.
It seems logical that the first several cranial nerves should be associated with the eye because the eye is at the front of the brain. If one can remember that the **nose is first** (in a race, the *nose* crosses the finish line *first* to **"win by a nose"**...the olfactory nerve is CN I) the next four can be remembered as being associated with the eye.

CN II: vision

CN III: superior rectus, medial rectus, inferior rectus, inferior oblique, parasympathetics (miosis and positive accommodation), levator palpebrae superioris

CN IV: superior oblique

CN V: sensory to eye (innervation is not confined to the eye)

CN VI: lateral rectus

HALF AND HALF
There are 12 cranial nerves. The first half (CN I - VI) supply the nose and eye. (the trigeminal nerve additionally supplies numerous other structures). The second half (CN VII - XII) has other responsibilities.

QUIZ 1
Cranial Nerves

Time for Quiz = 20 minutes.
For questions 1-14, choose the single best answer.

_____1) Which cranial nerve supplies the lateral rectus muscle?
  a) optic nerve
  b) trochlear nerve
  c) oculomotor nerve
  d) ophthalmic nerve
  e) none of the above

_____2) Which nerve carries both sensory and motor fibers?
  a) mandibular nerve
  b) maxillary nerve
  c) ophthalmic nerve
  d) oculomotor nerve
  e) none of the above

_____3) Which nerve is cranial nerve I?
  a) oculomotor
  b) ophthalmic
  c) optic
  d) abducens
  e) none of the above

_____4) Olfactory cells synapse in the
  a) brain
  b) olfactory tract
  c) olfactory bulb
  d) mucous membrane of the nasal cavity
  e) none of the above

_____5) Which nerve relays pain from the cornea of the eye?
  a) optic nerve
  b) oculomotor nerve
  c) ophthalmic nerve
  d) olfactory nerve
  e) none of the above

_____6) The smallest cranial nerve is the
  a) olfactory nerve
  b) abducens nerve
  c) optic nerve
  d) trochlear nerve
  e) none of the above

_____7) Which fibers cross at the optic chiasm?
  a) fibers transmitting signals from the medial side of each eye
  b) fibers transmitting signals for the right visual field of the right eye
  c) both a and b
  d) fibers transmitting signals from the lateral side of each eye
  e) none of the above

_____8) Which nerve supplies the lateral pterygoid muscle?
  a) maxillary
  b) abducens
  c) mandibular
  d) oculomotor
  e) none of the above

_____9) The fibers of what type of cells travel in the optic nerve?
  a) ganglion
  b) pseudounipolar
  c) both a and b
  d) olfactory
  e) none of the above

_____10) Which nerve supplies the levator palpebrae superioris?
  a) ophthalmic nerve
  b) trochlear nerve
  c) oculomotor nerve
  d) mandibular nerve
  e) none of the above

_____11) What muscle does the trochlear nerve supply?
  a) superior rectus
  b) superior oblique
  c) lateral rectus
  d) inferior oblique
  e) none of the above

_____12) What fibers travel in an optic tract?
      a) ipsilateral fibers conducting signals from the contralateral visual field
      b) contralateral fibers conducting signals from the ipsilateral visual field
      c) both a and b
      d) ipsilateral fibers conducting signals from the ipsilateral visual field
      e) none of the above

_____13) What is the cranial nerve number of the vestibulocochlear nerve?
      a) VII
      b) VIII
      c) IX
      d) X
      e) none of the above

_____14) A patient presents with decreased vision in the right visual fields of both eyes. What structure represents the most likely location of the problem?
      a) right optic tract
      b) right optic nerve
      c) left optic tract
      d) optic chiasm
      e) none of the above

For questions 15-20, use the following directions:
    a......1,2,3 are correct
    b......1,3 are correct
    c......2,4 are correct
    d......only 4 is correct
    e......all are correct

_____15) Which of the following nerves are trigeminal nerve branches?
      1) mandibular nerve
      2) maxillary nerve
      3) ophthalmic nerve
      4) nerve to tensor tympani

_____16) What may be found in the trigeminal ganglion?
      1) parasympathetic cell bodies
      2) somatic efferent (motor) fibers
      3) parasympathetic postganglionic fibers
      4) somatic afferent (sensory) cell bodies

_____17) Which nerves supply striated muscles?
      1) CN IV
      2) mandibular nerve
      3) CN VI
      4) maxillary nerve

_____18) Which muscles are supplied by the oculomotor nerve?
      1) superior rectus muscle
      2) lateral rectus muscle
      3) inferior rectus muscle
      4) superior oblique muscle

_____19) Which of the following cranial nerve numbers are correct?
      1) The glossopharyngeal nerve is CN XII.
      2) The trochlear nerve is CN VI.
      3) The hypoglossal nerve is CN IX.
      4) The facial nerve is CN VII.

_____20) Which of the following cells are pseudounipolar in structure?
      1) visceral afferent cells
      2) retinal ganglion cells
      3) somatic afferent cells
      4) olfactory cells

QUIZ 1: Cranial Nerves

1) e – The lateral rectus muscle *abducts* the eye and is supplied by the *abducens* nerve (CN VI). The optic nerve relays special sensory signals related to vision. The trochlear nerve innervates the superior oblique muscle. The oculomotor nerve supplies the superior rectus, medial rectus, inferior rectus, inferior oblique and levator palpebrae superioris muscles. The ophthalmic nerve is a sensory nerve that forms the V1 division of the trigeminal nerve (CN V).

2) a – The trigeminal nerve is formed by a sensory root and a motor root. The trigeminal is the primary somatic sensory nerve of the anterior head. As such, all three trigeminal divisions carry somatic afferent fibers that return to the brain stem via the sensory root. These divisions include the ophthalmic nerve (V1 division), maxillary nerve (V2 division), and mandibular nerve (V3 division). The trigeminal nerve also supplies the four muscles of mastication, tensor tympani, tensor veli palatini, mylohyoid, and the anterior belly of the digastric muscle. The motor root joins the mandibular division to supply these muscles. The mandibular nerve is therefore the only trigeminal division to carry motor fibers.

3) e – The olfactory nerve is CN I. The oculomotor nerve is CN III. The ophthalmic nerve is the V1 division of the trigeminal nerve (CN V). The optic nerve is CN II. The abducens nerve is CN VI.

4) c – Olfactory cells are bipolar cells found in the upper nasal mucosa. Peripheral processes extend to the mucosal surface and project small sensory receptors, olfactory hairs, into the nasal cavity. Central processes travel away from the mucosal surface and synapse in the olfactory bulb. Postsynaptic fibers then travel in the olfactory tract back to the brain. When stimulated by smell, a signal is transmitted from the olfactory hair to the bulb and subsequently, the brain.

5) c – The ophthalmic nerve is the V1 division of the trigeminal nerve. The trigeminal nerve is the primary somatic sensory nerve of the anterior head. In addition to the cornea and conjunctiva of the eye, the trigeminal also supplies skin of the face, subcutaneous tissues, mucous membranes of the mouth, gums, teeth, and anterior 2/3 of the tongue. The other divisions of the trigeminal nerve include the maxillary nerve (V2 division) and mandibular nerve (V3 division). The optic nerve is composed of special sensory fibers that relay signals related to vision. The oculomotor innervates four extraocular muscles, the levator palpebrae superioris, and carries parasympathetic fibers responsible for miosis and positive accommodation. The olfactory nerve is CN I and transmits sensory signals associated with smell.

6) d – The trochlear nerve is CN IV and innervates one extraocular muscle, the superior oblique. The trochlear nerve is just before the largest cranial nerve, the trigeminal nerve (CN V), in cranial nerve sequence.

7) c – Fibers carrying visual information from both the medial and lateral sides of an eye initially travel in the ipsilateral optic nerve. At the optic chiasm, fibers from the medial or nasal half of each eye cross to travel in the contralateral optic tract and arrive at the contralateral side of the brain. Sensory cells in the retina of the medial side of each eye transmit visual information from light rays arriving from the opposite side of the visual field. The medial side of the right eye transmits information from the right lateral visual field; the medial side of the left eye transmits information from the left lateral visual field. Fibers which cross at the optic chiasm are therefore responsible for lateral or peripheral vision. Due to the fiber's crossing at the optic chiasm, each optic tract carries fibers from the ipsilateral half of each eye and relays visual signals from the contralateral visual field. The *right* optic tract carries fibers from the *right* or lateral half of the right eye and the *right* or medial half of the left eye. Both fiber groups relay signals related to the *left* visual field. The *left* optic tract carries fibers from the *left* (or lateral) half of the left eye and the *left* (or medial) half of the right eye. The left optic tract therefore carries visual signals associated with the *right* visual field.

8) c – The mandibular nerve is the only trigeminal nerve (CN V) division to carry motor fibers. As such, it supplies all eight muscles innervated by the trigeminal nerve. These include the four muscles of mastication (masseter, temporalis, medial pterygoid, lateral pterygoid), tensor tympani, tensor veli palatini, mylohyoid, and anterior belly of digastric. The maxillary nerve is the V2 division of the trigeminal nerve. Like the V1 division, the ophthalmic nerve, the maxillary nerve carries only somatic afferent fibers; no motor fibers are present. The abducens nerve is CN VI and innervates the lateral rectus muscle. This muscle *abducts* the eye. The oculomotor nerve is CN III and supplies four extraocular muscles and the levator palpebrae superioris. The four extraocular muscles include the superior rectus, medial rectus, inferior rectus, and inferior oblique. The levator palpebrae superioris raises the upper eyelid.

9) a – Ganglion cells are *bipolar* sensory cells found in the retina. The dendritic tree extends toward the pigmented layer of the retina and synapses with other sensory cells carrying visual information from rods and cones. Central processes (axons) of ganglion cells travel toward the brain and form the tissue of the optic nerve (CN II). Olfactory cells are bipolar special sensory cells associated with the olfactory nerve (CN I).

10) c – The levator palpebrae superioris raises the upper eyelid. The oculomotor nerve additionally supplies four extraocular muscles: the superior rectus, medial rectus, inferior rectus, and inferior oblique. The ophthalmic nerve is a sensory nerve and the V1 division of the trigeminal nerve (CN V). The trochlear nerve innervates the superior oblique muscle. The mandibular nerve is the V3 division of the trigeminal nerve. It is the only trigeminal division that carries motor fibers and supplies the four muscles of mastication, tensor tympani, tensor veli palatini, anterior belly of the digastric, and mylohyoid.

11) b – The trochlear nerve is named for the trochlea, a pulley-like apparatus in the upper medial corner of the orbit created by the tendon of the superior oblique muscle passing through a ring of dense connective tissue and cartilage. The superior rectus and inferior oblique are innervated by the oculomotor nerve. The lateral rectus muscle *abducts* the eye and is supplied by the *abducens* nerve.

12) a – See #7 answer explanation.

13) b – The vestibulocochlear nerve is CN VIII. The facial nerve is CN VII. The glossopharyngeal nerve is CN IX. The vagus nerve is CN X.

14) c – See #7 answer explanation.

15) e – The ophthalmic nerve is the V1 division if the trigeminal nerve. The maxillary nerve is the V2 division. The mandibular nerve is the V3 division. Along with the tensor tympani, the trigeminal nerve also supplies the tensor veli palatini, anterior belly of digastric, mylohyoid, and the four muscles of mastication (masseter, temporalis, medial pterygoid, lateral pterygoid).

16) d – The trigeminal ganglion is a somatic sensory ganglion. As such, it houses somatic afferent cell bodies. Both parasympathetic cell bodies and parasympathetic postganglionic fibers may be found in one of the four parasympathetic ganglia of the head: ciliary, pterygopalatine, otic, and submandibular. The motor root of the trigeminal nerve joins the mandibular nerve (V3 division) after its origination from the trigeminal ganglion.

17) a – The trochlear nerve is CN IV and supplies the superior oblique muscle. The abducens nerve is CN VI and supplies the lateral rectus muscle. The mandibular nerve is the V3 division of the trigeminal nerve and the only trigeminal division that carries motor fibers. The maxillary nerve is the V2 trigeminal division. Like the V1 division, it is purely a sensory nerve.

18) b – The oculomotor nerve (CN III) supplies the superior rectus, medial rectus, inferior rectus, and inferior oblique muscles. It also supplies the levator palpebrae superioris, which raises the upper eyelid. The lateral rectus muscle

abducts the eye and is supplied by the *abducens* nerve (CN VI). The trochlear nerve (CN IV) innervates the superior oblique muscle.

19) d – The glossopharyngeal nerve is CN IX. The trochlear nerve is CN IV. The abducens nerve is CN VI. The hypoglossal nerve is CN XII.

20) b – Afferent cells of both the visceral and somatic systems are pseudounipolar. One axon extends out from the cell body to divide into a central and peripheral process. Retinal ganglion cells are multipolar. Numerous dendrites extend from each ganglion cell toward the peripheral surface of the retina to synapse with sensory cells relaying visual information from rods and cones. An axon travels centrally within the optic nerve to reach the brain. Olfactory cells are bipolar. One process leaves the cell body to travel peripherally and extend small olfactory hairs into the nasal cavity. A second process exits the cell body and travels in a central direction to synapse in the olfactory bulb. From there, a postsynaptic fiber travels to the CNS.

CRANIAL NERVES VII-XII

CN VII = facial nerve. Although the facial nerve is named for its innervation of the muscles of facial expression, it has numerous responsibilities. The facial nerve is one of the four parasympathetic cranial nerves. As such, it carries parasympathetic fibers that innervate lacrimal, nasal, and salivary glands. Somatic afferent fibers supply skin of the auricle of the ear and behind the ear. Special visceral afferent fibers relay taste sensation from the anterior two thirds of the tongue. In addition to the muscles of facial expression, the facial nerve also supplies the stapedius, stylohyoid, and posterior belly of digastric.

> **The facial nerve frowns, cries, and spits.**
> It innervates muscles of facial expression, the lacrimal gland, and two salivary glands.

Parasympathetic responsibilities of the facial nerve were covered in the previous chapter. Preganglionic visceral efferent cell bodies located in the lacrimal nucleus extend preganglionic fibers to the pterygopalatine (sphenopalatine) ganglion to synapse with postganglionic cell bodies. From there, postganglionic fibers travel out to innervate the lacrimal gland and glands of the nasal and oral cavities. Preganglionic cell bodies in the superior salivatory nucleus extend preganglionic fibers to the submandibular (submaxillary) ganglion. Postganglionic fibers then course to the submandibular (submaxillary) and sublingual glands. It should be noted that there is often a mixture of cranial nerve innervation to the salivary glands; it is not as "black or white" as what is commonly presented. By way of various branches, both the facial and glossopharyngeal nerves frequently contribute secretomotor fibers to each of the three salivary glands: the submandibular, sublingual, and parotid glands.

An **auricular branch** comes off the facial to join an auricular branch of the vagus nerve to supply sensory innervation to skin of the auricle of the ear and behind the ear. Because the facial nerve carries somatic afferent fibers, it must be associated with a ganglion in which to house the pseudounipolar cell bodies.

FIGURE 7.12
SKIN SUPPLIED BY AURICULAR BRANCHES OF FACIAL AND VAGUS NERVES

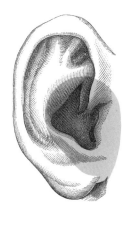

The **geniculate ganglion** is the sensory ganglion of the facial nerve. It appears as a dilated area of the facial nerve located at a sharp posterior turn the nerve makes before exiting the stylomastoid foramen. The word *geniculum* is Latin for *little knee*. The word describes structures that make sharp, knee-like bends. The geniculate ganglion contains pseudounipolar neuron cell bodies of two fiber types: general somatic afferent and special visceral afferent. General somatic afferent neurons transmit sensory information from somatic structures of the ear and soft palate. Special visceral afferent neurons comprise the majority of cells in the ganglion and relay signals related to taste sensation.

Peripheral processes travel from pseudounipolar somatic neurons within the ganglion to skin of the external acoustic meatus, behind the auricle of the ear, and mucous membranes of the soft palate. Central processes continue with the facial nerve back to the brain stem. When a sensory receptor is stimulated, a somatic afferent message is transmitted to the brain. A similar structure exists for pseudounipolar neurons relaying taste sensation, except the peripheral processes travel to taste buds of the anterior tongue.

The facial nerve is one of three cranial nerves that carry special visceral afferent fibers that conduct signals of taste sensation. As previously mentioned, the facial nerve is responsible for taste sensation to the anterior 2/3 of the tongue. This information is transmitted by way of a facial branch, the chorda tympani. The glossopharyngeal nerve (CN IX) relays taste signals from the posterior 1/3 of the tongue. The vagus nerve transmits taste signals originating from the extreme posterior aspect of the tongue and epiglottis. Coincidently, the facial, glossopharyngeal, and vagus represent three of the four parasympathetic cranial nerves.

It seems appropriate that three out of four parasympathetic cranial nerves relay signals related to taste. After all, digestion is a parasympathetic function and taste is the sensory modality most closely associated with digestion. The only parasympathetic nerve not associated with taste is the oculomotor nerve, obviously not a "taste" nerve.

Cranial nerves 7, 9, 10 relay taste.
If it were not for cranial nerve 8, which transmits signals related to hearing and balance, the cranial nerves that relay taste sensation would be in perfect sequence.

Their order of origination (seventh, ninth, and tenth) relative to other cranial nerves is appropriate for the area they supply (tongue and epiglottis).

The **chorda tympani** is a facial nerve branch that originates prior to the cranial nerve's exit from the temporal bone of the skull. The chorda tympani takes a separate path and exits the skull at a location different from that of its parent nerve. It joins the lingual nerve between the medial and lateral pterygoid muscles. The lingual nerve is a branch of the mandibular (V3) division of the trigeminal nerve and conveys general sensation from the anterior 2/3 of the tongue. Sensation from the anterior 2/3 of the tongue is therefore supplied by two cranial nerves. General sensation is provided by the trigeminal nerve (CN V); taste sensation is relayed by the facial nerve (CN VII). Both general and taste sensation from the posterior 1/3 of the tongue is transmitted by only one cranial nerve, the glossopharyngeal nerve (CN IX).

Although the majority of fibers that travel in the chorda tympani are special visceral afferent fibers associated with taste, general visceral efferent fibers are also present. These fibers consist of preganglionic parasympathetic fibers traveling from the superior salivatory nucleus to synapse with postganglionic cell bodies in the submandibular (submaxillary) ganglion. Postganglionic parasympathetic fibers leave the ganglion and innervate the submandibular (submaxillary) and sublingual glands.

The **nerve to stapedius** is a small branch that also originates prior to the exit of the facial nerve from the skull. The stapedius is an extremely small muscle that originates from the pyrimidal eminence of the wall of the tympanum and inserts on the posterior neck of the stapes, the ear ossicle for which it is named. Like the tiny muscle supplied by the trigeminal nerve, the tensor tympani, contraction dampens excessive ossicle movement during loud, repetitive noises, limiting damage to middle ear structures.

The facial nerve emerges from the skull through the stylomastoid foramen and soon gives a branch that travels up and behind the ear to supply the auricularis posterior and occipitalis muscles. The auricularis posterior originates from the mastoid process and inserts on the cartilage of the ear. Upon contraction, it pulls the auricle of the ear backward. The occipitalis originates from the highest nuchal line of the occipital bone and inserts on the aponeurosis of the scalp. Upon contraction, it pulls the scalp back.

Separate branches originate from the facial nerve and supply the posterior belly of the digastric muscle and stylohyoid muscle. The digastric muscle has two bellies. The prefix *di-* means two or divergent. The anterior belly originates below the chin on the mandible. It is innervated by the mylohyoid branch of the inferior alveolar nerve. The inferior alveolar is a branch of the mandibular (V3) division of the trigeminal nerve (CN V). The posterior belly originates on the mastoid process of the temporal bone. Both bellies insert by way of an intermediate tendon on the hyoid bone. The digastric functions to lower the mandible and raise the hyoid bone. The stylohyoid muscle originates on the styloid process of the temporal bone. This is not far from the origination of the posterior belly of the digastric muscle; thus, both muscles are in a position to be supplied by the same cranial nerve. The stylohyoid inserts on the hyoid bone and moves the hyoid posterior and superior upon contraction, pulling the tongue in the same direction.

The facial nerve continues into the tissue of the parotid gland to divide into terminal branches that subsequently leave the parotid and supply muscles of facial expression. The facial branches are named with respect to the region of the head and neck they supply. The most superior is the temporal branch. The most inferior is the cervical branch. The branches are listed in order from superior to inferior. There is variation in the specific muscles innervated by particular branches.

The **temporal branch** supplies the auricularis anterior, auricularis superior, frontalis, and corrugator supercilii muscles. The auricularis anterior muscle pulls the auricle of the ear forward; the auricularis superior pulls the auricle up. The frontalis muscle runs vertically across the forehead. It raises the eyebrows and skin of the forehead upon contraction. The corrugator supercilii is located just above the upper eyelids, between the frontalis and upper portion of orbicularis oculi. The word *cilia* is Latin for eyelid. The corrugator supercilii pulls the eyebrow down and in, as if squinting. This muscle may alternatively be supplied by the zygomatic branch.

The **zygomatic branch** innervates the orbicularis oculi and procerus muscles. The orbicularis oculi surrounds each eye and closes the eyelid upon contraction. The word *orbicular* describes a circular structure, such as an orbit. *Oculi* refers to the eye. The procerus originates from fascia over the bridge of the nose and inserts on skin of the medial forehead above the nose. With contraction it pulls the medial eyebrows down, creating a puzzled look. At times, the zygomatic branch will supply facial muscles associated with the upper lip that are otherwise supplied by the buccal branch.

The **"3 columns"** of the oculomotor nerve (CN III) holds the eyes open (oculomotor supplies levator palpebrae superioris).

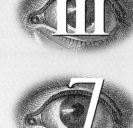

The **"hook"** of the facial nerve (CN 7) closes the eyes. (facial supplies orbicularis oculi).

The **buccal branch** is responsible for the innervation of muscles surrounding the nose and mouth. The levator labii superioris raises the upper lip. The levator labii superioris alaeque nasi is located just medial and flares the nostril in addition to raising the lip. The risorius stretches from fascia of the lateral neck to skin of the angle of the mouth. Its contraction pulls the angle of the mouth laterally, as if smiling with closed lips. The buccinator runs from the mandible and maxilla to the orbicularis oris muscle at the angle of the mouth. Its contraction pulls the check and angle of the mouth in, as if puckering. The compressor naris is also known as the nasalis muscle. It originates from the maxilla and inserts on the ala of the nose. It functions to flare the nostril. The levator anguli oris raises the angle of the mouth upon stimulation. The orbicularis oris surrounds the mouth. Contraction causes the lips to project forward, as if forming a kiss. The zygomaticus major originates from the zygomatic bone and inserts at the angle of the mouth. Contraction pulls the angle of the mouth up and out, as if smiling with open lips. The zygomaticus minor is medial to the major and inserts on the orbicularis oris and levator labii superioris muscles. Its contraction pulls the upper lip up and out.

The **mandibular branch** supplies the depressor anguli oris and depressor labii inferioris muscles. The depressor anguli oris originates from the lateral mandible and inserts at the angle of the mouth. Contraction pulls down the angle of the mouth, as if frowning. The depressor labii inferioris originates from the lower anterior aspect of the mandible and inserts on the lower portion of orbicularis oris and skin of the lower lip. Contraction lowers the lower lip.

Finally, the **cervical branch** descends the neck to supply the platysma. The platysma is a thin sheet of superficial muscle fibers located immediately beneath skin of the anterior neck. It originates from cervical fascia and inserts on the underside of the mandible and skin surrounding the mouth. The longitudinally-directed ridges that appear in skin of the anterior neck during periods of straining or "bearing down" are the result of platysma muscle contraction.

"To Zanzibar By Motor Car"

This mnemonic displays the correct order, from superior to inferior, of facial nerve branches to muscles of facial expression:

Temporal ➔ Zygomatic ➔ Buccal ➔ Mandibular ➔ Cervical

FIGURE 7.13
MUSCLES OF FACIAL EXPRESSION AND SUPERFICIAL MUSCLES OF NECK

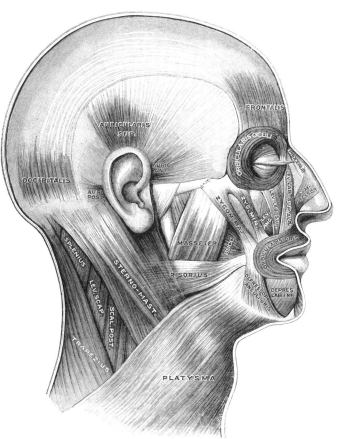

These facial nerve branches should not be confused with nerves that arise from other cranial nerves. For instance, the zygomatic, buccal, and mandibular nerves are branches of the trigeminal nerve.

The word *facial* has 6 letters; the facial nerve has 6 responsibilities

1) **parasympathetic** to pterygopalatine ganglion for lacrimal glands and glands of nasal and oral cavities

2) **parasympathetic** to submandibular ganglion for submandibular and sublingual glands

3) **sensory** to skin of external acoustic meatus, skin behind the ear, and mucous membranes of soft palate

4) **taste** to anterior 2/3 of tongue

5) **five muscles not on face**: stapedius, auricularis posterior, occipitalis, posterior belly of digastric, stylohyoid

6) **muscles of facial expression**

Similarities Between Trigeminal and Facial Nerves

1) Each is an odd numbered cranial nerve: 5 (CN V) and 7 (CN VII).
2) Each has extensive innervations of the anterior head and is challenging to learn.
3) Each is associated with one sensory ganglion: trigeminal ganglion (CN V) and geniculate ganglion (CN VII).
4) Each innervates a particular group of muscles: muscles of mastication (CN V) and muscles of facial expression (CN VII). Both groups are supplied by special visceral efferent fibers.
5) In addition to these muscle groups, CN V supplies four other muscles and CN VII supplies five other muscles. Seven is higher than five and CN VII supplies a higher number of additional muscles.
   - each supplies a small muscle of the tympanum
     - tensor tympani via V (V also supplies another "tensor")
     - stapedius via VII (VII also supplies another muscle that starts with "st-")
   - each supplies a "-ylohyoid" muscle
     - mylohyoid via V
     - stylohyoid via VII
     M of <u>m</u>ylohyoid comes before *s* of <u>s</u>tylohyoid and V comes before VII.
   - each supplies a belly of the digastric
     - anterior belly via V
     - posterior belly via VII
     anterior comes before posterior and V comes before VII
   - In addition, V supplies tensor veli palatini. VII supplies auricularis posterior and occipitalis

CN VIII = vestibulocochlear nerve. The vestibulocochlear nerve is named for the vestibule and cochlea of the inner ear. The vestibule is a sensory structure associated with balance and equilibrium; the cochlea functions in the perception of sound. The vestibulocochlear nerve is also known as the acoustic nerve and relays sensory information related to balance and sound. The vestibulocochlear nerve is formed by the combination of two roots, a vestibular and cochlear root. The vestibular is the medially-located root and the cochlear is laterally-located. After their respective points of origin, the two join and pass into the internal acoustic meatus alongside the facial nerve (CN VII). The vestibulocochlear then divides back into its two components and each branch runs to its own sensory ganglion.

> The vestibular root is associated with equilibrium. It is in a medial location because it needs to be closer to the center of gravity to maintain balance. The cochlear root is associated with hearing; it is in a lateral position so it is closer to the outside and can hear better.

The **vestibular root** transmits sensory information related to equilibrium and balance. A *vestibule* is a space at the entrance of a canal. Bipolar sensory neurons are located in the **vestibular ganglion**. Peripheral processes extend from these cells to the saccule, the utricle, and the three semicircular ducts. Central processes travel with the vestibular root back to the brain stem.

Signals associated with sound sensation are transmitted by the **cochlear root**. A *cochlea* is a spiral form such as a snail shell. Bipolar sensory neurons are found in the **cochlear (spiral) ganglion**. Peripheral processes are distributed to the spiral organ of Corti in the cochlear duct. Central processes travel to the brain stem with the cochlear root.

> A *cochlea* is a spiral form such as a shell. Consider an island native who creates *sound* by blowing into a hole at the end of a conch shell.

FIGURE 7.14
STRUCTURES OF THE EAR

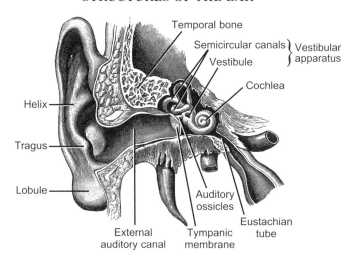

CN IX = **glossopharyngeal nerve** (210). The word root *gloss(o)* refers to the tongue. *Pharyngeal* clearly refers to the pharynx. This nerve provides general and taste sensation to the posterior 1/3 of the tongue and sensation to most of the pharynx. It also contributes to the motor innervation of pharyngeal muscles. Like the facial nerve (CN VII), the glossopharyngeal has a variety of functions. It carries parasympathetic fibers that ultimately supply the parotid gland. Somatic afferent fibers relay sensory signals from the middle ear, eustachian tube, pharynx, and posterior 1/3 of tongue. Motor fibers supply the stylopharyngeus muscle and contribute to the innervation of other pharyngeal muscles. Finally, visceral afferent fibers relay sensory signals from baroreceptors and carotid bodies of the carotid artery sinus. These sensory receptors transmit sensory information related to blood pressure and respiration control, respectively. Other visceral afferents transmit taste sensation from the posterior 1/3 of the tongue.

The glossopharyngeal originates from the medulla oblongata very near the origin of the vagus nerve and exits the skull by way of the jugular foramen. It travels down behind the stylopharyngeus muscle and courses to the posterior pharynx and base of the tongue.

The stylopharyngeus muscle is the only muscle innervated entirely by the glossopharyngeal nerve. When stimulated, the muscle functions to raise or elevate the pharynx. Other pharyngeal muscles are supplied by a combination of glossopharyngeal and vagus nerve branches. These innervations are described in the cervical nerve chapter.

Sensation is transmitted from the middle ear cavity (tympanum), inner surface of tympanic membrane, auditory (eustachian) tube, posterior 1/3 of the tongue, and mucous membranes of the soft palate, pharynx, and tonsils. In addition, sensory signals relay taste from the posterior 1/3 of the tongue and regulatory information from the carotid sinus. All these sensory fibers necessitate the presence of ganglia to house their associated pseudounipolar cell bodies. The **superior ganglion** is not always present and appears as an enlargement of the glossopharyngeal nerve as the nerve enters the jugular foramen. The **inferior ganglion** is a larger ganglion and is located at the point of exit of the nerve from the foramen.

The **tympanic nerve** (209) is a glossopharyngeal branch also known as the nerve of Jacobson. It travels to the middle ear to contribute to the tympanic plexus. This plexus supplies the mucous membrane of the tympanum, the middle ear cavity. The tympanic plexus may also receive contribution from the facial nerve and sympathetic input from the internal carotid plexus. Glossopharyngeal fibers that course through the plexus form the **lesser petrosal nerve**. The lesser petrosal is considered a branch of the glossopharyngeal nerve, even though it physically appears to originate from the tympanic plexus. The word *petrosal* refers to the petrous portion of the temporal bone. The lesser petrosal nerve carries preganglionic parasympathetic fibers that originated from cell bodies located in the inferior salivatory nucleus and course to the otic ganglion. From there, postganglionic fibers travel on to supply the parotid gland. As mentioned in the discussion of the facial nerve, each of the three salivary glands usually obtains some degree of secretomotor innervation from both the facial (CN VII) and glossopharyngeal (CN IX) nerves.

The **carotid branch** (207) provides sensory innervation to the carotid sinus of the carotid artery. The carotid sinus is the dilated area of the common carotid artery at its bifurcation into the internal and external carotid arteries. Within the walls of the carotid sinus are baroreceptors, which are stretch receptors that function in blood pressure control. The carotid body is a grouping of chemoreceptors located at the superior aspect of the fork of the common carotid artery. These chemoreceptors detect changes in oxygen content, carbon dioxide content, and pH of the blood and are used in the regulation of respiration. Afferent signals from baroreceptors and chemoreceptors are transmitted to the brain stem via the carotid branch, which is also known as the **afferent nerve of Hering**.

The glossopharyngeal is a "jack of all trades, but a master of none."

1) **General visceral efferent**: It is the primary supplier of parasympathetic fibers to only one salivary gland, the parotid.
2) **Special visceral afferent**: It supplies taste to only the posterior 1/3 of the tongue.
3) **Special visceral efferent**: Only one muscle, the stylopharyngeus, is innervated solely by it and no other nerve.
4) **General somatic afferent**: It relays sensory information from a variety of "small" areas: mucous membranes of tympanum, auditory tube, posterior pharynx, tonsil, etc.
5) **General visceral afferent**: It supplies only a small area of one blood vessel, the carotid sinus (baroreceptors, carotid body).

CN X = vagus (**29**, 49, 232, 236, 237, 241, 244, 255). As stated in the previous chapter, the word *vagus* is derived from a Latin word which means *wandering*. This nerve goes many places and performs many tasks.

A *vaga*bond is a *wanderer*.

Although the trigeminal nerve (CN V) is the largest cranial nerve, the vagus nerve is the longest. The vagus transmits sensory information from skin of the external acoustic meatus, skin behind the ear, and mucous membranes of the pharynx and larynx. Taste sensation is relayed from the extreme posterior aspect of the tongue and epiglottis. Similar to transmission of afferent signals from the carotid body by the glossopharyngeal nerve, the vagus conducts information related to blood oxygen content, carbon dioxide content, and pH from receptors of the aortic body. Motor innervation is provided to muscles of the pharynx, esophagus, and larynx. The vagus is responsible for parasympathetic visceral input to thoracic and abdominal viscera. It supplies the digestive tract to the distal level of the left (splenic) flexure of the large colon. Beyond the left colic flexure, sacral parasympathetic fibers provide the innervation. Due to its extensive distribution, the specific branches, courses, anatomic relationships, and innervations of the vagus nerve are covered in other chapters.

The vagus nerve originates from the medulla oblongata between the glossopharyngeal nerve (above) and accessory nerve (below). All three nerves exit the skull by way of the jugular foramen. Similar to the glossopharyngeal, the vagus is associated with both a superior and inferior sensory ganglion, although the superior vagal ganglion is more consistently present than that of the glossopharyngeal.

The **superior vagal ganglion** is also known as the jugular ganglion. It appears as a rounded enlargement of the vagus nerve as the nerve passes through the jugular foramen. Most of the peripheral processes of pseudounipolar neurons within the ganglion travel in the auricular branch of the vagus and transmit sensory signals from skin of the external acoustic meatus and behind the auricle of the ear. Some peripheral fibers transmit sensory signals from mucous membranes of the pharynx. Central processes travel with the vagus nerve back to the medulla.

The vagus nerve receives the internal branch of the accessory nerve (CN XI) just above the inferior vagal ganglion. This accessory nerve contribution is the origin of many of the motor fibers that subsequently travel out in vagal branches to supply muscles of the pharynx and larynx.

The **inferior vagal ganglion** is also known as the nodose ganglion. It appears as an elongated dilation of the vagus nerve soon after the nerve exits the jugular foramen. Peripheral processes of pseudounipolar neurons travel out in the internal branch of the superior laryngeal nerve (internal laryngeal nerve (34)) to relay sensory signals from mucous membranes of the larynx. Additional peripheral processes travel in other vagal branches and transmit signals from the esophagus, trachea, bronchi, and other visceral structures of the thorax and abdomen. Central processes travel back up the vagus and pass through the superior vagal ganglion without synapsing to reach the medulla.

Similarities Between Glossopharyngeal and Vagus Nerves

1) They are next to each other in cranial nerve sequence (CN IX and CN X).
2) Each carries parasympathetic fibers (general visceral efferent).
3) Each exits skull via the jugular foramen (so does the accessory nerve (CN XI)).
4) Each is associated with two sensory ganglia: a superior and inferior ganglion (the superior ganglion of CN IX may be absent).
5) Each supplies sensation to mucous membranes of the pharynx, although IX is the dominant nerve (general somatic afferent fibers).
6) Each supplies muscles of the pharynx, although X is the dominant nerve (special visceral efferent fibers). X additionally supplies muscles of the larynx.
7) Each carries general visceral afferent fibers (they are the only two cranial nerves to do so).
8) Each transmits taste sensation (special visceral afferent fibers).
9) Each carries 5 different fiber types (the most carried by any cranial nerve).

CN XI = accessory nerve. The accessory nerve can be remembered for providing "accessory" fibers to the vagus nerve by way of the internal branch. The accessory nerve (CN XI) is composed of a cranial root and a spinal root. The **cranial root** originates from the medulla oblongata (just inferior to the origin of the vagus nerve) and forms the internal branch or internal *ramus*. The internal branch joins the vagus nerve proximal to the inferior vagal ganglion and provides additional "accessory" innervation to structures supplied by the vagus. The **spinal root** is created by branches from the C1-C5 spinal segments; thus, this *cranial* nerve obtains "accessory" contribution from the *spinal* cord. The spinal root forms the external branch or external *ramus*. It is this spinal root or external branch that becomes the **spinal accessory nerve** (26), the visually apparent nerve that is often referred to as the accessory nerve. Contributing branches from the C2, C3, and C4 spinal segments (13, 17, 21) can be seen in Figure 1 of the poster.

The *internal* ramus comes from the brain, which is *internal* to the skull.

The *external* ramus is formed by cervical spinal segments, which are *external* to the skull.

The spinal accessory nerve is a motor nerve. It supplies one muscle entirely and contributes to the innervation of another. It travels out to innervate the trapezius muscle of the posterior neck and upper back. The trapezius originates from the occipital bone and C7-T12 spinous processes. It inserts on the acromion and spine of the scapula and the clavicle. The trapezius functions to lift or "shrug" the shoulders. Similar to the trapezium bone of the carpus, the trapezius muscle is named for its shape. A trapezium is an irregular shape with four sides. The spinal accessory nerve also

gives a branch that combines with a branch from the C2 spinal segment to form a nerve that supplies the sternocleidomastoid muscle. This is the prominent muscle of the anterior neck which is easily identifiable in most people. The sternocleidomastoid is named for its origins and insertion. The muscle has two heads. The *"sterno-"* component of the name is related to the origination of the sternal head from the manubrium of the sternum. The *"-cleido-"* component is a Greek word root describing the clavicle. It refers to the origination of the clavicular head from the medial third of the clavicle. Both heads insert on the mastoid process of the temporal bone, with some insertion occurring at the superior nuchal line of the occipital bone. The sternocleidomastoid turns the head from side to side and is the predominant flexor of the cervical vertebral column.

CN XI has an identity crisis.

The anatomy and terminology concerning the accessory nerve can be misleading. The accessory nerve is CN XI and is formed by a cranial and spinal root. Although the accessory is a *cranial* nerve, its cranial root joins the vagus nerve. These cranial fibers originate from the accessory, but subsequently travel in vagal branches; the structures they innervate are considered supplied by the vagus nerve. This merger occurs early, so the actual accessory nerve is frequently not seen. The nerve that is often visualized, the spinal accessory nerve, is formed by the spinal root. The spinal accessory nerve is a motor nerve that supplies the trapezius and sternocleidomastoid muscles. The spinal accessory nerve is frequently called the accessory nerve, which is technically not correct.

FIGURE 7.15
MUSCLES SUPPLIED BY SPINAL ACCESSORY NERVE

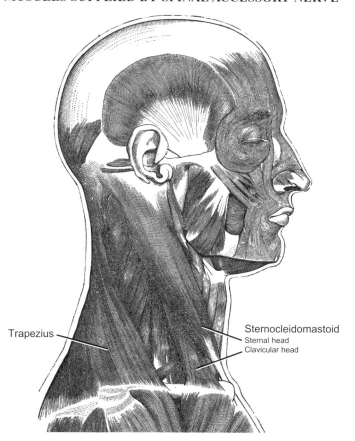

Trapezius

Sternocleidomastoid
Sternal head
Clavicular head

CN XII = hypoglossal nerve (28). *Hypo* means *below* or *lower*. The word root *gloss(o)* refers to the tongue. This motor nerve travels down to supply the extrinsic and intrinsic muscles of the tongue. *Extrinsic* muscles are *ex*ternal to the tongue and attach the tongue to other structures. Extrinsic muscles include the styloglossus, genioglossus, and hyoglossus muscles. Intrinsic muscles form the tissue of the tongue and include the chondroglossus, longitudinalis inferior linguae, longitudinalis superior linguae, transversus linguae, and verticalis linguae muscles. Both word roots, *gloss(o)* and *lingu(a)* refer to the tongue. Except for the palatoglossus muscle, which is supplied by vagal fibers from the pharyngeal plexus and discussed in chapter eight, all muscles with the combining form *gloss(o)* or *lingu(a)* in their names are supplied by the hypo*gloss*al nerve. These muscles work together in a complex fashion to provide the diverse movement patterns of the tongue.

The glossopharyngeal nerve (CN IX) should not be confused with the hypoglossal nerve (CN XII). The **hypoglossal** nerve travels **below** the **tongue** to innervate the muscles which move the tongue.

In addition to innervating intrinsic and extrinsic muscles of the tongue, the hypoglossal nerve serves as a "carrier" for other fibers which innervate striated muscles of the neck. Early in its course, the hypoglossal is joined by fibers from the C1 and C2 spinal nerves (20). These fibers later branch from the hypoglossal, forming the **superior root of the ansa cervicalis** (6). The *ansa cervicalis* is a motor nerve *loop* of the *neck* formed by a superior root and inferior root. The inferior root (12) is composed

of other fibers from the C2 spinal nerve (19) and C3 spinal nerve (18). The ansa cervicalis (7) innervates the sternohyoid muscle, sternothyroid muscle, and the superior and inferior bellies of the omohyoid muscle. Although it physically appears to branch from the hypoglossal nerve, the superior root contains no hypoglossal fibers. After the takeoff of the superior root, other C1 and C2 fibers continue with the hypoglossal a short distance and subsequently branch off to innervate the thyrohyoid and geniohyoid muscles. Again, hypoglossal fibers do not contribute. The ansa cervicalis and its innervations are described in greater detail in chapter eight.

The hypoglossal nerve is CN XII. As such, it is the *last* cranial nerve available for the C1 and C2 ventral rami fibers to "catch a ride with." Because it is the last cranial nerve, it is also the cranial nerve closest to the C1 and C2 spinal segments.

Because the cranial nerves are numbered in the order they originate from the ventral side of the brain, a particular cranial nerve number could be estimated following an evaluation of the cranial nerve name and where, generally speaking, the function of that cranial nerve would be located relative to the brain. For instance, the glossopharyngeal nerve, by name, innervates the tongue and the pharynx. The hypoglossal nerve, by name, innervates structures below the tongue. This would imply that it would originate "further back" or more posterior and inferior on the brain as compared to the glossopharyngeal nerve. Indeed, the glossopharyngeal nerve is cranial nerve IX and the hypoglossal nerve is cranial nerve XII.

FIGURE 7.16
NERVES ASSOCIATED WITH TONGUE AND MUSCLES INNERVATED BY HYPOGLOSSAL NERVE

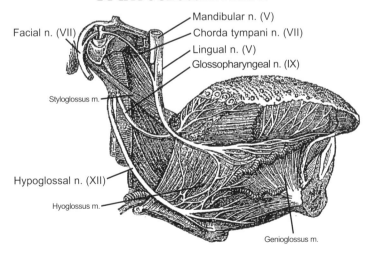

FIGURE 7.17
RELATIONSHIP OF CRANIAL NERVES TO THE BRAIN

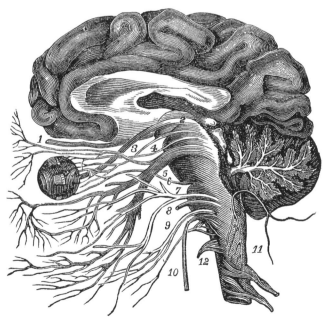

QUIZ 2
Cranial Nerves

Time for Quiz = 20 minutes.
For questions 1-14, choose the single best answer.

_____1) Which nerve innervates the auricularis posterior muscle?
   a) facial nerve
   b) trigeminal nerve
   c) hypoglossal nerve
   d) spinal accessory nerve
   e) none of the above

_____2) The medial root of CN VIII is the
   a) motor root
   b) cranial root
   c) cochlear root
   d) spinal root
   e) none of the above

_____3) The sensory ganglion associated with the facial nerve is the
   a) gasserian ganglion
   b) geniculate ganglion
   c) jugular ganglion
   d) nodose ganglion
   e) none of the above

_____4) Which statements concerning the hypoglossal nerve are true?
   a) It may have both a superior and inferior ganglion.
   b) It carries general somatic afferent fibers.
   c) It supplies mucous membranes of the pharynx.
   d) All the above
   e) None of the above

_____5) The spinal accessory nerve is formed by
   a) the external ramus of CN XI
   b) the external ramus of CN IX
   c) the internal ramus of CN XI
   d) the spinal root of CN XII
   e) none of the above

_____6) The styloglossus muscle is innervated by the
   a) glossopharyngeal nerve
   b) facial nerve
   c) hypoglossal nerve
   d) spinal accessory nerve
   e) none of the above

_____7) The inferior vagal ganglion is also known as the
   a) gasserian ganglion
   b) nodose ganglion
   c) spiral ganglion
   d) jugular ganglion
   e) none of the above

_____8) The vagus nerve is joined by
   a) the cranial root of the glossopharyngeal nerve
   b) the external ramus of the glossopharyngeal nerve
   c) the internal ramus of the accessory nerve
   d) the spinal root of the accessory nerve
   e) none of the above

_____9) Sensory information concerning blood pressure and respiration control are relayed by
   a) CN IX
   b) CN XI
   c) CN VII
   d) CN XII
   e) none of the above

_____10) What information may be transmitted by cell bodies located in the superior vagal ganglion?
   a) touch sensation from skin of the external acoustic meatus
   b) touch sensation from mucous membranes of the pharynx
   c) both a and b
   d) touch sensation from the tongue
   e) none of the above

____11) The depressor labii inferioris muscle is supplied by which facial nerve branch?
- a) cervical
- b) zygomatic
- c) buccal
- d) mandibular
- e) none of the above

____12) Muscles supplied by the facial nerve include the
- a) orbicularis oculi
- b) anterior belly of digastric
- c) both a and b
- d) temporalis
- e) none of the above

____13) Peripheral processes of cell bodies located the cochlear ganglion travel to the
- a) organ of corti
- b) saccule
- c) utricle
- d) semicircular ducts
- e) none of the above

____14) Which of the following plays the largest role in the regulation of respiration?
- a) carotid sinus
- b) carotid body
- c) baroreceptors
- d) semicircular ducts
- e) none of the above

For questions 15-20, use the following directions:
- **a……1,2,3 are correct**
- **b……1,3 are correct**
- **c……2,4 are correct**
- **d……only 4 is correct**
- **e……all are correct**

____15) Which cranial nerves relay signals related to taste?
- 1) facial nerve
- 2) vagus nerve
- 3) glossopharyngeal nerve
- 4) trigeminal nerve

____16) Which of the following are branches of CN IX?
- 1) tympanic branch
- 2) lesser petrosal nerve
- 3) auricular branch
- 4) afferent nerve of Hering

____17) Which ganglia are associated with the facial nerve?
- 1) pterygopalatine
- 2) gasserian
- 3) submandibular
- 4) nodose

____18) Which cranial nerves contribute an auricular branch?
- 1) facial nerve
- 2) vestibulocochlear nerve
- 3) vagus nerve
- 4) hypoglossal nerve

____19) Which ganglia are associated with the vagus nerve?
- 1) semilunar
- 2) jugular
- 3) spiral
- 4) inferior

____20) Which statements concerning the chorda tympani are true?
- 1) It is a branch of CN VIII.
- 2) It leaves the skull from a different location than that of its parent nerve.
- 3) It relays signals of taste from the posterior 1/3 of the tongue.
- 4) It joins the lingual nerve.

QUIZ 2: Cranial Nerves

1) a – The facial nerve (CN VII) innervates both the auricularis posterior and occipitalis muscles. In addition, it also supplies the muscles of facial expression, the stapedius, the stylohyoid, and the posterior belly of digastric. The trigeminal nerve (CN V) supplies the muscles of mastication, tensor tympani, tensor veli palatini, mylohyoid, and anterior belly of digastric muscle. The hypoglossal nerve (CN XII) supplies the intrinsic and extrinsic muscles of the tongue. The spinal accessory nerve (component of CN XI) innervates the trapezius muscle and contributes to the innervation of the sternocleidomastoid muscle.

2) e – The vestibulocochlear nerve is CN VIII and is formed by two roots. The vestibular root is medial to the cochlear root and is associated with balance. The cochlear root is associated with sound.

3) b – The geniculate ganglion is the sensory ganglion of the facial nerve (CN VII). It contains cell bodies of neurons transmitting taste signals from the anterior 2/3 of the tongue and those relaying signals from skin of the external acoustic meatus, skin behind the auricle of the ear, and mucous membranes of the soft palate. The gasserian ganglion is another name for the trigeminal ganglion. The jugular ganglion is the same as the superior vagal ganglion. The nodose ganglion is a different name for the inferior vagal ganglion.

4) e – All answers apply to the glossopharyngeal nerve (CN IX). The hypoglossal nerve (CN XII) supplies the extrinsic and intrinsic muscles of the tongue.

5) a – The accessory nerve (CN XI) is composed of a cranial root and a spinal root. The cranial root originates from the medulla oblongata and forms the internal branch or internal *ramus*. The internal branch joins the vagus nerve (CN X) proximal to the inferior vagal ganglion and provides additional "accessory" innervation to structures of the pharynx, palate, larynx, and thoracic viscera supplied by the vagus. The spinal root is created by branches from the C1-C5 spinal segments and forms the external branch or external *ramus*. It is this spinal root or external branch that becomes the spinal accessory nerve, the visually apparent nerve often referred to as the accessory nerve.

6) c – The hypoglossal nerve is CN XII and supplies the intrinsic and extrinsic muscles of the tongue. The extrinsic muscles include the styloglossus, genioglossus, and hyoglossus. *Gloss(o)-* is a Greek word root referring to the tongue. Except for the palatoglossus muscle, which is supplied by vagal fibers from the pharyngeal plexus and discussed in Chapter Nine, all muscles with the word root *-gloss-* in their name are supplied by the hypo*gloss*al nerve.

7) b – The inferior vagal ganglion is also known as the nodose ganglion. The gasserian and semilunar are other names for the trigeminal ganglion. The spiral or cochlear ganglion is associated with the vestibulocochlear nerve (CN VIII) and contains sensory cell bodies that relay signals related to sound. The jugular ganglion is another name for the superior vagal ganglion.

8) c – See #5 answer explanation.

9) a – The carotid branch of the glossopharyngeal nerve (CN IX) is also known as the afferent nerve of Hering and provides sensory innervation to the carotid sinus of the carotid artery. The carotid sinus is the dilated area of the common carotid artery at its bifurcation into the internal and external carotid arteries. Within the walls of the carotid sinus are baroreceptors, which are stretch receptors that function in blood pressure control. The carotid body is an area at the superior aspect of the fork that contains chemoreceptors that monitor blood oxygen, carbon dioxide, and pH. These chemoreceptors send signals that are used in the control of respiration.

10) c – The superior vagal or jugular ganglion houses pseudounipolar cell bodies of sensory neurons. Peripheral processes of many of these neurons travel out with the auricular branch of

the vagus (CN X) to relay sensory signals from skin of the external acoustic meatus and behind the auricle of the ear. Other pseudounipolar cell bodies found in the ganglion transmit signals from mucous membranes of the pharynx. General (touch) sensation of the anterior 2/3 of the tongue is provided by the trigeminal nerve (CN V). General sensation of the posterior 1/3 of the tongue is transmitted by the glossopharyngeal nerve (CN IX).

11) d – The mandibular branch of the facial nerve (CN VII) supplies the depressor labii inferioris and depressor anguli oris muscles. The cervical branch supplies the platysma muscle. The zygomatic branch innervates the orbicularis oculi and procerus muscles. The buccal branch supplies the levator labii superioris, levator labii superioris alaeque nasi, risorius, buccinator, compressor naris (nasalis), levator anguli oris, orbicularis oris, zygomaticus major, and zygomaticus minor muscles.

12) a – The orbicularis oculi is a muscle of facial expression and is innervated by the zygomatic branch of the facial nerve (CN VII). The anterior belly of the digastric muscle is supplied by branches of the trigeminal nerve (CN V). The posterior belly of the digastric is innervated by the facial nerve. Branches of the trigeminal nerve also supply the temporalis, one of the four muscles of mastication.

13) a – Bipolar sensory neurons associated with sound are found in the cochlear (spiral) ganglion. Peripheral processes are distributed to the spiral organ of Corti in the cochlear duct. Central processes travel back with the cochlear root to the brain stem. Peripheral processes extend from cell bodies in the vestibular ganglion to the saccule, the utricle, and the three semicircular ducts. Central processes travel to the brain stem with the vestibular root and transmit signals related to balance and equilibrium.

14) b – See #9 answer explanation.

15) a – By way of the chorda tympani, the facial nerve (CN VII) transmits taste signals from the anterior 2/3 of the tongue. The glossopharyngeal nerve (CN IX) relays taste signals from the posterior 1/3 of the tongue. The vagus nerve (CN X) transmits signals related to taste from the extreme posterior aspect of the tongue and epiglottis. Although the trigeminal nerve (CN V) is responsible for general sensation of the anterior 2/3 of the tongue via the lingual nerve, it transmits no signals related to taste.

16) e – The afferent nerve of Hering is also known as the carotid branch of the glossopharyngeal nerve (CN IX).

17) b – The pterygopalatine (sphenopalatine) and submandibular (submaxillary) ganglia are the two parasympathetic efferent ganglia associated with the facial nerve (CN VII). The pterygopalatine ganglion is the location of postganglionic cell bodies that extend parasympathetic postganglionic fibers to the lacrimal glands and small glands of the nasal and oral cavities. The submandibular ganglion houses cell bodies that extend postganglionic fibers to the submandibular (submaxillary) and sublingual glands. The geniculate ganglion is the sensory ganglion associated with the facial nerve. It houses pseudounipolar cell bodies of two types. Special visceral afferent neurons relay taste signals from the anterior 2/3 of the tongue. General somatic afferent neurons provide sensory innervation to skin of the external acoustic meatus, skin behind the auricle of the ear, and mucous membranes of the soft palate. The gasserian ganglion, along with the semilunar ganglion, is another name for the trigeminal ganglion, the sensory ganglion of the trigeminal nerve (CN V). The nodose ganglion is a different name for the inferior vagal ganglion, one of two sensory ganglia of the vagus nerve (CN X).

18) b – The auricular branches intermix to supply skin of the external acoustic meatus, external auditory canal, and behind the auricle of the ear. The vestibulocochlear nerve (CN VIII) transmits signals associated with sound and equilibrium from inner ear structures but does not provide an auricular branch. The hypoglossal nerve (CN XII) is a motor nerve that supplies the intrinsic and extrinsic muscles of the tongue.

19) c – The vagus nerve (CN X) is associated with two sensory ganglia. The superior vagal ganglion is also known as the jugular ganglion and appears as a rounded enlargement of the vagus as it travels through the jugular foramen. The inferior vagal ganglion is also known as the nodose ganglion and appears as an elongated enlargement of the vagus distal to its exit from the foramen. The semilunar ganglion, along with the gasserian ganglion, is another name for the trigeminal ganglion, the sensory ganglion of the trigeminal nerve (CN V). The spiral ganglion is another name for cochlear ganglion, the sensory ganglion of the vestibulocochlear nerve (CN VIII) that is associated with sound.

20) c – The chorda tympani is a branch of the facial nerve (CN VII). It joins a trigeminal (CN V) branch, the lingual nerve, and transmits taste signals from the anterior 2/3 of the tongue. The glossopharyngeal nerve is responsible for taste sensation from the posterior 1/3 of the tongue.

CLASSIFICATION OF CRANIAL NERVES

Depending on the type of fibers that travel within a particular cranial nerve, the nerve can be classified as a sensory, motor, or mixed cranial nerve. A sensory nerve carries afferent fibers only. A motor nerve carries efferent fibers. A mixed nerve carries both.

Cranial nerves conduct the special senses. Signals related to smell, sight, sound, taste, and touch are transmitted by cranial nerves. Each of the first three senses requires only one cranial nerve to transmit the sensory information. The olfactory nerve relays information relating to smell. The optic nerve is responsible for the perception of sight. The vestibulocochlear nerve transmits signals associated with sound. In addition, the vestibulocochlear nerve also relays signals associated with equilibrium or balance. Because the function of these three nerves is confined to sensory transmission, each is broadly classified as a sensory cranial nerve.

There are four cranial nerves that transmit signals of the other two senses, taste and touch. Coincidently, each of these nerves is classified as a mixed cranial nerve; the nerve possesses both sensory and motor function. The four mixed cranial nerves are the trigeminal nerve, the facial nerve, the glossopharyngeal nerve, and the vagus nerve.

As described, taste sensation is provided by three of the four mixed cranial nerves. Taste to the anterior 2/3 of the tongue is by way of the facial nerve. Taste to the posterior 1/3 of the tongue is provided by the glossopharyngeal nerve. The vagus nerve may transmit taste signals from the extreme posterior aspect of the tongue and epiglottis.

Touch sensation is transmitted by all four of the mixed cranial nerves. The trigeminal nerve is the cranial nerve with the largest responsibility for touch sensation. It innervates the entire face, mouth, anterior 2/3 of the tongue, gums, and teeth. The facial nerve conducts information from mucous membranes of the soft palate. The glossopharyngeal nerve provides touch sensation to the middle ear, posterior 1/3 of the tongue, and pharynx. The vagus nerve also conveys touch signals from the pharynx and additionally supplies the larynx. Finally, the facial and vagus nerves transmit touch signals from skin of the external acoustic meatus and behind the ear. As will be discussed later, touch sensation to the neck and back of the head is provided by spinal nerves.

> **There are 4 mixed cranial nerves.**
> - 3 transmit taste (trigeminal does not)
> - all 4 transmit touch (trigeminal is the main "touch" cranial nerve)
>   - touch = somatic afferent

There are five cranial nerves classified as motor nerves. Included are the oculomotor nerve, trochlear nerve, abducens nerve, accessory nerve, and hypoglossal nerve. Although the oculomotor nerve also carries parasympathetic fibers, no innate sensory fibers are carried by any of these five nerves. The first three nerves are involved in extraocular eye movement. They are also located toward the front of the brain (CN III, CN IV, CN VI). The last two cranial nerves innervate muscles of the neck. As may be surmised by their innervation assignment, these nerves are located toward the back of the brain. In fact, they are the two cranial nerves which originate from the most posterior and inferior locations (CN XI, CN XII).

> Consider the sensory nerves at one end of the cranial nerve spectrum, the mixed nerves in an intermediate position, and the motor nerves at the other end of the spectrum.
>
> **Just remember 3, 4, 5**
>
> | | SENSORY | MIXED | MOTOR |
> |---|---|---|---|
> | # of cranial nerves | 3 | 4 | 5 = **12 cranial nerves** |

> This mnemonic displays in cranial nerve sequence the nerves that are <u>s</u>ensory (s), <u>m</u>otor (m), or <u>b</u>oth sensory and motor (b).
>
> | I | II | III | IV | V | VI | VII | VIII | IX | X | XI | XII |
> |---|---|---|---|---|---|---|---|---|---|---|---|
> | <u>S</u>ome | <u>S</u>ay | <u>M</u>oney | <u>M</u>akes | <u>B</u>usiness. | <u>M</u>y | <u>B</u>rother | <u>S</u>ays | <u>B</u>ad | <u>B</u>usiness. | <u>M</u>y! | <u>M</u>y! |

CLASSIFICATION OF CRANIAL NERVE FIBERS

The classification of cranial nerves and associated ganglia has been described. Attention will turn to the classification of the various fibers that travel in these structures. Much of the challenge associated with learning the cranial nerves can be attributed to the classification of the diverse fiber types that travel in different cranial nerves. Not only must the physical anatomy of each nerve be learned, but the type of fibers that travel in each nerve or nerve branch must also be known.

EFFERENT	CRANIAL NERVE
General somatic – striated muscles originating from myotomes (extraocular muscles, neck muscles, tongue muscles)	III, IV, VI, XI, XII
Special visceral – striated muscles originating from branchial arches (muscles of facial expression, mastication, pharynx, larynx)	V, VII, IX, X
General visceral – smooth muscle of glands and viscera	III, VII, IX, X

AFFERENT

General somatic – skin of face, mucous membrane of mouth, pharynx, larynx	V, VII, IX, X
General visceral – visceral structures of head, neck, thorax, abdomen	IX, X
Special sensory – smell and sight	I, II
Special somatic – inner ear (hearing and equilibrium)	VIII
Special visceral – taste	VII, IX, X

The nerve fiber classification is not as complex as it may initially appear. The terminology creates an uneasy "bulkiness of description" that dissipates with familiarity. With a little review and interpretation, the classification becomes much less arduous and easier to understand. In many instances, the reader will find that a certain classification is already known and/or understood. It simply becomes an issue of learning the language and applying the terminology of the categories.

The word *afferent* is synonymous with sensory; *efferent* is synonymous with motor. A nerve fiber is described as somatic or visceral based upon the type of tissues supplied. *Somatic* tissues are those associated with the body wall. *Visceral* tissues are those associated with the viscera. In some instances the tissue type is unclear and is determined by the embryological derivation of the tissue.

The terms *general* and *special* are rather self-explanatory. A fiber is classified as a *general* somatic or *general* visceral fiber if the supplied tissue conforms to the usual characteristics of a somatic or visceral tissue, respectively. The word *special* designates an unusual characteristic or composition of the tissue.

Cranial nerve innervation of striated muscles demonstrate the differences in tissue classification that exist. Striated muscles embryologically derived from myotomes, such as extraocular muscles of the eye and tongue muscles, are somatic in origin. Like striated muscles of the body wall and extremities, these muscles are said to be innervated by **general somatic efferent fibers**. The oculomotor (III), trochlear (CN IV), abducens (CN VI), spinal accessory CN XI), and hypoglossal (CN XII) nerves are the cranial

nerves which carry these fibers. The oculomotor, trochlear, and abducens nerves supply extraocular muscles. The spinal accessory nerve innervates the sternocleidomastoid and trapezius muscles of the neck and upper back. Finally, the hypoglossal nerve supplies intrinsic and extrinsic muscles of the tongue.

Striated muscles derived from the branchial arches are visceral in origin. Such muscles include the muscles of facial expression, mastication, the pharynx, and the larynx. The nerve fibers that supply these muscles are classified as **special visceral efferent fibers.** Since these striated muscles are not "typical" visceral structures, their innervating fibers are given the designation of *special*. The cranial nerves that carry these fibers include the trigeminal (V), facial (VII), glossopharyngeal (IX), and vagus (X) nerves. The trigeminal nerve supplies muscles of mastication. The facial nerve innervates muscles of facial expression. The glossopharyngeal nerve supplies muscles of the pharynx. The vagus supplies muscles of both the pharynx and larynx.

Because special visceral efferent fibers are only found in cranial nerves, **general visceral efferent** fibers are only specified as such when discussing cranial nerves. With other nerves, these fibers are merely referred to as visceral efferent fibers; there is no reason to differentiate them as *general* visceral efferent. Out of the twelve cranial nerves, it is the four parasympathetic cranial nerves that carry general visceral efferent fibers. These nerves include the oculomotor (CN III), facial (CN VII), glossopharyngeal (CN IX), and vagus (CN X) nerves. The visceral responsibilities of each nerve were covered in the previous chapter.

Just as there are general somatic and general visceral efferent fibers, there are also general somatic and general visceral *afferent* fibers. **General somatic afferent** fibers are those which transmit sensory signals from somatic structures. This involves conduction of signals related to touch, pain, and proprioception. The trigeminal nerve (CN V) is the cranial nerve primarily responsible for transmission of general somatic afferent signals. In fact, the trigeminal nerve provides sensation to virtually all skin of the face, tissues below the skin, mucous membranes of the mouth, anterior tongue, gums, and teeth. The trigeminal ganglion is a very large ganglion of the head; the significant size is required to house the numerous somatic afferent cell bodies that supply this considerable tissue mass. In addition to the trigeminal nerve, the facial (CN VII), glossopharyngeal (CN IX), and vagus (CN X) nerves also carry general somatic afferent fibers. All three nerves conduct afferent signals from somatic tissues associated with the ear. The glossopharyngeal and vagus nerves also transmit sensory signals from mucous membranes of the mouth and pharynx.

> The two types of fibers that travel in the trigeminal nerve are opposite in every category.
>
> **Special** *visceral* efferent   and   **General** *somatic* afferent

General visceral afferent fibers are those which transmit sensory information from visceral structures. These fibers are found in two of the four parasympathetic cranial nerves, the glossopharyngeal (CN IX) and vagus nerves (CN X). Sensory signals from baroreceptors of the carotid sinus and chemoreceptors of the carotid body are conducted by the glossopharyngeal nerve. The vagus nerve carries sensory information from numerous visceral structures. This includes afferent signals from the aortic body that are related to blood pressure, oxygen content, carbon dioxide content, and pH.

There are two unique cranial nerves that cannot be classified as either somatic or visceral. Each is associated with one of the special senses, smell and sight. The olfactory nerve (CN I) relays signals responsible for the perception of smell. The olfactory nerve is associated with sensory neuron cell bodies located in the mucous membrane of the upper nasal cavity. From these cell bodies, afferent fibers travel back to synapse in the olfactory bulb. Similarly, neuron cell bodies associated with the optic nerve (CN II) are found in the retina. From these cell bodies, afferent fibers course to the brain. These two nerves are classified as **special sensory afferent** cranial nerves.

Sound and balance are special sensory modalities initiated by the activation of sensory receptors in somatic structures. The cochlea is the somatic structure associated with sound; the vestibule is associated with balance and equilibrium. Because sensory signals are initiated in somatic structures, the nerve fibers that transmit signals of sound and balance are classified as **special somatic afferent** fibers. The vestibulocochlear nerve (CN VIII) is the only cranial nerve to carry this fiber type.

Taste buds are visceral structures. Signals that relay the perception of taste are conducted in **special visceral afferent** fibers. These fibers are found in the three cranial nerves associated with taste sensation: the facial (CN VII), glossopharyngeal (CN IX), and vagus (CN X) nerves.

TASTE = SVA (Special visceral afferent)

3 letters (T for taste, S for special, and V for visceral) are toward the end of the alphabet (R **S** **T** U **V** W) and one letter (U) is skipped.

The **3 nerves** that carry SVA fibers (facial, glossopharyngeal, vagus) are toward the end of the cranial nerve sequence (CN VII, IX, and X) and one cranial nerve (the vestibulocochlear nerve [CN VIII]) is skipped.

There are 4 "Specials."

Only 1 is efferent (*special* visceral efferent). There is only one "special" type of striated muscle, the striated muscles derived from branchial arches.

3 are afferent; more afferent fiber types are required because the "special" senses are afferent by nature (they are sensory): smell and sight = 1 (*special* sensory afferent), sound and balance = 1 (*special* somatic afferent), taste = 1 (*special* visceral afferent).

Uncomplicate the Complicated.

General somatic efferent – extraocular muscles, neck muscles, intrinsic and extrinsic muscles of tongue
- The nerves that supply extraocular muscles must be toward the front (III, IV, VI). The only nerves ahead of any of them supply smell (I) and sight (II) and the nerve which provides somatic sensory to eye (V). The nerves that supply muscles of the neck (XI) and tongue (XII) must be toward the back.

Special visceral efferent – muscles of mastication, facial expression, pharynx, larynx
- mastication (V), facial expression (VII), pharynx (IX, X), larynx (X)

General visceral efferent – smooth muscle of glands, viscera, blood vessels
- the 4 parasympathetic cranial nerves (III, VII, IX, X)

General somatic afferent – skin of face, ear, mucous membrane of mouth, pharynx, larynx, gums, tongue, teeth
- mostly trigeminal nerve (V), but VII, IX, X carry fibers

General visceral afferent – visceral structures of neck, thorax, abdomen
- the 2 parasympathetic nerves that carry visceral sensory fibers (IX, X)

Special sensory afferent – smell and sight (I, II)

Special somatic afferent – sound and balance (VIII)

Special visceral afferent – taste (VII, IX, X)

The spinal nerves are introduced in the next chapter and the remainder of the book is devoted to their description. Unlike cranial nerves, there are no "special" fibers which course in spinal nerves. There are no special visceral efferent, special sensory afferent, special somatic afferent, or special visceral afferent fibers in spinal nerves. As discussed earlier, this leaves only general somatic efferent, general visceral efferent, general somatic afferent, and general visceral afferent fibers. Since no differentiation is required, the word *general* is often left off their description.

Somatic efferent fibers originate from cell bodies located in the spinal cord. Their axons leave the cord in ventral roots of spinal nerves. All spinal nerves carry somatic fibers.

Visceral efferent fibers enter spinal nerves by two routes, depending on the autonomic system involved. Sympathetic fibers enter by way of gray rami communicans that branch from the sympathetic chain. Most spinal nerves therefore carry sympathetic fibers. Parasympathetic fibers are isolated to sacral spinal nerves at the S2 - S4 levels of the spinal cord. There is no parasympathetic supply to spinal nerves that originate above the S2 level.

The structure of the afferent systems that travel in spinal nerves is more uniform. Afferent cell bodies of both the somatic and visceral systems are located in the dorsal root ganglion of the spinal nerve in which their respective fibers travel.

QUIZ 3
Cranial Nerves

Time for Quiz = 20 minutes.
For questions 1-12, choose the single best answer.

_____1) Which cranial nerve carries special visceral efferent fibers?
    a) optic nerve
    b) trochlear nerve
    c) oculomotor nerve
    d) facial nerve
    e) none of the above

_____2) What type of fibers may be found in the optic nerve?
    a) general somatic efferent
    b) special visceral afferent
    c) special visceral efferent
    d) special sensory afferent
    e) none of the above

_____3) Which cranial nerve carries general somatic afferent fibers?
    a) CN I
    b) CN VI
    c) CN III
    d) CN XII
    e) none of the above

_____4) What type of cell bodies may be found in the geniculate ganglion?
    a) general somatic afferent
    b) special visceral afferent
    c) both a and b
    d) general visceral efferent
    e) none of the above

_____5) Which cranial nerve carries special sensory afferent fibers?
    a) vestibulocochlear nerve
    b) optic nerve
    c) oculomotor nerve
    d) hypoglossal nerve
    e) none of the above

_____6) What type of cell bodies may be found in the superior vagal ganglion?
    a) general somatic afferent
    b) general visceral efferent
    c) special visceral efferent
    d) special somatic afferent
    e) none of the above

_____7) Which cranial nerve carries general visceral afferent fibers?
    a) CN II
    b) CN IV
    c) CN III
    d) CN IX
    e) none of the above

_____8) What type of fibers may be found in the abducens nerve?
    a) general somatic efferent
    b) special visceral afferent
    c) special visceral efferent
    d) special sensory afferent
    e) none of the above

_____9) Which cranial nerve carries general somatic efferent fibers?
    a) olfactory nerve
    b) facial nerve
    c) trigeminal nerve
    d) vestibulocochlear nerve
    e) none of the above

_____10) What may be found in the spiral ganglion?
    a) special somatic afferent cell bodies that relay signals related to equilibrium
    b) special somatic afferent cell bodies that relay signals related to sound
    c) special visceral afferent cell bodies that relay signals related to sound
    d) special visceral afferent cell bodies that relay signals related to taste
    e) none of the above

____11) General visceral efferent fibers are inherent to which cranial nerve?
- a) abducens nerve
- b) vestibulocochlear nerve
- c) oculomotor nerve
- d) hypoglossal nerve
- e) none of the above

____12) Which cranial nerve carries special visceral afferent fibers?
- a) olfactory nerve
- b) hypoglossal nerve
- c) oculomotor nerve
- d) trigeminal nerve
- e) none of the above

For questions 13-20, use the following directions:
- **a......1,2,3 are correct**
- **b......1,3 are correct**
- **c......2,4 are correct**
- **d......only 4 is correct**
- **e......all are correct**

____13) Which cranial nerves carry special visceral efferent fibers?
1) glossopharyngeal nerve
2) hypoglossal nerve
3) trigeminal nerve
4) vestibulocochlear nerve

____14) Which cranial nerves are classified as pure sensory nerves?
1) CN II
2) CN VIII
3) CN I
4) CN VII

____15) Which fibers may travel in the oculomotor nerve?
1) special visceral afferent
2) general visceral efferent
3) general visceral afferent
4) general somatic efferent

____16) Which cranial nerves carry special sensory afferent fibers?
1) optic nerve
2) oculomotor nerve
3) olfactory nerve
4) vestibulocochlear nerve

____17) Structures supplied by general somatic efferent fibers include the
1) muscles of facial expression
2) intrinsic muscles of the tongue
3) muscles of mastication
4) extraocular muscles

____18) Which fibers may travel in CN IX?
1) special visceral afferent
2) special visceral efferent
3) general somatic afferent
4) general visceral efferent

____19) Which cranial nerves are classified as mixed nerves?
1) vestibulocochlear nerve
2) hypoglossal nerve
3) abducens nerve
4) facial nerve

____20) Which cranial nerves carry general visceral efferent fibers?
1) CN VI
2) CN VII
3) CN IV
4) CN IX

QUIZ 3: Cranial Nerves

1) d – Special visceral efferent fibers innervate striated muscles derived from branchial arches. Such muscles include the muscles of facial expression, mastication (chewing), the pharynx, and the larynx. Cranial nerves that carry special visceral efferent fibers include the trigeminal (V), facial (VII), glossopharyngeal (IX), and vagus (X) nerves. The trigeminal nerve innervates the four muscles of mastication. The facial nerve is named for its innervation of the muscles of facial expression. The glossopharyngeal nerve supplies muscles of the pharynx. The vagus supplies muscles of both the pharynx and larynx.

2) d – The olfactory nerve (CN I) and optic nerve (CN II) are the two cranial nerves that carry special sensory afferent fibers. These nerves provide for the special sensory modalities of smell and sight, respectively. General somatic efferent fibers supply striated muscles originating from myotomes and are found in the oculomotor (CN III), trochlear (CN IV), abducens (CN VI), spinal accessory (CN XI) and hypoglossal (CN XII) nerves. Special visceral afferent fibers transmit signals relating to taste and are found in the facial (CN VII), glossopharyngeal (CN IX), and vagus (CN X) nerves. Special visceral efferent fibers supply striated muscles that originate from branchial arches. These fibers travel in the trigeminal (CN V), facial (CN VII), glossopharyngeal (CN IX), and vagus (CN X) nerves.

3) e – General somatic afferent fibers are those which transmit sensory signals from somatic structures. This involves conduction of signals related to touch, pain, and proprioception. The trigeminal nerve (CN V) is the cranial nerve primarily responsible for transmission of general somatic afferent signals. The trigeminal nerve provides sensation to virtually all skin of the face, tissues below the skin, mucous membranes of the mouth, tongue, and the teeth. The facial (CN VII), glossopharyngeal (CN IX), and vagus (CN X) nerves also carry general somatic afferent fibers. The facial and vagus nerves conduct signals from skin of the external acoustic meatus and behind the ear. Additionally, the facial nerve supplies mucous membranes of the soft palate; the vagus supplies membranes of the pharynx and larynx. The glossopharyngeal supplies mucous membranes of the middle ear and pharynx.

4) c – The geniculate ganglion is the sensory ganglion of the facial nerve (CN VII). It houses pseudounipolar cell bodies of two fiber types. The majority of cell bodies are special visceral afferent and relay signals related to taste from the anterior 2/3 of the tongue. General somatic afferent neuron cell bodies are also present. These cell bodies transmit sensory signals from skin of the external acoustic meatus, skin behind the auricle of the ear, and mucous membranes of the soft palate. General visceral efferent cell bodies are found in parasympathetic efferent ganglia. The pterygopalatine (sphenopalatine) and submandibular (submaxillary) are the two parasympathetic ganglia associated with the facial nerve.

5) b – The olfactory nerve (CN I) and optic nerve (CN II) are the two cranial nerves that carry special sensory afferent fibers. These nerves provide for the special sensory modalities of smell and sight, respectively. The vestibulocochlear nerve (CN VIII) is formed by special somatic fibers that transmit information related to sound and balance. The facial (CN VII), glossopharyngeal (CN IX), and vagus (CN X) nerves carry special visceral afferent fibers that relay signals responsible for taste sensation.

6) a – The superior vagal ganglion is also known as the jugular ganglion. It is the location of pseudounipolar cell bodies of general somatic afferent and general visceral afferent neurons. General somatic afferent neurons relay sensory signals from skin of the external acoustic meatus, skin behind the auricle of the ear, and mucous membranes of the pharynx and larynx. General visceral afferent neurons conduct sensory signals from visceral structures of the head, neck, and upper torso.

7) d – General visceral afferent fibers transmit sensory information from visceral structures such as glands, viscera, and blood vessels. Among the twelve cranial nerves, these fibers are

found in two of the four that carry parasympathetic fibers, the glossopharyngeal (IX) and vagus (X) nerves.

8) a – General somatic efferent fibers supply striated muscles originating from myotomes and are found in the oculomotor (CN III), trochlear (CN IV), abducens (CN VI), spinal accessory (CN XI) and hypoglossal (CN XII) nerves. Special visceral afferent fibers transmit signals relating to taste and are found in the facial (CN VII), glossopharyngeal (CN IX), and vagus (CN X) nerves. Special visceral efferent fibers supply striated muscles that originate from branchial arches. These fibers travel in the trigeminal (CN V), facial (CN VII), glossopharyngeal (CN IX), and vagus (CN X) nerves. The olfactory nerve (CN I) and optic nerve (CN II) are the two cranial nerves that carry special sensory afferent fibers. These nerves provide for the special sensory modalities of smell and sight, respectively.

9) e – General somatic efferent fibers supply somatic structures that contribute to the formation of the body wall and extremities. This includes striated muscles embryologically originated from myotomes. In the head and neck, such muscles consist of extraocular muscles, intrinsic and extrinsic muscles of the tongue, and voluntary muscles of the neck. The cranial nerves that carry general somatic efferent fibers include the oculomotor (III), trochlear (IV), abducens (VI), accessory (XI), and hypoglossal (XII) nerves. The first three nerves supply extraocular muscles. The spinal accessory nerve innervates the sternocleidomastoid and trapezius muscles of the neck. The hypoglossal nerve supplies both extrinsic and intrinsic muscles of the tongue.

10) b – The spiral ganglion is also known as the cochlear ganglion and houses special somatic afferent cell bodies that transmit signals associated with the perception of sound. The vestibular ganglion is the location of special somatic afferent cell bodies that relay signals associated with equilibrium and balance.

11) c – General visceral efferent fibers innervate smooth muscle of glands, viscera, and blood vessels. Among the twelve cranial nerves, these fibers are inherent to the four that carry *parasympathetic* fibers (the four parasympathetic cranial nerves of the parasympathetic or craniosacral system). Because they provide parasympathetic fibers, no blood vessels are supplied; the parasympathetic system does not innervate smooth muscle of blood vessels. The four parasympathetic cranial nerves that carry these general visceral efferent fibers include the oculomotor (III), facial (VII), glossopharyngeal (IX), and vagus (X) nerves. General visceral efferent fibers of the sympathetic system originate from the superior cervical ganglion and join various cranial nerve branches. These fibers supply glands and blood vessels.

12) e – The facial (CN VII), glossopharyngeal (CN IX), and vagus (CN X) nerves carry special visceral afferent fibers that relay signals responsible for taste sensation. The olfactory nerve (CN I) and optic nerve (CN II) are the two cranial nerves that carry special sensory afferent fibers. The hypoglossal (CN XII) and oculomotor (CN III) nerves are motor nerves and therefore carry general somatic efferent fibers. In addition to special visceral efferent fibers that innervate the muscles of mastication, the trigeminal nerve (CN V) carries general somatic afferent fibers that transmit sensory information from somatic structures of the anterior head.

13) b – See #1 answer explanation.

14) a – There are three cranial nerves broadly categorized as sensory nerves: the olfactory (CN I), optic (CN II), and vestibulocochlear (CN VIII) nerves. Four cranial nerves contain both sensory and motor fibers and are described as mixed cranial nerves. These include the trigeminal (CN V), facial (CN VII), glossopharyngeal (IX), and vagus (CN X) nerves. Finally, five cranial nerves are motor nerves: the oculomotor (CN III), trochlear (CN IV), abducens (CN VI), accessory (*spinal* accessory – CN XI), and hypoglossal (CN XII) nerves.

15) c – General visceral efferent fibers supply smooth muscle of visceral structures. These fibers

travel in the four parasympathetic cranial nerves: the oculomotor (CN III), facial (CN VII), glossopharyngeal (CN IX), and vagus (CN X) nerves. Parasympathetic fibers of the oculomotor nerve supply the ciliary muscle and pupillary aperture. General somatic efferent fibers supply striated muscles originating from myotomes and are found in the oculomotor (CN III), trochlear (CN IV), abducens (CN VI), spinal accessory (CN XI) and hypoglossal (CN XII) nerves.

16) b – See #5 answer explanation.

17) c – See #9 answer explanation. Muscles derived from branchial arches are supplied by special visceral efferent fibers. Such muscles include the muscles of facial expression, mastication (chewing), the pharynx, and the larynx.

18) e – Special visceral afferent fibers transmit signals relating to taste and are found in the facial (CN VII), glossopharyngeal (CN IX), and vagus (CN X) nerves. Special visceral efferent fibers supply striated muscles that originate from branchial arches. These fibers travel in the trigeminal (CN V), facial (CN VII), glossopharyngeal (CN IX), and vagus (CN X) nerves. General somatic afferent fibers provide sensation to somatic structures of the head. These fibers are located in the trigeminal (CN V), facial (VII), glossopharyngeal (CN IX), and vagus (CN X) nerves. General visceral efferent fibers innervate smooth muscle of glands, viscera, and blood vessels. Among the twelve cranial nerves, these fibers are found in the four that carry parasympathetic fibers: the oculomotor (III), facial (VII), glossopharyngeal (IX), and vagus (X) nerves.

19) d – See #14 answer explanation.

20) c – See #11 answer explanation.

"The reason grandparents and grandchildren get along so well is that they have a common enemy."

– Sam Levenson

CLINICAL CORRELATION

A cranial nerve exam is an integral component of a basic neurologic exam. Not only does it evaluate the integrity of peripheral segments of each cranial nerve, but it assesses the central nuclei and tracts present in the brain and brain stem. Peripheral nerves can be damaged with traumatic injury, infection, tumor, or impingement by other anatomic structures. Central structures may be additionally affected by anoxic injury, seizure activity, head injury, or stroke. Abnormalities detected with the exam can be correlated with clinical signs and systems to determine the most likely location of the problem. Further laboratory and radiologic studies can then narrow down possible causes.

A cranial nerve exam can be competently accomplished in just a few minutes. Other portions of a basic neurologic exam include testing for mental status, cerebellar function, reflexes, and sensation. The following description is an overview of a basic neurologic exam. It is by no means intended to serve as a comprehensive examination. This overview is followed by a discussion of tests for cranial nerve function.

Mental status can be informally assessed during a brief conversation with the patient. Typically, it should be established that the patient is alert and oriented to four entities: person, place, time, and situation. Does the patient know who he/she is? Does he/she know where he/she is? Is the date, day of the week, and/or time of the day known? Finally, can the patient express in a logical manner the events that transpired which brought about the current situation?

The cerebellum is the portion of the brain associated with proprioception, equilibrium, and balance. It is responsible for unconscious coordination of various muscular contractions that provide certain body postures, positions, movements, balance, and locomotion. Tests of cerebellar function include repetitive alternating movements, gait, heel-to-toe walking, and the Romberg test.

There are several **repetitive alternating movements** which can quickly be accessed. The patient can be asked to touch the thumb to the tip of each finger of the same hand in successive order from the small finger to the index finger and back again. The speed is increased as the test is performed. The exam is then repeated in the opposite hand. Another repetitive movement test involves the patient's extending both arms out laterally, away from the body. The patient bends one elbow and touches the nose with an outstretched finger of one hand and returns the arm to an extended position while the nose is touched with a finger of the opposite hand. The arms are alternated and speed is increased as the exam is performed. Once the patient appears comfortable, he/she is asked to continue performing the motion with the eyes shut.

Gait is accessed by asking the patient to walk across the room while the examiner looks for any signs of awkwardness, difficulty, spasticity, widely spaced feet, or shuffling. Upon establishment of adequate gait, the patient can be asked to perform **heel-to-toe** walking. As one foot contacts the ground, the heel of the other foot leaves the ground and touches the toe of the contact foot. The lifted foot then extends forward to contact the ground as the patient walks. This is repeated in an alternating fashion with the heel of each foot contacting the toes of the opposite foot prior to extending forward to complete the step.

To perform the **Romberg test**, the patient is asked to stand straight with the legs and feet together. Arms are at the side. The patient's eyes are then closed. The examiner looks for signs of obvious loss of balance with eye closure. Significant loss of balance is a positive Romberg test. Most normal patients will sway a little. In addition, the patient can be asked to alternatively lift one foot while continuing to stand on the other. This is then alternated to the other leg. The movement is repeated with the eyes open and closed.

Reflexes can be divided into superficial and deep tendon. Exams for both types of reflexes check the integrity of certain spinal segments. These spinal segments may be affected by disease states confined to the spine or by processes located in higher structures, such as the brain or brain stem.

Superficial reflexes include the abdominal and plantar reflexes. To elicit an **abdominal reflex**, a sharp edge of an object is scraped against the skin of the abdomen. This object may be a thin piece of plastic, wood, or cardboard. The umbilicus should move slightly toward the area that is scraped. The exam is repeated in all four quadrants of the abdomen: upper right, upper left, lower right, lower left. Upper abdominal reflexes evaluate the intactness of the T7-T9 spinal levels. Lower abdominal reflexes check the T10-T12 levels.

The patient is placed in a sitting or supine position to evaluate the **plantar reflex**. A pointed structure is rubbed across the skin of the lateral foot from the heel to the base of the little toe. Many reflex hammers have a curved point at the end of the handle to serve in this capacity. At the base of the small toe, the pointed object curves under the side of the foot and travels in a medial direction across skin of the sole to the base of the great toe. There should be plantar flexion of all toes. Dorsiflexion of the great toe is known as a positive **Babinski sign** and is indicative of central nervous system pathology in adult patients. Many ticklish patients will have some dorsiflexion of the great toe. This can be controlled with a firm grip on the foot.

There are six **deep tendon reflexes** that are commonly checked. Each is graded 0-4+. A grade of 2+ is considered normal. A grade of 0 denotes no reflex response. A grade of 4+ is considered hyperactive and may be associated with some degree of clonus. **Clonus** is a spastic alternating contraction and relaxation of a certain muscle or group of muscles induced by forcibly extending the muscle. Clonus is indicative of upper motor neuron disease of the brain or brain stem.

Testing for clonus is one of the six deep tendon reflex exams commonly performed. The patient is placed in a reclined position. The back of the lower leg is supported by one of the examiner's hands while the other hand suddenly and forcefully dorsiflexes the foot. The foot is maintained in a dorsiflexed position for several seconds while both hands feel for repetitive contraction and relaxation of calf muscles. The exam is then repeated on the other side.

Each of the other five deep tendon reflex exams involves striking the tendon of a particular striated muscle or muscle group with a reflex hammer and evaluating the response of the muscles associated with the tendon. The exam is performed on both the right and left sides for each tendon and each response is given a score of 0-4+. The five tendons include the **brachioradialis** at the medial wrist/distal forearm, **biceps** at the anterior elbow, **triceps** at the posterior distal arm, **patellar** below the knee cap, and **Achilles** at the posterior distal leg above the heel. Both the brachioradialis and biceps reflex check the integrity of the C5 and C6 spinal segments. The triceps reflex evaluates the C6-C8 levels. The patellar tests the L2-L4 levels. Finally, the Achilles checks the S1 and S2 segments.

There are several subtypes of sensation that are commonly tested: touch, pain, temperature, vibration, and digit position. Exams are performed on both the right and left sides with the patient's eyes closed. The patient is asked to note the location and describe the stimulus. He or she is also asked if the stimulus was proximal or distal (above or below) the previous stimulus. Any abnormality is mapped out. The cause of the impairment could be in a distal location. A specific nerve injury or peripheral neuropathy could cause localized abnormalities. Alternatively, the pathology could be found in the spinal cord, brain stem, or brain.

Touch sensation is evaluated with a light object such as a cotton swab. Skin is barely touched in various locations at the distal aspects of each extremity and slowly progressed in a proximal direction. The patient is asked to specify the location of touch the instant he or she feels it. At times, the examiner may ask the patient to determine the location of sensation when no touch is applied. This validates patient cooperation in performance of the exam.

A sharp object like a sterile needle is used to test for **pain** sensation. In a variable pattern, the skin is lightly poked with the sharp object. This object in intermittently exchanged for a dull object, such as a fingertip. Each time the surface of the skin is contacted, the patient is asked to determine the location and describe the stimulus.

Hot and cold objects are applied to the patient's skin to evaluate **temperature** sensation. A warm cloth could be periodically substituted with an alcohol pad. Alternatively, small bags or exam gloves could be filled with warm and cold water. As in the evaluation of touch and pain sensation, the skin is contacted in a variable and unpredictable fashion. The patient is asked to describe the stimulus each time the skin is contacted.

A tuning fork is required to test for **vibration** sensation. The fork is stroked against an object and the base is placed over a bony prominence. The patient is asked to note the location and describe the stimulus. Possible contact points include knuckles of fingers and toes, ankle, wrist, knee, elbow, hip, shoulder, clavicle, and sternum.

A finger and toe from each extremity is used to test for **digit position**. As in the other sensory exams, the patient's eyes are closed. The digit to be tested is grasped by the examiner. From a neutral position, the digit is raised or lowered and the patient is asked which direction the digit moved. Several movements up or down are performed with each digit. Each time the digit is returned to a neutral position before proceeding with the next

movement. After the exam is satisfactorily completed, a digit of another extremity is tested. This is continued until all four extremities have been evaluated.

CRANIAL NERVE EXAM

The following is a representation of a basic cranial nerve exam. There are a variety of ways to conduct the evaluation. Other procedures not presented here may also substantiate cranial nerve function. In the basic exam, each cranial nerve is quickly tested for gross function. More precise testing, such as that performed in vision and hearing examinations, can be performed if time permits and equipment is available.

CN I: Olfactory nerve. The patient's eyes are closed and a fragrant material is placed at the opening of one naris while the other naris is shut. In an optimal exam, several fragrances are tested in each naris and the patient is asked to identify each. If nothing else, the patient should be able to distinguish between sweet and bitter. Commonly available substances that can be used include perfume, coffee, fruit, mint, and flavored lip gloss or balm.

CN II: Optic nerve. One eye is closed and the patient is asked to read or identify objects from a card or book held a short distance away from the open eye. The patient is directed to look forward without moving the eye. Upon successful identification of the visual stimuli, new material is placed in a different area until all four quadrants of the visual field are tested. The opposite eye is then closed and the exam is repeated with new visual stimuli. In the absence of visual props, the examiner may hold out a different number of fingers in each visual field and ask the patient to identify the number.

CN III, IV, VI: Oculomotor, Trochlear, and Abducens nerves. The patient is asked to keep the head immobile and focus on an outstretched finger of the examiner. The finger is slowly moved forward to touch the patient's nose while the ability of the patient to converge is noted. The finger is slowly backed away and moved through all six fields of gaze. Included are the medial, upper inner, upper outer, lateral, lower outer, and lower inner fields.

FIGURE 7.18
FIELDS OF GAZE

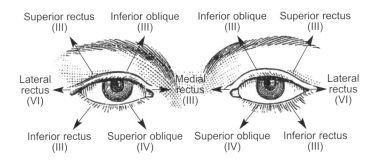

Eye movements are evaluated for smoothness and symmetry. Both eyes are examined at the same time. As the finger is moved lateral to the patient's left eye, movements induced by the medial rectus of the right eye is compared to that of the lateral rectus of the left eye. The same is true for the opposite side. With head injury or suspected elevated intracranial pressure, particular attention is paid to the lateral gaze of each eye. Because of its long course, the abducens nerve is especially susceptible to injury with increased intracranial pressure.

CN V: Trigeminal nerve. Motor function is tested by asking the patient to bite down while the examiner feels the muscles of mastication contract. Downward pressure is placed on the mandible to test the strength of contraction. Sensory function is tested on both sides of the face for each of the three trigeminal nerve divisions. Sensory exams are performed as described for the basic neurologic exam. Light touch, pain, and temperature sensation are evaluated. A tongue blade or soft-tipped applicator can be used to test touch sensation of the tongue and oral mucosa.

CN VII: Facial nerve. Motor function is evaluated by asking the patient to make a group of facial expressions. The ability to raise the eyebrows tests the temporal branch. Squeezing the eyes closed tests the zygomatic branch. Flaring the nostrils and smiling with the lips closed are two tests that evaluate the zygomatic and/or buccal branch. Puffing out the cheeks with the mouth closed and protruding the lips in a pursed position (as if to form a kiss) are two tests more specific to the buccal branch. Smiling with the teeth showing tests the buccal and mandibular branches. Frowning is specific for the mandibular branch. To check the cervical branch, the patient is asked to extend the neck and bear down or strain while the examiner looks for longitudinally directed lines of platysma contraction.

Facial nerve taste function is evaluated by asking the patient to blindly identify a substance as tasting salty or sweet. The facial nerve supplies the anterior 2/3 of the tongue, the location of taste buds that convey salty and sweet sensations. For the sake of convenience, facial taste function is usually performed concurrent with that of the glossopharyngeal nerve. The glossopharyngeal innervates the posterior 1/3 of the tongue, the location of taste buds that transmit sour and bitter sensations. The patient is allowed to drink water between tastes. Symmetric pharyngeal muscle contraction and ease of swallowing is noted, evaluating glossopharyngeal and vagus motor function.

CN VIII: Vestibulocochlear nerve. The vestibular division of the vestibulocochlear nerve is evaluated with the Romberg test. The cochlear division is grossly tested by asking the patient close his

or her eyes while the examiner lightly rubs his or her fingers together just outside one of the patient's ears. The patient informs the examiner at the instant sound is heard. This is alternated between the two ears with variable lengths of time between each audible stimulus. The patient may occasionally be asked if a sound was heard when none was created. As with sensory examinations, this is to validate patient cooperation.

CN IX: Glossopharyngeal nerve. The taste function of the glossopharyngeal nerve is usually evaluated with that of the facial nerve. The motor function is often evaluated with that of the vagus nerve. During the taste exam, smooth and symmetric swallowing was noted, owing more to adequate vagus rather than glossopharyngeal function. While the vagus is the predominant motor nerve of the pharynx, the glossopharyngeal is the predominant sensory nerve. Both nerves are therefore evaluated in performance of the gag reflex.

CN X: Vagus nerve. Vagus and glossopharyngeal function are evaluated simultaneously. Adequate swallowing was previously established during the taste exam. The gag reflex involves touching the back of the pharynx with a soft-tipped applicator while noting upward and symmetric contraction of the soft palate. The uvula should move upward in a midline position, not deviating to one side or the other. This may require a tongue blade to depress the tongue and a light to visualize pharyngeal structures. The same should occur by asking the patient to say "ahh," although glossopharyngeal sensory function is not evaluated.

CN XI: Spinal accessory nerve. Although the spinal accessory nerve is only a component of the accessory nerve, it is the only segment which is peripherally available for routine testing. The cranial root of CN XI joins the vagus early in its course. The spinal accessory nerve is evaluated by asking the patient to lift or "shrug" each shoulder to evaluate trapezius muscle function. To test sternocleidomastoid function, the head is turned against mild to moderate resistance from side-to-side and up-and-down.

CN XII: Hypoglossal nerve. The hypoglossal is the motor nerve of the tongue. As such, its exam involves an evaluation of tongue movement. The patient is asked to stick his or her tongue out in a midline position while symmetry is noted. The tongue is then moved to the left, right, up, and down.

SUMMARY OF CHAPTER BOXES

1) Mnemonics

I.	II.	III.	IV.	V.	VI.	VII.	VIII.	IX.	X.	XI.	XII.
Oh,	Oh,	Oh,	The	Twins	Are	Facing	Very	Good	Vacations	And	Holidays
Oh,	Oh,	Oh,	The	Trail	Away	From	Virginia	Gets	Vigorous	And	Hot

If substitute Acoustic for Vestibulocochlear and Spinal Accessory for Accessory:

I.	II.	III.	IV.	V.	VI.	VII.	VIII.	IX.	X.	XI.	XII.
On	Old	Olympus	Towering	Tops	A	Fin	And	German	Viewed	Some	Hops

2) **Left to Left; Right to Right** –

- Fibers of the *left* eye travel in the *left* optic nerve. Fibers of the *left* half of the left eye and *left* half of the right eye travel in the *left* optic tract. These fibers transmit signals related to the *right* visual field.

- Fibers of the *right* eye travel in the *right* optic nerve. Fibers of the *right* half of the right eye and *right* half of the left eye travel in the *right* optic tract. These fibers transmit signals related to the *left* visual field.

3) Olfactory (CN I) comes before optic (CN II) in alphabetic order.

4) **ONE** nose and **TWO** eyes. Olfactory nerve = CN I and optic nerve = CN II.

5) **So For Nose.** Trochlear nerve (CN IV) function is evaluated by having the patient look down and in, toward the nose.

6) A pulley (trochlea) is usually *above* the object it is moving. Thus, the trochlear nerve supplies the *superior* oblique muscle.

7) The smallest (**t**rochlear nerve – CN IV) and largest (**t**rigeminal nerve – CN V) cranial nerves are next to one another and both names start with a "t."

8) It only makes sense that the mandibular nerve is *the* trigeminal branch that carries motor fibers. After all, the trigeminal nerve supplies the muscles of mastication.

9) To subdue an alligator or crocodile, the arms are placed around the *lateral* side of its mouth to hold its jaws shut. The *lateral* **pterygoid** is the human muscle of mastication that opens the lower jaw.

10) **HALF AND HALF:** Half the striated muscles supplied by the trigeminal nerve (4) are muscles of mastication (masseter, temporalis, medial pterygoid, lateral pterygoid) Half (4) are not (tensor tympani, tensor veli palatini, anterior belly of digastric, mylohyoid).

11) *Tensor* = **tense** *veli* = **soft** *palatini* = **palate** It is contraction of the tensor veli palatini that opens the auditory tube and "clears the ears."

12) The *tensor tympani tenses* the *tympanic* membrane.

13) Due to tensor tympani contraction, the perception of the voice you hear when you talk sounds different from an audio recording of it.

14) The **t**rigeminal nerve innervates the **t**wo **t**ensors, the **t**ensor veli palatini and **t**ensor tympani.

15) The *abduc*ens nerve *abduc*ts the eye. It innervates the lateral rectus muscle.

16) $LR_6SO_4$3 = innervation of extraocular muscles.

17) $E_1Y_2E_3$: 3 cranial nerves supply extraocular muscles.

18) *Rectus* is a Latin word for *straight*.

19) **CN II - VI are associated with the eye.** The **nose is first** (olfactory nerve is CN I: "win by a nose.")
CN II: vision
CN III: superior rectus, medial rectus, inferior rectus, inferior oblique, parasympathetics (miosis and positive accommodation), levator palpebrae superioris
CN IV: superior oblique
CN V: sensory to eye (innervation is not confined to the eye)
CN VI: lateral rectus

20) **HALF AND HALF:** 12 cranial nerves. The first half (CN I - VI) supply the nose and eye (the trigeminal nerve also supplies other structures). The second half (CN VII - XII) has other responsibilities.

21) **The facial nerve frowns, cries, and spits:** It innervates muscles of facial expression, the lacrimal gland, and two salivary glands.

22) **3 out of 4 parasympathetic** cranial nerves relay **taste** signals. Digestion is a parasympathetic function and taste is the sensory modality most closely associated with it. The **oculomotor** nerve is the only parasympathetic nerve not associated with taste.

23) **Cranial nerves 7, 9, 10 relay taste.** If it were not for cranial nerve 8 (vestibulocochlear), the "taste" cranial nerves would be in perfect sequence. Their order of origination (seventh, ninth, and tenth) is appropriate for the area they supply (front of tongue, back of tongue, epiglottis).

24) The **"3 columns"** of the oculomotor nerve (CN III) hold the eyes open. The **"hook"** of the facial nerve (CN 7) closes the eyes.

25) "**T**o **Z**anzibar **B**y **M**otor **C**ar" = facial nerve branches to muscles of facial expression (temporal, zygomatic, buccal, mandibular, cervical).

26) **The word *facial* has 6 letters; the facial nerve has 6 responsibilities:**
(1) parasympathetic to pterygopalatine ganglion for lacrimal glands and glands of nasal and oral cavities (2) parasympathetic to submandibular ganglion for submandibular and sublingual glands (3) sensory to skin of external acoustic meatus and behind ear (4) taste to anterior 2/3 of tongue (5) muscles of facial expression (6) five other muscles: stapedius, auricularis posterior, occipitalis, posterior belly of digastric, and stylohyoid.

27) **Similarities between Trigeminal and Facial Nerves:**
(1) Each is odd numbered (CN V and CN VII). (2) Each has extensive innervations (3) Each is associated with one sensory ganglion: trigeminal ganglion (CN V) and geniculate ganglion (CN VII). (4) Each innervates a group of muscles supplied by special visceral efferent fibers: muscles of mastication (CN V) and muscles of facial expression (CN VII). (5) In addition, V supplies four other muscles; VII supplies five other muscles:
- Each supplies a small muscle of the tympanum: tensor tympanum (V) and stapedius (VII).
- Each supplies a "-ylohyoid" muscle: mylohyoid (V) and stylohyoid (VII).
- Each supplies a belly of the digastric: anterior belly (V) and posterior belly (VII).
- In addition, V supplies tensor veli palatini. VII supplies auricularis posterior and occipitalis.

28) The **vestibular root** is associated with **equilibrium**. It is in a **medial** location to be closer to the center of gravity to maintain balance. The **cochlear root** is associated with **hearing**; it is in a **lateral** position, so it is closer to the outside and can hear better.

29) A *cochlea* is a **spiral form** such as a shell. An island native creates *sound* by blowing into a hole at the end of a conch shell.

30) **The glossopharyngeal is a "jack of all trades, but a master of none."**
(1) **General visceral efferent**: Parasympathetic fibers to only one salivary gland, the parotid.
(2) **Special visceral afferent**: Taste to only the posterior 1/3 of the tongue.
(3) **Special visceral efferent**: Only one muscle, the stylopharyngeus, is innervated solely by it and no other nerve.
(4) **General somatic afferent**: It relays sensory information from a variety of "small" areas: mucous membranes of tympanum, auditory tube, posterior pharynx, tonsil, etc.
(5) **General visceral afferent**: It supplies only a small

area of one blood vessel, the carotid sinus (baroreceptors, carotid bodies).

31) A *vaga*bond is a *wanderer*.

32) **Similarities between Glossopharyngeal and Vagus Nerves:** (1) They are next to each other (CN IX and CN X). (2) Each carries parasympathetic fibers. (3) Each exits skull via the jugular foramen. (4) Each is associated with two sensory ganglia: a superior and inferior ganglion (the superior ganglion of CN IX may be absent). (5) Each supplies sensation to mucous membranes of the pharynx, although IX is the dominant nerve. (6) Each supplies muscles of the pharynx, although X is the dominant nerve (X additionally supplies muscles of the larynx). (7) Each carries general visceral afferent fibers (they are the only two cranial nerves to do so). (8) Each transmits taste. (9) Each carries 5 different fiber types (the most carried by any cranial nerve).

33) The ***internal*** ramus of CN XI is from the brain, which is ***internal*** to the skull. The ***external*** ramus is formed by cervical spinal segments, which are ***external*** to the skull.

34) **CN XI has an identity crisis:** The accessory nerve is CN XI and is formed by a cranial and spinal root. Although the accessory is a *cranial* nerve, its cranial root joins the vagus nerve. This merger occurs early so the actual accessory nerve is not seen. The nerve that can be identified, the spinal accessory nerve, is formed by the *spinal* root.

35) The glossopharyngeal nerve (CN IX) should not be confused with the hypoglossal nerve (CN XII). The ***hypoglossal*** nerve travels ***below*** the ***tongue*** to innervate the muscles that move the tongue.

36) The **hypoglossal** nerve is **CN XII** and is the ***last*** cranial nerve available for the C1 and C2 ventral rami fibers to **"catch a ride with."** Because it is the last cranial nerve, it is also the cranial nerve closest to the C1 and C2 spinal segments.

37) There are **4 mixed cranial nerves:**
- 3 transmit taste (trigeminal does not)
- all 4 transmit touch (trigeminal is the main "touch" cranial nerve). touch = somatic afferent.

38)

	SENSORY	MIXED	MOTOR	
# of cranial nerves =	3	4	5	= 12 cranial nerves

39) S = <u>s</u>ensory, M = <u>m</u>otor, B = <u>b</u>oth sensory and motor

I	II	III	IV	V	VI	VII	VIII	IX	X	XI	XII
<u>S</u>ome	Say	Money	Makes	Business.	My	Brother	Says	Bad	Business.	My!	My!

40) The 2 fiber types in the trigeminal nerve are total opposites: **SVE** vs **GSA**

41) **TASTE = SVA** (Special visceral afferent): 3 letters (T for <u>t</u>aste, S for <u>s</u>pecial, and V for <u>v</u>isceral) are toward the end of the alphabet ➜ …R <u>S</u> <u>T</u> U <u>V</u> W

42) **There are 4 "Specials."**
   • Only 1 is efferent (*special* visceral efferent). There is only one "special" type of muscle, the striated muscles derived from branchial arches.
   • 3 are afferent; more afferent fiber types are required because the "special" senses are afferent: smell and sight = 1 (*special* sensory afferent), sound and balance = 1 (*special* somatic afferent), taste = 1 (*special* visceral afferent)

43) **Uncomplicate the Complicated**
   General somatic efferent – extraocular muscles, neck muscles, intrinsic and extrinsic muscles of tongue
   • The nerves that supply extraocular muscles must be toward the front (III, IV, VI). The only nerves ahead of any of them supply smell (I) and sight (II) and the nerve which provides somatic sensory to eye (V). The nerves that supply muscles of the neck (XI) and tongue (XII) must be toward the back.
   Special visceral efferent – muscles of mastication, facial expression, pharynx, larynx
   • mastication (V), facial expression (VII), pharynx (IX, X), larynx (X)
   General visceral efferent – smooth muscle of glands, viscera, blood vessels
   • the 4 parasympathetic cranial nerves (III, VII, IX, X)
   General somatic afferent – skin of face, ear, mucous membrane of mouth, teeth
   • mostly trigeminal nerve (V), but VII, IX, X carry fibers
   General visceral afferent – visceral structures of head, neck, thorax, abdomen
   • the 2 parasympathetic nerves that carry visceral sensory fibers (IX, X)
   Special sensory afferent – smell and sight (I, II)
   Special somatic afferent – sound and balance (VIII)
   Special visceral afferent – taste (VII, IX, X)

END OF CHAPTER TEST

Time for Exam = 60 minutes.
For questions 1-42, choose the single best answer.

_____1) An example of structures supplied by general somatic efferent fibers is the
   a) muscles of mastication
   b) extrinsic muscles of tongue
   c) muscles of the pharynx
   d) muscles of facial expression
   e) none of the above

_____2) Which nerve supplies the levator palpebrae superioris?
   a) oculomotor nerve
   b) trochlear nerve
   c) facial nerve
   d) ophthalmic nerve
   e) none of the above

_____3) Which cranial nerve carries general visceral afferent fibers?
   a) olfactory nerve
   b) vagus nerve
   c) trigeminal nerve
   d) hypoglossal nerve
   e) none of the above

_____4) Which muscle functions to open the mouth?
   a) masseter
   b) lateral pterygoid
   c) tensor veli palatini
   d) medial pterygoid
   e) none of the above

_____5) Which cranial nerve is associated with a trochlea?
   a) CN III
   b) CN IV
   c) CN VIII
   d) CN VI
   e) none of the above

_____6) Which statement concerning the ansa cervicalis is true?
   a) It innervates the styloglossus muscle.
   b) The inferior root branches from the hypoglossal nerve.
   c) The superior root branches from the glossopharyngeal nerve.
   d) It innervates the sternothyroid muscle.
   e) None of the above

_____7) What type of fibers may be found in the olfactory nerve?
   a) general somatic efferent
   b) special visceral afferent
   c) special visceral efferent
   d) special sensory afferent
   e) none of the above

_____8) Fibers which cross at the optic chiasm to travel in the contralateral optic tract originate from
   a) the medial side of the right eye
   b) the lateral side of the left eye
   c) both a and b
   d) the lateral side of the right eye
   e) none of the above

_____9) Which cranial nerve carries general somatic efferent fibers?
   a) optic nerve
   b) facial nerve
   c) abducens nerve
   d) vestibulocochlear nerve
   e) none of the above

_____10) Pain sensation from the eye is transmitted by the
   a) optic nerve
   b) olfactory nerve
   c) abducens nerve
   d) trigeminal nerve
   e) none of the above

____11) What type of fibers may be found in CN III?
- a) general somatic efferent
- b) special visceral afferent
- c) special visceral efferent
- d) special sensory afferent
- e) none of the above

____12) The olfactory tract is composed of
- a) central processes of olfactory cells
- b) peripheral processes of olfactory cells
- c) central processes of cells that synapsed in the olfactory bulb
- d) peripheral processes of cells that synapsed in the olfactory bulb
- e) none of the above

____13) What is a vestibule?
- a) a somatic structure associated with equilibrium
- b) a space at the entrance of a canal
- c) both a and b
- d) a somatic structure associated with hearing
- e) none of the above

____14) Which nerve innervates the risorius muscle?
- a) oculomotor nerve
- b) facial nerve
- c) trigeminal nerve
- d) spinal accessory nerve
- e) none of the above

____15) What type of fibers may be found in the abducens nerve?
- a) general somatic efferent
- b) special somatic afferent
- c) special visceral efferent
- d) special sensory afferent
- e) none of the above

____16) The geniculate ganglion is named for its
- a) crescent shape
- b) acute bend
- c) spiral shape
- d) position in the geniculate foramen
- e) none of the above

____17) Which cranial nerve carries special visceral efferent fibers?
- a) CN I
- b) CN IV
- c) CN V
- d) CN VIII
- e) none of the above

____18) What muscle opens the auditory tube upon contraction?
- a) tensor veli palatini
- b) tensor tympani
- c) temporalis
- d) stylopharyngeus
- e) none of the above

____19) What type of fibers may be found in the spinal accessory nerve?
- a) general somatic efferent
- b) special visceral afferent
- c) special visceral efferent
- d) special somatic afferent
- e) none of the above

____20) What is the tympanum?
- a) a bone of the skull
- b) an organ associated with equilibrium
- c) the middle ear cavity
- d) an ear ossicle
- e) none of the above

____21) Which cranial nerve carries special sensory afferent fibers?
- a) CN VIII
- b) CN I
- c) CN IV
- d) CN VII
- e) none of the above

____22) Which nerve innervates the tensor tympani muscle?
- a) trigeminal nerve
- b) facial nerve
- c) glossopharyngeal nerve
- d) vagus nerve
- e) none of the above

_____23) What type of fibers may be found in the vestibulocochlear nerve?
 a) general visceral efferent
 b) special visceral efferent
 c) special somatic afferent
 d) special visceral afferent
 e) none of the above

_____24) Which nerve is associated with the jugular ganglion?
 a) trigeminal
 b) facial
 c) vagus
 d) glossopharyngeal
 e) none of the above

_____25) Which cranial nerve carries general visceral efferent fibers?
 a) CN VI
 b) CN IX
 c) CN I
 d) CN XII
 e) none of the above

_____26) Which nerve innervates the stylopharyngeus muscle?
 a) facial nerve
 b) hypoglossal nerve
 c) trigeminal nerve
 d) vagus nerve
 e) none of the above

_____27) What type of fibers may be found in the trigeminal nerve?
 a) general somatic efferent
 b) special visceral efferent
 c) general visceral afferent
 d) special somatic afferent
 e) none of the above

_____28) Fibers from what location in the eye may travel in the right optic tract?
 a) medial half of right eye
 b) lateral half of right eye
 c) lateral half of left eye
 d) all the above
 e) none of the above

_____29) Which nerve forms one of the three major divisions of the trigeminal nerve?
 a) optic nerve
 b) chorda tympani nerve
 c) submandibular nerve
 d) pterygopalatine nerve
 e) none of the above

_____30) Which muscle is innervated by CN VIII?
 a) masseter
 b) sternocleidomastoid
 c) orbicularis oris
 d) genioglossus
 e) none of the above

_____31) What is a cochlea?
 a) a space at the entrance of a canal
 b) a somatic structure associated with hearing
 c) both a and b
 d) a somatic structure associated with balance
 e) none of the above

_____32) The middle ear cavity is located in the
 a) ethmoid bone
 b) temporal bone
 c) sphenoid bone
 d) zygomatic bone
 e) none of the above

_____33) An example of structures supplied by special visceral efferent fibers is the
 a) extrinsic muscles of the tongue
 b) extraocular muscles
 c) sternocleidomastoid
 d) pharyngeal muscles
 e) none of the above

_____34) Which nerve is responsible for "clearing the ears" after rapid changes in altitude?
 a) glossopharyngeal
 b) facial
 c) trigeminal
 d) vagus
 e) none of the above

____35) Which cranial nerve innervates the cochlea?
    a) CN IX
    b) CN V
    c) CN VII
    d) CN X
    e) none of the above

____36) What nerve innervates the trapezius muscle?
    a) spinal accessory nerve
    b) facial nerve
    c) trigeminal nerve
    d) hypoglossal nerve
    e) none of the above

____37) What type of fibers may be found in CN VII?
    a) general somatic efferent
    b) general visceral efferent
    c) special somatic afferent
    d) special sensory afferent
    e) none of the above

____38) Olfactory cells are located in the
    a) brain
    b) olfactory bulb
    c) olfactory tract
    d) nasal mucosa
    e) none of the above

____39) Which cranial nerve carries special visceral afferent fibers?
    a) vestibulocochlear nerve
    b) facial nerve
    c) trochlear nerve
    d) trigeminal nerve
    e) none of the above

____40) A patient presents with decreased peripheral vision. What structure represents the most likely location of the problem?
    a) right optic tract
    b) right optic nerve
    c) left optic tract
    d) optic chiasm
    e) none of the above

____41) Which cranial nerve carries general somatic afferent fibers?
    a) olfactory nerve
    b) abducens nerve
    c) trigeminal nerve
    d) hypoglossal nerve
    e) none of the above

____42) Which statements concerning the maxillary nerve are true?
    a) It is a facial nerve branch that supplies muscles of facial expression.
    b) It becomes the infraorbital nerve.
    c) It is the V3 division of the trigeminal nerve.
    d) It carries motor fibers.
    e) None of the above

_____

For questions 43-60, use the following directions:
    a......1,2,3 are correct
    b......1,3 are correct
    c......2,4 are correct
    d......only 4 is correct
    e......all are correct

____43) Which fibers may travel in CN VIII?
    1) general somatic efferent
    2) special visceral afferent
    3) general somatic afferent
    4) special somatic afferent

____44) Which cranial nerve exits the skull via the jugular foramen?
    1) vagus nerve
    2) glossopharyngeal nerve
    3) accessory nerve
    4) hypoglossal nerve

____45) Which cranial nerve carries general somatic efferent fibers?
    1) hypoglossal nerve
    2) abducens nerve
    3) spinal accessory nerve
    4) trigeminal nerve

____46) What may be found in the gasserian ganglion?
    1) special visceral afferent cell bodies
    2) special visceral efferent fibers
    3) general visceral efferent cell bodies
    4) general somatic afferent cell bodies

_____47) What statements about the superior oblique muscle is true?
    1) Its contraction causes the eye to rotate inferiorly (look down).
    2) It is innervated by the trochlear nerve.
    3) Its contraction causes the eye to abduct (look out, laterally).
    4) Its function is evaluated by having the patient look down and in (adduct).

_____48) Which statements concerning the cochlear ganglion are true?
    1) Central processes of its cell bodies are lateral to those of the vestibular ganglion.
    2) Peripheral processes of its cell bodies travel to the semicircular ducts.
    3) It is associated with the transmission of signals related to sound.
    4) It is associated with CN VII.

_____49) Which cranial nerves carry special visceral efferent fibers?
    1) CN IX
    2) CN XII
    3) CN V
    4) CN VIII

_____50) Muscles of facial expression include the
    1) buccinator
    2) temporalis
    3) frontalis
    4) hyoglossus

_____51) Which fibers may travel in CN V?
    1) general somatic afferent
    2) general visceral efferent
    3) special visceral efferent
    4) special sensory afferent

_____52) Which muscles are supplied by the oculomotor nerve?
    1) superior oblique
    2) ciliary
    3) lateral rectus
    4) medial rectus

_____53) Which cranial nerves are classified as mixed nerves?
    1) CN VIII
    2) CN XII
    3) CN VI
    4) CN VII

_____54) Muscles innervated by the trigeminal nerve include the
    1) tensor tympani
    2) mylohyoid
    3) masseter
    4) posterior belly of digastric

_____55) Which fibers may travel in the facial nerve?
    1) special visceral efferent
    2) general visceral efferent
    3) general somatic afferent
    4) special visceral afferent

_____56) Which nerves carry motor fibers that innervate striated muscle?
    1) lingual
    2) chorda tympani
    3) maxillary
    4) vagus

_____57) Structures supplied by special visceral efferent fibers include the
    1) pharyngeal muscles
    2) muscles of mastication
    3) laryngeal muscles
    4) extraocular muscles

_____58) Which statements concerning olfactory cells are true?
    1) They are multipolar.
    2) Cell bodies are located in the nasal mucosa.
    3) Central processes travel in the olfactory tract.
    4) Peripheral processes are associated with olfactory hairs.

_____59) Which cranial nerves are classified as pure motor nerves?
    1) CN X
    2) CN IV
    3) CN IX
    4) CN XII

_____60) Which statements about the geniculate ganglion are true?
    1) It is the location of special visceral afferent cell bodies.
    2) It is the location of general somatic afferent cell bodies.
    3) It is associated with CN VII.
    4) It is the location of multipolar cell bodies.

END OF CHAPTER TEST: Answers and Explanations

1) b – General somatic efferent fibers supply somatic structures that contribute to the formation of the body wall and extremities. These structures include striated muscles embryologically originated from myotomes. Such muscles consist of extraocular muscles, intrinsic and extrinsic muscles of the tongue, and muscles of the neck. Muscles derived from branchial arches are supplied by special visceral efferent fibers. Such muscles include the muscles of facial expression, mastication (chewing), the pharynx, and the larynx.

2) a – The oculomotor nerve also supplies four extraocular muscles: the superior rectus, medial rectus, inferior rectus, and inferior oblique. The trochlear nerve innervates the superior oblique muscle. The facial nerve supplies the muscles of facial expression, auricularis posterior, occipitalis, stapedius, stylohyoid, and posterior belly of digastric. The ophthalmic nerve is the V1 division of the trigeminal nerve and carries only sensory fibers.

3) b – General visceral afferent fibers transmit sensory information from visceral structures such as glands, viscera, and blood vessels. Among the twelve cranial nerves, these fibers are found in two of the four that carry parasympathetic fibers, the glossopharyngeal (IX) and vagus (X) nerves.

4) d – The four muscles of mastication are the masseter, temporalis, medial pterygoid, and lateral pterygoid. All are supplied by the trigeminal nerve (CN V). Of the four muscles, only the lateral pterygoid functions to open the lower jaw. All others close the lower jaw. The tensor veli palatini is also supplied by the trigeminal nerve and functions to tense the soft palate and open the auditory (eustachian) tube.

5) b – A trochlea is a pulley-like structure. The trochlear nerve (CN IV) is named for its innervation of a muscle that is associated with a pulley-like apparatus. The trochlear nerve innervates one of the extraocular muscles, the superior oblique. This muscle is located in the medial orbit and its tendon passes through a ring of dense connective tissue and cartilage in the upper medial orbit. The tendon then travels obliquely to insert on the upper outer surface of the eyeball. Upon contraction, this "pulley" allows the superior oblique to depress (look down) and abduct (look outward, laterally) the eye.

6) d – The ansa cervicalis is a motor nerve loop of the neck formed by a superior and inferior root. The superior root is formed by C1 and C2 spinal nerve branches that join the hypoglossal nerve (CN XII) early in its course and subsequently branch from it. The ansa cervicalis innervates the sternothyroid muscle, sternohyoid muscle, and the superior and inferior bellies of the omohyoid muscle. The styloglossus muscle, along with the genioglossus and hyoglossus, is an extrinsic muscle of the tongue and is innervated by the hypoglossal nerve.

7) d – The olfactory nerve (CN I) and optic nerve (CN II) are the two cranial nerves that carry special sensory afferent fibers. These nerves provide for the special sensory modalities of smell and sight, respectively. General somatic efferent fibers supply striated muscles originating from myotomes and are found in the oculomotor (CN III), trochlear (CN IV), abducens (CN VI), spinal accessory (CN XI) and hypoglossal (CN XII) nerves. Special visceral afferent fibers transmit signals relating to taste and are found in the facial (CN VII), glossopharyngeal (CN IX), and vagus (CN X) nerves. Special visceral efferent fibers supply striated muscles that originate from branchial arches. These fibers travel in the trigeminal (CN V), facial (CN VII), glossopharyngeal (CN IX), and vagus (CN X) nerves.

8) a – Fibers from the medial or nasal half of each eye cross at the optic chiasm to travel in the contralateral optic tract. Fibers from the lateral half of each eye do not cross and therefore travel in the ipsilateral optic tract.

9) c – General somatic efferent fibers supply somatic structures that contribute to the formation of the body wall and extremities. This includes

striated muscles embryologically originated from myotomes. In the head and neck, such muscles consist of extraocular muscles, intrinsic and extrinsic muscles of the tongue, and voluntary muscles of the neck. The cranial nerves which carry general somatic efferent fibers include the oculomotor (III), trochlear (IV), abducens (VI), accessory (XI), and hypoglossal (XII) nerves. The first three nerves supply extraocular muscles. The spinal accessory nerve innervates the sternocleidomastoid and trapezius muscles of the neck. The hypoglossal nerve supplies both extrinsic and intrinsic muscles of the tongue.

10) d – The ophthalmic nerve is a sensory nerve and the V1 division of the trigeminal nerve. Among other duties, it transmits sensory signals from the eye. The optic nerve relays visual signals. The olfactory nerve transmits signals associated with smell. The abducens nerve is a motor nerve that innervates the lateral rectus muscle.

11) a – General somatic efferent fibers supply striated muscles originating from myotomes and are found in the oculomotor (CN III), trochlear (CN IV), abducens (CN VI), spinal accessory (CN XI) and hypoglossal (CN XII) nerves. Special visceral afferent fibers transmit signals relating to taste and are found in the facial (CN VII), glossopharyngeal (CN IX), and vagus (CN X) nerves. Special visceral efferent fibers supply striated muscles that originate from branchial arches. These fibers travel in the trigeminal (CN V), facial (CN VII), glossopharyngeal (CN IX), and vagus (CN X) nerves. The olfactory nerve (CN I) and optic nerve (CN II) are the two cranial nerves that carry special sensory afferent fibers. These nerves provide for the special sensory modalities of smell and sight, respectively.

12) c – Olfactory cells are bipolar cells found in the upper nasal mucosa. Peripheral processes extend to the mucosal surface and project small sensory receptors, olfactory hairs, into the nasal cavity. Central processes travel away from the mucosal surface and synapse in the olfactory bulb. Postsynaptic fibers then travel in the olfactory tract back to the brain. When

stimulated by smell, a signal is transmitted from the olfactory hair to the bulb and subsequently, the brain.

13) c – The vestibule is a somatic structure associated with balance and equilibrium. The word *vestibule* describes a space at the entrance of a canal. The cochlea is a somatic structure associated with hearing. The word *cochlea* describes a spiral or shell-shaped form. Both structures are innervated by the vestibulocochlear nerve (CN VIII).

14) b – The risorius is a muscle of facial expression supplied by the buccal branch of the facial nerve (CN VII).

15) a – See #11 answer explanation. Special somatic afferent fibers transmit signals relating to sound and balance and are located in the vestibulocochlear nerve (CN VIII).

16) b – The geniculate ganglion is the sensory ganglion of the facial nerve. It appears as a dilated area of the facial nerve located at a sharp posterior turn the nerve makes before exiting the stylomastoid foramen. The word *geniculum* is Latin for *little knee*. The word describes anatomic structures that make sharp, knee-like bends.

17) c – Special visceral efferent fibers innervate striated muscles derived from branchial arches. Such muscles include the muscles of facial expression, mastication (chewing), the pharynx, and the larynx. Cranial nerves that carry special visceral efferent fibers include the trigeminal (V), facial (VII), glossopharyngeal (IX), and vagus (X) nerves. The trigeminal nerve innervates the four muscles of mastication. The facial nerve is named for its innervation of the muscles of facial expression. The glossopharyngeal nerve supplies muscles of the pharynx. The vagus supplies muscles of both the pharynx and larynx.

18) a – The auditory tube is also known as the eustachian tube and runs from the middle ear cavity to the pharynx. When opened, it equalizes middle ear pressure with that of the external environment. The tensor veli palatini, tensor tympani, and temporalis are all supplied

by the trigeminal nerve (CN V). The temporalis is a muscle of mastication. The stylopharyngeus is innervated by the glossopharyngeal nerve (CN IX).

19) a – See #11 and #15 answer explanations.

20) c – The tympanum is the middle ear cavity and is located in the temporal bone of the skull. Many anatomic structures are named for their relationship to the middle ear. Examples include the tympanic plexus, tensor tympani muscle, and chorda tympani nerve. Organs of equilibrium include the saccule, utricle, and semicircular ducts. Ear ossicles include the malleus, incus, and stapes.

21) b – See #7 answer explanation.

22) a – The tensor tympani muscle is a small muscle of the middle ear and is innervated by the trigeminal nerve (CN V). The tensor tympani originates from cartilage of the auditory tube and greater wing of the sphenoid bone. It inserts on the manubrium of the malleus bone, the ear ossicle that contacts the tympanic membrane. Contraction pulls the tympanic membrane in a medial direction, increasing the tension on it. This dampens membrane movement in an effort to prevent damage to middle ear structures during particularly loud and repetitive noises.

23) c – Special somatic afferent fibers transmit signals relating to sound and balance and are located in the vestibulocochlear nerve (CN VIII). General visceral efferent fibers supply smooth muscle of visceral structures. These fibers travel in the four parasympathetic cranial nerves: the oculomotor (CN III), facial (CN VII), glossopharyngeal (CN IX), and vagus (CN X) nerves. Special visceral efferent fibers supply striated muscles that originate from branchial arches. These fibers travel in the trigeminal (CN V), facial (CN VII), glossopharyngeal (CN IX), and vagus (CN X) nerves. Special visceral afferent fibers transmit signals relating to taste and are found in the facial (CN VII), glossopharyngeal (CN IX), and vagus (CN X) nerves.

24) c – The vagus nerve (CN X) is associated with two sensory ganglia. The superior vagal ganglion is also known as the jugular ganglion because it arises as the vagus travels through the jugular foramen. The inferior vagal ganglion is also known as the nodose ganglion.

25) b – General visceral efferent fibers innervate smooth muscle of glands, viscera, and blood vessels. Among the twelve cranial nerves, these fibers are found in the four that carry parasympathetic fibers: the oculomotor (III), facial (VII), glossopharyngeal (IX), and vagus (X) nerves.

26) e – The stylopharyngeus muscle is the only muscle that is innervated in its entirety by the glossopharyngeal nerve (CN IX).

27) b – See #15 and #17 answer explanations. General visceral afferent fibers transmit sensory signals from visceral structures and are found in the glossopharyngeal (CN IX) and vagus (CN X) nerves.

28) b – See #8 answer explanation.

29) e – Tri = 3. The trigeminal nerve is CN V. It is divided into three divisions which originate from the trigeminal ganglion: the ophthalmic nerve (V1), maxillary nerve (V2), and mandibular nerve (V3).

30) e – The vestibulocochlear nerve is CN VIII and carries no motor fibers. The masseter is a muscle of mastication and is supplied by the trigeminal nerve (CN V). The sternocleidomastoid is a neck muscle innervated by branches from the spinal accessory nerve (component of CN XI) and second cervical (C2) spinal nerve. The orbicularis oris is a muscle of facial expression supplied by the facial nerve (CN VII). Finally, the genioglossus is an extrinsic muscle of the tongue and is innervated by the hypoglossal nerve (CN XII).

31) b – See #13 answer explanation.

32) b – See # 20 answer explanation.

33) d – Special visceral efferent fibers innervate striated muscles that are embryologically derived from branchial arches. Such muscles include the muscles of facial expression, mastication (chewing), the pharynx, and the larynx. General somatic efferent fibers supply somatic structures that contribute to the formation of the body wall and extremities. These structures include striated muscles embryologically originated from myotomes. Such muscles consist of extraocular muscles, intrinsic and extrinsic muscles of the tongue, and muscles of the neck. The sternocleidomastoid is a striated muscle of the neck supplied by general somatic efferent fibers of the spinal accessory nerve.

34) c – See #18 answer explanation.

35) e – See #13 answer explanation.

36) a – The spinal accessory nerve is a motor nerve formed by the external branch (ramus) or spinal component of the accessory nerve (CN XI). In addition to innervating the trapezius, the spinal accessory also gives a branch which combines with a branch from the C2 spinal nerve to supply the sternocleidomastoid muscle.

37) b – General visceral efferent fibers supply smooth muscle of visceral structures. These fibers travel in the four parasympathetic cranial nerves: the oculomotor (CN III), facial (CN VII), glossopharyngeal (CN IX), and vagus (CN X) nerves.

38) d – See #12 answer explanation.

39) b – The facial (CN VII), glossopharyngeal (CN IX), and vagus (CN X) nerves carry special visceral afferent fibers that relay signals responsible for taste sensation. The vestibulocochlear nerve (CN VIII) is formed by special somatic afferent fibers that transmit information related to sound and balance. The trochlear nerve (CN IV) is a motor nerve. In addition to special visceral efferent fibers that innervate the muscles of mastication, the trigeminal nerve (CN V) carries general somatic afferent fibers that transmit sensory information from somatic structures of the head.

40) d – Fibers carrying visual information from both the medial and lateral sides of an eye initially travel in the ipsilateral optic nerve. At the optic chiasm, fibers from the medial or nasal half of each eye cross to travel in the contralateral optic tract and arrive at the contralateral side of the brain. Sensory cells in the retina of the medial side of each eye transmit visual information from light rays arriving from the opposite side of the visual field. The medial side of the right eye transmits information from the right lateral visual field; the medial side of the left eye transmits information from the left lateral visual field. Fibers that cross at the optic chiasm are therefore responsible for lateral or peripheral vision. Due to the fiber crossing at the optic chiasm, each optic tract carries fibers from the ipsilateral half of each eye and relays visual signals from the contralateral visual field. The *right* optic tract carries fibers from the *right* (or lateral) half of the right eye and the *right* (or medial) half of the left eye. Both fiber groups relay signals related to the *left* visual field. The *left* optic tract carries fibers from the *left* (or lateral) half of the left eye and the *left* (or medial) half of the right eye. The left optic tract therefore carries visual signals associated with the *right* visual field. Visual abnormalities associated with peripheral vision are frequently found in patients with a pituitary tumor. The pituitary gland is located near the optic chiasm; pituitary swelling can encroach on tissue of the optic chiasm and negatively affect signal transmission by fibers crossing at that location.

41) c – General somatic afferent fibers are those that transmit sensory signals from somatic structures. This involves conduction of signals related to touch, pain, and proprioception. The trigeminal nerve (CN V) is the cranial nerve primarily responsible for transmission of general somatic afferent signals. The trigeminal nerve provides sensation to virtually all skin of the face, tissues below the skin, mucous membranes of the mouth, tongue, and the teeth. The facial (CN VII), glossopharyngeal (CN IX), and vagus (CN X) nerves also carry general somatic afferent fibers.

42) b – The maxillary nerve is the V2 division of the

trigeminal nerve. Once it enters the infraorbital canal, it is known thereafter as the infraorbital nerve. The infraorbital nerve exits the skull via the infraorbital foramen and supplies anterior skin below the orbit. The mandibular nerve is the V3 division of the trigeminal nerve and the only trigeminal division to carry motor fibers.

43) d – Special somatic afferent fibers transmit signals relating to sound and balance and are located in the vestibulocochlear nerve (CN VIII).

44) a – The hypoglossal nerve exits the skull through the hypoglossal canal.

45) a – See #9 answer explanation. The trigeminal nerve carries special visceral efferent fibers that innervate muscles of mastication.

46) d – The gasserian or semilunar ganglion is often simply referred to as the trigeminal ganglion and is the somatic sensory ganglion of the trigeminal nerve (CN V). As such, it houses general somatic afferent cell bodies. The motor root of the trigeminal nerve joins the mandibular nerve (V3 division) after the origination of the mandibular from the trigeminal ganglion. For this reason, special visceral efferent fibers do not travel in the ganglion. Special visceral afferent cell bodies relay signals related to the perception of taste; they are only found in sensory ganglia associated with the three cranial nerves that convey taste signals: facial (CN VII), glossopharyngeal (CN IX), and vagus (CN X) nerves. Parasympathetic (general visceral efferent) cell bodies are confined to one of the four parasympathetic efferent ganglia of the head: ciliary, pterygopalatine, otic, and submandibular.

47) e – See #5 answer explation. Contraction of the superior oblique causes the eye to depress (look down) and abduct (look outward, laterally). Because the inferior rectus also depresses the eye, the lateral rectus also abducts the eye, and the depressing action of the superior oblique is optimized from an adducted position, superior oblique function is clinically tested by having the patient look toward the nose, down (depression) and in (adduction). This is a frequent cause of confusion because the muscle's action is to rotate the eye down and out (abduction).

48) b – The vestibulocochlear nerve (CN VIII) is formed by the combination of two roots, a cochlear and vestibular root. The cochlear root transmits information related to sound perception and is lateral to the vestibular root. The vestibular root transmits information related to equilibrium and balance. After originating separately, the two join and pass into the internal acoustic meatus alongside the facial nerve (CN VII). The vestibulocochlear then divides back into its two components and each branch runs to its respective sensory ganglion. Bipolar sensory neurons in the cochlear (spiral) ganglion extend peripheral processes to the spiral organ of Corti in the cochlear duct. Central processes travel back to the brain stem with the cochlear root. Bipolar sensory neurons in the vestibular ganglion distribute peripheral processes to the saccule, the utricle, and the three semicircular ducts. Central processes travel to the brain stem with the vestibular root.

49) b – See #17 answer explanation.

50) b – The frontalis muscle runs vertically across the forehead and raises the eyebrows and skin of the forehead upon contraction. It is supplied by the temporal branch of the facial nerve (CN VII). The buccinator runs from the mandible and maxilla to the orbicularis oris muscle at the angle of the mouth. Its contraction pulls the cheek and angle of the mouth in, as if puckering. The buccinator is innervated by the buccal branch of the facial. The temporalis is a muscle of mastication and is supplied by the trigeminal nerve (CN V). It originates from the temporal fossa of the side of the skull and inserts on the coronoid process of it mandible. The temporalis closes the jaw upon contraction. The hyoglossus is an extrinsic muscle of the tongue and is innervated by the hypoglossal nerve (CN XII).

51) b – See #17 and #41 answer explanations.

52) c – The oculomotor nerve (CN III) supplies the superior rectus, medial rectus, inferior rectus, inferior oblique and levator palpebrae superioris muscles. In addition, it carries parasympathetic fibers that stimulate the ciliary muscle to contract. This contraction loosens the tension on the suspensory ligaments and allows the lens to assume a more spherical shape, providing positive accommodation for near-sighted vision. The trochlear nerve (CN IV) innervates the superior oblique muscle. The lateral rectus muscle *abducts* the eye and is supplied by the *abducens* nerve (CN VI).

53) d – See #47 answer explanation.

54) a – The posterior belly of the digastric muscle is innervated by the facial nerve (CN VII). The trigeminal nerve (CN V) supplies the anterior belly of the digastric.

55) e – Special visceral efferent fibers supply striated muscles that originate from branchial arches. These fibers travel in the trigeminal (CN V), facial (CN VII), glossopharyngeal (CN IX), and vagus (CN X) nerves. The trigeminal nerve innervates muscles of mastication. The facial nerve supplies muscles of facial expression. The glossopharyngeal nerve supplies muscles of the pharynx. The vagus supplies muscles of both the pharynx and larynx. General visceral efferent fibers innervate smooth muscle of glands, viscera, and blood vessels. Among the twelve cranial nerves, these fibers are found in the four that carry parasympathetic fibers: the oculomotor (III), facial (VII), glossopharyngeal (IX), and vagus (X) nerves. General somatic afferent fibers provide sensation to somatic structures of the head. These fibers are located in the trigeminal (CN V), facial (VII), glossopharyngeal (CN IX), and vagus (CN X) nerves. Special visceral afferent fibers transmit signals relating to taste and are found in the facial (CN VII), glossopharyngeal (CN IX), and vagus (CN X) nerves.

56) d – The vagus nerve (CN X) carries special visceral efferent fibers that innervate striated muscles of the pharynx and larynx. The lingual nerve is a sensory branch of the trigeminal (CN V) and provides general sensation to the anterior 2/3 of the tongue. The chorda tympani is a sensory branch of the facial nerve (CN VII) that joins the lingual nerve and relays signals related to taste from the anterior 2/3 of the tongue. The maxillary nerve is the V2 division of the trigeminal nerve and is a sensory nerve. It carries no motor fibers.

57) a – See #33 answer explanation.

58) c – The olfactory nerve (CN I) transmits information related to the sense of smell and is composed of a tract and a bulb. The olfactory tract travels forward from the brain and ends in a dilated terminal portion, the olfactory bulb. Olfactory cells are sensory cells located in the mucous membrane of the upper nasal cavity. These cells are bipolar; each cell has one peripheral and one central process. Peripheral processes travel to the mucosal surface to project small olfactory hairs into the cavity. Central processes travel away from the mucosal surface and end in the olfactory *bulb*. In the bulb, these processes synapse with cells that extend fibers centrally, forming the olfactory *tract*.

59) c – See #47 answer explanation.

60) a – The geniculate ganglion is the sensory ganglion of the facial nerve (CN VII). It contains pseudounipolar cell bodies of two types. Special visceral afferent cell bodies transmit taste signals from the anterior 2/3 of the tongue. General somatic afferent cell bodies relay signals from skin of the external acoustic meatus, skin behind the auricle of ear, and mucous membranes of the soft palate.

"Success is the result of hard work that overcomes all forms of disappointment and moments of discouragement. Success is not achieved through complex strategies. It is achieved only through conscientiously carrying out the duties of your office and exercising the responsibilities of leadership...nothing else will prevail."

– Attila the Hun

CHAPTER EIGHT

THE SPINAL NERVES

The **spine** is formed by the spinal cord and vertebral column. The **spinal cord** is the nerve tissue that extends from the brain, travels through the foramen magnum of the skull, and courses inferiorly within the bony protection of the vertebral column. The spinal cord serves as the origin of **spinal nerves**. Just as cranial nerves originate directly from the brain and brain stem, spinal nerves originate directly from the spinal cord.

The **vertebral column** is the bony case protecting the spinal cord. The column consists of **33 vertebrae** grouped according to the region of the body they are located. There are **7 cervical vertebrae** (neck), **12 thoracic vertebrae** (chest), and **5 lumbar vertebrae** (loin/abdomen). The five vertebrae below the lumbar vertebrae fuse to form the **sacrum**. Finally, the **coccyx** forms the inferior tip of the spinal cord and is produced by the fusion of four vertebrae. Grossly, there are **24 true vertebrae**, one sacrum, and one coccyx. The C1 and C2 vertebrae (the first and second cervical vertebrae) are known as the **atlas** and **axis**, respectively.

HALF AND HALF

There are **24 true vertebrae. Half are attached to ribs** (12 thoracic vertebrae) and **half are not** (7 cervical and 5 lumbar vertebrae...7 + 5 = 12).

Almost Half and Half: 5 and 4 are almost equal. The sacrum is noticeably larger (formed by fusion of 5 vertebrae) than the coccyx (formed by fusion of 4 vertebrae).
5 + 4 = 9

24 + 9 = 33 total vertebrae

Segments of the spinal cord should be distinguished from vertebrae of the vertebral column. With the exception of the sacrum, no vertebrae are shown in Figure 2 of the poster. The spinal cord is depicted as a series of blocks designated C1 through L5. These blocks represent **spinal cord segments**. They are drawn to aid the student in learning the spinal segment contribution to various nerves. It is important to realize that these blocks represent the actual nervous tissue of the spinal cord, not the bony vertebrae of the vertebral column. For instance, there are only seven cervical vertebrae, yet eight cervical spinal cord segments have been drawn (C1-C8). This is because there are eight pairs of

cervical spinal nerves. A spinal cord segment can simply be considered a region of spinal cord tissue that serves as the origin for a pair of spinal nerves.

There are a total of **31 pairs of spinal nerves** originating directly from the spinal cord. Each pair consists of a right and left spinal nerve. Almost every spinal nerve is associated with a particular vertebra. The location of the exit of the nerve from the spine is correlated with that vertebra.

---

33 Vertebrae Protect 31 Spinal Segments
Hypothetically, more *outer* vertebrae are required to enclose and protect the *inner* spinal segments.

Each cervical spinal nerve exits immediately above its respective vertebrae except the C8 nerve. The first cervical nerve pair exit above the C1 vertebrae (atlas). The C2 spinal nerve exits through the intervertebral foramen between the C1 and C2 vertebrae. The C3 nerve exits between the C2 and C3 vertebrae and so on. This pattern continues until the eighth cervical nerve is reached. There is no C8 vertebra. The C8 spinal nerve makes its exit between the C7 and T1 vertebrae. To phrase it differently, each of the cervical spinal nerves exits above its respective vertebra except the C8 nerve, which exits below the C7 vertebra. Thus, there are eight cervical spinal nerves but only seven cervical vertebrae.

Each thoracic and lumbar spinal nerve exits the spine below its respective vertebra. The T1 nerve exits the intervertebral foramen between the T1 and T2 vertebrae. The T12 nerve exits between the T12 and L1 vertebrae. Likewise, the L5 nerve leaves the spinal column between the L5 vertebrae and the sacrum.

FIGURE 8.1
Relationship of cervical spinal nerves to cervical vertebrae. (Anterior View)

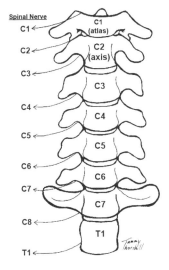

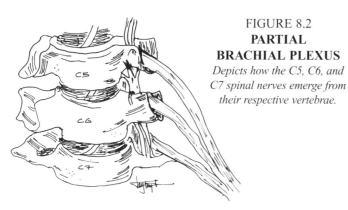

FIGURE 8.2
**PARTIAL
BRACHIAL PLEXUS**
*Depicts how the C5, C6, and
C7 spinal nerves emerge from
their respective vertebrae.*

The first four sacral spinal nerves exit the sacrum through **four sacral foramina.** You can remember that four sacral foramina exist because they are the "remnants" of the four intervertebral foramina located between each of the **five fused sacral vertebrae.** Because there were five vertebrae, there were four *inter*vertebral foramina.

The fifth sacral spinal nerve exits below the sacrum. Representing the last pair of spinal nerves is the coccygeal nerve, which runs along the coccyx.

FIGURE 8.3
*Relationship of spinal
nerves to corresponding
vertebrae. (Sagital View)*

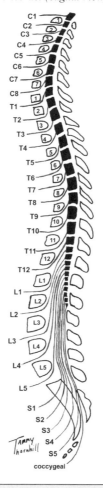

The head and neck are "above" or superior to the rest of the body. Spinal nerves which exit the vertebral column in the neck (the cervical spinal nerves) exit **"above"** or superior to their respective vertebrae. The exception is the C8 nerve, which does not have a vertebra. Those that leave the cord in the torso (vertebral regions which are **"below" the head and neck**, such as the thoracic and lumbar spinal nerves), exit the intervertebral foramen **"below"** their respective vertebra (inferior to their vertebra). For example, the C6 spinal nerve exits above the C6 vertebra (between the C5 and C6 vertebrae). The T11 spinal nerve exits below the T11 vertebra (between the T11 and T12 vertebrae).

There are five sacral spinal nerves. The S1-S4 spinal nerves leave the spine by way of four sacral foramina. The **fifth sacral spinal nerve (S5)** (87) exits below the sacrum. Representing the last pair of spinal nerves is the **coccygeal nerve** (86), which runs along the first part of the coccyx. Thus, there are a total of **33 vertebrae and 31 pair of spinal nerves**. Spinal nerves generally innervate tissue that is below their level of origination from the spinal cord.

All thirty-one spinal segments are represented in Figure 2 of the poster. The C1-C8, T1-T12, and L1-L5 spinal segments are depicted as twenty-five separate blocks. The image of the sacrum serves as a reference point. The upper four sacral spinal nerves exit through sacral foramina. These four sacral foramina represent the S1-S4 spinal segments. The S5 spinal nerve and coccygeal nerve exit below the sacrum.

To decrease clutter and improve image clarity, many of the spinal nerves are not drawn in Figure 2 of the poster. Although every nerve is not drawn, a representative of that nerve is present. These representations are explained as the material is reached in the text. It is important to realize that each spinal segment gives rise to a pair of spinal nerves, a right one and left one. One or the other is usually all that is shown in the poster.

SPINAL NERVE STRUCTURE

A spinal nerve is formed by the combination of a **dorsal root** with a **ventral root.** The dorsal root comes off the dorsal (or posterior) side of the spinal cord. The ventral root comes off the ventral (or anterior) side of the cord. Because each spinal segment is the origin of a pair of spinal nerves, each spinal segment is the origin of two dorsal roots and two ventral roots. The right dorsal root combines with the right ventral root; the left dorsal root combines with the left ventral root. Dorsal roots carry afferent (or sensory) nerve fibers toward the cord. Ventral roots carry efferent (or motor) fibers away from the cord.

Dorsal roots carry sensory, afferent information that is also said to be ascending; the flow of transmission is from sensory receptors upward, toward the brain. Only one afferent neuron participates in nerve signal transmission outside the central nervous system (CNS). This pseudounipolar neuron is located within the **dorsal root ganglion** of the dorsal root. The neuron has only one appendage or exten-

---

C8 and Coccyx
is why # of vertebrae do not equal # spinal segments

Start at 30:
C8 = spinal cord segment, but no vertebrae = 1 additional spinal segment = 31 spinal cord segments
Coccyx = 4 vertebrae, but only 1 coccygeal nerve = 3 additional vertebrae = 33 vertebrae

Otherwise: 12 thoracic spinal segments = 12 thoracic vertebrae
5 lumbar spinal segments = 5 lumbar vertebrae
5 sacral spinal segments = 5 sacral vertebrae

FIGURE 8.4
**FORMATION OF A PAIR OF SPINAL NERVES
FROM THE SAME SPINAL SEGMENT**

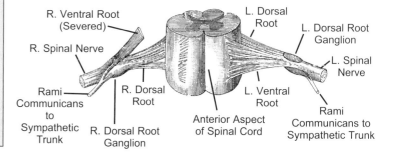

R. Ventral Root
(Severed)

R. Spinal Nerve

Rami
Communicans
to
Sympathetic
Trunk

R. Dorsal Root
Ganglion

R. Dorsal
Root

Anterior Aspect
of Spinal Cord

L. Ventral
Root

L. Dorsal
Root

L. Dorsal Root
Ganglion

L. Spinal
Nerve

Rami
Communicans to
Sympathetic Trunk

sion from the cell body. This appendage is an axon; no dendrites are present. The lone axon travels out to divide into two branches. The longer branch travels out to a peripheral sensory receptor and is analogous to a dendrite because it receives information. The shorter branch courses to the spinal cord. When the sensory receptor is activated, an afferent signal is transmitted to the spinal cord.

Both somatic and autonomic afferent fibers travel in the dorsal roots. The neuron structure is similar for both systems in that one pseudounipolar neuron is housed in the dorsal root ganglion. With the somatic system, the peripheral sensory receptor is located in a somatic tissue. Examples of such receptors include a touch receptor of the skin or a pain receptor of a bone or muscle. With the autonomic or visceral system, the sensory receptor is located in a visceral tissue. Examples include a stretch receptor of an artery or a pain receptor of a viscus.

Everyone likes to get his or her back *(posterior)* scratched. This is sensory, afferent information which travels through the dorsal *(posterior)* roots.

Dorsal back scratch is **afferent sensory** information via **dorsal** root.

DorSal roots carry Sensory information.

Ventral roots are formed by motor fibers. Motor fibers carry information that is efferent; the flow of nerve transmission is outward, toward the muscles and away from the brain and spinal cord. This pattern of neurotransmission is also said to be descending. Signals flow from the brain downward, toward the muscles.

Like the dorsal roots, the ventral roots can be formed by both somatic and autonomic (visceral) fibers. Somatic fibers innervate somatic structures; visceral fibers innervate visceral structures. The efferent neurons of both systems are multipolar. They possess an axon and numerous dendrites.

The efferent somatic system is a one-neuron system. Only one neuron participates in efferent transmission outside the CNS. The somatic neuron cell body is located in the ventral horn of the spinal cord. Its axon travels out by way of a ventral root to enter a spinal nerve. It courses peripherally to innervate a skeletal muscle fiber. The synapse between the somatic efferent axon and skeletal muscle fiber is known as a **motor end plate.**

The efferent visceral system is a two-neuron system. Two neurons participate in efferent transmission outside the CNS. Similar to the somatic efferent neuron, the cell body of the preganglionic visceral efferent neuron is located in the ventral horn of the spinal cord. Its axon leaves the cord in a ventral root and travels peripherally to synapse with the postganglionic neuron in a peripheral autonomic ganglion. The postganglionic axon then continues distally to supply the effector organ: a cardiac or smooth muscle cell of a visceral structure (see Figure 5.14).

The ventral and dorsal root of each side of the spinal cord segment combine to form a **spinal nerve trunk.** Again, there are two spinal nerve trunks, a right and left, for each spinal cord segment. Each trunk continues outward to divide into **dorsal** and **ventral rami.** The Latin word *ramus* simply means branch. The plural form of the word is *rami.* The dorsal rami are the spinal nerve *branches* which travel dorsally or posteriorly to supply posterior tissues. The

ventral rami are spinal nerve *branches* which travel ventrally or anteriorly to supply anterior tissues. The trunks often divide while still within the cover of the vertebral column. As a result, dorsal and ventral rami are usually the nerves seen exiting the spine.

Think of a **spinal nerve as a tree**.
• It is formed by **roots** (one dorsal root and one ventral root).
• The combination of roots forms a spinal nerve **trunk**.
• The trunk soon divides into dorsal and ventral rami (**branches**).

Because most of the mass of the body is anterior (or ventral) to the spinal cord, there is significantly more tissue for the ventral rami to supply. It should be no surprise that most of the body's spinal nerve branches originate from ventral rami. In fact, the majority of nerves depicted in Figures 1, 2, and 3 of the poster are spinal nerve ventral rami branches. The dorsal rami course posteriorly to innervate skin and muscles of the posterior head, neck, and torso.

In humans, *ventral* is synonymous with *anterior. Dorsal* is synonymous with *posterior.* The spine is located in the dorsal or posterior aspect of the body. Most of the mass of the body lies ventral or anterior to the spine. The *ventral* rami branches comprise most of the spinal nerve branches because most of the mass and structures are *ventral* to the spine. The only structures *dorsal* to the spine are muscles and skin of the *dorsal* (or posterior) aspect of the head, neck, back, and buttocks.

Even though the lower spinal nerves exit the vertebral column from locations as inferior as below the sacrum, the actual **spinal cord ends at the L1-L2 vertebral level.** Roots of spinal segments located below this level, including both dorsal and ventral roots, branch from the cord at the L1-L2 level and travel inferiorly as individual nerve roots within the dura mater. The spinal nerves formed by these roots eventually turn lateral to exit the vertebral column through an intervertebral or sacral foramen.

The tapered, cone-shaped ending of the actual cord at L1-L2 is called the **conus medullaris.** The Latin word *conus* describes a structure that is shaped like a cone. The word *medulla* refers to the internal portion of a structure.

The **filum terminale** is the thin, centralized structure that extends distally from the conus medullaris. The word *filum* is Latin for thread or thread-like. *Terminale* denotes that this structure represents the terminal aspect of the spinal cord. The filum terminale acts as a securing line that travels inferiorly to attach to the coccyx and hold the spinal cord in place.

Below the conus medullaris, the continuation of the inferiorly-traveling spinal nerve roots is collectively known as the **cauda equina.** *Cauda* is Latin for tail. The word *equine* refers to a horse. The cauda equina is named for its visual similarity to a horse's tail.

VENTRAL RAMI

As ventral rami branches travel out to innervate anterior structures, they form various nerve plexuses. A **plexus** is merely a group of nerves. Each spinal nerve plexus is formed by a proximal group of ventral rami branches. These proximal branches

FIGURE 8.5
SPINAL CORD AND ASSOCIATED STRUCTURES

(Reproduced with permission from Seidel, H.M., Ball, J.W., Dains, J.E., Benedict, G.W.: Mosby's Guide to Physical Examination, 6th ed. St. Louis, Mosby Elsevier, 2006)

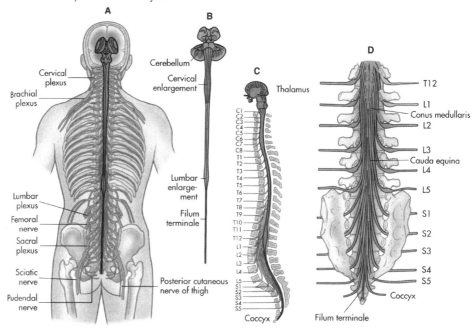

FIGURE 8.6
SPINAL SEGMENT CONTRIBUTION TO THE VENTRAL RAMI PLEXUSES

- C1 / C2 / C3 / C4 — **Cervical Plexus**
- C5 / C6 / C7 / C8 / T1 — **Brachial Plexus**
- T2 / T3 / T4 / T5 / T6 / T7 / T8 / T9 / T10 / T11 / T12 — **Intercostal Nerves**
- L1 / L2 / L3 / L4 — **Lumbar Plexus**
- L5 / S1 / S2 / S3 / S4 — **Sacral Plexus**
- S5
- Coccygeal

combine with one another in unique and specific ways to form nerves which supply a particular area. There are four large spinal nerve plexuses: the cervical plexus, the brachial plexus, the lumbar plexus, and the sacral plexus. These plexuses, along with their branches, will be the focus of remaining chapters. They are introduced here so their spinal segment composition may be learned.

The ventral rami of the upper cervical spinal nerves form the **cervical plexus**. This includes ventral rami from C1-C4. The majority of innervation to the cervical plexus actually comes from the ventral rami of C2-C4. The C1 ventral ramus is small and may contribute by way of a small branch to C2. The word *cervical* describes the neck. The cervical plexus is the origin of many of the nerves that supply structures of the posterior head, neck, and skin of the upper torso.

The lower cervical and first thoracic spinal nerves contribute to the **brachial plexus**. The brachial plexus is formed by ventral rami branches from C5-C8 and T1. Although most of the C4 ventral ramus participates in the cervical plexus, a portion may also contribute to the brachial plexus via a small branch of communication with C5. The word *brachial* pertains to the arm. The brachial plexus supplies structures associated with the shoulder or pectoral girdle and upper extremity.

The ventral rami of the thoracic spinal nerves do not participate in a plexus. Instead, they form the **intercostal nerves.** These nerves travel parallel to ribs and supply skin and muscles of the chest and anterior abdominal wall. The word *costa* means rib. The *inter*costal nerves are the nerves which travel *between* the ribs. Much of the mass of the thorax and abdomen is occupied by visceral organs. Because these organs are supplied by the autonomic nervous system, the thoracic spinal nerves do not have as much of an innervation responsibility. There is therefore no need for a thoracic spinal nerve plexus.

The upper lumbar ventral rami contribute to the **lumbar plexus.** Specifically, the L1, L2, L3, and a portion of the L4 ventral rami combine to form the plexus. The lumbar plexus supplies structures of the anterior aspect of the hip girdle and lower extremity. Except for one nerve that innervates skin of the medial leg (below knee), all innervation of the lumbar plexus is confined to anterior tissues above the knee, including structures of the hip girdle and thigh.

Finally, the remaining portion of the L4 ventral ramus and all of the L5, S1, S2, S3, and S4 ventral rami form the **sacral plexus.** The combination of the remaining portion of the L4 ventral ramus and the entire L5 ventral ramus forms the **lumbosacral trunk** (133). This trunk represents lumbar contribution to the sacral plexus. The sacral plexus is responsible for innervating structures of the posterior hip girdle and posterior thigh. With the exception of one lumbar plexus cutaneous nerve, the sacral plexus also supplies all tissues located below the knee. For descriptive purposes, the lumbar and sacral plexuses are often combined into one plexus, the **lumbosacral plexus.**

HALF AND HALF
There are 8 cervical spinal segments. The first half (C1-C4) form the cervical plexus. The second half (C5-C8) contribute to the brachial plexus (along with the T1 spinal nerve).

SPINAL NERVES GO DOWN, NOT UP (AFFECTED BY GRAVITY)
Spinal nerves usually supply tissues located below their level of origination from the spinal cord. For example, it is mostly cervical spinal nerves (C5-C8) that travel down to form the brachial plexus. The brachial plexus supplies the arm. In accordance with this principle, a portion of the L4 ventral ramus and all of the L5 ventral ramus travel down to contribute to the lower-lying sacral plexus. There is no sacral contribution to the superiorly-located lumbar plexus.

QUIZ 1
Spinal Nerve

Time for Quiz = 25 minutes.
For questions 1-15, choose the single best answer.

____ 1) Ventral rami branches of the cervical spinal nerves contribute to the
      a) cervical plexus
      b) brachial plexus
      c) both a and b
      d) thoracic plexus
      e) none of the above

_____ 2) How many vertebrae are in the vertebral column, excluding the sacrum and coccyx?
      a) 28
      b) 31
      c) 33
      d) 24
      e) none of the above

_____ 3) Spinal nerve dorsal roots carry nerve fibers which are
      a) afferent
      b) sensory
      c) both a and b
      d) efferent
      e) none of the above

_____ 4) What nerves are usually seen exiting the intervertebral foramen of the spinal cord?
      a) dorsal roots
      b) ventral roots
      c) both a and b
      d) ventral rami
      e) none of the above

_____ 5) Where does the filum terminale end?
      a) L1-L2 vertebral level
      b) L5 vertebral level
      c) sacrum
      d) coccyx
      e) none of the above

_____ 6) From which of the following nerve structures do most peripheral nerves directly originate?
      a) ventral roots
      b) ventral rami
      c) dorsal rami
      d) dorsal roots
      e) none of the above

_____ 7) Where does the C1 spinal nerve exit the vertebral column?
      a) immediately above the axis
      b) immediately below the axis
      c) immediately above the atlas
      d) immediately below the atlas
      e) both a and d

_____ 8) Ventral rami branches of the lumbar spinal nerves contribute to the
      a) lumbar plexus
      b) sacral plexus
      c) both a and b
      d) they do not contribute to a plexus
      e) none of the above

_____ 9) Moving distally from the spinal cord, a spinal nerve is formed by the combination of
      a) a dorsal root and ventral root
      b) a dorsal ramus and ventral ramus
      c) a dorsal root and dorsal ramus
      d) a dorsal root and ventral ramus
      e) none of the above

_____ 10) The brachial plexus is formed by
      a) only cervical dorsal rami branches
      b) both cervical and thoracic dorsal rami branches
      c) only cervical ventral rami branches
      d) both cervical and thoracic ventral rami branches
      e) none of the above

_____ 11) Where does the actual structure of the spinal cord end?
      a) coccyx
      b) L2
      c) sacrum
      d) L5
      e) none of the above

_____12) As a spinal nerve travels distally, it divides into
- a) a dorsal root and ventral root
- b) a dorsal ramus and ventral ramus
- c) a dorsal root and ventral ramus
- d) a dorsal root and dorsal ramus
- e) none of the above

_____13) Where does the C8 spinal nerve exit the vertebral column?
- a) between the C7 and C8 vertebrae
- b) between the C8 and T1 vertebrae
- c) between the C7 and T1 vertebrae
- d) there is no C8 spinal nerve
- e) none of the above

_____14) The C1 vertebra is known as the
- a) axis
- b) atlas
- c) coccyx
- d) avis
- e) none of the above

_____15) The sacral plexus is formed by
- a) lumbar and sacral ventral rami
- b) only sacral ventral rami
- c) lumbar and sacral ventral roots
- d) only sacral ventral roots
- e) none of the above

_____

For questions 16-25, use the following directions:
- **a......1,2,3 are correct**
- **b......1,3 are correct**
- **c......2,4 are correct**
- **d......only 4 is correct**
- **e......all are correct**

_____16) Which of the following spinal segments contribute to the sacral plexus?
1. L4
2. S1
3. L5
4. S4

_____17) Which of the following is true concerning the pattern of nerve transmission of spinal nerves?
1. Dorsal rami primarily carry only afferent nerve transmission.
2. Dorsal rami primarily carry only sensory nerve transmission.
3. Ventral rami primarily carry only descending nerve transmission.
4. Spinal nerves usually supply tissues which are below the level of origination of the spinal nerve from the spinal cord.

_____18) Which of the following is true concerning the terminal aspect of the spinal cord?
1. The S5 spinal nerves exit the vertebral column below the sacrum.
2. The filum terminale is composed of the conus medullaris and cauda equina.
3. The conus medullaris ends at the approximate L2 vertebral level.
4. The spinal cord ends at the approximate L5 vertebral level.

_____19) What is the correct location of exit from the vertebral column for the following spinal nerves?
1. The C4 nerves exits immediately below the C3 vertebra.
2. The C7 nerve exits immediately above the T1 vertebra.
3. The L5 nerve exits immediately above the sacrum.
4. The T12 nerve exits immediately above the T12 vertebra.

_____20) The C8 spinal nerve contributes to the
1. thoracic plexus
2. cervical plexus
3. intercostal nerves
4. brachial plexus

_____21) Which of the following spinal segments contribute to the lumbar plexus?
1. L1
2. L2
3. L4
4. L5

_____22) The S1 spinal nerve contributes to the
1. cervical plexus
2. lumbar plexus
3. intercostal nerves
4. sacral plexus

_____23) Which of the following structures compose the cauda equina?
1. conus medullaris
2. L1 nerve root
3. T12 nerve root
4. S4 nerve root

_____24) The L4 spinal nerve contributes to the
1. intercostal nerves
2. sacral plexus
3. thoracic plexus
4. lumbar plexus

_____25) Which structures are routinely found within a dorsal root ganglion?
1. a sympathetic afferent neuron cell body
2. a somatic afferent neuron cell body
3. a parasympathetic afferent neuron cell body
4. a pseudounipolar neuron cell body

QUIZ 1: Spinal Nerve Answers and Explanations

1) c – Half the cervical ventral rami (C1-C4) contribute to the cervical plexus and the other half (C5-C8), along with the T1 ventral ramus, contribute to the brachial plexus. Remember, the cervical ventral rami are "half and half." There is no thoracic ventral rami plexus. The thoracic ventral rami instead form the intercostal nerves.

2) d – There are 7 cervical vertebrae, 12 thoracic vertebrae, and 5 lumbar vertebrae. Remember "half and half"…half of the true vertebrae are attached to ribs (the 12 thoracic vertebrae) and half are not (the 7 cervical and 5 lumbar vertebrae 7+5=12).

3) c – Dorsal roots carry sensory fibers, whereas ventral roots carry motor fibers. Sensory fibers are afferent because they are traveling to the brain. They are therefore also said to be ascending because they are traveling from the sensory receptor, up, toward the brain. The *dorsal* roots carry sensory information, such as the sensation obtained from a "*dorsal* back scratch."

4) d – The structure of a spinal nerve is similar to that of a tree. A dorsal and ventral *root* originates from the same side of the spinal cord and unites to form a spinal nerve *trunk*. The trunk then divides into dorsal and ventral rami (*branches*). This division often occurs within the bony cover of the vertebral column, so the dorsal and ventral rami are the nerves actually seen exiting the spine.

5) d – The actual structure of the spinal cord ends at the L1-L2 vertebral level. The tapered ending of the spinal cord at this level is known as the conus medullaris. The centralized, thread-like nerve structure which continues from the spinal cord to end at the coccyx is the filum terminale. The filum terminale fixates the spinal cord to the coccyx. The lower spinal nerve roots exit the conus medullaris and continue distally within the dura mater. The combination of these nerve roots is collectively known as the cauda equina (horse's tail).

6) b – See #4 answer explanation. Dorsal rami are the branches that course dorsally to supply posterior structures, such as skin and muscles. The ventral rami are branches that travel anteriorly to supply structures. Because the spine is a dorsal structure, most of the mass of the body is anterior to it. There is therefore more tissue for the ventral rami to supply. It is no surprise that most spinal nerve branches directly originate from ventral rami nerves.

7) c – The atlas is the C1 vertebrae. All cervical spinal nerves exit the vertebral column above their respective vertebra except the C8 spinal nerve. Because there are only 7 cervical vertebrae, no C8 vertebra exists. The C8 spinal nerve exits between the C7 and T1 vertebrae. Subsequently, all thoracic and lumbar spinal nerves exit below their respective vertebrae.

8) c – The lumbar plexus is formed by ventral rami branches from L1, L2, L3, and part of L4. The sacral plexus is formed by the other portion of the L4 ventral ramus and all of the L5, S1, S2, S3, and S4 ventral rami.

9) a – See #4 and #6 answer explanations. The word *ramus* is the singular form of the word *rami*.

10) d – The brachial plexus is formed by ventral rami branches from the C5, C6, C7, C8, and T1 spinal nerves. Because most of the mass of the body is anterior to the spine, most spinal nerve branches are ventral rami branches. All of the large spinal nerve plexuses are formed by ventral rami nerves. This includes the cervical, brachial, lumbar, and sacral plexuses.

11) b – See #5 answer explanation.

12) b – See #4 and #6 answer explanations.

13) c – See #7 answer explanation.

14) b – Remember, the atlas "holds the head up," just as in Greek mythology Atlas "holds the world up."

15) a – See #4, #6 and #10 answer explanations. The sacral plexus is formed by a portion of the L4 ventral ramus and all of the L5, S1, S2, S3, and S4 ventral rami.

16) e – The sacral plexus is formed by a combination of lumbar and sacral ventral rami. A portion of the L4 ventral ramus combines with the entire L5 ventral ramus to form the lumbosacral trunk, which serves as the lumbar contribution to the sacral plexus. Ventral rami from S1, S2, S3, and S4 also contribute to the plexus.

17) d – Answer E would be correct if answer possibilities 1-3 said *roots* instead of *rami*. Spinal nerve structure is similar to that of a tree. Dorsal and ventral *roots* combine to a spinal nerve *trunk*. Dorsal roots carry sensory information. Because this information is traveling toward the brain, it is afferent nerve transmission. It is also ascending transmission because the flow of transmission is upward, from sensory receptors toward the brain. Ventral roots carry motor fibers. The flow of nerve transmission is therefore both efferent and descending. Spinal nerve trunks divide into dorsal and ventral rami (*branches*), which are the nerves usually seen exiting the vertebral column. Each type of ramus carries both motor and sensory fibers. Dorsal rami course dorsally to supply posterior structures. Ventral rami course ventrally to supply anterior structures. A particular spinal nerve usually innervates a region of tissue that is below the level of origination of the spinal nerve from the spinal cord.

18) b – See #5 answer explanation.

19) b – There are 8 cervical spinal nerves, yet only 7 cervical vertebrae. Each cervical nerve exits above its respective vertebra, except the C8 nerve, which exits between the C7 and T1 vertebrae. There is no C8 vertebra. The T1-L5 spinal nerves exit below their respective vertebrae. For example, the T1 nerve exits between the T1 and T2 vertebrae. The T12 nerve exits between the T12 and L1 vertebrae. The L1 nerve exits between the L1 and L2 vertebrae. The L5 nerve exits between the L5

vertebra and sacrum. The S1-S4 spinal nerves exit through four sacral foramina. The S5 nerve exits below the sacrum. The coccygeal nerve represents the last pair of spinal nerves and continues inferiorly to end at the coccyx.

20) d – The brachial plexus is formed by ventral rami from the C5, C6, C7, C8, and T1 spinal cord segments. Ventral rami from the C1, C2, C3, and C4 spinal segments form the cervical plexus. There is no large thoracic spinal nerve plexus.

21) a – The lumbar plexus is formed by the L1, L2, L3 spinal nerve ventral rami and a portion of the L4 ventral ramus. The other portion of the L4 ventral ramus combines with the entire L5 ventral ramus to form the lumbosacral trunk. The lumbosacral trunk contributes to the sacral plexus.

22) d – See #16 answer explanation. Remember, spinal nerves usually supply tissue located below their level of origination from the spinal cord. Although there is lumbar contribution to the sacral plexus, there is no sacral contribution to the lumbar plexus.

23) d – See #5 answer explanation. The conus medullaris and/or spinal cord ends at the L2 vertebral level. Because of this, spinal nerve roots that originate from spinal cord segments below the L2 level (such as the S4 nerve root) must exit from the tapered conus medullaris and travel inferiorly as part of the cauda equina. The T12 and L1 nerve roots, by contrast, are able to branch directly from the spinal cord because the spinal cord has not yet ended.

24) c – See #21 answer explanation.

25) e – A spinal nerve is formed by the union of one dorsal root with one ventral root. The ventral root carries efferent (motor) signals, which are signals that travel in the direction away from the brain. Peripheral *efferent* neurons are *multipolar* in structure. This includes efferent neurons of both the somatic and autonomic (sympathetic and parasympathetic) nervous systems. One axon and numerous dendrites

arise from a multipolar neuron. Somatic efferent pathways innervate muscles, causing contraction and/or relaxation. Visceral efferent pathways innervate glands, organs, and other visceral structures supplied by the autonomic nervous system. The dorsal root carries afferent (sensory) signals, which are signals that travel toward the brain. Somatic afferent pathways transmit sensory signals from somatic structures such as skin, muscles, and bones. Visceral afferent pathways transmit sensory signals from visceral structures such as internal organs, glands, and vessels. Peripheral *afferent* neurons of both the somatic and autonomic systems are *pseudounipolar* in structure and are found in dorsal root ganglia of spinal nerves and sensory ganglia of cranial nerves. Each dorsal root ganglion contains afferent pseudounipolar cell bodies of both the somatic and visceral (autonomic) systems. A particular cranial nerve sensory ganglion may contain somatic cell bodies exclusively, visceral cell bodies exclusively, or a combination of both types of afferent neuron cell bodies. A pseudounipolar neuron has only one appendage, a lone axon, that originates from the cell body. As opposed to a unipolar neuron, this axon quickly divides into a long and short branch. The longer branch travels to a peripheral sensory receptor and is analogous to a dendrite because it receives information. The shorter branch travels to the spinal cord (dorsal root ganglion) or brain stem (cranial nerve sensory ganglion). When the sensory receptor is activated, a sensory signal is transmitted to the CNS. Unipolar neurons are found in invertebrates. One axon extends from the cell body and contains areas that are axonal (transmit information) and areas that are dendritic (receive information) in function.

DORSAL RAMI

Spinal nerve dorsal rami do not participate in the formation of plexuses. Because the innervation responsibility is not as large or diverse as that of the ventral rami, there is no requirement for complicated plexus formation. After branching from the spinal nerve trunks, dorsal rami merely course posteriorly to supply skin and muscles of the posterior head, neck, and torso.

Due to the high degree of variability in the specific back muscles that each nerve innervates, many dorsal rami nerves are not named. With a few exceptions, there is no definitive relationship between a particular dorsal rami nerve and a particular muscle it supplies. If no specific structure is reliably supplied, it is impossible to positively identify the nerve, except to note where it comes from. A nerve name would serve little purpose. Adding to this ambiguity is the fact that many muscles of the back are often vaguely formed, consisting of sheets of muscle with multiple, varied points of origination and/or insertion along the vertebral column. Instead of having a specific name, most dorsal rami nerves are simply known as the *dorsal ramus* of the spinal nerve from which they originated (e.g. T4 dorsal ramus). Each muscle is then said to be innervated in a nonspecific fashion by cervical, thoracic, and/or lumbar dorsal rami. There is often a combination of innervation from dorsal rami of different spinal regions. For instance, the spinalis muscle of the thorax, spinalis thoracis, is supplied by thoracic dorsal rami branches. It is not unusual to find lumbar dorsal rami branches also contributing.

Like other spinal nerve branches, each dorsal ramus usually provides innervation to an area of tissue that is below the level of origination of the spinal nerve from the spinal cord. The upper cervical dorsal rami are the exceptions. In addition to supplying skin and muscles of the posterior neck, they also supply skin and muscles of the posterior head. The thoracic dorsal rami innervate back muscles and skin of the thoracic and upper lumbar areas. Lumbar dorsal rami supply posterior tissue of the lower lumbar and upper sacral areas. Finally, sacral dorsal rami supply the lower sacral area.

CERVICAL SPINAL NERVES ARE THE EXCEPTIONS

1) They originate in the neck. All others originate in the trunk.
2) They exit the spine above their respective vertebra.
3) They have an extra spinal nerve (C8), which does not have a vertebra.
4) Some of their **dorsal rami** branches innervate specific muscles and have nerve names (covered in the next chapter).
5) Some innervate skin and muscles which are located **above** the level of spinal nerve origination from the spinal cord.

CERVICAL SPINAL NERVES LIKE TO BE ABOVE

Cervical spinal nerves originate from *__above__* (neck), exit *__above__* their respective vertebrae, and some supply tissue located *__above__* their level of origination.

Because of the lack of specificity in the dorsal rami innervation of the back muscles, these muscles will be grouped together and described in this chapter. Later chapters are devoted to body regions supplied mostly by ventral rami branches. In those chapters, the specific ventral rami nerves, along with the muscles and areas of skin they supply, will be described.

Before proceeding, the term *back* muscles should be explained. A more proper name would actually be spinal or vertebral muscles; these muscles attach to and support the spine. Back muscles course longitudinally, parallel to the vertebral column. They originate or insert on the vertebrae and function to support and extend the vertebral column. Although called *back* muscles, some function to extend the neck and/or head.

There are numerous other muscles of the back that are not anatomically considered *back* muscles. In the upper torso, there are a number of muscles that are part of the shoulder girdle and function in movement of the upper extremity. Although considered back muscles by the lay public, these muscles are not true *back* muscles of anatomic description. They include the trapezius, rhomboids, levator scapulae, supraspinous, teres minor, teres major, and latissimus dorsi. An athletic trainer may argue that these are *the* back muscles. There are other posterior muscles located in the lower torso that are also not considered back muscles. They are part of the pelvic girdle and function in movement of the lower extremity. For discussion here, the term *back* muscles is specific for muscles that attach to and provide movement of the spine. The back muscles are some of the largest and strongest in the body. It is no surprise that a strained back or neck is so painful.

FIGURE 8.7
SPINAL NERVE DORSAL RAMI
The superficial layer of muscle and fascia is removed on the right, revealing the deeper-located back muscles. Note that the upper cervical dorsal rami course superiorly.

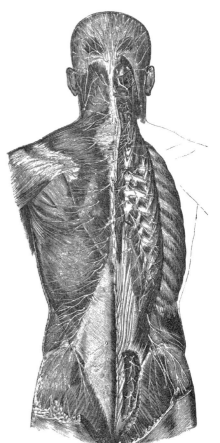

The following table groups back muscles innervated by spinal nerve dorsal rami. There are several similarities among these muscles. All run longitudinally, in the same direction as the spine. Some are virtually parallel with the spine. Some may be short and some quite long, but all travel upward from their point of origination to insert on vertebrae that are above their level of origination. There are muscles that travel up and insert on the vertebrae immediately above their origination.

Others skip multiple vertebrae before inserting. A few ascend to insert on the skull. **A muscle's origin is the fixed point of origination. Its insertion is the point of attachment to the bone or other structure it moves upon contraction.** Since all these muscles are on the posterior aspect of the vertebral column, all function to extend the vertebral column. Some may also turn or twist the vertebral column, depending upon how *unparallel* they are to the spine. In the neck, similar structural relationships act to extend and turn the head. To better understand and remember the origins, insertions, and actions of back muscles, the basic anatomy of vertebrae should be reviewed.

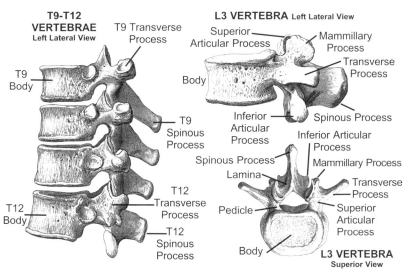

FIGURE 8.8
VERTEBRAL STRUCTURES
Although vertebrae from different regions of the spine have obvious structural differences, all are formed by the same general components.

Generally speaking, the table starts with the deep back muscles and moves more superficially.

SUBOCCIPITAL MUSCLES The posterior muscles that connect atlas, axis, and skull. All 4 muscles are innervated by cervical dorsal rami branches, including the greater occipital and suboccipital nerves	**Obliquus capitis superior** – extends head and pulls head laterally	originates from transverse process of atlas and travels upward and medially to insert on occipital bone of skull.
	Obliquus capitis inferior – turns atlas and head to side	originates from spinous process of axis and travels upward and laterally to insert on transverse process of atlas.
	Rectus capitis posterior major – extends head	originates from spinous process of axis and travels upward and laterally to insert on occipital bone of skull. It skips the atlas.
	Rectus capitis posterior minor – extends head	originates from posterior tubercle of atlas and travels up to insert on occipital bone of skull.
SEGMENTAL MUSCLES They travel from the process of one vertebra to insert on the same process of vertebra immediately above. Depending on the specific muscle, there can be slight medial or lateral slant, but overall, these muscle fibers run parallel to spine.	**Interspinales** – extend vertebral column	originate from each side of a spinous process of a vertebra and travel straight up to insert on the spinous process of vertebra immediately above. Present in cervical and lumbar spine; not in thoracic spine. Innervated by cervical and lumbar dorsal rami. Thoracic dorsal rami may contribute, depending on location of muscles.
	Intertransversarii – bend vertebral column to the side	originate from the transverse process of a vertebra and travel straight up to insert on the transverse process of the vertebra immediately above. In neck, there are anterior intertransversarii innervated by cervical ventral rami and posterior intertransversarii innervated by cervical dorsal rami. Intertransversarii are usually absent in thorax. Lumbar intertransversarii are supplied by dorsal rami.
TRANSVERSOSPINALIS MUSCLES From their origination, they travel up or superiorly while slanting medially to reach their insertion.	**Long rotators** – rotate vertebral column toward opposite side	originate from transverse process of one vertebra and insert on the spinous process of second vertebra above it (skips one vertebra). For the most part, cervical long rotators innervated by cervical dorsal rami, thoracic by thoracic, and lumbar by lumbar.
	Short rotators – rotate vertebral column toward opposite side	insert on spinous process of the vertebra immediately above the vertebra they originate from. For the most part, cervical dorsal rami supply cervical short rotators, thoracic supply thoracic, and lumbar supply lumbar.
	Multifidi muscles – extend and twist vertebral column	present the entire length of spine. Originate from sacrum, iliac spine, erector spinae tendon, and lumbar vertebrae (all for lumbar multifidi); transverse processes of upper lumbar and thoracic vertebrae (for thoracic multifidi), and articular processes of lower 3-5 cervical vertebrae (for cervical multifidi). Each travels upward or cephalically to insert on spinous processes of vertebrae that are 2-4 vertebrae above their origination. Innervated by a combination of cervical, thoracic, and lumbar dorsal rami. There is no clear structural division of the multifidi muscles. For that reason, the cumulative total mass of these individual muscles is known as a single muscle, the **multifidus muscle**.

TRANSVERSOSPINALIS MUSCLES *(cont.)*	**Semispinalis** – extends and twists vertebral column Semispinalis capitis extends head (look up)	present from occipital bone of skull to the lower six thoracic vertebrae. The semi-spinalis is actually formed by three separate muscles. The **semispinalis capitis** originates from transverse processes of the upper thoracic and lower cervical verte-brae to travel up and insert on occipital bone of skull. The **semispinalis cervicis** (neck) originates from transverse processes of upper thoracic vertebrae and inserts on spinous processes of middle cervical vertebrae. The semispinalis capitis travels on top of (or superficial to) the semispinalis cervicis muscle. The **semispinalis thoracis** originates from transverse processes of the lower six thoracic vertebrae and inserts on upper thoracic and lower cervical spinous processes. The semi-spinalis capitis is innervated by cervical dorsal rami branches including the suboc-cipital and greater occipital nerves. There can also be some thoracic dorsal rami contribution. The semispinalis cervicis and semispinalis thoracis receive innerva-tion from cervical and/or thoracic dorsal rami branches.
ERECTOR SPINAE MUSCLES This makes up the largest muscle mass of the back. These muscles originate from the sacrum, iliac crest, lumbar vertebrae, and lower thoracic verte-brae. They run up seem-ingly parallel to vertebral column to make their insertion. There is little, if any, medial or lateral slant as they travel up.	**Spinalis** – extends vertebral column; spinalis capitis extends head	the most medial group of the erector spinae. It can be composed of 3 muscles that all originate from, and insert on, spinous processes. The **spinalis thoracis** is almost always present. It originates from lower thoracic and upper lumbar verte-brae. It travels up to insert on upper thoracic vertebrae. When present, the **spinalis cervicis** originates from lower cervical and upper thoracic vertebrae and travels up to insert on upper cervical vertebrae. The **spinalis capitis** muscle is usually blend-ed with the larger semispinalis capitis muscle. Dorsal rami from thoracic and cer-vical spinal nerves innervate these muscles.
	Longissimus – extends vertebrae; longissimus capitis extends head	the intermediate, middle muscle of the erector spinae. The same common theme should become apparent. The longissimus also consists of 3 muscles: **longissimus thoracis, longissimus cervicis,** and **longissimus capitis.** All originate from trans-verse processes of vertebrae and insert on transverse processes of vertebrae located above, except the capitis, which inserts on the mastoid process of the temporal bone. Both cervical and thoracic dorsal rami branches innervate the longissimus thoracis and longissimus cervicis. The innervation of the longissimus capitis is probably limited to the dorsal rami of the cervical spinal nerves.
	Iliocostalis – extends ver-tebrae	the most lateral muscle of the erector spinae. It also is actually formed by 3 mus-cles: **iliocostalis lumborum, iliocostalis thoracis,** and **iliocostalis cervicis.** These muscles originate from the iliac crest (lumborum), ribs #6-12 (thoracis), and ribs #3-6 (cervicis). They travel up multiple levels to insert on transverse processes of vertebrae and/or ribs located above their origination. Depending on their location, they may be innervated by cervical, thoracic, or lumbar dorsal rami branches.
SPLENIUS MUSCLE The most superficial back muscles that are located in the posterior neck. They originate relatively medial-ly and slant laterally as they travel up to their insertion. The word *spleni-um* refers to a bandage or band-like structure. These muscles are named for their appearance as a band-age wrapped around the neck.	**Splenius capitis** – extends and turns head	originates from the lower cervical and upper thoracic spinous processes and travels up to insert on the lateral aspect of the posterior skull (lateral occipital bone and/or temporal bone). It receives cervical dorsal rami contribution.
	Splenius cervicis – extends and turns vertebrae and head	originates from spinous processes of the upper thoracic vertebrae and travels up to insert on transverse processes of the upper cervical vertebrae. It usually receives only cervical dorsal rami innervation. Occasionally, thoracic dorsal rami also con-tribute.

Transversospinalis ∧	Long and short rotators Multifidi Semispinalis	by traveling or slanting medially to insert on spinous processes of vertebrae above their origination, these muscles must *transverse* the **spine**.
Erector Spinae ∣∣	Spinalis Longissimus Iliocostalis	have little, if any, slant as they travel up the spine. Because of this, their stimulation causes only extension and no rotation of spine. They are *erectors* of the **spine**.
Splenius ∨	Splenius capitis Splenius cervicis	since they originate from the spinous processes of vertebrae, they must slant laterally to their insertion in order to turn the head and neck. They look like a *splenium* around the neck.

FIGURE 8.9
ERECTOR SPINAE
Posterior View

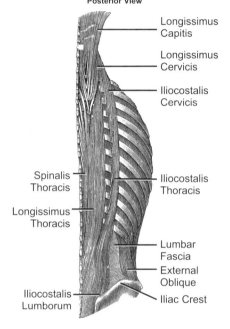

Longissimus Capitis
Longissimus Cervicis
Iliocostalis Cervicis
Spinalis Thoracis
Iliocostalis Thoracis
Longissimus Thoracis
Lumbar Fascia
External Oblique
Iliocostalis Lumborum
Iliac Crest

The **spin**alis muscle is part of the erector **spin**ae and hence, travels essentially parallel to the **spine**. The **semi**spinalis muscle is part of the transversospinalis and therefore travels upward with a medial slant. It is **semi**-parallel to the spine.

TRANSVERSOSPINALIS MUSCLES "TRANSVERSE" THE SPINE

The transversospinalis muscles are named for the fact that most originate on the *transverse* processes of vertebrae and insert on *spinous* processes of vertebrae located above. They therefore have a medial slant.

In order to "rotate" the spine, the *short and long rotators* must have a slant, because a muscle parallel to the spine cannot rotate it.

The **semispinalis** is *semi*-parallel to the spine.

The *multifidus* is also part of the transversospinalis group, a group that originates and inserts on *multiple* or **different** vertebral processes (originates on transverse, inserts on spinous).

FIGURE 8.10
MUSCLES OF THE POSTERIOR NECK AND UPPER BACK

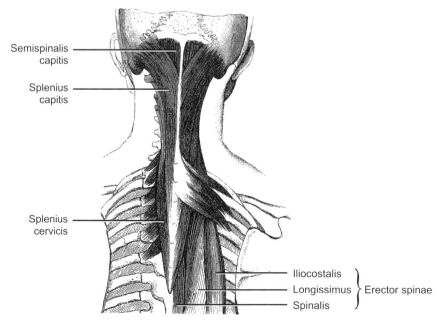

Semispinalis capitis
Splenius capitis
Splenius cervicis
Iliocostalis
Longissimus } Erector spinae
Spinalis

QUIZ 2
Spinal Nerve

Time for Quiz = 18 minutes.
For questions 1-11, choose the single best answer.

_____1) Which group of back muscles is the obliquus capitis superior muscle in?
    a) segmental muscles
    b) transversospinalis muscles
    c) erector spinae muscles
    d) suboccipital muscles
    e) none of the above

_____2) Which of the following muscles is the most lateral of the erector spinae group of back muscles?
    a) spinalis
    b) semispinalis
    c) longissimus
    d) iliocostalis
    e) none of the above

_____3) From their point of origination, which of the following back muscles travel essentially parallel to the long axis of the spine?
    a) interspinales
    b) long rotators
    c) multifidi muscles
    d) splenius cervicis
    e) none of the above

_____4) Which group of back muscles are the multifidi muscles in?
    a) suboccipital muscles
    b) segmental muscles
    c) transversospinalis muscles
    d) erector spinae
    e) none of the above

_____5) Which of the following muscles is the most medial of the erector spinae group of back muscles?
    a) spinalis
    b) semispinalis
    c) multifidus
    d) longissimus
    e) none of the above

_____6) From their point of origination, which of the following back muscles travel medially to reach their insertion?
    a) semispinalis
    b) splenius cervicis
    c) spinalis
    d) longissimus
    e) none of the above

_____7) Which group of back muscles are the interspinales muscles in?
    a) segmental muscles
    b) suboccipital muscles
    c) splenius muscles
    d) erector spinae muscles
    e) none of the above

_____8) Muscles which are anatomically classified as back muscles function to
    a) move the lower extremity
    b) flex the spine
    c) extend the spine
    d) all of the above
    e) none of the above

_____9) Which group of back muscles is the longissimus muscle a member of?
    a) transversospinalis muscles
    b) erector spinae muscles
    c) splenius muscles
    d) segmental muscles
    e) none of the above

_____10) From their point of origination, which of the following back muscles travel laterally to reach their insertion?
    a) splenius cervicis
    b) splenius capitis
    c) both a and b
    d) longissimus
    e) none of the above

_____11) Which group of back muscles is the splenius cervicis a member of?
    a) erector spinae muscles
    b) segmental muscles
    c) suboccipital muscles
    d) transversospinalis muscles
    e) none of the above

For questions 12-18, use the following directions:
   a......1,2,3 are correct
   b......1,3 are correct
   c......2,4 are correct
   d......only 4 is correct
   e......all are correct

____12) Which of the following muscles are in the suboccipital group of back muscles?
   1. obliquus capitis superior
   2. rectus capitis posterior minor
   3. obliquus capitis inferior
   4. rectus capitis posterior major

____13) Which of the following muscles are in the transversospinalis group of back muscles?
   1. long rotators
   2. multifidi muscles
   3. short rotators
   4. semispinalis

____14) Muscles anatomically classified as back muscles function to
   1. move the upper extremity
   2. flex the spine
   3. move the lower extremity
   4. extend the spine

____15) Which of the following muscles are in the erector spinae group of back muscles?
   1. spinalis
   2. longissimus
   3. iliocostalis
   4. semispinalis

____16) Which of the following muscles are in the splenius group of back muscles?
   1. splenius thoracis
   2. splenius cervicis
   3. splenius lumborum
   4. splenius capitis

____17) Which statements concerning the cutaneous innervation of thoracic and lumbar dorsal rami are true?
   1. A particular dorsal ramus usually supplies skin that is more medial than skin supplied by the dorsal ramus of the spinal nerve immediately above it.
   2. A particular dorsal ramus usually supplies skin that is more medial than skin supplied by the dorsal ramus of the spinal nerve immediately below it.
   3. They usually supply skin that is above or superior to their spinal segment level of origin.
   4. They usually supply skin that is below or inferior to their spinal segment level of origin.

____18) Which of the following muscles are in the segmental group of back muscles?
   1. interspinales
   2. short rotators
   3. intertransversarii
   4. multifidi muscles

QUIZ 2: Spinal Nerve Answers and Explanations

1) d – The suboccipital muscles are formed by four muscles that connect the atlas, axis, and skull. The suboccipital group of muscles consist of the obliquus capitis superior, obliquus capitis inferior, rectus capitis posterior major, and rectus capitis posterior minor. The obliquus capitis superior originates from the transverse process of the atlas and travels superiorly and medially to insert on the occipital bone of the skull. It extends the head and pulls the head laterally.

2) d – The erector spinae group of back muscles is formed by the spinalis, longissimus and iliocostalis muscles. The spinalis is the most medial. The longissimus is in an intermediate position. The iliocostalis is the most lateral. The semispinalis muscle is part of the transversospinalis group of back muscles.

3) a – The interspinales muscles, along with the intertransversarii muscles, form the group of back muscles known as the segmental muscles. The segmental muscles travel from the process of one vertebra to insert on the same process of the vertebra immediately above. The long rotators and multifidi muscles, along with the short rotators and semispinalis muscles, form the transversospinalis group of back muscles. These muscles travel medially to reach their point of insertion. The splenius cervicis, along with the splenius capitis, forms the splenius group of muscles. They are the most superficial back muscles located in the neck. From their origination, they slant laterally to reach their insertion.

4) c – The transversospinalis group of muscles is formed by the long rotators, short rotators, multifidi, and semispinalis muscles. From their origination, the transversospinalis muscles travel superiorly while slanting medially to reach their insertion.

5) a – See #2 answer explanation. The multifidus muscle is actually the cumulative muscle mass formed by all the individual multifidi muscles, which are part of the transversospinalis group of back muscles.

6) a – The semispinalis is part of the transversospinalis group of muscles. This group travels medially to reach their insertion. The splenius cervicis, along with the splenius capitis, forms the splenius group of muscles. They are the most superficial back muscles located in the neck. From their origination, they slant laterally to reach their insertion. The spinalis, longissimus, and iliocostalis collectively form the erector spinae group of back muscles. They make up the largest muscle mass of the back and travel parallel to the vertebral column.

7) a – See #3 answer explanation.

8) c – Muscles anatomically classified as back muscles are those that primarily support and extend the spine. Some cause the spine to bend laterally. In the neck, back muscles may extend the neck and/or head. Some cause the head to bend laterally. Because back muscles are located posterior to the spine, there is no way for them to flex the spine. Although muscles affecting movement of the upper and lower extremities may be located in the posterior torso (back), they are not anatomically classified as back muscles.

9) b – The erector spinae group of back muscles is formed by the spinalis, longissimus and iliocostalis muscles. They make up the largest muscle mass of the back and travel parallel to the vertebral column.

10) c – The splenius group of muscles is formed by the splenius capitis and splenius cervicis muscles. They are the most superficial back muscles located in the neck. From their origination, they slant laterally to reach their insertion. The longissimus, along with the spinalis and iliocostalis, forms the erector spinae group of muscles.

11) e – The splenius cervicis, along with the splenius capitis, forms the splenius group of muscles. The erector spinal group of back muscles is formed by the spinalis, longissimus and iliocostalis muscles. The segmental group of back muscles is formed by the interspinales and

intertransversarii muscles. The suboccipital group of muscles consist of the obliquus capitis superior, obliquus capitis inferior, rectus capitis posterior major, and rectus capitis posterior minor. Finally, the transversospinalis group of muscles is formed by the long rotators, short rotators, multifidi, and semispinalis muscles.

12) e – The suboccipital muscles are formed by four muscles that connect the atlas, axis, and skull. They are innervated by cervical dorsal rami branches, including the suboccipital and greater occipital nerves.

13) e – The transversospinalis group of muscles is formed by the long rotators, short rotators, multifidi, and semispinalis muscles. From their origination, the transversospinalis muscles travel superiorly while slanting medially to reach their insertion.

14) d – See #8 answer explanation.

15) a – See #2 answer explanation. The erector spinae group of muscles make up the largest muscle mass of the back. They travel parallel to the vertebral column.

16) c – See #11 answer explanation. There is no splenius thoracis (thorax) or splenius lumborum (lumbar).

17) d – Thoracic and lumbar dorsal rami usually innervate skin located below the spinal cord segment level of origin. Although there is often a repetitive back and forth pattern in which one nerve supplies a medial area of skin and the next lower nerve supplies a lateral area, there is no definite order of innervation for any particular random thoracic dorsal ramus nerve and the nerve immediately above or below it.

18) b – See #3 answer explanation.

"The man who reads nothing at all is better educated than the man who reads nothing but newspapers."

– Thomas Jefferson

CLINICAL CORRELATION

As discussed earlier, spinal nerves tend to innervate tissues located below their level of origination. This is evidenced by the segmental pattern of spinal nerve cutaneous innervation. A **dermatome** is a specific area of skin which is supplied by a certain spinal nerve segment. Regardless of whether the area is supplied by dorsal or ventral rami, the primary focus is placed on the spinal segment responsible for the innervation.

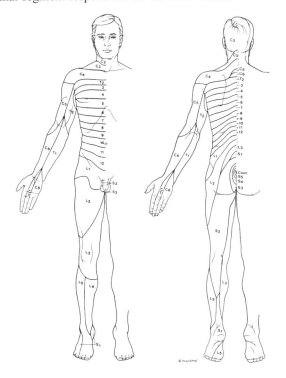

FIGURE 8.11
DERMATOMES
(Reproduced from Scott DB: Techniques of Regional Anaethesia, *Norwalk, 1989, Appleton & Lange.)*

Dermatomes exist in consistent patterns. This allows the drawing and assimilation of dermatome patterns into **dermatome maps or charts.** Dermatome charts are widely distributed and used for a variety of diagnostic clinical situations. Neurologic changes, such as weakness, numbness, or burning/tingling pain, which fit a particular dermatomal pattern, give clues to the etiology and location of the disease process.

In some cases, one entire dermatome on each side of the spinal cord may be supplied by only one spinal nerve. This solitary spinal nerve has a name, and these individual names and cutaneous innervations will be covered in later chapters. For example, the ulnar nerve supplies medial skin of both the palmar and dorsal sides of the hand. A review of a dermatomal chart reveals that the C8 spinal segment is responsible for the innervation of the medial hand.

Although memorizing the entire dermatomal chart would certainly prove beneficial, there are several notable or "key" dermatomes from which the spinal segmental contribution to other areas can be estimated.

Back of head C2
Back of neck C3
Back of shoulders C4
Outer arm C5
Thumb C6
Middle finger C7
Little finger C8
Inner (medial) forearm T1
Inner (medial) arm T2
Nipple line T4
Immediately below sternum T7
Umbilicus (navel) T10
Lateral anterior thigh L2
Anterior knee L3
Medial anterior leg (below knee) L4
Lateral leg (below knee)/Great toe L5
Little toe S1
Target on buttocks (S5 is bulls eye) S2-S5

Dermatome: formed by 3, remembered by 3

Derm – a – tome ..... derm = skin, tome = segment.
   1   2   3
Attempt to memorize the dermatomes in groups of **3.**

The umbilicus or navel ("belly button") is the previous point of attachment of the umbilical cord. It is therefore the point where life begins. It will also be the point where the memorization of dermatomes begins ➔ **T10...where life begins (umbilicus)** Subtract **3 = T7 = immediately below sternum.** Subtract **3 = T4 = nipple line.**

The C1 spinal nerve is small and does not significantly contribute to the dermatomes. **3 groups of 3:**

     (1) **C2 = back of head**
     (2) **C3 = back of neck**
     (3) **C4 = back of shoulders**

     (1) **C6 = thumb**
     (2) **C7 = middle finger**
     (3) **C8 = small finger**

     (1) **L2 = anterior thigh**
     (2) **L3 = anterior knee**
     (3) **L4 = medial anterior leg**

Then simply remember **L5 = great toe** and **S1 = small toe** and the **sacral target of S2-S5** is perirectal.

Like other aspects of anatomy, variations exist in dermatomal patterns from one individual to another. In addition, there are differences in the way dermatomes are specifically mapped out in different dermatome charts. Regardless of these differences, a particular dermatome chart is valuable in alerting the clinician to the general region of disease. The specific area of pathology can then be pinpointed with other tests.

The following clinical situations should provide insight into the clinical usefulness of dermatomes. A dermatomal pattern of disease may suggest not only certain disease processes, but also their location. After associating this pattern with other pathologic signs and symptoms, the proper laboratory and radiologic tests can be ordered to confirm the suspected diagnosis.

A 64-year-old male presents with a two week history of right lateral chest and abdominal pain associated with a rash. The pain is described as itching and burning and is fairly severe. Examination reveals a crusty rash confined to the T8-T9 dermatomal area.

Herpes zoster is a condition commonly known as **shingles** and is caused by the varicella-zoster virus. Varicella-zoster is one of several types of herpes viruses. Herpes simplex type I is the cause of cold sores/fever blisters of the lips and mouth. Herpes simplex type II is the etiology of genital herpes.

The varicella-zoster virus is also the cause of chicken pox. Whether or not an individual has ever had the clinical manifestations of chicken pox, a person with herpes zoster has been previously exposed to the virus. The virus normally remains in a dormant state within the dorsal root ganglia of spinal nerves. For uncertain reasons, the virus may become active in certain individuals. It spreads from the dorsal root (sensory) ganglion distally along the spinal nerve. During this period, the individual may experience itching, burning, or shooting pains in the area supplied by the spinal nerve. The virus continues peripherally with the nerve until it reaches the skin, causing an erythematous (red), vesicular (vesicles) rash. As the vesicles rupture, a crust is formed which may last a month, even longer in complicated cases. The virus usually remains confined to one spinal cord dermatomal level. Occasionally, in severe cases, the spinal nerve above or below the infected spinal nerve may also be involved. Treatment includes antiviral, anti-inflammatory and pain medications. These may be combined with needle injections. The manifestations are usually transient, but permanent nerve damage, lasting pain, and permanent skin disfigurement can occur.

A 24-year-old male is involved in a motorcycle accident. He appears to have several peripheral bone fractures but is awake and able to communicate. On physical exam, he cannot feel a pinprick of the skin on both sides of the body below the xyphoid process of the sternum. He can feel it across his chest, arms, and neck.

Spinal cord injury is the most likely cause of the neurologic deficit in this situation. Multiple peripheral bone fractures establish this as a high-impact injury. The fact that the deficit is present on both sides of the spinal cord makes spinal cord injury more likely to be the cause than peripheral nerve injury. Time is of the essence in this situation. The spinal cord may not be completely transected (severed), and other potentially correctable causes could be found and treated. The cord could be compressed due to a fracture or dislocation of the vertebral column or simply contused (bruised) due to G-forces associated with the injury.

Due to the location of the sensory change, a spinal cord injury is suspected at the T6-T7 level. Appropriate radiologic studies, such as X-rays and CT (computed tomography) scans, would further delineate the extent of injury and are ordered immediately. Depending on the results, the patient may be rushed to the operating room for an emergency spinal cord decompression and/or stabilization of the vertebral column. A spinal cord decompression is

indicated when there is a bone fragment or other structure impinging on nerve tissue of the cord. With removal of the offending agent, the hope is that the neurologic deficit will improve. The patient may also be taken to surgery for stabilizing an otherwise unstable vertebral column in an effort to prevent further spinal cord injury. This may involve the use of plates, rods, screws, and/or bone grafts to fuse the fragments of fractured vertebrae together. Alternatively, if nothing correctable is found, the patient will be monitored and treated with various anti-inflammatory and pain medications. If indicated, drugs specific for spinal cord injury may be used.

Unfortunately, with complete transection of the spinal cord, little can be done to improve the outcome. When one considers the billions of nerve fibers and synapses present in the cord, the great challenge of treating spinal cord transection becomes evident. Because of the complexity of individual nerve pathways, the two severed ends cannot simply be reattached to one another and be expected to work. A spinal cord transection occurring above the C5-T1 spinal segments (the brachial plexus) results in **quadriplegia**. The word element *quadri-* means *four*. The word element *-plegia* means *paralysis*. All four extremities are paralyzed. If the transaction occurs within the C5-T1 segments, some use of the upper extremities may be maintained. Below the T1 spinal segment, a transection results in **paraplegia**. The word element *para-* means *beside* or *beyond*. The lower portion of the body, including the legs, is paralyzed. Because the upper body remains functional, the patient is "beyond total paralysis." If the transaction occurs in the lower lumbar cord, the patient may maintain some use of the legs. There is a tremendous amount of ongoing research in spinal cord injury. New medications and treatment modalities provide hope. Perhaps more promising treatment options will be available in the future.

A 43-year-old female presents with a four month history of progressive numbness and tingling of the lateral aspect of her right arm. She also notes a sporadic pain that shoots down her right arm upon assuming certain head and neck positions. The pain is described as "sharp and electric shock-like." It shoots down her arm to the level of the right index finger.

Degenerative disease of the spine is a common cause of medical evaluation and treatment. The cause is often due to encroachment on nerve tissue of the spinal cord or nerve root by a herniated intervertebral disc, bone osteophyte, or bone fragment. The cervical and lumbar areas of the spine are the most commonly affected. Even though the site of pathology is located in the spine, the pain is often felt in the tissues supplied by the affected spinal nerves. This is why the patient may experience pain radiating down the arm or leg with cervical or lumbar disease of the spine. Due to the location of the numbness and pain in this patient, the specific site of pathology is suspected to be the C5, C6, C7 area. Although more than one interspace is often involved, the C5-C6 interspace seems to be the most likely location of the problem. Radiologic studies like MRI (magnetic resonance imaging) of the spine are ordered and the results are correlated to the clinical signs and symptoms of the patient. If the MRI results are consistent with the clinical picture of the patient, treatment may begin. In this scenario, it is likely that a herniated disc at C5-C6 is compressing the diagonally descending C6 nerve root. Depending on the severity of disease, options include anti-inflammatory and pain medications, epidural steroid injections, and surgical decompression.

SUMMARY OF CHAPTER BOXES

1) **Half and Half:** 24 true vertebrae…half (12) are associated with ribs, half are not (7 cervical + 5 lumbar = 12 vertebrae). Sacrum formed by fusion of 5 vertebrae; coccyx by fusion of 4 vertebrae (sacrum is larger). Not exactly half and half, but as close as an odd # (9) can get: 5 sacral + 4 coccygeal = 9 fused vertebrae. 24 true vertebrae + 9 fused vertebrae = **33 total vertebrae**

2) **33 vertebrae protect 31 spinal segments.** Hypothetically, more vertebrae are required because they are exterior to the spinal segments.

3) **Head and neck are *above* torso.** Cervical spinal nerves exit spine *above* their respective vertebra (except C8, which does not have a respective vertebra). Spinal nerves exiting the spine in the torso (lumbar and sacral spinal nerves), exit below their respective vertebra.

4) **C8 and Coccyx is why # of vertebrae do not equal # spinal segments**
Start at 30: **C8** = spinal cord segment, but no vertebra = 1 additional spinal segment = 31 spinal cord segments. **Coccyx** = 4 vertebrae, but only 1 coccygeal nerve = 3 additional vertebrae = 33 vertebrae
Otherwise:
12 thoracic spinal segments = 12 thoracic vertebrae
5 lumbar spinal segments = 5 lumbar vertebrae
5 sacral spinal segments = 5 sacral vertebrae

5) **First four sacral spinal nerves exit via sacral foramina.** Four sacral foramina result from the four intervertebral spaces of five fused vertebrae. Fifth sacral nerve exits below sacrum. Last spinal nerve is coccygeal nerve, which runs along coccyx.

6) *Dorsal* back scratch is afferent **sensory** information via *dorsal* root.

7) Dor**S**al roots carry **S**ensory information.

8) **Spinal nerve as tree:** 1) formed by **roots** 2) combination of roots forms **trunk** 3) trunk divides into dorsal and ventral rami (**branches**).

9) **Spine in dorsal (posterior) aspect of body.** Most mass is *ventral* to it, so most tissues are supplied by *ventral* rami. Dorsal rami only supply skin and muscles on the dorsal or posterior body (tissues posterior to the spine).

10) **Half and Half:** There are 8 cervical spinal nerves. The first half (C1-C4) forms cervical plexus. The second half (C5-C8) forms brachial plexus (along with T1 spinal nerve).

11) **Spinal nerves go down, not up (affected by gravity).** Most spinal nerves supply tissues located below (or inferior to) their spinal segment level of origination. Example: lumbar nerves contribute to sacral plexus via lumbosacral trunk. There is no sacral contribution to the lumbar plexus.

12) **Cervical spinal nerves are exceptions:** 1) originate in neck. All others originate in torso. 2) exit above their respective vertebra 3) have an extra nerve (C8), which does not have a respective (C8) vertebra 4) Some of their dorsal rami innervate specific muscles and have nerve names. 5) Some supply tissues located *above* their spinal segment level of origination.

13) **Cervical spinal nerves like to be *above*:** originate from *above* (neck), exit *above* their respective vertebrae, some supply tissues *above* their level of origination.

14) *Spin*alis is part of erector *spin*ae group and travels parallel to *spine*. *Semi*spinalis is part of transversospinalis group and travels superiorly with a medial slant. It is *semi*-parallel to spine.

15) **Transversospinalis muscles *"transverse"* the spine:** named for their origination on *transverse* processes and insertion on *spinous* processes of vertebrae located above their vertebrae of origination (results in medial slant). To *rotate* the spine, **short and long *rotators*** must have a slant because a parallel muscle cannot rotate the spine. The **semispinalis** is *semi*-parallel to the spine. The *multi*fidus is also part of the transversospinalis group, a group which originates and inserts on *multi*ple or **different vertebral processes** (originates on transverse, inserts on spinous).

16) **CLINICAL CORRELATION:**
DERM – A – TOME
1   2   3
Dermatome = formed by 3, remembered by 3
derm = skin, tome = segment
memorize dermatomes in groups of 3:
T-10 (where life begins = umbilicus), subtract **3** = T7 (beneath sternum), subtract **3** = T4 (nipple line). **3 GROUPS OF 3:**
1) **C2** = back of head 2) **C3** = back of neck 3) **C4** = back of shoulders
1) **C6** = thumb 2) **C7** = middle finger 3) **C8** = small finger
1) **L2** = anterior thigh 2) **L3** = anterior knee 3) **L4** = medial anterior leg
Additionally, **L5** = great toe, **S1** = small toe, sacral "target" of **S2-S5** is perirectal.

END OF CHAPTER TEST

Time for Exam = 50 minutes.
For questions 1-31, choose the single best answer.

_____1) Where does the T1 spinal nerve exit the vertebral column?
   a. between the C7 and T1 vertebrae
   b. between the C8 and T1 vertebrae
   c. between the T1 and T2 vertebrae
   d. immediately below the T2 vertebrae
   e. none of the above

_____2) Which group of back muscles is the obliquus capitis inferior muscle in?
   a. segmental muscles
   b. transversospinalis muscles
   c. suboccipital muscles
   d. erector spinae muscles
   e. none of the above

_____3) Which of the following is true?
   a. The vertebral column is formed by the spine and spinal cord.
   b. The spinal nerves are formed from the vertebral column.
   c. The spine is formed by the vertebral column and spinal cord.
   d. The spinal cord is formed by a combination of vertebrae.
   e. None of the above

_____4) Where does the conus medullaris end?
   a. L1-L2
   b. L5
   c. S5
   d. coccyx
   e. none of the above

_____5) Which group of back muscles are the semispinalis muscles in?
   a. segmental muscles
   b. splenius muscles
   c. erector spinae muscles
   d. transversospinalis muscles
   e. none of the above

_____6) The C2 vertebra is known as the
   a. atis
   b. atlas
   c. avis
   d. axis
   e. none of the above

_____7) Ventral rami branches of the sacral spinal nerves contribute to the
   a. lumbar plexus
   b. sacral plexus
   c. both a and b
   d. they do not contribute to a plexus
   e. none of the above

_____8) Where does the L5 spinal nerve exit the vertebral column?
   a. between the L4 and L5 vertebrae
   b. between the L5 and L6 vertebrae
   c. between the L6 vertebrae and the sacrum
   d. below the sacrum
   e. none of the above

_____9) Which of the following is true concerning the cutaneous innervation of the thoracic dorsal rami?
   a. They usually supply skin that is more medial than skin supplied by the dorsal ramus of the spinal nerve immediately above it.
   b. They usually supply skin that is more medial than skin supplied by the dorsal ramus of the spinal nerve immediately below it.
   c. Both a and b
   d. They usually supply skin that is above their spinal segment level of origin.
   e. None of the above

_____10) Which group of back muscles are the intertransversarii muscles in?
   a. erector spinae muscles
   b. segmental muscles
   c. splenius muscles
   d. transversospinalis muscles
   e. none of the above

_____11) How many vertebrae are in the vertebral column, including the sacrum and coccyx?
   a. 31
   b. 33
   c. 24
   d. 27
   e. none of the above

_____12) How many spinal nerves exit the vertebral column by way of sacral foramina?
   a. none
   b. three
   c. four
   d. five
   e. none of the above

_____13) How many vertebrae usually fuse to form the coccyx?
   a. 4
   b. 3
   c. 5
   d. 2
   e. none of the above

_____14) Which of the following muscles is the most medial of the erector spinae group of back muscles?
   a. rectus capitis posterior major
   b. rectus capitis posterior minor
   c. multifidus
   d. splenius cervicis
   e. none of the above

_____15) Where does the C8 spinal nerve exit the vertebral column?
   a. there is no C8 spinal nerve
   b. between the C8 and C9 vertebrae
   c. between the C7 and C8 vertebrae
   d. between the C8 and T1 vertebrae
   e. none of the above

_____16) Spinal nerve dorsal roots carry fibers which are
   a. efferent
   b. sensory
   c. both a and b
   d. motor
   e. none of the above

_____17) What is usually seen exiting the intervertebral foramen of the spinal cord?
   a. dorsal rami
   b. ventral rami
   c. both a and b
   d. ventral roots
   e. none of the above

_____18) From their point of origination, which of the following back muscles travel essentially parallel to the long axis of the spine?
   a. short rotators
   b. intertransversarri
   c. semispinalis
   d. splenius cervicis
   e. none of the above

_____19) Which group of back muscles is the iliocostalis muscle a member of?
   a. transversospinalis muscles
   b. suboccipital muscle
   c. erector spinae muscles
   d. segmental muscles
   e. none of the above

_____20) Most peripheral spinal nerve branches directly originate from which of the following nerve structures?
   a. dorsal rami
   b. dorsal roots
   c. ventral roots
   d. ventral rami
   e. none of the above

_____21) Which of the following muscles is the most lateral of the erector spinae group of back muscles?
   a. spinalis
   b. splenius cervicis
   c. longissimus
   d. iliocostalis
   e. none of the above

_____22) Ventral rami branches of the thoracic spinal nerves contribute to the
   a. thoracic plexus
   b. brachial plexus
   c. both a and b
   d. lumbar plexus
   e. none of the above

_____23) From their point of origination, which of the following back muscles travel medially to reach their insertion?
    a. intertransversarii muscles
    b. iliocostalis
    c. multifidi muscles
    d. splenius capitis
    e. none of the above

_____24) Moving distally from the spinal cord, a spinal nerve is formed by the combination of
    a. a right dorsal root and left dorsal root
    b. a right dorsal ramus and right ventral ramus
    c. a left dorsal root and left ventral root
    d. a right dorsal ramus and left ventral ramus
    e. none of the above

_____25) The cervical plexus is formed directly by
    a. only cervical ventral root branches
    b. cervical and thoracic ventral root branches
    c. only cervical dorsal root branches
    d. cervical and thoracic dorsal root branches
    e. none of the above

_____26) Muscles which are anatomically classified as back muscles function to
    a. support the spine
    b. flex the spine
    c. both a and b
    d. move the upper extremity
    e. none of the above

_____27) Where does the C1 spinal nerve exit the vertebral column?
    a. between the C1 and C2 vertebrae
    b. between the atlas and axis
    c. both a and b
    d. above the C1 vertebra
    e. none of the above

_____28) The sacral plexus is formed by
    a. lumbar and sacral dorsal rami
    b. lumbar and sacral ventral roots
    c. lumbar and sacral ventral rami
    d. only sacral ventral rami
    e. none of the above

_____29) From their point of origination, which of the following back muscles travel laterally to reach their insertion?
    a. intertransversarii muscles
    b. splenius cervicis
    c. spinalis
    d. semispinalis
    e. none of the above

_____30) What is the name of the tapered, distal end of the actual spinal cord?
    a. cauda equina
    b. filum terminale
    c. conus medullaris
    d. S5 spinal root
    e. none of the above

_____31) The spinal nerve thoracic plexus is formed by
    a. thoracic and lumbar ventral rami branches
    b. thoracic and lumbar ventral root branches
    c. only thoracic ventral rami branches
    d. only thoracic ventral root branches
    e. none of the above

For questions 32-50, use the following directions:
    a.......1,2,3 are correct
    b.......1,3 are correct
    c.......2,4 are correct
    d.......only 4 is correct
    e.......all are correct

_____32) What is the correct total number of vertebrae for each section of the vertebral column?
    1. five sacral vertebrae fuse to form the sacrum
    2. eight cervical vertebrae
    3. twelve thoracic vertebrae
    4. four lumbar vertebrae

_____33) The T1 spinal nerve contributes to the
    1. thoracic plexus
    2. 1st intercostal nerve
    3. cervical plexus
    4. brachial plexus

_____34) Which muscles are in the suboccipital group of back muscles?
    1. spinalis
    2. iliocostalis
    3. longissimus
    4. rectus capitis posterior major

_____35) Which of the following are true concerning spinal nerve structure?
    1. Dorsal and ventral roots combine to form spinal nerve trunks.
    2. Dorsal and ventral roots are the nerves seen exiting the vertebral column.
    3. Spinal nerves split into dorsal and ventral rami.
    4. Dorsal rami primarily carry sensory nerve transmission.

_____36) Which muscles are part of the segmental group of back muscles?
    1. long rotators
    2. intertransversarii
    3. multifidi muscles
    4. interspinales

_____37) Which spinal segments contribute to the brachial plexus?
    1 T1
    2. T2
    3. C8
    4. C3

_____38) Muscles anatomically classified as back muscles function to
    1. support the spine
    2. bend the spine sideways (laterally)
    3. extend the spine
    4. extend the neck (head)

_____39) The L5 spinal nerve contributes to the
    1. intercostal nerves
    2. lumbar plexus
    3. thoracic plexus
    4. sacral plexus

_____40) Which of the following is true concerning the filum terminale?
    1. It extends from the conus medullaris.
    2. It is the terminal component of the vertebral column.
    3. It fixates the spinal cord to the coccyx.
    4. It ends at the approximate L2 vertebral level.

_____41) What is the correct location of exit from the vertebral column for the following spinal nerves?
    1. The C3 nerve exits immediately below the C3 vertebra.
    2. The C8 nerve exits immediately below the C7 vertebra.
    3. The L4 nerve exits immediately above the L4 vertebra.
    4. The T12 nerve exits immediately below the T12 vertebra.

_____42) Which muscles are part of the transversospinalis group of back muscles?
    1. interspinales
    2. spinalis
    3. intertransversarii
    4. semispinalis

_____43) Which spinal segments contribute to the sacral plexus?
    1. L2
    2. L4
    3. L3
    4. S4

_____44) Which muscles are part of the splenius group of back muscles?
    1. splenius cervicis
    2. splenius thoracis
    3. splenius capitis
    4. semispinalis

_____45) Which of the following is true concerning the terminal aspect of the spinal cord?
    1. The cauda equina is the tapered end of the actual spinal cord.
    2. The filum terminale is formed by spinal nerve roots traveling inferiorly.
    3. The conus medullaris ends at the coccyx.
    4. The spinal cord ends at the L1-L2 vertebral level.

____46) Which of the following is true regarding the pattern of nerve transmission of spinal nerves?
1. Dorsal roots carry afferent nerve transmission.
2. Ventral roots carry ascending nerve transmission.
3. Ventral roots carry motor signal conduction.
4. Spinal nerves usually supply tissues that are above the level of origination of the spinal nerve from the spinal cord.

____47) Which of the following spinal segments contribute to the lumbar plexus?
1. L1
2. L4
3. L2
4. L5

____48) Which muscles are part of the erector spinae group of back muscles?
1. longissimus
2. spinalis
3. iliocostalis
4. multifidi muscles

____49) What is the correct total number of spinal cord segments for each region of the spinal cord?
1. twelve thoracic spinal segments
2. five lumbar spinal segments
3. five sacral spinal segments
4. seven cervical spinal segments

____50) Which of the following structures compose the cauda equina?
1. L4 nerve root
2. L1 nerve root
3. S3 nerve root
4. conus medullaris

END OF CHAPTER TEST: Answers and Explanations

1) c – All cervical spinal nerves exit the vertebral column above their respective vertebra except the C8 spinal nerve. There are only 7 cervical vertebrae. Because there is no C8 vertebra, the C8 spinal nerve exits between the C7 and T1 vertebrae. Subsequently, all thoracic and lumbar spinal nerves exit below their respective vertebrae.

2) c – The suboccipital muscles are formed by four muscles that connect the atlas, axis, and skull. The suboccipital group of muscles consists of the obliquus capitis superior, obliquus capitis inferior, rectus capitis posterior major, and rectus capitis posterior minor. The obliquus capitis inferior muscle originates from the spinous process of axis and travels superiorly and laterally to insert on the transverse process of the atlas. It turns the atlas and head to the side.

3) c – The spinal cord is the actual nerve tissue. It is protected by the bony vertebral column. Together, they form the spine.

4) a – The actual structure of the spinal cord ends at the L1-L2 vertebral level. The tapered ending of the spinal cord at this level is known as the conus medullaris. The centralized, thread-like nerve structure which continues from the spinal cord to attach to the coccyx is the filum terminale. The lower spinal nerve roots exit the conus medullaris and continue distally within the dura mater. The combination of these nerve roots is collectively known as the cauda equina (horse's tail).

5) d – From their origination, the transversospinalis muscles travel superiorly while slanting medially to reach their insertion. The segmental group of muscles is formed by the interspinales and intertransversarii. The splenius group is composed of the splenius capitis and splenius cervicis. Finally, the erector spinae group of muscles is formed by the spinalis, longissimus and iliocostalis muscles.

6) d – The axis is the C2 vertebra. The **t** of atlas (C1 vertebrae) comes before the **x** of axis (C2 vertebra).

7) b – The lumbar plexus is formed by ventral rami branches from L1, L2, L3, and part of L4. The sacral plexus is formed by the other portion of the L4 ventral ramus and all of the L5, S1, S2, S3, and S4 ventral rami.

8) e – See #1 answer explanation. The L5 spinal nerve exits the vertebral column between the L5 vertebra and sacrum.

9) e – Thoracic dorsal rami usually innervate skin located below their spinal segment level of origin. Although there is often a repetitive back and forth pattern in which one nerve supplies a medial area of skin and the next lower nerve supplies a lateral area, there is no definite order of innervation for any particular random thoracic dorsal ramus nerve and the nerve immediately above or below it.

10) b – The segmental group of back muscles is formed by the interspinales and intertransversarii muscles. The segmental muscles travel from the process of one vertebra to insert on the same process of the vertebra immediately above. Interspinales muscles originate and insert on spinous processes. Intertransversarii originate and insert on transverse processes.

11) b – There are 7 cervical vertebrae, 12 thoracic vertebrae, and 5 lumbar vertebrae. In addition, there are usually 5 vertebrae that fuse to form the sacrum and 4 vertebrae that fuse to form the coccyx.

12) c – Four sacral spinal nerves (S1-S4) exit the vertebral column via sacral foramina. If one can remember that the sacrum is formed by the fusion of 5 vertebrae, it is easy to remember that there are 4 sacral foramina (1 between each of the 5 fused vertebrae). The fifth sacral spinal nerve (S5) exits below the sacrum. The coccygeal nerve represents the last pair of spinal nerves and continues down to end at the coccyx.

13) a – The coccyx is a bone forming the inferior tip of the vertebral column. It is usually formed by the fusion of 4 vertebrae.

14) e – The erector spinae group of back muscles is formed by the spinalis, longissimus and ilio-costalis muscles. The spinalis is the most medial. The longissimus is in an intermediate position. The iliocostalis is the most lateral. Both the rectus capitis posterior major and minor are part of the suboccipital group of muscles. The multifidi muscles (the multi-fidus) are part of the transversospinalis group of back muscles. The splenius cervicis, along with the splenius capitis, forms the splenius group of muscles.

15) e – See #1 answer explanation.

16) b – Dorsal roots carry sensory fibers, whereas ventral roots carry motor fibers. Sensory fibers are afferent because they are traveling to the brain. They are therefore also said to be ascending because they are traveling from the sensory receptor, up, toward the brain. Remember, *dorsal* roots carry sensory infor-mation from a "*dorsal* back scratch."

17) c – The structure of a spinal nerve is similar to that of a *tree*. The dorsal and ventral *roots* originate from the same side of the spinal cord and unite to form a spinal nerve *trunk*. The trunk then divides into dorsal and ventral rami (*branches*). This division often occurs within the bony cover of the vertebral column, so the dorsal and ventral rami are the nerves usually seen exiting the spine.

18) b – The intertransversarii muscles, along with the interspinales, form the group of back muscles known as the segmental muscles. They travel from the process of one vertebra to insert on the same process of the vertebra immediately above. The short rotators and semispinalis muscles, along with the long rotators and multifidi muscles, form the transversospinalis group of back muscles. These muscles travel medially to reach their point of insertion. The splenius cervicis, along with the splenius capitis, forms the splenius group of muscles. They are the most superficial back muscles located in the neck. From their origination, they slant laterally to reach their insertion.

19) c – The erector spinae group of back muscles is formed by the spinalis, longissimus and ilio-costalis muscles. They make up the largest muscle mass of the back and travel parallel to the vertebral column.

20) d – See #17 answer explanation. Dorsal rami are the spinal nerve branches which course dor-sally to supply posterior structures, such as skin and muscles. The ventral rami are branches that travel anterior to supply struc-tures. Because the spine is a dorsal structure, most of the mass of the body is anterior to it. There is therefore more tissue for the ventral rami to supply. It is no surprise that most spinal nerve branches directly originate from ventral rami branches.

21) d – See #14 answer explanation.

22) b – The T1 ventral ramus, along with the C5-C8 ventral rami, contributes to the brachial plexus. There is no thoracic ventral rami plexus. Instead, the thoracic ventral rami, including the remainder of the T1 ventral ramus, form intercostal nerves.

23) c – The multifidi muscles are part of the transver-sospinalis group of back muscles. From their origination, the transversospinalis muscles trav-el superiorly while slanting medially to reach their insertion. The intertransversarii, along with the interspinales, form the group of back muscles known as the segmental muscles. The segmental muscles travel from the process of one vertebra to insert on the same process of the vertebra immediately above. The iliocostalis is part of the erector spinae group of back mus-cles. They make up the largest muscle mass of the back and travel parallel to the vertebral col-umn. Finally, the splenius capitis, along with the splenius cervicis, forms the splenius group of muscles. They are the most superficial back muscles located in the neck. From their origina-tion, they slant laterally to reach their insertion.

24) c – A spinal segment is an area of the spinal cord that serves as the origin of a pair of spinal nerves, a right one and left one. The structure of a spinal nerve is similar to that of a tree. A dorsal and ventral root originates from the same side of the spinal cord and combines to form a spinal nerve trunk. The trunk travels out and divides into dorsal and ventral rami

(branches). Dorsal rami are the branches that travel dorsally to supply posterior structures. Ventral rami are the branches that travel ventrally to supply anterior structures.

25) e – The cervical plexus is formed solely by ventral *rami* branches from the C1-C4 spinal cord segments. A spinal nerve is formed by the proximal combination of a ventral *root* with a dorsal *root*. The spinal nerve continues distally to divide into dorsal and ventral rami. Because most of the mass of the body is anterior to the spine, most spinal nerve branches are ventral rami branches. All of the large spinal nerve plexuses are formed by ventral rami nerves. This includes the cervical, brachial, lumbar, and sacral plexuses.

26) a – Muscles anatomically classified as back muscles are those that primarily support and extend the spine. Some cause the spine to bend laterally. In the neck, back muscles may extend the neck and/or head. Some cause the head to bend laterally. Because back muscles are located posterior to the spine, there is no way for them to flex the spine. Although muscles affecting movement of the upper and lower extremities may be located in the posterior torso (back), they are not anatomically classified as back muscles.

27) d – See #1 answer explanation. The atlas is the C1 vertebra. The axis is the C2 vertebra.

28) c – See #25 answer explanation. The sacral plexus is formed by a portion of the L4 ventral ramus and all of the L5, S1, S2, S3, and S4 ventral rami.

29) b – See #18 and #19 answer explanations.

30) c – See #4 answer explanation.

31) e – There is no thoracic plexus formed by spinal nerves. Instead of contributing to a plexus, thoracic ventral rami form intercostal nerves. The thoracic plexuses that exist are autonomic plexuses, which are part of the autonomic nervous system.

32) b – There are 7 cervical vertebrae, 12 thoracic vertebrae, and 5 lumbar vertebrae. In addition, there usually are 5 vertebrae that fuse to form the sacrum and 4 vertebrae that fuse to form the coccyx. Although there are only seven cervical vertebrae, there are eight cervical spinal cord segments. The C1 nerve exits the vertebral column above the C1 vertebra. The C8 nerve exits the vertebral column between the C7 and T1 vertebrae. There is no C8 vertebra.

33) c – The T1 spinal nerve contributes both to the brachial plexus and the 1st intercostal nerve. The brachial plexus is formed by ventral rami from the C5, C6, C7, C8, and T1 spinal nerves. In addition, each of the twelve thoracic spinal nerves forms one of twelve intercostal nerves. The cervical plexus is formed by ventral rami from the C1-C4 spinal nerves. There is no large thoracic spinal nerve plexus.

34) d – See #2 answer explanation. The obliquus capitis superior muscle originates from the transverse process of the atlas and travels superiorly and medially to insert on the occipital bone of the skull. It extends the head and pulls the head laterally. The other three incorrect answers, spinalis, iliocostalis, and longissimus muscles, make up the erector spinae group of back muscles.

35) b – Spinal nerve structure is similar to that of a *tree*. Dorsal and ventral *roots* combine to a spinal nerve *trunk*. Dorsal roots carry sensory information. Because this information is traveling toward the brain, it is afferent nerve transmission. It is also ascending transmission, because the flow of transmission is upward, from sensory receptors toward the brain. Ventral roots carry motor fibers. The flow of nerve transmission is therefore both efferent and descending. Spinal nerve trunks divide into dorsal and ventral rami (*branches*), which are the nerves usually seen exiting the vertebral column. Each type of ramus carries both motor and sensory fibers. Dorsal rami course dorsally to supply posterior structures. Ventral rami course ventrally to supply anterior structures. A particular spinal nerve usually innervates a region of tissue that is below its origination.

36) c – See #10 answer explanation. Both the long rotators and multifidi muscles are part of the transversospinalis group of back muscles.

37) b – The brachial plexus is formed by ventral rami from the C5, C6, C7, C8, and T1 spinal cord segments. The T2 spinal nerve forms the 2nd intercostal nerve. The C3 spinal nerve contributes to the cervical plexus (along with C1, C2, and C4).

38) e – See #26 answer explanation.

39) d – The lumbar plexus is formed by ventral rami from the L1, L2, and L3 spinal nerves along with a portion of the L4 spinal nerve ventral ramus. The other portion of the L4 ventral ramus combines with the entire L5 ventral ramus to form the lumbosacral trunk. The lumbosacral trunk contributes to the sacral plexus.

40) b – See #4 answer explanation. The filum terminale is the terminal component of the spinal cord. The coccyx is the terminal component of the vertebral column.

41) c – See #1 answer explanation.

42) d – The transversospinalis group of muscles is formed by the long rotators, short rotators, multifidi, and semispinalis muscles. From their origination, the transversospinalis muscles travel superiorly while slanting medially to reach their insertion. The interspinales muscles, along with the intertransversarii muscles, form the group of back muscles known as the segmental muscles. The spinalis is part of the erector spinae group of back muscles.

43) c – The sacral plexus formed by a combination of lumbar and sacral ventral rami. A portion of the L4 ventral ramus combines with the entire L5 ventral ramus to form the lumbosacral trunk, which serves as the lumbar contribution to the sacral plexus. Ventral rami from S1, S2, S3, and S4 also contribute to the plexus.

44) b – See #18 answer explanation. There is no splenius thoracis. The semispinalis muscles are part of the transversospinalis group of back muscles.

45) d – See #4 answer explanation.

46) b – See #35 answer explanation.

47) a – See #39 answer explanation.

48) a – See #19 answer explanation. The multifidi muscles are part of the transversospinalis group of back muscles.

49) a – A spinal cord segment is a region of spinal cord tissue which serves as the origin for a pair of spinal nerves. There are eight cervical spinal nerves, twelve thoracic spinal nerves, five lumbar nerves, and five sacral nerves. The coccygeal nerve represents the final pair of spinal nerves, bringing the total number of spinal nerves to 31.

50) b – See #4 answer explanation. The conus medullaris and/or spinal cord ends at the L2 vertebral level. Nerve roots that originate from spinal cord segments below the L2 level exit from the tapered conus medullaris and travel inferiorly as individual nerve roots. Collectively, these roots form the cauda equina. The roots eventually form spinal nerves that travel lateral to exit the vertebral column. Roots that originate from spinal segments above L2 simply branch from the spinal cord.

"No tree grows strong without constant wind; it makes the roots stronger."

– Seneca

CHAPTER NINE

CERVICAL PLEXUS AND NERVES OF THE NECK

The nerves discussed in this chapter include members of the cervical plexus, glossopharyngeal nerve (cranial nerve IX), vagus nerve (cranial nerve X), spinal accessory nerve (a component of cranial nerve XI), hypoglossal nerve (cranial nerve XII), phrenic nerve, and the upper cervical dorsal rami branches. The neck has a significant number of vital structures in a fairly compact space. The complex functions of vocalization and swallowing require a high number of intricate muscles. Not only are the spine, esophagus, trachea, blood vessels, and thoracic duct present, but a large number of nerves also travel in this confined area. To avoid clutter and facilitate learning, these nerves are spread over several illustrations on the poster.

FIGURE 9.1
STRUCTURES OF THE UPPER AIRWAY
(median plane)

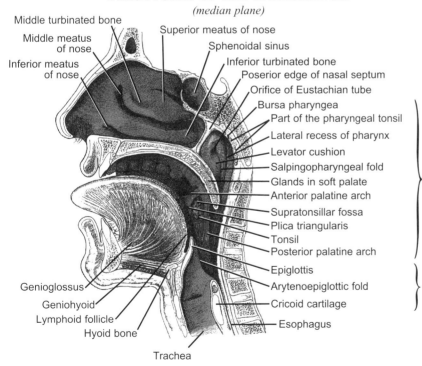

Middle turbinated bone
Middle meatus of nose
Inferior meatus of nose
Superior meatus of nose
Sphenoidal sinus
Inferior turbinated bone
Poserior edge of nasal septum
Orifice of Eustachian tube
Bursa pharyngea
Part of the pharyngeal tonsil
Lateral recess of pharynx
Levator cushion
Salpingopharyngeal fold
Glands in soft palate
Anterior palatine arch
Supratonsillar fossa
Plica triangularis
Tonsil
Posterior palatine arch
Epiglottis
Arytenoepiglottic fold
Cricoid cartilage
Esophagus
Genioglossus
Geniohyoid
Lymphoid follicle
Hyoid bone
Trachea
Pharynx
Larynx

Based on general function, neck muscles can be grossly divided into three types: those that move and support the head and cervical spine, those involved in phonation and swallowing, and those that function in vocalization and protection of the larynx. There are a significant number of skeletal muscles that originate and/or insert on the skull or vertebral column and function to move and support these two structures. Muscles of the pharynx are used to phonate and swallow. Muscles of the larynx are used

to vocalize and protect the larynx from entry of foreign substances.

As repeatedly noted, there is a great deal of variability in anatomy. One nerve may come off the C2 ventral ramus of one individual and the C3 ventral ramus of another. Just as there is variability in actual individual anatomy, there is also variability in the way some of the fine details are taught. One anatomy text may describe the nerve to the thyrohyoid as originating from the ansa cervicalis. Another text may describe the nerve as originating from the hypoglossal nerve, which sends a branch to the ansa cervicalis. In truth, the nerve fibers which supply the thyrohyoid are from the same source as those which form the ansa cervicalis, but they travel with the hypoglossal nerve. Technically, both answers are correct.

Figure 1 of the poster displays the upper three vertebrae. This includes the atlas, axis, and C3 vertebrae as viewed from the front. The upper cervical spinal nerves, like all spinal nerves, divide into ventral and dorsal rami. The ventral rami form the cervical plexus. Dorsal rami branches form the suboccipital nerve, greater occipital nerve, 3rd occipital nerve, and various unnamed motor nerves. With the exception of a trunk that divides into the great auricular and transversus colli nerves, all ventral rami branches are located on the left side of the spinal column (visually appearing on the right). Most are colored yellow. The dorsal rami branches are seen on the right side of the vertebral column (visually appearing on the left). They are colored purple because dorsal rami innervate structures on the posterior aspect of the head and neck (**p**urple = **p**osterior).

> Again, objects of anatomy are described as right or left with respect to the subject's right or left. For example, the subject's left spinal accessory nerve appears visually to the right of the vertebral column in Figure 1 of the poster because the observer is facing the subject.

In addition to the ventral and dorsal rami branches, there is another nerve that originates from upper cervical spinal segments. The **spinal accessory nerve** (26) is a component of the **accessary nerve** (CN XI) and was described in chapter six. Branches from the first five cervical spinal segments unite to form the **external ramus** of the accessory nerve. The external ramus emerges from the spine as the spinal accessory nerve. Contributing branches from the C2, C3, and C4 spinal segments (13, 17, 21) can be seen in Figure 1 of the poster. The spinal accessory nerve is a motor nerve that supplies one muscle entirely and contributes to the innervation of another. As described in chapter six, the spinal accessory nerve innervates the trapezius muscle and is the origin of a branch that combines with a C2 ventral ramus branch to supply the sternocleidomastoid muscle.

CERVICAL VENTRAL ROOT BRANCHES

The cervical plexus is formed by the ventral rami of the first four cervical spinal nerves. The C1 ventral ramus is small and may contribute to the plexus via a **branch of communication to C2** (27). Because of this, many consider the plexus to be formed by the ventral rami of C2-C4. Depending on how it is viewed, either C1-C4 or C2-C4 is correct. The brachial plexus is formed by the ventral rami of C5-C8 and T1.

The C2 ventral ramus is the origin of five nerves which will be covered here. Included are four branches to other nerve structures and a branch that forms a nerve solely by itself. These branches are described in this order for organizational purposes only. The student should avoid the misconception that the C2 ventral ramus, along with all subsequent ventral rami, gives off branches in the same order as described in this text.

The first C2 ventral ramus nerve is the **motor branch** (23) which combines with **a branch from the spinal accessory nerve** (25) to form the **nerve to the sternocleidomastoid** (24).

The second branch of the C2 ventral ramus combines with a branch from the C3 ventral ramus to form a nerve trunk. As seen in Figure 1 of the poster, this trunk soon divides into two nerves, the great auricular and transversus colli nerves. Both are cutaneous (sensory) nerves. The **great auricular nerve** (4) continues up the neck, usually in close proximity to the external jugular vein. It supplies the skin of the ear and in front of the ear. The word *auricular* pertains to the ear. The **transversus colli nerve** (5) is also known as the transverse cervical nerve. The word *transversus* inherently refers to the transverse course this nerve takes. *Colli* describes the neck. This nerve travels forward and cuts across or transverses the front of the neck, supplying skin of this area.

The **branch to the hypoglossal nerve** (20) is the third C2 ventral ramus branch. This branch contains fibers from the C1 and C2 ventral rami. The **hypoglossal nerve** (28) is a motor nerve and is cranial nerve XII. Some of the C1 and C2 fibers that travel with the hypoglossal later branch off to form the **superior root of the ansa cervicalis** (6).

Although it physically appears to branch from the hypoglossal nerve, the **superior root** (6) is composed of C1 and C2 ventral rami fibers. Hypoglossal fibers do not contribute. After the takeoff of the superior root, the remaining C1 and C2 fibers continue with the hypoglossal nerve to innervate the thyrohyoid and geniohyoid muscles. Here also, hypoglossal fibers do not contribute. The thyrohyoid originates from the thyroid cartilage and inserts on the greater horn of the hyoid bone. The muscle raises the larynx upon contraction. The geniohyoid originates from the inferior genial tubercle of the anterior mandible (chin). It inserts on the body of the hyoid bone. Upon contraction, the geniohyoid pulls the hyoid bone anteriorly. Because these muscles are inner-

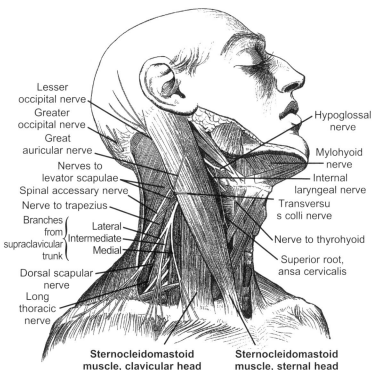

FIGURE 9.2
SUPERFICIAL NERVES OF THE NECK

Lesser occipital nerve
Greater occipital nerve
Great auricular nerve
Nerves to levator scapulae
Spinal accessory nerve
Nerve to trapezius
Branches from supraclavicular trunk { Lateral / Intermediate / Medial
Dorsal scapular nerve
Long thoracic nerve

Hypoglossal nerve
Mylohyoid nerve
Internal laryngeal nerve
Transversus colli nerve
Nerve to thyrohyoid
Superior root, ansa cervicalis

Sternocleidomastoid muscle, clavicular head   **Sternocleidomastoid muscle, sternal head**

vated by nerve fibers from the same basic source as those of the ansa cervicalis, they are occasionally described as supplied by the ansa cervicalis, even though the innervating nerves physically appear to branch from the hypoglossal nerve.

The fourth C2 ventral ramus is the **branch to the inferior root of the ansa cervicalis** (19). This branch comes off the C2 ventral ramus and combines with a branch from the C3 ventral ramus to form the inferior root of the ansa cervicalis.

> **SUPERIOR ROOT:** branches from hypoglossal nerve, but is formed by fibers that arise from *superior* spinal cord segments (C1 and C2 ventral rami)
>
> **INFERIOR ROOT:** formed by fibers from *inferior* spinal cord segments (C2 and C3 ventral rami)

The **ansa cervicalis** is a motor nerve that forms a loop in the neck. The word *ansa* describes a loop-like structure. *Cervicalis* refers to the neck (cervical). The ansa cervicalis and its contributors are colored silver in Figure 2 of the poster, similar to a silver necklace which "loops" around the neck. As described, the ansa cervicalis is formed by the union of a superior and inferior root. The **superior root** (6) is comprised of C1 and C2 ventral rami fibers that travel with and branch from the hypoglossal nerve. The **inferior root** (12) is formed by ventral rami branches from C2 and C3. The C2 ventral ramus therefore contributes to the ansa cervicalis by two routes.

The ansa cervicalis is the origin of several **muscular branches** (7) that supply the sternohyoid muscle, sternothyroid muscle, and the superior and inferior bellies of the omohyoid muscle. Both the sternohyoid and sternothyroid originate from the manubrium of the sternum. The sternohyoid inserts on the body of the hyoid bone; the sternothyroid inserts on the thyroid

FIGURE 9.3
STRUCTURES IN A DEEPER DISSECTION OF THE NECK

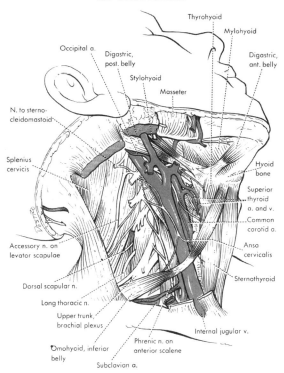

(Reproduced with permission from Hollinshead, W.H., Rosse, C.: Textbook of Anatomy, 4th ed. Philadelphia, Harper & Row, 1985)

cartilage. The omohyoid originates on the superior aspect of the scapula and, like the sternohyoid, inserts on the body of the hyoid bone. Because they are located immediately below the hyoid bone, these three neck muscles are classified as infrahyoid muscles. They function to lower the hyoid bone and larynx, as occurs immediately following swallowing or during maneuvers such as low-pitched phonation. By opposing suprahyoid muscles, they stabilize the hyoid bone and provide a foundation to support tongue movement.

Muscles Innervated by Ansa Cervicalis	Muscles Innervated by C1, C2 Ventral Rami Fibers via Hypoglossal Nerve
Sternohyoid	Thyrohyoid
Sternothyroid	Geniohyoid
Omohyoid	

Finally, the fifth C2 ventral ramus branch forms the **lesser occipital nerve** (22). The lesser occipital nerve is a sensory nerve that courses up to supply skin just behind the ear. The previously-described great auricular nerve supplies skin of the ear and immediately in front of the ear. There are also other "occipital" nerves. All are named with reference to the location of the tissues supplied. The occiput is the back of the head. The lesser occipital nerve is the only "occipital" nerve which is a ventral ramus branch. The others are dorsal ramus branches.

The C3 ventral ramus is next. It has four branches of significance. The first two combine with branches of the C2 ventral ramus to form nerves previously discussed. These include the **branch to the trunk that forms the great auricular** (4) **and transversus colli** (5) **nerves** and the **branch to the inferior root of the ansa**

cervicalis (18). Incidentally, the remaining two C3 ventral ramus branches combine with C4 ventral ramus branches to form the two nerves described next. Thus, all significant C3 ventral rami branches combine with other cervical ventral rami branches.

The third **C3 ventral rami branch** (16) combines with a branch from the C4 ventral ramus to form the supraclavicular trunk. The **supraclavicular trunk** (11) is a sensory nerve named for its location superior to the clavicle. It gives rise to three **supraclavicular nerves** (8, 9, 10), which innervate skin of the anterior chest over the first two ribs.

The fourth and final **C3 ventral rami branch** combines with branches from C4 and C5 ventral rami to form the phrenic nerve. The **phrenic nerve** (47, 234, 235, 238, 239) passes down the neck lateral to the vagus nerve on each side of the spinal cord. It descends through the chest in close approximation to the heart and great vessels to reach and supply the diaphragm. The diaphragm is the large, dome-like muscle of respiration that separates the thorax from the abdomen. The word *phrenic* pertains to the diaphragm.

> Since the diaphragm is required for respiration (i.e. to keep you alive) there is an easy rhyme that helps to remember the ventral rami contribution to the phrenic nerve...
> **"C3, C4, C5 – keeps you alive"**

> **C3 IS IN MIDDLE OF CERVICAL PLEXUS (C2-C4)**
> Coincidentally, it contributes its ventral rami branches equally with ventral rami branches from the other two cervical segments. It contributes four branches:
>
> -2 branches combine with C2 branches (branch to trunk that forms great auricular and transversus colli nerves, branch to inferior root of ansa cervicalis)
>
> -2 branches combine with C4 branches (branch to supraclavicular trunk, branch to phrenic nerve)

Finally, branches of the C4 ventral ramus will be mentioned. There are three branches of significance and two have already been discussed. These include the **branch to the supraclavicular trunk** (14) and **branch to the phrenic nerve** (47). The only C4 branch not yet described is a possible **branch to the C5 ventral ramus** (15). When present, this represents C4 contribution to the brachial plexus.

> **Top to Bottom = 5, 4, 3**
> C2 has 5 ventral rami branches, C3 has 4, C4 has 3.
>
> **Top to Bottom: (C2) → (C3) → (C4)**
> 5   4   3

Although considered a contributor to the brachial plexus and not part of the cervical plexus, it is important to remember that the C5 spinal segment also gives branches that join those of upper cervical segments. Along with C1-C4, the C5 segment contributes to the spinal accessory nerve. The C5 ventral ramus also gives a branch that combines with that of the C3 and C4 ventral rami to form the phrenic nerve.

> There are two nerves (a right and a left) for every nerve shown in Figure 1 of the poster. Both dorsal rami and ventral rami exit from each side of the vertebrae. For example, there are two greater occipital nerves, a right and left, even though only the right one is drawn. There are also two hypoglossal, spinal accessory, and ansa cervicalis nerves.

FIGURE 9.4
A STILL DEEPER DISSECTION OF THE NECK

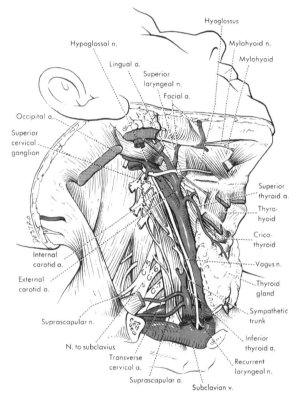

(Reproduced with permission from Hollinshead, W.H., Rosse, C.: Textbook of Anatomy, 4th ed. Philadelphia, Harper & Row, 1985)

CERVICAL DORSAL ROOT BRANCHES

The dorsal rami of the upper three cervical spinal nerves will now be described. Most dorsal rami branches that originate below the C3 spinal level form various unnamed nerves that innervate muscles of the posterior neck and back. Most of these muscular branches are not drawn. It is important to realize that they do exist. The lesser occipital nerve was mentioned earlier as a C2 ventral ramus branch. The first three cervical dorsal rami branches are also "occipital" nerves. All are named with reference to the occiput, the posterior aspect of the head.

The C1 dorsal ramus gives rise to the **suboccipital nerve** (3).

This nerve courses around the top of the atlas (C1 vertebra) to descend behind it and supply muscles of the posterior head and neck. This includes the semispinalis capitis, rectus capitis posterior major, rectus capitis posterior minor, obliquus capitis superior, and obliquus capitis inferior. All were described in the previous chapter. The semispinalis capitis is part of the transversospinalis group of back muscles. The other four muscles comprise the suboccipital group of back muscles. The suboccipital group forms the suboccipital triangle.

> The **sub**occipital nerve is the C1 dorsal ramus. C1 is the most superior spinal segment, so it is immediately beneath the skull and hence, the occiput. It is **sub**-occipital.

The C2 dorsal ramus forms the **greater occipital nerve** (2). The greater occipital nerve usually gives several muscular branches before traveling up the posterior aspect of the head with the occipital artery. Like the suboccipital nerve, the greater occipital nerve contributes to the innervation of the semispinalis capitis, rectus capitis posterior major and rectus capitis posterior minor muscles. In addition, the greater occipital nerve also has sensory properties, innervating the skin of the back of the head. The suboccipital nerve has no sensory properties.

> **THE GREATER OCCIPITAL NERVE
> IS GREAT**
>
> It is the only "occipital" nerve
> with both sensory and motor functions.
>
> The C2 spinal segment is the origin of the "**greatest**" number of ventral rami branches (5). It is appropriate that the C2 dorsal ramus would produce the "**greater**" occipital nerve. Also note that the C2 spinal cord segment is responsible for both the "lesser" occipital nerve (ventral ramus) and "greater" occipital nerve (dorsal ramus).

Finally the **third occipital nerve** (1) is formed from the C3 dorsal ramus. Like many nerves, it is not always present. It ascends medial to the greater occipital nerve to supply skin of the posterior head and upper neck.

> **3**rd occipital nerve = C**3** dorsal ramus

> Consider the upper 3 cervical dorsal rami to exist in a spectrum of position and function. At the top (C1), the suboccipital nerve is a motor nerve. In an intermediate position (C2), the greater occipital nerve is a mixed nerve. At the bottom (C3), the 3rd occipital nerve is a sensory nerve.

FIGURE 9.5
STRUCTURES OF THE POSTERIOR NECK

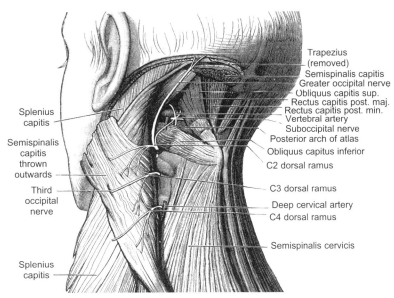

FIGURE 9.6
CERVICAL PLEXUS

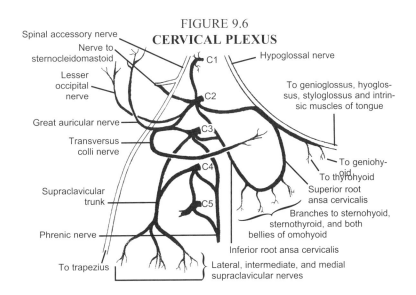

The following table is included as a summary of the cervical plexus (C2-C4).

BRANCHES OF SPINAL SEGMENT		BRANCHES OF VENTRAL RAMUS	BRANCHES OF DORSAL RAMUS
C1	Br. to spinal accessory nerve	Communicating branch to C2 ventral ramus	Suboccipital nerve *(motor)*
C2	Br. to spinal accessory nerve	1) Br. to nerve to sternocleidomastoid *(motor)* 2) Br. to great auricular and transversus colli nerves *(sensory)* 3) Br. to hypoglossal nerve *(motor)* 4) Br. to inferior root of ansa cervicalis *(motor)* 5) Lesser occipital nerve *(sensory)*	Greater occipital nerve *(mixed)*
C3	Br. to spinal accessory nerve	1) Br. to great auricular and transversus coli nerves *(sensory)* 2) Br. to inferior root of ansa cervicalis *(motor)* 3) Br. to supraclavicular trunk *(sensory)* 4) Br. to phrenic nerve *(motor)*	3rd Occipital nerve *(sensory)*
C4	Br. to spinal accessory nerve	1) Br. to supraclavicular trunk *(sensory)* 2) Br. to phrenic nerve *(motor)* 3) Possible branch to C5 ventral ramus *(brachial plexus)*	Muscular branches
C5	Br. to spinal accessory nerve	1) Br. to phrenic nerve *(motor)* 2) Brachial plexus *(mixed)*	Muscular branches

QUIZ 1
Cervical Plexus and Nerves of the Neck

Time for Quiz = 32 minutes.
For questions 1-18, choose the single best answer.

_____1) Which nerve innervates the trapezius muscle?
  a) hypoglossal nerve
  b) greater occipital nerve
  c) suboccipital nerve
  d) ansa cervicalis
  e) none of the above

_____2) Skin behind the ear is supplied by which nerve?
  a) suboccipital nerve
  b) transversus colli nerve
  c) supraclavicular trunk
  d) spinal accessory nerve
  e) none of the above

_____3) The C1 dorsal ramus contributes to the formation of which of the following nerves?
  a) spinal accessory nerve
  b) suboccipital nerve
  c) both a and b
  d) lesser occipital nerve
  e) none of the above

_____4) Which muscles are supplied by the spinal accessory nerve?
  a) trapezius
  b) sternocleidomastoid
  c) both a and b
  d) sternohyoid
  e) none of the above

_____5) Which nerve innervates the sternothyroid muscle?
  a) spinal accessory nerve
  b) ansa cervicalis
  c) hypoglossal nerve
  d) transversus colli nerve
  e) none of the above

_____6) Which muscles are innervated by the suboccipital nerve?
  a) rectus capitis posterior major
  b) trapezius
  c) omohyoid
  d) hyoglossus
  e) none of the above

_____7) Which nerve supplies skin of the anterior neck?
  a) great auricular nerve
  b) transversus colli nerve
  c) ansa cervicalis
  d) spinal accessory nerve
  e) none of the above

_____8) The inferior root of the ansa cervicalis contains fibers from:
  a) C2 ventral ramus
  b) C3 ventral ramus
  c) both a and b
  d) C4 ventral ramus
  e) none of the above

_____9) Which nerve innervates the sternocleidomastoid muscle?
  a) a branch from the C3 ventral ramus
  b) spinal accessory nerve
  c) both a and b
  d) ansa cervicalis
  e) none of the above

_____10) Which muscles are supplied by the greater occipital nerve?
  a) rectus capitis posterior major
  b) rectus capitis posterior minor
  c) semispinalis capitis
  d) all of the above
  e) none of the above

_____11) Which of the following muscles are supplied by the lesser occipital nerve?
      a) semispinalis capitis
      b) hyoglossus
      c) sternothyroid
      d) trapezius
      e) none of the above

_____12) Which nerve innervates the thyrohyoid muscle?
      a) C1 and C2 ventral rami fibers which travel with the hypoglossal nerve
      b) transversus colli nerve
      c) supraclavicular trunk
      d) spinal accessory nerve
      e) none of the above

_____13) The superior root of the ansa cervicalis contains fibers from the
      a) C2 ventral ramus
      b) C3 ventral ramus
      c) both a and b
      d) C4 ventral ramus
      e) none of the above

_____14) Which muscles are ultimately innervated by the supraclavicular trunk?
      a) sternocleidomastoid
      b) sternohyoid
      c) hyoglossus
      d) thyrohyoid
      e) none of the above

_____15) Which nerve innervates the semispinalis capitis muscle?
      a) greater occipital nerve
      b) suboccipital nerve
      c) both a and b
      d) 3rd occipital nerve
      e) none of the above

_____16) Which nerve supplies skin of the posterior head?
      a) suboccipital nerve
      b) greater occipital nerve
      c) both a and b
      d) transversus colli nerve
      e) none of the above

_____17) The suboccipital nerve contains fibers from the
      a) C1 dorsal ramus
      b) C1 ventral ramus
      c) C2 dorsal ramus
      d) C2 ventral ramus
      e) none of the above

_____18) The nerve to sternocleidomastoid contains nerve fibers from the
      a) C2 ventral ramus
      b) spinal accessory nerve
      c) both a and b
      d) hypoglossal nerve
      e) none of the above

For questions 19-32, use the following directions:
    a.......1,2,3 are correct
    b.......1,3 are correct
    c.......2,4 are correct
    d.......only 4 is correct
    e.......all are correct

_____19) Which of the following are purely motor nerves?
      1. ansa cervicalis
      2. spinal accessory nerve
      3. hypoglossal nerve
      4. suboccipital nerve

_____20) Which statements concerning the spinal accessory nerve are true?
      1. It is a component of CN XII.
      2. It is purely a motor nerve.
      3. It supplies the sternohyoid muscle.
      4. It is formed by branches from the C1-C5 spinal segments.

_____21) Which of the following nerves could contain fibers from the C1 ventral ramus?
      1. supraclavicular trunk
      2. inferior root ansa cervicals
      3. phrenic nerve
      4. superior root ansa cervicalis

_____22) Which of the following nerves are cervical dorsal rami branches?
      1. suboccipital nerve
      2. 3rd occipital nerve
      3. greater occipital nerve
      4. lesser occipital nerve

_____23) The inferior root of the ansa cervicalis contains fibers from the
    1. C4 ventral ramus
    2. C1 ventral ramus
    3. hypoglossal nerve
    4. C2 ventral ramus

_____24) Which statements about the great auricular nerve are true?
    1. The C3 ventral ramus contributes to its formation.
    2. The C2 ventral ramus contributes to its formation.
    3. It is purely a sensory nerve.
    4. It supplies the trapezius muscle.

_____25) Which of the following are branches of the C2 ventral ramus?
    1. branch to the trunk that forms the great auricular and transversus colli nerves
    2. branch to hypoglossal nerve
    3. branch to nerve to sternocleidomastoid
    4. lesser occipital nerve

_____26) Which nerve structures contain fibers from the C4 ventral ramus?
    1. transversus colli nerve
    2. lesser occipital nerve
    3. inferior root ansa cervicalis
    4. supraclavicular trunk

_____27) Which statements are true concerning the ansa cervicalis?
    1. The inferior root branches from the hypoglossal nerve.
    2. The superior root branches from the glossopharyngeal nerve.
    3. It supplies both muscle and skin.
    4. It innervates infrahyoid muscles.

_____28) Which of the following are purely sensory nerves?
    1. transversus colli nerve
    2. 3rd occipital nerve
    3. lesser occipital nerve
    4. greater occipital nerve

_____29) Which nerves contain fibers from the C3 ventral ramus?
    1. great auricular nerve
    2. inferior root ansa cervicalis
    3. phrenic nerve
    4. supraclavicular trunk

_____30) Which of the following are mixed nerves, having both sensory and motor responsibilities?
    1. supraclavicular trunk
    2. suboccipital nerve
    3. ansa cervicalis
    4. greater occipital nerve

_____31) Which statements concerning the transversus colli nerve are true?
    1. The C2 ventral ramus contributes to its formation.
    2. It is purely a sensory nerve.
    3. The C3 ventral ramus contributes to its formation.
    4. It supplies skin behind the ear.

_____32) The superior root of the ansa cervicalis contains fibers from the
    1. C3 ventral ramus
    2. hypoglossal nerve
    3. C4 ventral ramus
    4. C2 ventral ramus

QUIZ 1: Cervical Plexus and Nerves of the Neck Answers and Explanations

1) e – The trapezius muscle is supplied by the spinal accessory nerve. The spinal accessory nerve forms the external ramus of the accessory nerve (CN XI). The spinal accessory nerve is formed by branches from the C1-C5 spinal segments.

2) e – The lesser occipital nerve is a sensory nerve supplying skin behind the ear. The lesser occipital nerve is a branch of the C2 ventral ramus. The transversus colli is a sensory nerve that supplies skin across the front of the neck. The supraclavicular trunk is a sensory nerve that supplies skin of the upper anterior chest. Both the suboccipital and spinal accessory nerves are motor nerves.

3) b – The suboccipital nerve is a motor nerve that supplies the semispinalis capitis, rectus capitis posterior major, rectus capitis posterior minor, obliquus capitis superior, and obliquus capitis inferior muscles.

4) c – The spinal accessory nerve is a division of the accessory nerve, CN XI. The spinal accessory nerve is formed by branches from the C1-C5 spinal segments. The spinal accessory nerve is a motor nerve that innervates the trapezius muscle and gives a branch that combines with a C2 ventral ramus branch to innervate the sternocleidomastoid muscle. The sternohyoid muscle is supplied by the ansa cervicalis nerve loop.

5) b – The ansa cervicalis is a motor nerve. The ansa cervicalis innervates infrahyoid muscles, including the sternohyoid, sternothyroid, and omohyoid muscles.

6) a – See #3 answer explanation. The trapezius muscle is supplied by the spinal accessory nerve (component of CN XI). The omohyoid muscle is supplied by the ansa cervicalis nerve loop. The hyoglossus muscle is innervated by the hypoglossal nerve (CN XII).

7) b – The transversus colli is a sensory nerve that supplies skin across the front of the neck. The

great auricular and transversus colli nerves arise from a common trunk formed by ventral rami branches from C2 and C3. The great auricular nerve is a sensory nerve that supplies skin of the ear and anterior to the ear. The ansa cervicalis and spinal accessory nerves are motor nerves.

8) c – The inferior root of the ansa cervicalis is formed by branches from the C2 and C3 ventral rami.

9) b – The sternocleidomastoid muscle is supplied by a nerve composed of branches from the C2 ventral ramus and spinal accessory nerve. The spinal accessory nerve is formed by branches from the C1-C5 spinal segments. It forms the external ramus of the accessory nerve (CN XI).

10) d – The suboccipital nerve also participates in the innervation of these three muscles.

11) e – The lesser occipital nerve is a branch of the C2 ventral ramus. It is a sensory nerve supplying skin behind the ear. The semispinalis capitis muscle is innervated by the suboccipital and greater occipital nerves. The hyoglossus muscle is innervated by the hypoglossal nerve (CN XII). The sternothyroid muscle is supplied by the ansa cervicalis nerve loop. Finally, the trapezius is supplied by the spinal accessory nerve (component of CN XI).

12) a – The superior root of the ansa cervicalis is formed by a branch of the hypoglossal nerve (CN XII) composed of C1 and C2 ventral rami nerve fibers which previously joined the hypoglossal by way of a C2 ventral ramus branch. After the superior root branches from the hypoglossal, the remaining C1 and C2 fibers continue with the hypoglossal to innervate the geniohyoid and thyrohyoid muscles.

13) a – See #12 answer explanation.

14) e – The supraclavicular trunk is a sensory nerve responsible for supplying skin of the anterior

chest over the first two ribs. The sternocleido-mastoid muscle is supplied by a nerve formed by branches from the C2 ventral ramus and spinal accessory nerve (component of CN XI). The sternohyoid muscle is supplied by the ansa cervicalis nerve loop. The hyoglossus muscle is innervated by the hypoglossal nerve (CN XII). The thyrohyoid muscle is supplied by C1 and C2 ventral rami fibers that travel with and branch from the hypoglossal nerve.

15) c – The third occipital nerve is formed from the C3 dorsal ramus. It is a sensory nerve that supplies skin of the posterior upper neck and lower head.

16) b – The greater occipital nerve is a mixed nerve, supplying both skin and muscle of the posterior head and neck. The suboccipital nerve is a motor nerve. The transversus colli is a sensory nerve that supplies skin across the front of the neck.

17) a – See #3 answer explanation.

18) c – The sternocleidomastoid muscle is supplied by a nerve formed by branches from the C2 ventral ramus and spinal accessory nerve (component of CN XI).

19) e – The ansa cervicalis innervates infrahyoid muscles, including the sternohyoid, sternothyroid, and omohyoid muscles. The spinal accessory nerve (component of CN XI) innervates the trapezius muscle and gives a branch which combines with a C2 ventral ramus branch to innervate the sternocleidomastoid muscle. The hypoglossal nerve (CN XII) supplies the intrinsic and extrinsic muscles of the tongue. The suboccipital nerve supplies the semispinalis capitis, rectus capitis posterior major, rectus capitis posterior minor, obliquus capitis superior, and obliquus capitis inferior muscles.

20) c – The spinal accessory nerve is a division of the accessory nerve, CN XI. It is formed by branches from the C1-C5 spinal segments. The sternohyoid muscle is supplied by the ansa cervicalis nerve loop.

21) d – The superior root of the ansa cervicalis is formed by a branch of the hypoglossal nerve (CN XII) composed of C1 and C2 ventral rami nerve fibers that previously joined the hypoglossal by way of a C2 ventral ramus branch. The inferior root is formed by ventral rami branches from the C2 and C3 spinal segments. The supraclavicular trunk is formed by branches from the C3 and C4 ventral rami. The phrenic nerve is formed by ventral rami branches from C3, C4, and C5 (C3, C4, C5...keeps you alive).

22) a – The suboccipital nerve is formed by the C1 dorsal ramus. The third occipital nerve is formed from the C3 dorsal ramus. The greater occipital nerve is formed by the C2 dorsal ramus. The lesser occipital nerve is a branch of the C2 ventral ramus.

23) d – The inferior root of the ansa cervicalis is formed by branches from the C2 and C3 ventral rami. The superior root is formed by a branch of the hypoglossal nerve (CN XII) composed of C1 and C2 ventral rami nerve fibers that previously joined the hypoglossal by way of a C2 ventral ramus branch.

24) a – See #7 answer explanation.

25) e – The other branch of the C2 ventral ramus is the branch to the inferior root of ansa cervicalis. The branch to the hypoglossal nerve (CN XII) contains C1 and C2 ventral rami fibers and forms the superior root of the ansa cervicalis.

26) d – The supraclavicular trunk is formed by branches from the C3 and C4 ventral rami. The transversus colli nerve, along with the great auricular nerve, branches from a trunk formed by ventral rami branches from C2 and C3. The lesser occipital nerve is a branch of the C2 ventral ramus. The inferior root of the ansa cervicalis is formed by branches from the C2 and C3 ventral rami.

27) d – See #5 and #23 answer explanations.

28) a – The greater occipital nerve is a mixed nerve, supplying both skin and muscle of the posterior head and neck.

29) e – Both the great auricular and transversus colli nerves originate from a trunk formed by ventral rami branches from C2 and C3. The inferior root of the ansa cervicalis is formed by branches from the C2 and C3 ventral rami. The phrenic nerve is formed by ventral rami branches from C3, C4, and C5 (C3, C4, C5... keeps you alive). The supraclavicular trunk is formed by branches from the C3 and C4 ventral rami.

30) d – The supraclavicular trunk is a sensory nerve.

It usually gives off three supraclavicular nerves that supply skin of the anterior chest over the first two ribs. The suboccipital nerve is a motor nerve which supplies muscles of the posterior triangle of the neck. The ansa cervicalis is a motor nerve that innervates infrahyoid muscles, including the sternohyoid, sternothyroid, and omohyoid muscles.

31) a – See #7 answer explanation.

32) d – See #5 and #23 answer explanations.

CRANIAL NERVES OF THE NECK

There are four cranial nerves with significant responsibilities in the neck. They include the glossopharyngeal nerve (CN IX), vagus nerve (CN X), spinal accessory nerve (a component of CN XI), and hypoglossal nerve (CN XII). It seems only logical that the last four cranial nerves (CN IX-XII) have a notable role in the neck. The two lowest nerves (CN XI, CN XII) are purely motor nerves, supplying muscles of the neck. The innervations of the spinal accessory nerve were described in the previous section.

The **hypoglossal nerve** (28) is cranial nerve XII. It is a motor nerve responsible for supplying muscles of the tongue. It supplies the genioglossus, hyoglossus, and styloglossus muscles, as well as the intrinsic muscles of the tongue. All work together in a complex fashion to provide the diverse movement patterns of the tongue. The intrinsic muscles form the substance of the tongue.

In addition to the innervation of tongue muscles, the hypoglossal nerve is also a carrier of C1 and C2 ventral rami fibers. A significant portion of these fibers branch off as the superior root of the ansa cervicalis. Other fibers continue with the hypoglossal to supply the thyrohyoid and geniohyoid muscles.

FIGURE 9.7
TONGUE AND ASSOCIATED MUSCLES

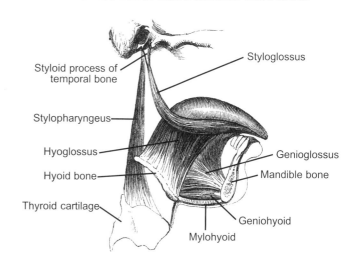

MUSCLES INNERVATED BY HYPOGLOSSAL NERVE

Extrinsic muscles of tongue	Intrinsic muscles of tongue
Genioglossus	Chondroglossus
Hyoglossus	Longitudinalis inferior linguae
Styloglossus	• (inferior longitudinal muscle of tongue)
	Longitudinalis superior linguae
	• (superior longitudinal muscle of tongue)
	Tranversus linguae
	• (transverse muscle of tongue)
	Verticalis linguae
	• (vertical muscle of tongue)

The words, *glossal* and *lingua*, both relate to the tongue. The combining form *gloss(o)* means tongue. It only makes sense that the hypo**glossal** nerve would innervate tongue muscles. Included are the extrinsic muscles of the tongue (genio**glossus**, hyo**glossus**, and stylo**glossus** muscles) and intrinsic muscles of the tongue (chondro**glossus**, longitudinalis inferior <u>linguae</u>, longitudinalis superior <u>linguae</u>, tranversus <u>linguae</u>, and verticalis <u>linguae</u> muscles).

To anchor the tongue, the extrinsic muscles of the ***tongue*** must originate from ***below*** or behind the tongue; they are therefore supplied by the ***hypo-glossal*** nerve.

FIGURE 9.8
MUSCLES OF THE NECK

Anterior view after removal of sternocleidomastoid muscle on both sides. The layers of muscle on the subject's left (visually appearing on the right) are deep to those of the subject's right (visually appearing on the left).

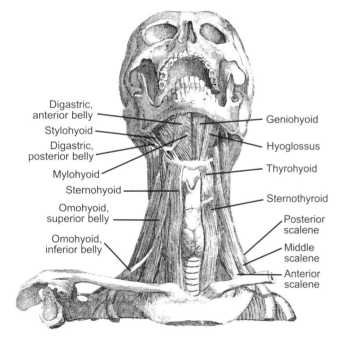

Digastric, anterior belly
Stylohyoid
Digastric, posterior belly
Mylohyoid
Sternohyoid
Omohyoid, superior belly
Omohyoid, inferior belly

Geniohyoid
Hyoglossus
Thyrohyoid
Sternothyroid
Posterior scalene
Middle scalene
Anterior scalene

Much of the remaining chapter focuses on the glossopharyngeal and vagus nerves. Both are mixed nerves, providing both sensory and motor function. They are also two of the four cranial nerves that provide parasympathetic innervation to visceral structures.

One of the paramount parasympathetic functions is digestion. Both the glossopharyngeal and vagus nerves play integral roles in digestive processes of the head and neck. Innervation is supplied to the parotid gland for salivation and muscles of the pharynx and esophagus for swallowing.

The **glossopharyngeal nerve** (210) arises from the lateral aspect of the medulla oblongata of the brain and exits the skull via the jugular foramen. It gives several sensory branches and at least one motor branch before continuing forward to supply taste and general sensation to the posterior 1/3 of the tongue.

MUSCLES ARE FREQUENTLY NAMED FOR THEIR ORIGINS AND INSERTIONS

The amount of new information encountered in anatomy can, at times, seem overwhelming to the beginning student. Instead of sheer memorization, it is often beneficial to learn **WHY** an anatomic structure is named what it is. Even if the student cannot remember details about a certain structure, an evaluation of the structure's name may provide clues as to where the structure is, what it does, and/or what structures are associated with it. This is especially true of muscles. Muscles are frequently named for their shape, structure, origin, insertion, or movement achieved upon contraction. Many muscles of the neck are named for their origin and insertion. If the origin and insertion are known, the function of the muscle can be deduced. From this, an educated guess can be made as to which nerve innervates it. Mastering this information will come with time and repetition.

To provide for the highly varied and intricate movements of swallowing and vocalization, the pharynx and larynx contain a significant number of small, very specialized muscles. Many are named for their origins and insertions. Below is a list of words that may appear in their names. Each represents an anatomic structure serving as an origin or insertion.

Arytenoid – arytenoid cartilage is at base of vocal cords (arytenoid = **"jug-shaped"**)

Epiglottic – epiglottis

Crico – cricoid cartilage is first cartilage of trachea located below thyroid cartilage (cricoid = **ring-shaped**)

Genio – superior or inferior genial tubercle (genial = **chin**)

Hyo – hyoid bone

Palato – palate

Sterno – sternum

Stylo – styloid process of temporal bone (styl- or stylo = a **pole**)

Thyro – Thyroid cartilage is large, protective cartilage of larynx. Forms "Adam's apple."

EXAMPLES: A muscle's origin is its fixed point of attachment. The insertion is the attachment to the bone or other structure it moves upon contraction. The thyrohyoid muscle originates on the thyroid cartilage and inserts on the hyoid bone. It elevates the hyoid bone and larynx upon contraction. The sternohyoid muscle originates on the sternum and inserts on the hyoid bone. It lowers the hyoid bone and larynx.

While both taste and general sensation to the posterior 1/3 of the tongue are provided by one cranial nerve, the glossopharyngeal, it takes fibers from two cranial nerves to supply these sensations to the anterior 2/3 of the tongue. The **lingual nerve** is a branch of the mandibular division (mandibular nerve) of the **trigeminal nerve**, cranial nerve V. Its fibers supply general sensation to the anterior 2/3 of the tongue. Near its origin, the lingual nerve receives the **chorda tympani** from the **facial nerve**, cranial nerve VII. Facial nerve fibers traveling in the lingual nerve provide taste sensation to the anterior 2/3 of the tongue.

> The glossopharyngeal nerve is named for its innervation of the tongue ("glosso") and pharynx ("pharyngeal"). Since the glossopharyngeal is already in the *back* of the throat supplying the pharynx, it also supplies the *back* of the tongue…it supplies taste and general sensation to the posterior 1/3 of tongue.

Although the glossopharyngeal nerve is a mixed nerve, its responsibilities in the neck are mostly sensory. There is one muscle it reliably innervates. Additionally, it may contribute to the innervation of two other muscles that are also supplied by the vagus nerve. Otherwise, most of its branches form sensory nerves of the neck.

The **tympanic branch** (209) travels to the middle ear to contribute to the tympanic plexus. This plexus supplies the mucous membrane of the tympanum, the middle ear cavity of the temporal bone of the skull. The word *tympanic* describes structures associated with the middle ear. The tympanic membrane is the eardrum. In addition to the glossopharyngeal branch, the tympanic plexus may also receive contribution from the facial nerve and sympathetic input from the internal carotid plexus. Glossopharyngeal fibers which course through the plexus form the **lesser petrosal nerve**. The lesser petrosal is considered a branch of the glossopharyngeal nerve, even though it appears to originate from the tympanic plexus. The word *petrosal* refers to the petrous part of the temporal bone. The lesser petrosal nerve carries preganglionic glossopharyngeal fibers to the **otic ganglion**. From there, postganglionic fibers continue on to supply the parotid gland, the largest of the salivary glands.

An **auricular branch** (208) can also exist. When present, this sensory branch joins the auricular branch of the vagus nerve and the smaller posterior auricular branch of the facial nerve to supply the lower rear external meatus of the ear.

The **carotid branch** (207) provides sensory innervation to the carotid sinus of the carotid artery. The carotid sinus is the dilated area of the common carotid artery where it bifurcates into the internal and external carotid arteries. The walls of the carotid sinus contain baroreceptors. *Bar(o)-* is a combining word form which means *weight*. Because of the relationship between weight and pressure, the combining form is often used to describe entities that are associated with *pressure*. A *baro*meter, for example, measures atmospheric pressure. Baroreceptors are stretch receptors that function in blood pressure control. The carotid body is an area of the superior aspect of the fork of the common carotid artery that is rich in chemoreceptors. These chemoreceptors detect changes in blood oxygen, carbon dioxide, and pH and function in regulation of respiration. The carotid branch is also

known as the **afferent nerve of Hering**. It is afferent because it is sending information from these sensory receptors to the brain.

The **nerve to stylopharyngeus muscle** (204) serves as the consistent motor branch of the glossopharyngeal nerve. The nerve emerges as the glossopharyngeal turns toward the tongue. When stimulated, the muscle functions to raise or elevate the pharynx.

> The nerve to the stylo**pharyngeus** muscle is provided by the glosso**pharyngeal** nerve.

FIGURE 9.9
GLOSSOPHARYNGEAL NERVE AND POSTERIOR STRUCTURES OF PHARYNX

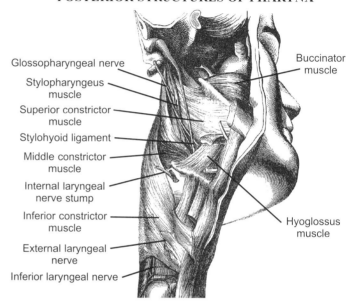

The glossopharyngeal nerve is also the origin of several **pharyngeal branches** (206). These branches, along with those of the vagus nerve, contribute to the pharyngeal plexus. The pharyngeal plexus is a meshwork of glossopharyngeal and vagus fibers. It is the origin of several sensory branches of the pharynx. It also innervates muscles functioning in phonation and swallowing.

Tonsillar branches (205) are sensory nerves that come off the glossopharyngeal in the pharynx. They supply sensation to the tonsils and nearby tissue.

The **vagus nerve** (**29**, 49, 232, 236, 237, 241, 244, 255) is cranial nerve X. The vagus nerve is a mixed cranial nerve with many functions. Predominately, it is known for its parasympathetic innervation of the thoracic and abdominal viscera. It also provides motor innervation to the pharynx (lift palate, swallow), larynx (move vocal cords, vocalize), and esophagus (swallow). Sensory innervation is provided to the esophagus, pharynx, larynx, and ear. The vagus nerve comes off the lateral aspect of the brain stem and exits the skull via the jugular foramen. It serves as the origin for several motor and sensory branches in the neck. It enters the thorax and continues into the abdomen. While the distribution of vagus nerve branches is extensive, only the ones innervating structures of the head and neck are discussed in this chapter.

Soon after its formation from the lateral aspect of the medulla oblongata, the vagus nerve produces a **meningeal branch** (30), which supplies the posterior dura of the brain. The dura mater is the outer fibrous membrane or "sac" that the brain and spinal cord are enclosed within. It is separated from the brain and spinal cord by cerebrospinal fluid (CSF).

The **auricular branch** (31) runs up to supply skin in areas of the rear middle ear, tympanic membrane, and external acoustic meatus. Often, auricular branches of the facial nerve (cranial nerve VII) and glossopharyngeal (cranial nerve IX) join it.

Another group of vagus nerve branches that associate with glossopharyngeal branches of the same name are the **pharyngeal branches** (32). These branches combine with pharyngeal branches of the glossopharyngeal to form the previously-mentioned pharyngeal plexus. This plexus is the origin of both sensory and motor nerves of the pharynx. Below is a list of muscles supplied by the pharyngeal plexus.

MUSCLES INNERVATED BY THE PHARYNGEAL PLEXUS

MUSCLE	FUNCTION
Uvulae	elevates uvula

• vagus fibers only

Superior constrictor muscle of pharynx .....constricts pharynx
• vagus fibers only

Middle constrictor muscle of pharynx ....constricts pharynx
• vagus and glossopharyngeal fibers

Inferior constrictor muscle of pharynx ......constricts pharynx
• vagus and glossopharyngeal fibers
• contribution also from glossopharyngeal nerve, ext. br. superior laryngeal and recurrent laryngeal nerves (the later two are vagus branches)

Palatoglossus ....elevates tongue
• vagus fibers only

Palatopharyngeal...constricts pharynx
• vagus fibers only

Levator veli palatini ....elevates soft palate
• vagus fibers only   (veli = a covering structure such as a veil)

Salpingopharyngeal....................................elevates pharynx
• vagus fibers only

The **superior laryngeal nerve** (33) is a vagus nerve branch often seen coming off the inferior vagal ganglion. It is a mixed nerve with both sensory and motor function. The superior laryngeal travels down and divides into two branches, the external and internal laryngeal nerves. The **external laryngeal nerve** (35) supplies the cricothyroid muscle and levator muscle of thyroid. The cricothyroid originates on the cricoid cartilage and inserts on the inferior horn of the thyroid cartilage; its contraction tenses the vocal cords. The levator muscle of the thyroid originates on the thyroid gland and inserts on the body of the hyoid bone. Contraction serves to immobilize the thyroid gland. In addition, the external laryngeal nerve often contributes to the innervation to the inferior constrictor muscle, which constricts the pharynx. The **internal laryngeal nerve** (34) supplies sensation to the inner mucous membrane of the larynx.

FIGURE 9.10
PHARYNGEAL MUSCLES AND DEEP STRUCTURES OF THE UPPER NECK

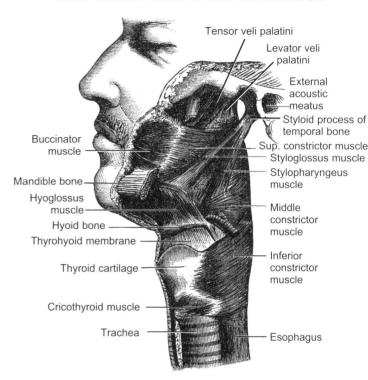

Tensor veli palatini
Levator veli palatini
External acoustic meatus
Styloid process of temporal bone
Sup. constrictor muscle
Styloglossus muscle
Stylopharyngeus muscle
Middle constrictor muscle
Inferior constrictor muscle
Esophagus
Buccinator muscle
Mandible bone
Hyoglossus muscle
Hyoid bone
Thyrohyoid membrane
Thyroid cartilage
Cricothyroid muscle
Trachea

Both the glossopharyngeal and vagus nerves contribute to the pharyngeal plexus. With exceptions, the glossopharyngeal can be considered the sensory nerve and the vagus the motor nerve.

Glossopharyngeal fibers, either from an actual nerve branch or by way of the pharyngeal plexus, provide sensory input to all areas of the pharynx between the auditory tube, above, and larynx, below. Maintaining its role as the sensory nerve of the pharynx, the glossopharyngeal also provides touch and taste sensation to the posterior 1/3 of the tongue. This is the portion of the tongue "closest" to the pharynx.

Vagus fibers contribute to the innervation of every muscle of the pharynx except the stylopharyngeus (glossopharyngeal). Even though innervation is supplied by the vagus, glossopharyngeal fibers may also contribute to the innervation of the middle and inferior constrictor muscles of the pharynx.

VAGUS = MOTOR
1 2 3 4 5   1 2 3 4 5

GLOSSO PHARYNGEAL = SENSORY
post. 1/3   all of **pharynx**
of **tongue**

FIGURE 9.11
VAGUS NERVES AND BRANCHES

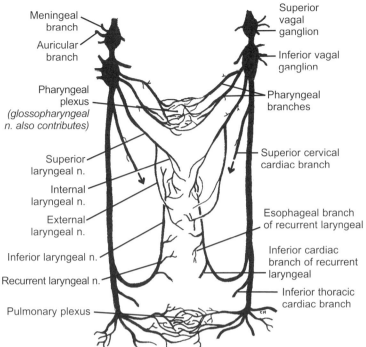

FIGURE 9.12
CARTILAGES OF LARYNX – ANTERIOR VIEW

POSTERIOR VIEW

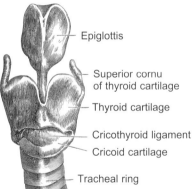

ANTERIOR VIEW WITH HYOID BONE AND THYROHYOID MEMBRANE REMOVED

The **superior cervical cardiac branch** (**37**, 245, 254) leaves the vagus while in the neck and descends to provide parasympathetic contribution to the cardiac plexus. The **cardiac plexus** (253) is the autonomic plexus surrounding the heart. Along with other vagus branches, parasympathetic input to the plexus is provided by both the superior cervical cardiac branch and the **inferior cardiac branch** (**48**, 246, 252), which usually originates from the vagus in the thorax. Sympathetic innervation to the cardiac plexus is by way of branches from paravertebral ganglia of the two sympathetic chains.

The **recurrent laryngeal nerve** (**46**, 233, 240, 242, 257) is a vagus branch also known as the **recurrent branch of the right or left vagus**. It is called the recurrent laryngeal nerve because it branches from the vagus while in the thorax and "backtracks" to the neck. It travels up between the esophagus and trachea to reach the larynx. Along the way, it gives several branches. The **inferior cardiac branch** (45) contributes additional parasympathetic innervation to the cardiac plexus. Care should be taken not to confuse this nerve with the inferior cardiac branch of the vagus nerve. The **esophageal branch** (43) innervates a portion of the esophagus.

The terminal branch of the recurrent laryngeal nerve is the **inferior laryngeal nerve** (41). A terminal branch is the last branch of a particular nerve structure. In many instances, a nerve simply divides into two terminal branches. In this case, the inferior laryngeal nerve can be considered the distal continuation of the recurrent laryngeal nerve. The inferior laryngeal nerve continues into the larynx to supply the intrinsic muscles of the larynx.

FIGURE 9.13
SUPERIOR VIEW OF LARYNGEAL OPENING TO TRACHEA

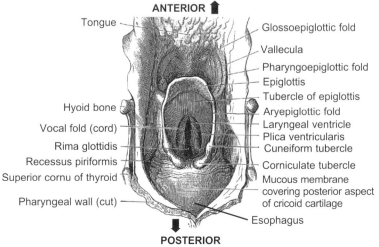

Muscles Innervated by Recurrent Laryngeal Nerve
(via Inferior Laryngeal Nerve)

Most are named with reference to their origin and insertion. These attachment points include the arytenoid cartilage, cricoid cartilage, thyroid cartilage, and epiglottis.

MUSCLE	FUNCTION
aryepiglottic	closes laryngeal entrance
oblique arytenoid	closes laryngeal entrance
thyroarytenoid	relaxes vocal folds
thyroepiglottic	closes laryngeal entrance
transverse arytenoid	brings arytenoid cartilage together
posterior cricoarytenoid	moves vocal folds apart
lateral cricoarytenoid	brings vocal folds together
vocalis	causes local changes in vocal fold tension

The first four muscles generally function to close the larynx in a sphincter-like fashion. This protects the larynx, trachea, and lungs from entrance of foreign substances, as may occur while eating, swimming, talking, etc. The second four, along with the cricothyroid muscle, cause changes of vocal cord and laryngeal structure as needed for vocalization and breathing.

FIGURE 9.14
LARYNGEAL MUSCLES, POSTERIOR VIEW

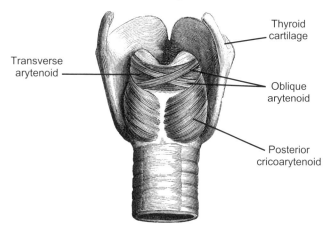

FIGURE 9.15
LARYNGEAL MUSCLES, RIGHT LATERAL VIEW
WITH THYROID CARTILAGE PARTIALLY REMOVED

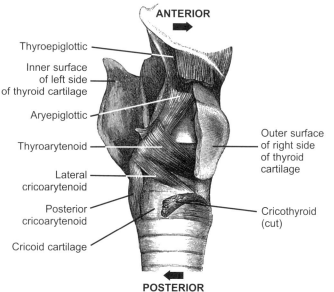

---

9 laryngeal muscles
1 2 3 4 5 6 7 8 9

Of these 9, the cricothyroid is the only muscle not supplied by the recurrent laryngeal nerve (via inferior laryngeal nerve). The cricothyroid is also the only laryngeal muscle on the *exterior* of the larynx. The other muscles are intrinsic muscles. The cricothyroid is supplied by the *external* laryngeal nerve (external branch of superior laryngeal nerve)

For exam purposes, the cricothyroid should be the laryngeal muscle name initially memorized. It is the only muscle on the exterior of the larynx. It is also the only laryngeal muscle not supplied by the recurrent laryngeal nerve. Others can simply be recognized as a laryngeal muscle…thus, the innervation is known. Proficiency in this material will come with time.

LARYNX (voice box) IS USED FOR SINGING

Just as a showgirl sings in *vegas* (Las Vegas), the larynx is supplied entirely by the *vagus* nerve (via its named branches). The superior laryngeal nerve provides the internal and external laryngeal nerves. The recurrent laryngeal nerve is the source of the inferior laryngeal nerve. Thus, there are three nerves which actually supply the larynx and each is a branch of a vagus nerve branch.

LARYNX IS SUPPLIED BY
TWO VAGUS BRANCHES

One from above ....**Superior laryngeal nerve**
(divides into internal and external laryngeal nerves)

One from below...........................**Inferior laryngeal nerve**
(terminal branch of recurrent laryngeal nerve)

FIGURE 9.16
VAGUS NERVE INNERVATION OF THE LARYNX
Right Lateral View

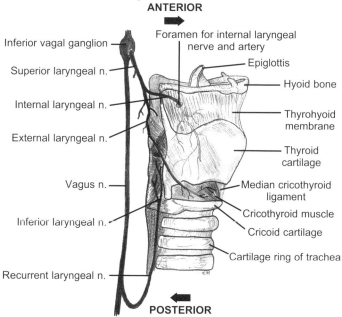

The "laryngeal" nerves are named accordingly

The "laryngeal" branches are all vagus nerve branches that provide innervation to muscles or mucosal lining of the larynx ("voice box"). The most proximal branch comes off higher or more <u>**superior**</u> in the neck than the more distal branches. Hence, it is called the <u>**superior**</u> laryngeal nerve. It subsequently branches into the <u>**external**</u> laryngeal nerve (supplying the cricothyroid muscle, levator muscle of thyroid, and inferior constrictor muscle of pharynx…all of which are **"external"** to the larynx) and <u>**internal**</u> laryngeal nerve (supplying the **"internal"** mucosal membrane of the larynx). The recurrent laryngeal nerve comes off the vagus nerve in the thorax and "backtracks" to the larynx. It is therefore "recurrent." Its terminal branch is the <u>**inferior**</u> laryngeal nerve, which is coming up from the <u>**inferior**</u>ly located recurrent laryngeal nerve. This nerve innervates all the muscles of the larynx except the cricothyroid, which is supplied by the external laryngeal nerve. The two laryngeal nerves innervating muscles of vocal cord movement and phonation are therefore the external laryngeal nerve (external branch of the superior laryngeal nerve) and inferior laryngeal nerve (terminal branch of the recurrent laryngeal nerve).

HELPFUL HINTS
FOR LEARNING MUSCLES AND INNERVATION OF THROAT (TONGUE, PHARYNX, AND LARYNX)
Learn the general innervations of the tongue, pharynx, and larynx and then learn to identify a muscle as belonging to one of these three groups.

TONGUE: Hypoglossal nerve supplies intrinsic and extrinsic muscles of tongue. Each muscle has "glossus" or "linguae" in name (or some derivation of each word). Caution: palatoglossus is supplied by vagus fibers via the pharyngeal plexus.

PHARYNX: The pharyngeal plexus supplies all pharyngeal muscles except stylopharyngeus, which is supplied by the glossopharyngeal nerve. Other direct glossopharyngeal branches may contribute to the innervation of the inferior constrictor muscle. The pharyngeal plexus is comprised of vagus and glossopharyngeal fibers. **Vagus fibers supply all muscles innervated by the pharyngeal plexus.** Glossopharyngeal fibers may additionally contribute to the innervation of the middle and inferior constrictor muscles. If a muscle can be identified as a pharyngeal muscle, then the innervation should be known. The uvulae muscle can be associated with the uvula, an obvious pharyngeal structure. The 3 constrictor muscles constrict the pharynx. Palatoglossus is discussed above. It is associated with the palate (pharyngeal structure). Palatopharyngeal, salpingopharyngeal, and stylopharyngeus muscles (stylopharyngeus supplied by glossopharyngeal) all have "pharyn" in name. Finally, the levator veli palatini raises the soft palate (pharyngeal structure). In summary, except for the stylopharyngeus muscle, all pharyngeal muscles are supplied by vagus nerve fibers of the pharyngeal plexus. The stylopharyngeus is supplied by a direct branch of the glossopharyngeal nerve. Other direct glossopharyngeal branches may contribute to the innervation of the inferior constrictor muscle. In addition, glossopharyngeal fibers of the pharyngeal plexus may aid in the supply of the middle and inferior constrictor muscles.

LARYNX: Vagus branches supply all laryngeal muscles. The epiglottis is the thumb-like structure above the larynx which closes, protecting the larynx during swallowing. The arytenoid cartilage is at the base of the vocal cords. These two structures are inherent laryngeal structures. Muscles are frequently named for their origins and insertions, which often give a clue as to the function. Every laryngeal muscle (except two) has "arytenoid" or "epiglottic" in its name (or some derivation of each word). The two exceptions include the vocalis, which seems the most appropriately named muscle for the voicebox, and the cricothyroid. The cricothyroid can be remembered as "the renegade" laryngeal muscle which is

1) the only laryngeal muscle exterior to the larynx
2) the only laryngeal not supplied by the recurrent laryngeal nerve
3) one of two laryngeal muscles without "arytenoid" or "epiglottic" in name

CRICOTHYROID = RENEGADE

PHARYNX AND LARYNX sound similar and each contains **9 MUSCLES**

Pharynx = 8 via pharyngeal plexus + 1 via glossopharyngeal n.
Larynx = 8 via recurrent (inferior) laryngeal n. + 1 via external laryngeal n.

FIGURE 9.17
CRICOTHYROID MUSCLE

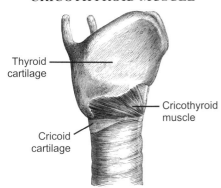

Thyroid cartilage

Cricothyroid muscle

Cricoid cartilage

MOTOR INNERVATION OF "THROAT" PROVIDED BY 3 CRANIAL NERVES

HYPOGLOSSAL: intrinsic and extrinsic muscles of tongue
GLOSSOPHARYNGEAL: stylopharyngeus, contribution to middle and inferior constrictor muscles of pharynx
VAGUS: everything else in pharynx and all of larynx!

OTHER CERVICAL INNERVATIONS

There are four muscles supplied by cranial nerves with a limited presence in the neck. All are described in chapter six. They are the mylohyoid, digastric, stylohyoid, and platysma muscles.

The mylohyoid muscle originates on the inner surface of the mandible and inserts on the hyoid bone and midline facial plane of muscles of the upper neck. It forms the floor of the mouth. It is supplied by the mylohyoid

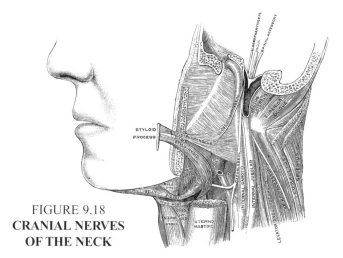

FIGURE 9.18
**CRANIAL NERVES
OF THE NECK**

branch of the inferior alveolar nerve. The inferior alveolar nerve is a branch of the mandibular nerve, which itself is a branch of the trigeminal nerve (CN V). The innervation of the mylohyoid is therefore ultimately provided by the trigeminal nerve.

MYLOHYOID = MOUTH via MANDIBULAR

The mylohyoid forms the floor of the mouth and is innervated by the mandibular nerve (br. of trigeminal n., CN V).

The digastric muscle has two bellies. The anterior belly originates below the chin on the mandible. The posterior belly originates on the mastoid process of the temporal bone. Both insert by way of an intermediate tendon on the hyoid bone. The word element *di-* means two or divergent. Either application is appropriate in the naming of this muscle. The anterior belly is supplied by the previously-mentioned mylohyoid branch of the inferior alveolar nerve. This seems logical, as the anterior belly is near the mylohyoid muscle. The posterior belly is innervated by the digastric branch of the facial nerve, cranial nerve VII. The posterior belly's origination from the mastoid process is behind the ear, a location very near the facial nerve. The digastric functions to lower the mandible and raise the hyoid bone.

The two remaining muscles are also supplied by the facial nerve. The stylohyoid originates on the styloid process of the temporal bone. This is not far from the origination of the posterior belly of the digastric muscle. As may be inferred from its name, the stylohyoid inserts on the hyoid bone. Upon contraction, it moves the hyoid bone posterior and superior, pulling the tongue in the same direction. The stylohyoid, mylohyoid and digastric muscles can be seen in Figure 9.8.

The platysma is the other "muscle" of the neck supplied by the facial nerve. The platysma is actually a thin sheet of superficial muscle fibers located just beneath the skin of the anterior neck. It originates from cervical fascia and inserts on the underside of the mandible. The platysma is innervated by the cervical branch of the facial nerve.

Similar to innervation of back muscles by unnamed dorsal rami branches, several muscles of the neck originate from the lateral and/or anterior aspect of the cervical vertebral column and are innervated by unnamed ventral rami branches. Because they are innervated in a variable fashion at or near their point of origination, there are no named nerves which supply them.

The rectus capitis anterior originates from the lateral side of

the atlas. The rectus capitis lateralis originates from the transverse process of the atlas. Both insert on the anterior and inferior aspect of the occipital bone and function to flex the skull. Both are also supplied by ventral rami branches from C1 and C2. The rectus capitis posterior major and rectus capitis posterior minor are part of the suboccipital group of back muscles and were previously described. Coincidently, they are innervated by dorsal rami branches from C1 and C2, the suboccipital and greater occipital nerves.

The longus colli muscle is similar to an anterior-located back muscle in that it originates from vertebrae, travels up, almost parallel to the spine, and inserts on vertebrae located above its point of origination. It originates from transverse processes and vertebral bodies of mid to low cervical and upper thoracic vertebrae. Fibers travel up to insert on transverse processes and vertebral bodies of cervical vertebrae. Just as back muscles function to support and extend the spine, the longus colli functions to support and flex the cervical spine. It is innervated by various unnamed ventral rami branches.

The levator scapulae is supplied by ventral rami branches of the mid-cervical spinal segments. Most commonly, this includes C3 and C4. The levator scapulae originates from the transverse processes of the first four vertebrae. The muscle inserts on the medial edge of the scapula. As its name may imply, the levator scapulae functions to elevate the scapula.

Finally, there are three scalene muscles: the anterior, middle, and posterior scalene muscles. All originate from transverse processes of cervical vertebrae. The anterior and middle insert on the first rib. The posterior inserts on the second rib. All are innervated in a variable fashion by ventral rami branches from C2-C7. Each muscle functions to raise the rib on which it inserts and flexes the neck sideways. Of interest, the brachial plexus travels between the anterior and middle scalene muscles to reach the arm.

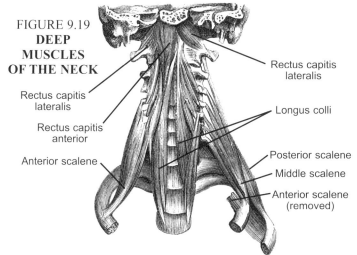

FIGURE 9.19
**DEEP
MUSCLES
OF THE NECK**

Rectus capitis lateralis
Rectus capitis lateralis
Rectus capitis anterior
Anterior scalene
Longus colli
Posterior scalene
Middle scalene
Anterior scalene (removed)

The brachial plexus is described in the next chapter. However, since this chapter is devoted to nerves of the neck, the brachial plexus should be mentioned. Formed by ventral rami of the lower four cervical and first thoracic spinal cord segments, most of the brachial plexus originates in the neck. Nerve structures of the plexus travel down to supply the arm. Figure 2 of the poster is drawn to facilitate learning the spinal cord segment contribution to the various nerves. It is a nerve *chart* and not an actual anatomically correct *picture*. The background of the subject's body is provided as a crude reference to demonstrate, generally speaking, where the nerves come from and where they go. It is not exactly anatomically correct. The fact that the brachial plexus originates in the neck may not be inherently obvious by simply viewing Figure 2.

QUIZ 2: Cervical Plexus and Nerves of the Neck

Time for Quiz = 34 minutes.
For questions 1-19, choose the single best answer.

_____1) Parasympathetic fibers are carried by which of the following nerves?
  a) vagus nerve
  b) glossopharyngeal nerve
  c) both a and b
  d) hypoglossal nerve
  e) none of the above

_____2) The stylopharyngeus muscle is supplied by which nerve?
  a) vagus nerve
  b) hypoglossal nerve
  c) spinal accessory nerve
  d) ansa cervicalis
  e) none of the above

_____3) The predominant motor nerve of the larynx is the
  a) internal laryngeal nerve
  b) glossopharyngeal nerve
  c) inferior laryngeal nerve
  d) external laryngeal nerve
  e) none of the above

_____4) The carotid branch of the glossopharyngeal nerve is also known as the
  a) superior laryngeal nerve
  b) lesser occipital nerve
  c) transversus colli nerve
  d) afferent nerve of Hering
  e) none of the above

_____5) The aryepiglottic muscle is supplied by the
  a) external laryngeal nerve
  b) recurrent laryngeal nerve
  c) internal laryngeal nerve
  d) hypoglossal nerve
  e) none of the above

_____6) Taste sensation to the anterior 2/3 of the tongue is provided by fibers of the
  a) chorda tympani
  b) facial nerve
  c) both a and b
  d) trigeminal nerve
  e) none of the above

_____7) The superior constrictor muscle of pharynx is supplied by
  a) vagus fibers of pharyngeal plexus
  b) glossopharyngeal fibers of pharyngeal plexus
  c) the hypoglossal nerve
  d) the recurrent laryngeal nerve
  e) none of the above

_____8) What is the carotid body?
  a) the dilated area of the common carotid artery where it divides into internal and external carotid arteries
  b) a grouping of chemoreceptors that monitor blood O_2, CO_2, and pH
  c) a passageway through which the carotid artery enters the skull
  d) a stretch receptor functioning in blood pressure regulation
  e) none of the above

_____9) Which nerve provides a tonsillar branch?
  a) glossopharyngeal nerve
  b) hypoglossal nerve
  c) spinal accessory nerve
  d) great auricular nerve
  e) none of the above

_____10) Which nerve structure innervates the palatoglossus muscle?
  a) hypoglossal nerve
  b) spinal accessory nerve
  c) glossopharyngeal nerve
  d) pharyngeal plexus
  e) none of the above

_____11) The predominant sensory nerve of the pharynx is the
  a) hypoglossal nerve
  b) trigeminal nerve
  c) glossopharyngeal nerve
  d) vagus nerve
  e) none of the above

_____12) The rectus capitis lateralis muscle is supplied by
   a) the greater occipital nerve
   b) the suboccipital nerve
   c) both a and b
   d) C1 and C2 ventral rami branches
   e) none of the above

_____13) What does the afferent nerve of Hering innervate?
   a) the parotid gland
   b) the tympanic plexus
   c) both a and b
   d) the carotid sinus
   e) none of the above

_____14) Which nerve structure supplies the salpingopharyngeal muscle?
   a) hypoglossal nerve
   b) recurrent laryngeal nerve
   c) pharyngeal plexus
   d) ansa cervicalis
   e) none of the above

_____15) What is the origin of the thyroarytenoid muscle?
   a) arytenoid cartilage
   b) thyroid cartilage
   c) hyoid bone
   d) sternum
   e) none of the above

_____16) The lateral cricoarytenoid muscle is innervated by the
   a) external laryngeal nerve
   b) internal laryngeal nerve
   c) inferior laryngeal nerve
   d) ansa cervicalis
   e) none of the above

_____17) The lingual nerve is a branch of the
   a) hypoglossal nerve
   b) trigeminal nerve
   c) glossopharyngeal nerve
   d) vagus nerve
   e) none of the above

_____18) The cricothyroid muscle is innervated by the
   a) external laryngeal nerve
   b) ansa cervicalis
   c) inferior laryngeal nerve
   d) pharyngeal plexus
   e) none of the above

_____19) Which nerves usually provides an auricular branch?
   a) spinal accessory nerve
   b) vagus nerve
   c) both a and b
   d) hypoglossal nerve
   e) none of the above

For questions 20-34, use the following directions:
   a.......1,2,3 are correct
   b.......1,3 are correct
   c.......2,4 are correct
   d.......only 4 is correct
   e.......all are correct

_____20) Which statements about the external laryngeal nerve are true?
   1. It is a branch of the superior laryngeal nerve.
   2. It contains vagus nerve fibers.
   3. It supplies the cricothyroid muscle.
   4. It supplies the inner mucous membrane of the larynx.

_____21) Which nerves exit the skull by way of the jugular foramen?
   1. vagus nerve
   2. facial nerve
   3. glossopharyngeal nerve
   4. hypoglossal nerve

_____22) Possible contributors to the tympanic plexus include the
   1. facial nerve
   2. internal carotid plexus
   3. glossopharyngeal nerve
   4. hypoglossal nerve

_____23) Which muscles are supplied by trigeminal nerve fibers?
   1. longus colli
   2. rectus capitis anterior
   3. levator scapulae
   4. anterior belly of digastric

____24) Glossopharyngeal nerve branches include the
1. tympanic branch
2. lesser petrosal nerve
3. nerve to stylopharyngeus
4. internal laryngeal nerve

____25) Which of the following are correct concerning the innervations of the tongue?
1. Motor is supplied by the hypoglossal nerve.
2. General sensation to the anterior 2/3 is via the trigeminal nerve.
3. Taste sensation to the posterior 1/3 is via the glossopharyngeal nerve.
4. General sensation to the posterior 1/3 is via the glossopharyngeal nerve.

____26) Which muscles are supplied by the hypoglossal nerve?
1. genioglossus
2. longitudinalis inferior linguae
3. hyoglossus
4. palatoglossus

____27) Which muscles are supplied by the inferior laryngeal nerve?
1. aryepiglottic
2. thyroarytenoid
3. vocalis
4. cricothyroid

____28) Which statements about the superior cervical cardiac branch are true?
1. It contributes parasympathetic input to the cardiac plexus.
2. It is also known as the afferent nerve of Hering.
3. It is a vagus nerve branch.
4. It supplies the thyroarytenoid muscle.

____29) Which muscles are supplied by facial nerve fibers?
1. levator scapulae
2. mylohyoid
3. posterior scalene
4. stylohyoid

____30) Which muscles may be supplied by the glossopharyngeal nerve fibers?
1. stylopharyngeus
2. inferior constrictor muscle of pharynx
3. middle constrictor muscle of pharynx
4. superior constrictor muscle of pharynx

____31) Recurrent laryngeal nerve branches include the
1. inferior cardiac branch
2. esophageal branch
3. inferior laryngeal nerve
4. external laryngeal nerve

____32) Contributors to the pharyngeal plexus include the
1. trigeminal nerve
2. hypoglossal nerve
3. facial nerve
4. glossopharyngeal nerve

____33) Which statements about the inferior laryngeal nerve are true?
1. All supplied muscles are intrinsic laryngeal muscles.
2. It contains vagus nerve fibers.
3. It supplies the oblique arytenoid muscle.
4. It is the terminal branch of the internal laryngeal nerve.

____34) Which of the following nerves supply the tongue?
1. glossopharyngeal nerve
2. trigeminal nerve
3. hypoglossal nerve
4. spinal accessory nerve

QUIZ 2: Cervical Plexus and Nerves of the Neck Answers and Explanations

1) c – The parasympathetic cranial nerves include the oculomotor (CN III), facial (CN VII), glossopharyngeal (CN IX), and vagus (CN X) nerves.

2) e – The glossopharyngeal nerve (CN IX) supplies the stylopharyngeus muscle.

3) c – The inferior laryngeal nerve is the terminal branch or distal continuation of the recurrent laryngeal nerve. The inferior laryngeal nerve supplies all muscles of the larynx except the cricothyroid, which is supplied by the external laryngeal nerve (external branch of the superior laryngeal nerve).

4) d – The afferent nerve of Hering is a sensory nerve carrying information to the brain from baroreceptors of the carotid artery sinus and chemoreceptors of the carotid body.

5) b – The aryepiglottic is a laryngeal muscle supplied by the recurrent laryngeal nerve (via the inferior laryngeal nerve).

6) c – The lingual nerve is a trigeminal nerve (CN V) branch that supplies general sensation to the anterior 2/3 of the tongue. Near its origin, the lingual nerve receives the chorda tympani branch from the facial nerve (CN VII). It is these facial nerve fibers from the chorda tympani that travel with the lingual nerve and provide taste sensation to the anterior 2/3 of the tongue.

7) a – The superior constrictor muscle of pharynx is supplied by vagus nerve (CN X) fibers from the pharyngeal plexus.

8) b – The carotid artery sinus is the dilated area of the common carotid artery where it bifurcates into the internal and external carotid arteries. The carotid body is a grouping of chemoreceptors at the fork of the common carotid. These chemoreceptors detect changes in blood oxygen, carbon dioxide, and pH and function in regulation of respiration. Baroceptors are stretch receptors that are located in the wall of the carotid sinus and function in blood pressure regulation.

9) a – The glossopharyngeal nerve (CN IX) is the primary sensory nerve of the pharynx. As such, it serves as the origin of tonsillar branches. These are sensory branches that supply the mucosa near the tonsil.

10) d – The palatoglossus muscle is supplied by vagus nerve (CN X) fibers from the pharyngeal plexus.

11) c – Both the glossopharyngeal (CN IX) and vagus (CN X) nerves are mixed nerves, providing motor and sensory functions. The glossopharyngeal nerve is the primary sensory nerve of the pharynx. The vagus nerve is the primary motor nerve of the pharynx.

12) d – The rectus capitis lateralis muscle, like the rectus capitis anterior, is supplied by ventral rami branches from C1 and C2. Coincidently, both the rectus capitis posterior major and rectus capitis posterior minor muscles are supplied by the suboccipital nerve (C1 dorsal ramus) and greater occipital nerve (C2 dorsal ramus).

13) d – See #4 and #8 answer explanations. The tympanic branch of the glossopharyngeal nerve (CN IX) is also known as the nerve of Jacobson and carries glossopharyngeal fibers to the tympanic plexus and subsequently, the parotid gland.

14) c – The salpingopharyngeal muscle is supplied by vagus nerve (CN X) fibers from the pharyngeal plexus.

15) b – Muscles are frequently named with reference to their origins and/or insertion. The origin is the fixed point of attachment of a muscle. The insertion is the attachment to the bone or other structure it moves. In many of the small, intricate muscles of the neck, the origin is referred to in the first part of the muscle name. The insertion is referred to in the second part of the name.

16) c – See #3 answer explanation.

17) b – The lingual nerve is a branch of the mandibu-

lar nerve (mandibular division of the trigeminal nerve (CN V)).

18) a – See #3 answer explanation.

19) b – Auricular branches are sensory nerves originating from the vagus (CN X) and facial (CN VII) nerves. The glossopharyngeal nerve (CN IX) can also contribute fibers. These branches supply tissue of the inferior and posterior external meatus of the ear.

20) a – The internal laryngeal nerve is the internal branch of the superior laryngeal nerve. It is a sensory nerve that supplies the inner mucous membrane of the larynx.

21) b – Both the vagus (CN X) and glossopharyngeal (CN IX) nerves exit the skull via the jugular foramen.

22) a – The glossopharyngeal nerve (CN IX) is the origin of a tympanic branch. This branch, along with possible input from the facial nerve and internal carotid plexus, contributes to the tympanic plexus.

23) d – The anterior belly of the digastric muscle is supplied by the mylohyoid branch of the inferior alveolar nerve. The inferior alveolar is a branch of the mandibular nerve, which itself is a branch of the trigeminal nerve (CN V). The posterior belly of the digastric is supplied by the facial nerve (CN VII).

24) a – The glossopharyngeal nerve (CN IX) is the origin of a tympanic branch, the fibers of which contribute to the tympanic plexus and form the lesser petrosal nerve. The lesser petrosal travels to the otic ganglion and innervates the parotid gland. The vagus nerve (CN X) is ultimately the source of the internal laryngeal nerve.

25) e – Taste sensation to the anterior 2/3 of the tongue is provided by the facial nerve (CN VII) via the chorda tympani.

26) a – The hypoglossal nerve (CN XII) supplies the intrinsic muscles (chondroglossus, longitudinalis superior linguae, longitudinalis inferior linguae, transversus linguae, verticalis linguae) and extrinsic muscles (genioglossus, hyoglos-

sus, and styloglossus) of the tongue. The palatoglossus muscle is supplied by vagus nerve (CN X) fibers from the pharyngeal plexus.

27) a – See #3 answer explanation. The inferior laryngeal nerve supplies the intrinsic muscles of the larynx.

28) b – The afferent nerve of Hering is the carotid branch of the glossopharyngeal nerve (CN IX). The thyroarytenoid, like other intrinsic muscles of the larynx, is supplied by the inferior laryngeal nerve (distal continuation of recurrent laryngeal nerve).

29) d – The levator scapulae muscle is supplied by ventral rami branches from C3 and C4. The mylohyoid muscle is supplied by the inferior alveolar nerve, which is a branch of the trigeminal nerve system. All three scalene muscles (anterior, middle, and posterior) are supplied by ventral rami branches from C2-C7.

30) a – The inferior constrictor muscle of pharynx is supplied by vagus (CN X) and glossopharyngeal (CN IX) fibers from the pharyngeal plexus, glossopharyngeal nerve, external laryngeal nerve (external branch of superior laryngeal nerve), and inferior laryngeal nerve (distal branch of recurrent laryngeal nerve). The middle constrictor muscle of pharynx is supplied by vagus and glossopharyngeal nerve fibers from the pharyngeal plexus. The superior constrictor muscle of pharynx is supplied only by vagus nerve fibers from the pharyngeal plexus.

31) a – The inferior laryngeal nerve is the terminal branch or distal continuation of the recurrent laryngeal nerve. The external laryngeal nerve is the external branch of the superior laryngeal nerve.

32) d – The glossopharyngeal nerve (CN IX), along with the vagus nerve (CN X), is the origin of pharyngeal branches. These contribute to the pharyngeal plexus.

33) a – The inferior laryngeal nerve is the terminal branch or distal continuation of the recurrent laryngeal nerve. It supplies the intrinsic muscles of the larynx, including the aryepiglottic, oblique

arytenoid, transverse arytenoid, posterior cricoarytenoid, lateral cricoarytenoid, thyroarytenoid, thyroepiglottic, and vocalis muscles. The cricothyroid is an extrinsic muscle of the larynx and is supplied by the external laryngeal nerve (external branch of superior laryngeal nerve).

34) a – The glossopharyngeal nerve (CN IX) supplies taste and general sensation to the posterior 1/3 of the tongue. General sensation to the anteri-or 2/3 is by way of the trigeminal nerve (CN V). Taste sensation to the anterior 2/3 of the tongue is transmitted by facial nerve (CN VII) fibers. The hypoglossal nerve (CN XII) is a motor nerve that supplies the intrinsic and extrinsic muscles of the tongue. The spinal accessory nerve (component of CN XI) is another motor nerve. It supplies the trapezius muscle and contributes to the innervation of the sternocleidomastoid muscle.

"A baby is born with a need to be loved – and never outgrows it."

– Frank A. Clark

CLINICAL CORRELATION

The phrenic nerve is responsible for innervation of the diaphragm. The word *phrenic* refers to the diaphragm. It describes anatomic structures that are associated with or located near the diaphragm. Phrenic vessels supply the diaphragm. The costophrenic angle is the lower lateral border between the ribs and diaphragm seen on chest x-rays. The word root *costo-* pertains to the ribs.

As previously described, the diaphragm is the large dome-like muscle which separates the thorax from the abdomen and functions in respiration. Most people are familiar with this muscle, but many do not know the actual mechanism by which it functions in respiration. The diaphragm is often mistakenly thought to contract against the lungs to force air out during expiration. In actuality, the reverse is true. Upon contraction, the diaphragm squeezes down on abdominal viscera, compressing abdominal contents and deepening thoracic volume. The increase in thoracic volume is transferred to the lungs, contributing to their expansion during inspiration. In fact, the diaphragm is responsi-ble for approximately 2/3 of the inspiratory effort in a resting state. The other 1/3 is provided by intercostal and other chest wall muscles. Most work in the same manner as the diaphragm, contracting during inspiration to expand thoracic volume. A negative pressure is created by the sudden increase in lung volume during inspiration. This negative pressure pulls air into the lungs. Expiration in the resting state is largely passive. The thorax returns to its original position, similar to an elastic recoil.

The phrenic nerve is formed by the combination of ventral rami branches from the third, fourth, and fifth cervical nerves. After emerging from the spine, the phrenic nerve must travel a considerable distance to reach and innervate the diaphragm. It courses between the sternocleidomastoid and anterior scalene muscles while in the neck. In the thorax, it travels in close proximity to the heart and great vessels. The specific thoracic anatomic relationships will be covered in chapter ten.

Like any nerve, the phrenic nerve can become damaged. The long trek through the neck and thorax increases exposure to possible injury. Anywhere along its lengthy path, the nerve could be damaged by trauma, tumor, infection, or some other form of injury. The nerve damage could result from a traumatic accident or inadvertent injury during surgery of the neck or thorax. Depending on the circumstances of the surgery, phrenic nerve injury may be unavoidable. The nerve injury may also be idiopathic, having no known cause.

Each phrenic nerve supplies the portion of diaphragm that lies on its respective side. In other words, each phrenic nerve innervates the ipsilateral hemidiaphragm. The combining word form *hemi-* designates half. With injury to the phrenic nerve, the ipsilateral hemidiaphragm becomes paralyzed. This is evidenced on chest x-ray by an elevation of the hemidiaphragm. As mentioned earlier, the diaphragm squeezes down on abdominal contents to increase intrathoracic volume. If paralyzed, there is no muscular tone to offset the upward pressure of the abdomen. The affected hemidiaphragm therefore appears elevated as compared to unaffected side.

FIGURE 9.20
DIAPHRAGM AND RELATIONSHIP TO OTHER VISCERAL ORGANS

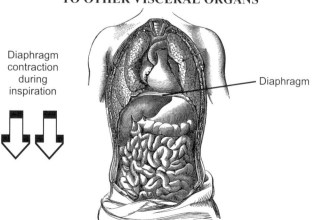

Diaphragm contraction during inspiration

Diaphragm

FIGURE 9.21

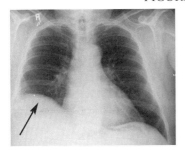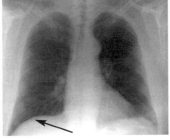

The chest x-ray on the left is from a patient with an elevated right hemidiaphragm, the result of right phrenic nerve injury. The chest x-ray on the right is from a patient with no such injury.

Because the diaphragm is responsible for 2/3 of the inspiratory effort in the resting state, one can simplistically deduce that each hemidiaphragm contributes approximately 1/3 of the overall inspiratory effort. Most patients adequately tolerate a paralyzed hemidiaphragm. There is enough respiratory reserve to compensate for the decreased diaphragmatic function. However, in patients with certain coexisting medical conditions, this may not be as well-tolerated. A paralyzed hemidiaphragm could become life-threatening in patients with disease processes that limit pulmonary reserve. Such processes include congestive heart failure (CHF), musculoskeletal disorders, and chronic obstructive pulmonary disease (COPD), a generalized disease class that includes emphysema and bronchitis.

As compared to unilateral hemidiaphragm paralysis, the outcome is not as promising if both hemidiaphragms become paralyzed. The likelihood of both phrenic nerves individually becoming damaged is fairly remote but can occur. When total diaphragm paralysis occurs, it is more frequently associated with a spinal cord transection above the C3-C5 spinal level. Not only would the function of both phrenic nerves lost, but spinal nerve innervation to chest wall muscles of respiration would also be lost. If the transection occurs within the C3-C5 level, some diaphragm function may persist, but most chest wall function would be lost. The patient would have very limited respiratory function.

In high cervical spinal cord transection, the patient is almost always dependent on mechanical ventilatory support. The amount of required support depends on where the cord transection occurs. The higher the spinal level, the more ventilator support required. A patient with a C1-C2 or C2-C3 transection requires full mechanical ventilation to survive. Between C3 and C5, the amount of phrenic nerve viability and hence, diaphragmatic function, is variable. The patient may be able to initiate a breath, but there would be little strength to maintain stable respiration, especially during times of stress. Such a patient often requires a mechanical ventilator to provide a certain amount of ventilatory "help" whenever a breath is initiated. Below C5, the patient should have full diaphragmatic function but may have limited chest wall function. This patient may be able to breath unassisted but would have limited function and reserve.

As opposed to physiologic ventilation, in which thoracic cavity expansion creates a negative pressure that pulls air into the lungs, mechanical ventilation is based on positive pressure. A mechanical ventilator simply squeezes or pushes air into the lungs. Because positive pressure is required to push air into the lungs, there must be a mechanism to deliver the air to the lungs while minimizing escape to the lower pressure of the atmosphere.

There are two basic types of conduits commonly used to transfer air under positive pressure between a mechanical ventilator and a patient's lungs. These include an **endotracheal tube** and **tracheostomy tube**. With both, the outer end is connected to a mechanical ventilation device and the inner end, when in place, lies within the lumen of the trachea. The inner end often has a cuff which can be inflated with air, thus sealing off the trachea and minimizing the escape of air. The lungs can then be adequately ventilated with positive pressure. An endotracheal tube is placed relatively noninvasively through the oral or nasal cavity. A tracheostomy tube requires surgical placement through tissues of the lower neck.

FIGURE 9.22
LOCATION OF ENDOTRACHEAL AND TRACHEOSTOMY TUBES

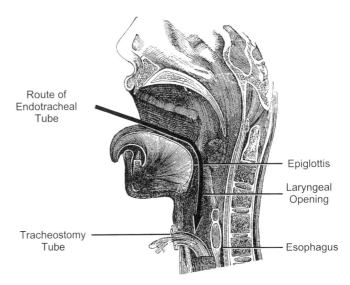

When mechanical ventilation is required for relatively short periods, such as needed for surgery or temporary periods of ventilation for patients in intensive care, an endotrachial tube is the preferred device. This "breathing tube" is placed directly through the mouth or nose and enters the trachea by way of the laryngeal opening between the vocal cords. With the use of a laryngoscope, the endotracheal tube is placed under direct vision, minimizing the likelihood of tissue trauma. The procedure of placing an endotracheal tube is known as endotracheal intubation. In common language, the procedure is simply referred to as an **intubation**. Endotracheal tubes are by far the most common type of airway conduit for positive pressure ventilation. As opposed to tracheostomy tubes, no invasive surgery is required for tube placement.

There are several obvious disadvantages that prevent the use of endotracheal tubes in cases such as cervical spinal cord transection where chronic mechanical ventilatory support is required. First, and most apparent, is oral and pulmonary hygiene. Secretions get deposited on the endotracheal tube. Over time, these deposits accumulate and become a source of infection. In addition, the tube curves through the mouth, pharynx, and larynx to reach the trachea. This creates tissue pressure points, which can lead to tissue ulcerations. Finally, the tube is relatively long. This provides additional surface area inside the tube for pulmonary secretions to collect, eventually occluding the tube.

There are other, less apparent, yet equally important aspects of endotracheal tube ventilation that preclude their use in chronic ventilatory assistance. This is especially true in cases like a C5-C6 cord transection, where the patient is able to breathe on his/her own but has very limited reserve and may require support. In this situation, it is important to minimize the work associated with breathing. This involves decreasing the resistance against breathing and increasing the efficiency of breathing. Improved efficiency occurs by minimizing work wasted on movement of air that does not participate in gas exchange.

As mentioned earlier, endotracheal tubes are relatively long. In addition, they are the same, rather narrow width throughout their length. The equation for the **resistance to gas flow (R)** in a straight tube is as follows:

$$R = \frac{8 \times length \times viscosity}{\pi r^4}$$

Because the length of the tube is in the numerator and radius of the tube (r) is in the denominator, anything that increases the length or decreases the radius (r) will increase the resistance to airflow and subsequently, the workload of breathing. Although it seems intuitive that the larger the radius of the tube, the less the resistance to breathing, the magnitude of this effect should be noted. Resistance is decreased by the radius of the tube to the 4th power (r^4).

In addition to increasing the resistance against breathing, the additional length of endotracheal tubes also decreases the efficiency of breathing by increasing dead space ventilation. **Dead space ventilation** is the amount of air/gas which is ventilated or "moved," but does not participate in gas exchange. Gas exchange occurs at the alveolar membrane. This is the respiratory epithelium of an alveolus, where oxygen is taken into the capillary beds and carbon dioxide is expelled. To reach the respiratory epithelium, air must travel through the **conductive airways**. These are the respiratory passageways through which air passes prior to gas exchange. They include the mouth and nasal cavities, pharynx, larynx, trachea, bronchi, and even the inner lumens of alveoli away from the respiratory epithelium. **Physiologic dead space** is the volume of air contained within the conductive airways. No gas exchange occurs in conductive airways. In most healthy individuals, physiologic dead space is usually equal to 2cc/kilogram (kg). Because 1 kilogram = 2.2 pounds (lb), a 220 lb man weighs 100 kg. His dead space ventilation would therefore be 200cc (dead space = 2cc/kg X 100kg = 200 cc). Dead space ventilation is a fairly constant value in each healthy individual because the anatomy and volume contained within the conductive airways does not change in normal circumstances. The amount of dead space ventilation in each breath will therefore not change. An endotracheal tube further lengthens the conductive airways and thereby increases physiologic dead space.

Tidal volume is the total volume of each breath during normal resting ventilation. For healthy individuals, this equates to approximately 6-8 cc/kg. A 100kg man would have a resting tidal volume of 600-800 cc. For this example, the tidal volume is said to be 600cc. Of this 600cc, 200cc is dead space and does not participate in gas exchange. The 400cc of air that participates in gas exchange is called **alveolar ventilation**. The **ratio of dead space to alveolar ventilation** in a normal, spontaneously breathing patient can be remembered as **1:2**.

To understand how dead space ventilation affects gas exchange and work of breathing, a spontaneously breathing patient should be considered. Just after exhalation and immediately before the next inhalation, most of the conductive airways are full of carbon dioxide. This was the last carbon dioxide that left the respiratory epithelium just before the conclusion of the expiration. There was not enough time or expiratory force to get the carbon dioxide out of the conductive airways prior to the next breath. Upon initiation of the next inhalation, it is this carbon dioxide-filled air that is first to present back to the respiratory epithelium. It is not until the continuation of the inhalation exceeds the conductive airway volume that "fresh" air makes it to the respiratory epithelium to participate in gas exchange.

Although the amount of physiologic dead space is constant for each breath, the amount of alveolar ventilation is not. Alveolar ventilation can be increased in healthy individuals by increasing the tidal volume, or more plainly, taking deeper breaths. A healthy patient has plenty of respiratory reserve to do this in times of stress. A patient with a cervical spinal cord transection, CHF, COPD, severe musculoskeletal disease, or any other cause of limited pulmonary reserve may not have the ability to increase alveolar ventilation. Because his/her ability to increase tidal volume is limited during spontaneous ventilation, the only way to effectively increase alveolar ventilation is to decrease dead space ventilation. Phrased differently, a patient with limited pulmonary reserve must breathe more efficiently. There is no reserve respiratory effort to waste on movement of air that does not participate in gas exchange. Dead space must be minimized.

FIGURE 9.23
TRACHEOSTOMY TUBE

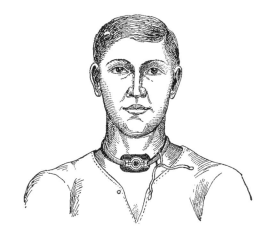

A tracheostomy tube is an airway conduit which is surgically placed in the lower anterior neck. A dissection is made through the skin, muscles, and other structures of the neck, a hole is made in the trachea, and a tracheostomy tube is placed directly into the lumen of the trachea. There are several aspects which make a tracheostomy tube the airway of choice for chronic ventilation support. First and most obvious, it is much easier to maintain good oral and pulmonary hygiene. Tracheostomy tubes are significantly shorter and often have wider lumens than endotracheal tubes. The resistance to airflow is therefore much lower. Most varieties have inner lumens which can be removed, cleaned, and/or replaced. Finally, tracheostomy tubes significantly decrease dead space ventilation by decreasing the length of the conductive airways through which ventilated air must pass. The mouth/nose, pharynx, larynx, and most of the cervical trachea are bypassed. A higher percentage of each tidal volume becomes alveolar ventilation and the patient breathes more efficiently.

In addition to chronic ventilation support, tracheostomy tubes are also used when the patency of the upper airway is in question. Upper airway damage can occur with traumatic injuries or surgery. Although the airway may be patent at a particular time, a tracheostomy tube may be electively placed in anticipation of probable tissue swelling and potential airway closure. Tumors, abscesses, and other infections can also necessitate the placement of a tracheostomy tube for airway protection. Some patients require a tracheostomy tube when long term ventilation is required for a potentially reversible cause, such as severe pneumonia. In many cases, the tracheostomy tube is removed once the threat to the airway or cause of respiratory decompensation is gone. With time, the tracheostomy site heals and these patients often resume a normal lifestyle.

X-RAYS

A paralyzed hemidiaphragm is only one of a seemingly inexhaustible supply of diagnoses made with the use of x-ray. Not only is knowledge of anatomy required to effectively read x-rays, but an insight into the process of x-ray formation and utilization helps to interpret what is viewed on film.

X-rays are a type of electromagnetic radiation. Radiation is a generalized term that describes a divergence from a common point. In anatomy, the word is used to describe various structures, such as nerve fiber tracts of the CNS. In common language, the word is often equated with electromagnetic radiation, which is the movement of atomic particles from a common source. Based on varying levels of energy, a spectrum is created among the different forms of electromagnetic radiation. X-rays are a high energy form. They travel at a speed near that of light.

HIGH ENERGY   **LOW ENERGY**

Gamma rays X-rays Ultraviolet Visible light Infrared Microwave Radar Radio

X-rays are the most well-known form of electromagnetic radiation used in medicine. Their use helped establish the medical field of radiology. Radiologists are physicians that specialize in the field. Not only do they read X-rays, but they use other forms of radiation for numerous diagnostic and therapeutic purposes.

For their use in medicine, x-rays are created by an x-ray tube. Within the outer housing of an x-ray tube are a filament and an anode. An electric current flows through the filament, causing it to become hot. The increase in thermal energy increases the kinetic energy of the atoms of the filament. As the kinetic energy increases, electrons are bounced from these atoms. A considerable voltage within the tube then accelerates these negatively-

charged electrons toward a metal anode. The positively-charged anode is frequently made of tungsten and has an angulated face. As the electrons strike the face of the anode, the dramatic decrease in kinetic energy is balanced by the creation of photons. A photon is a particle of radiant energy. The angle of the face directs the photons in a certain direction. The outer housing acts as a filter so that most of the particles leaving the x-ray tube are within the limits of the x-ray partition of the electromagnetic radiation spectrum.

FIGURE 9.24
BASIC MECHANISM OF A X-RAY TUBE

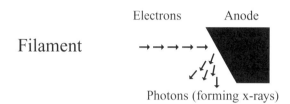

To take an x-ray, an x-ray tube is placed on one side of a patient. X-ray film is placed on the other side of the structures to be viewed. X-rays must pass through various tissues to reach the film. Tissues absorb x-rays at varying degrees, depending on the density of the tissue. Structures that absorb x-rays are said to be **radiopaque**. Structures that do not are described as **radiolucent**.

FIGURE 9.25
EARLY GENERATION X-RAY TUBE

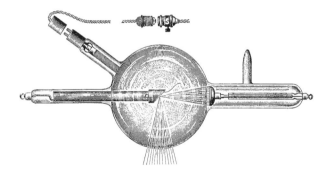

During development, regions of film exposed to x-rays turn dark. Regions not exposed to x-rays turn white or light. Bone is radiopaque and therefore absorbs x-rays. The film appears white in areas of film previously covered by overlying bone. Air is radiolucent and does not absorb X-rays. Regions of film which were under air-filled structures appear dark. Examples of such structures include air-filled lungs and gas in the digestive tract.

SUMMARY OF CHAPTER BOXES

1) Anatomic structures described right or left based on the subjects right or left. Example: left accessory nerve appears visually to right of spine.

2) Ansa cervicalis: **Superior root** from *superior* cervical spinal segments – branches from hypoglossal n., but composed of C1 and C2 ventral rami fibers. **Inferior root** from *inferior* segments – C2 and C3 ventral rami branches.

3) Phrenic nerve: C3, C4, C5…keeps you alive.

4) C3 in middle of cervical plexus (C2-C4). It contributes ventral rami branches equally with the other 2 cervical segments: 2 branches combine with C2 branches, 2 branches combine with C3 branches.

5) **Top to Bottom = 5, 4, 3.** C2 has 5 ventral rami branches. C3 has 4. C4 has 3.

6) Suboccipital nerve = C1 dorsal ramus. C1 is immediately below skull (occiput)…it is *suboccipital*.

7) Greater occipital nerve is great! It is the only "occipital" nerve with both motor and sensory functions.

8) C2 has *greatest* # of ventral rami branches (5). C2 dorsal ramus = *greater* occipital nerve. C2 is origin of both the *greater* (dorsal ramus) and *lesser* (ventral ramus) occipital nerves.

9) <u>3</u>rd occipital nerve = C<u>3</u> dorsal ramus

10) Upper 3 cervical dorsal rami exist in a spectrum of position and function: C1 (suboccipital n.) = motor, C2 (greater occipital n.) = mixed, C3 (3rd occipital n.) = sensory.

11) "glossal" and "lingua" relate to the tongue. The hypo<u>glossal</u> n. supplies intrinsic and extrinsic muscles of the tongue. To anchor the tongue, the extrinsic muscles must originate ***below*** or behind the ***tongue***. They are therefore innervated by the ***hypo glossal*** nerve.

12) Muscles are often named for origins and insertions: **Arytenoid** – arytenoid cartilage, **Epiglottic** – epiglottis, **Crico** – cricoid cartilage, **Genio** – genial = chin, **Hyo** – hyoid bone, **Palato** – palate, **Sterno** – sternum, **Stylo** – styloid process of temporal bone, **Thyro** – thyroid cartilage

13) The glossopharyngeal n. is named for its innervation of the tongue (glosso) and pharynx. Since the glossopharyngeal is already in the *back* of the throat supplying the pharynx, it also supplies the *back* of the tongue (taste and general sensation to the posterior 1/3 of tongue).

14) Nerve to stylo<u>pharyngeus</u> muscle provided by glossopharyngeal nerve.

15) Vagus n. is primary motor nerve of pharynx (supplies all muscles except stylopharyngeus). Glossopharyngeal n. is primary sensory nerve of pharynx. $V_1A_2G_3U_4S_5 = M_1O_2T_3O_4R_5$
GLOSSO (post. 1/3 tongue) **PHARYNGEAL** (all of pharynx) = sensory

16) **9 $L_1A_2R_3Y_4N_5G_6E_7A_8L_9$ MUSCLES:** cricothyroid is the only one not supplied by recurrent laryngeal n. (via inferior laryngeal n.). It is also the only one on the *exterior* of the larynx…it is supplied by the *external* laryngeal nerve (external branch of superior laryngeal n.).

17) Larynx (voice box) is used for singing. Just as a showgirl sings in Las **Vegas**, the larynx is supplied entirely by the **vagus** nerve via 2 branches: one from above – superior laryngeal n. (divides into internal and external laryngeal nerves), and one from below – inferior laryngeal n. (terminal branch of recurrent laryngeal n.).

18) "Laryngeal" nerves are named accordingly. All are vagus branches. The superior laryngeal n. divides into the *external* laryngeal n. (supplies cricothyroid, levator muscle of thyroid, and inferior constrictor…all are *external* of larynx) and *internal* laryngeal n. (supplies *internal* mucosal membrane of larynx). The recurrent laryngeal n. originates in thorax and "backtracks" to larynx. Its terminal branch, the *inferior* laryngeal n., approaches the larynx from an *inferior* position to supply all laryngeal muscles except the cricothyroid.

19) **Helpful Hints for Throat: <u>Tongue</u>** – Hypoglossal n. supplies all intrinsic and extrinsic tongue muscles. All muscles have "glossus" or "linguae" in name. Caution: palatoglossus is supplied by vagus fibers from pharyngeal plexus.
<u>Pharynx</u> – Vagus fibers supply all muscles except stylopharyngeus. Glossopharyngeal fibers may contribute to middle and inferior constrictors. Pharyngeal muscles include the 3 constrictors (superior, middle, inferior), muscles named for pharyngeal structures (uvulae = uvula, palatoglossus = palate, levator veli palatine = soft palate), and muscles with "pharyn" in name (palatopharyngeal, salpingopharyngeal, stylopharyngeus).
<u>Larynx</u> – Vagus branches supply all muscles. All muscles have "arytenoid" or "epiglottic" in name except two: vocalis and cricothyroid (renegade for 3 reasons). **Pharynx and larynx sound similar and each contains 9 muscles.**

20) Motor of throat via 3 cranial nerves: **Hypoglossal** = intrinsic and extrinsic muscles of tongue.
Glossopharyngeal = stylopharyngeus, contribution to middle and inferior constrictor muscles of pharynx.
Vagus = everything else in pharynx and all of larynx!

21) <u>M</u>ylohyoid = <u>M</u>outh via <u>M</u>andibular.

END OF CHAPTER TEST

Time for Exam = 80 minutes
For questions 1-51, choose the single best answer.

_____1) The lesser occipital nerve contains nerve fibers from the
   a) C2 ventral ramus
   b) C3 ventral ramus
   c) both a and b
   d) C3 dorsal ramus
   e) none of the above

_____2) The digastric muscle is innervated by the
   a) trigeminal nerve
   b) facial nerve
   c) both a and b
   d) hypoglossal nerve
   e) none of the above

_____3) Which of the following nerves is a branch of the C2 ventral ramus?
   a) 3rd occipital nerve
   b) branch to the glossopharyngeal nerve
   c) branch to the phrenic nerve
   d) branch to the supraclavicular trunk
   e) none of the above

_____4) The carotid branch of the glossopharyngeal nerve is also known as the
   a) external laryngeal nerve
   b) 3rd occipital nerve
   c) afferent nerve of Hering
   d) lesser petrosal nerve
   e) none of the above

_____5) Which nerve innervates the longitudinalis inferior linguae muscle?
   a) glossopharyngeal nerve
   b) ansa cervicalis
   c) hypoglossal nerve
   d) spinal accessory nerve
   e) none of the above

_____6) An auricular branch is usually provided by the
   a) vagus nerve
   b) facial nerve
   c) both a and b
   d) hypoglossal nerve
   e) none of the above

_____7) Which muscles are supplied by the greater occipital nerve?
   a) rectus capitis posterior major
   b) trapezius
   c) omohyoid
   d) hyoglossus
   e) none of the above

_____8) The levator veli palatini muscle is supplied by the
   a) facial nerve
   b) trigeminal nerve
   c) pharyngeal plexus
   d) hypoglossal nerve
   e) none of the above

_____9) The supraclavicular trunk contains nerve fibers from the
   a) C1 ventral ramus
   b) C2 ventral ramus
   c) C3 ventral ramus
   d) all of the above
   e) none of the above

_____10) The lesser petrosal nerve is a branch of which nerve?
   a) hypoglossal nerve
   b) glossopharyngeal nerve
   c) vagus nerve
   d) facial nerve
   e) none of the above

_____11) Which nerve innervates the sternohyoid muscle?
   a) ansa cervicalis
   b) hypoglossal nerve
   c) external laryngeal nerve
   d) inferior laryngeal nerve
   e) none of the above

_____12) The predominant motor nerve of the pharynx is the
   a) ansa cervicalis
   b) spinal accessory nerve
   c) glossopharyngeal nerve
   d) vagus nerve
   e) none of the above

_____13) The diaphragm is supplied by the
     a) spinal accessory nerve
     b) hypoglossal nerve
     c) glossopharyngeal nerve
     d) vagus nerve
     e) none of the above

_____14) What is the origin of the sternohyoid muscle?
     a) manubrium of the sternum
     b) thyroid cartilage
     c) cricoid cartilage
     d) hyoid bone
     e) none of the above

_____15) Skin of the posterior head is supplied by the
     a) 3rd occipital nerve
     b) greater occipital nerve
     c) both a and b
     d) suboccipital nerve
     e) none of the above

_____16) Which of the following nerves innervates the palatoglossus muscle?
     a) vagus fibers of the pharyngeal plexus
     b) glossopharyngeal fibers of the pharyngeal plexus
     c) hypoglossal nerve
     d) recurrent laryngeal nerve
     e) none of the above

_____17) The third occipital nerve innervates the
     a) rectus capitis posterior major muscle
     b) sternocleidomastoid muscle
     c) omohyoid muscle
     d) genioglossus muscle
     e) none of the above

_____18) Which nerve emerges from the tympanic plexus?
     a) chorda tympani
     b) lesser petrosal nerve
     c) nerve of Hering
     d) lingual nerve
     e) none of the above

_____19) The spinal accessory nerve contains nerve fibers from the
     a) C1 spinal segment
     b) C3 spinal segment
     c) C5 spinal segment
     d) all of the above
     e) none of the above

_____20) The vocalis muscle is innervated by the
     a) external laryngeal nerve
     b) inferior laryngeal nerve
     c) superior laryngeal nerve
     d) glossopharyngeal nerve
     e) none of the above

_____21) The ansa cervicalis innervates the
     a) stylohyoid muscle
     b) cricothyroid muscle
     c) omohyoid muscle
     d) all of the above
     e) none of the above

_____22) What is a carotid sinus?
     a) chemoreceptor which monitors blood O_2
     b) the bifurcation of a common carotid artery into internal and external carotid arteries
     c) stretch receptor functioning in the blood pressure regulation
     d) passageway through which carotid artery enters skull
     e) none of the above

_____23) The semispinalis capitis muscle is innervated by the
     a) greater occipital nerve
     b) 3rd occipital nerve
     c) both a and b
     d) lesser occipital nerve
     e) none of the above

_____24) Which nerves provides taste sensation for the anterior 2/3 of the tongue?
     a) trigeminal nerve
     b) glossopharyngeal nerve
     c) hypoglossal nerve
     d) vagus nerve
     e) none of the above

_____25) Vagus nerve fibers supply which muscle?
     a) cricothyroid
     b) palatoglossus
     c) posterior cricoarytenoid
     d) all the above
     e) none of the above

____26) Which muscles are supplied by the spinal accessory nerve?
  a) trapezius
  b) sternothyroid
  c) both a and b
  d) semispinalis capitis
  e) none of the above

____27) Which nerve provides a tonsillar branch?
  a) hypoglossal nerve
  b) glossopharyngeal nerve
  c) ansa cervicalis
  d) transversus colli nerve
  e) none of the above

____28) Which nerve innervates the geniohyoid muscle?
  a) spinal accessory nerve
  b) external laryngeal nerve
  c) C1 and C2 ventral rami fibers which travel with the hypoglossal nerve
  d) inferior laryngeal nerve
  e) none of the above

____29) The anterior, middle, and posterior scalene muscles are innervated by
  a) the spinal accessory nerve
  b) the ansa cervicalis
  c) dorsal rami branches from C2-C7
  d) the pharyngeal plexus
  e) none of the above

____30) Parasympathetic fibers are carried by which of the following nerves?
  a) vagus nerve
  b) hypoglossal nerve
  c) both a and b
  d) ansa cervicalis
  e) none of the above

____31) Which nerve innervates the omohyoid muscle?
  a) recurrent laryngeal nerve
  b) superior laryngeal nerve
  c) facial nerve
  d) ansa cervicalis
  e) none of the above

____32) The middle constrictor muscle of pharynx is supplied by the
  a) hypoglossal nerve
  b) facial nerve
  c) pharyngeal plexus
  d) recurrent laryngeal nerve
  e) none of the above

____33) Which muscles are supplied by C1 and C2 ventral rami fibers which branch from the hypoglossal nerve?
  a) styloglossus
  b) hyoglossus
  c) both a and b
  d) cricothyroid
  e) none of the above

____34) Taste and general sensation to the posterior 1/3 of the tongue is provided by the
  a) facial nerve
  b) glossopharyngeal nerve
  c) vagus nerve
  d) trigeminal nerve
  e) none of the above

____35) Which nerve supplies the rectus capitis posterior major muscle?
  a) greater occipital nerve
  b) suboccipital nerve
  c) both a and b
  d) unnamed cervical ventral rami branches
  e) none of the above

____36) A tympanic branch arises from the
  a) vagus nerve
  b) glossopharyngeal nerve
  c) transversus colli nerve
  d) hypoglossal nerve
  e) none of the above

____37) Which muscle is innervated by the suboccipital nerve?
  a) palatopharyngeal
  b) hyoglossus
  c) trapezius
  d) cricothyroid
  e) none of the above

_____38) What is the insertion of the cricothyroid muscle?
        a) cricoid cartilage
        b) hyoid bone
        c) thyroid cartilage
        d) arytenoid cartilage
        e) none of the above

_____39) Which muscle is supplied by the hypoglossal nerve?
        a) palatoglossus
        b) stylohyoid
        c) styloglossus
        d) sternothyroid
        e) none of the above

_____40) The oblique arytenoid muscle is supplied by the
        a) pharyngeal plexus
        b) ansa cervicalis
        c) recurrent laryngeal nerve
        d) hypoglossal nerve
        e) none of the above

_____41) What area of skin does the spinal accessory nerve most commonly supply?
        a) posterior to ear
        b) posterior neck
        c) anterior neck
        d) upper anterior chest
        e) none of the above

_____42) The rectus capitis anterior muscle is supplied by which nerve structure?
        a) suboccipital nerve
        b) greater occipital nerve
        c) both a and b
        d) C1 and C2 ventral rami branches
        e) none of the above

_____43) The superior root of the ansa cervicalis contains fibers from the
        a) C1 ventral ramus
        b) C2 ventral ramus
        c) both a and b
        d) C3 ventral ramus
        e) none of the above

_____44) The anterior 2/3 of the tongue is innervated by which nerve?
        a) CN V
        b) CN VII
        c) both a and b
        d) CN IX
        e) none of the above

_____45) Which muscles are supplied by the phrenic nerve?
        a) palatopharyngeal
        b) sternohyoid
        c) cricothyroid
        d) thyroarytenoid
        e) none of the above

_____46) The afferent nerve of Hering originates from which nerve?
        a) facial nerve
        b) glossopharyngeal nerve
        c) hypoglossal nerve
        d) vagus nerve
        e) none of the above

_____47) Which nerve supplies the skin of the ear?
        a) great auricular nerve
        b) suboccipital nerve
        c) both a and b
        d) transversus colli nerve
        e) none of the above

_____48) The cricothyroid muscle is innervated by
        a) C1 and C2 ventral rami fibers from the hypoglossal nerve
        b) the ansa cervicalis
        c) the external laryngeal nerve
        d) the inferior laryngeal nerve
        e) none of the above

_____49) The greater occipital nerve contains fibers from the
        a) C1 dorsal ramus
        b) C1 ventral ramus
        c) C2 dorsal ramus
        d) C2 ventral ramus
        e) none of the above

_____50) Nerves that contribute to the pharyngeal plexus include the
   a) hypoglossal nerve
   b) spinal accessory nerve
   c) both a and b
   d) ansa cervicalis
   e) none of the above

_____51) Which muscles are ultimately innervated by the supraclavicular trunk?
   a) trapezius
   b) mylohyoid
   c) palatopharyngeal
   d) thyroarytenoid
   e) none of the above

For questions 52-80, use the following directions:
   a.......1,2,3 are correct
   b.......1,3 are correct
   c.......2,4 are correct
   d.......only 4 is correct
   e.......all are correct

_____52) Possible contributors to the tympanic plexus include the
   1. facial nerve
   2. hypoglossal nerve
   3. glossopharyngeal nerve
   4. trigeminal nerve

_____53) Which statements are true concerning the inferior root of the ansa cervicalis?
   1. It contributes to the innervation of the thyrohyoid muscle.
   2. It is purely a motor nerve.
   3. The C4 ventral ramus contributes to its formation.
   4. The C2 ventral ramus contributes to its formation.

_____54) Muscles supplied by the hypoglossal nerve include the
   1. styloglossus
   2. transversus linguae
   3. genioglossus
   4. palatoglossus

_____55) Which nerves are purely sensory nerves?
   1. supraclavicular trunk
   2. suboccipital nerve
   3. transversus colli nerve
   4. ansa cervicalis

_____56) Recurrent laryngeal nerve branches include the
   1. inferior cardiac branch
   2. inferior laryngeal nerve
   3. esophageal branch
   4. internal laryngeal nerve

_____57) Nerve structures containing fibers from the C5 spinal segment include the
   1. phrenic nerve
   2. spinal accessory nerve
   3. brachial plexus
   4. supraclavicular trunk

_____58) Which muscles are supplied by the inferior laryngeal nerve?
   1. transversus linguae
   2. cricothyroid
   3. palatopharyngeal
   4. thyroarytenoid

_____59) Which statements concerning the transversus colli nerve are true?
   1. It arises from the same trunk as the great auricular nerve.
   2. It is purely a sensory nerve.
   3. The C3 ventral ramus contributes to its formation.
   4. The C4 ventral ramus contributes to its formation.

_____60) Which muscles are supplied by trigeminal nerve fibers?
   1. mylohyoid
   2. stylohyoid
   3. anterior belly of digastric
   4. posterior belly of digastric

_____61) Which statements about the spinal accessory nerve are true?
   1. It provides innervation to the trapezius muscle.
   2. It provides innervation to the omohyoid muscle.
   3. It provides innervation to the sternocleidomastoid muscle.
   4. It supplies skin of the posterior neck.

_____62) Which muscles may be supplied by the glossopharyngeal nerve fibers?
1. palatopharyngeal
2. inferior constrictor muscle of pharynx
3. superior constrictor muscle of pharynx
4. stylopharyngeus

_____63) Which nerves are cervical dorsal rami branches?
1. suboccipital nerve
2. lesser occipital nerve
3. 3rd occipital nerve
4. branch to spinal accessory nerve

_____64) Which statements about the internal laryngeal nerve are true?
1. It innervates the intrinsic muscles of the larynx.
2. It contains vagus nerve fibers.
3. It is a branch of the recurrent laryngeal nerve.
4. It supplies the inner mucous membrane of the larynx.

_____65) The inferior root of the ansa cervicalis contains fibers from the
1. C1 ventral ramus
2. C4 ventral ramus
3. hypoglossal nerve
4. C3 ventral ramus

_____66) Which of the following are correct concerning the innervation of the tongue?
1) Taste sensation to the anterior 2/3 is via the trigeminal nerve.
2) General sensation to the anterior 2/3 is via the facial nerve.
3) Taste sensation to the posterior 1/3 is via the hypoglossal nerve.
4) Motor is supplied by the hypoglossal nerve.

_____67) Which statements about the superior root of the ansa cervicalis are true?
1. It branches from the glossopharyngeal nerve.
2. It is a mixed nerve having both muscle and skin innervations.
3. It contains fibers from the C4 ventral ramus.
4. It contains fibers from the C1 ventral ramus.

_____68) Which muscles are supplied by facial nerve fibers?
1. rectus capitis anterior
2. anterior scalene
3. longus colli
4. posterior belly of digastric

_____69) Nerves containing fibers from the C2 ventral ramus include the
1. inferior root ansa cervicalis
2. superior root ansa cervicalis
3. transversus colli nerve
4. suboccipital nerve

_____70) Which statements about the inferior laryngeal nerve are true?
1. It innervates extrinsic and intrinsic laryngeal muscles.
2. It is the terminal branch of the recurrent laryngeal nerve.
3. It supplies the inner mucous membrane of the larynx.
4. It innervates the transverse arytenoid muscle.

_____71) Which of the following are purely motor nerves?
1. ansa cervicalis
2. greater occipital nerve
3. hypoglossal nerve
4. transversus colli nerve

_____72) Glossopharyngeal nerve branches include the
1. nerve of Hering
2. lingual nerve
3. nerve to stylopharyngeus
4. inferior laryngeal nerve

_____73) Which nerve structures may contain fibers from the C4 spinal segment?
1. spinal accessory nerve
2. supraclavicular trunk
3. phrenic nerve
4. brachial plexus

_____74) Which statements about the superior cervical cardiac branch are true?
1) It contributes to the cardiac plexus.
2) It is the origin of the lesser petrosal nerve.
3) It contains vagus fibers.
4) It innervates the carotid sinus.

____75) The superior root of the ansa cervicalis contains fibers from the
      1. C3 ventral ramus
      2. hypoglossal nerve
      3. C4 ventral ramus
      4. C1 ventral ramus

____76) Which nerves supply the tongue?
      1. hypoglossal nerve
      2. trigeminal nerve
      3. glossopharyngeal nerve
      4. facial nerve

____77) Nerves containing fibers from the C1 spinal segment include the
      1. superior root ansa cervicalis
      2. suboccipital nerve
      3. spinal accessory nerve
      4. phrenic nerve

____78) Which of the following are mixed nerves, having both sensory and motor responsibilities?
      1. ansa cervicalis
      2. lesser occipital nerve
      3. 3rd occipital nerve
      4. greater occipital nerve

____79) Which statements about the ansa cervicalis are true?
      1. The inferior root branches from the hypoglossal nerve.
      2. It is a mixed nerve with both muscle and skin innervations.
      3. It supplies the thyroepiglottic muscle.
      4. It supplies the sternohyoid muscle.

____80) Nerves containing fibers from the C3 ventral ramus include the
      1. superior root of ansa cervicalis
      2. transversus colli nerve
      3. 3rd occipital nerve
      4. supraclavicular trunk

END OF CHAPTER TEST: Answers and Explanations

1) a – The lesser occipital nerve is formed by a C2 ventral ramus branch. It is a sensory nerve that supplies skin posterior to the ear.

2) c – The anterior belly of the digastric muscle is supplied by the mylohyoid branch of the inferior alveolar nerve. The inferior alveolar is a branch of the mandibular nerve, which itself is a branch of the trigeminal nerve (CN V). The posterior belly of the digastric is supplied by the facial nerve (CN VII).

3) e – The third occipital nerve is formed from the C3 dorsal ramus. The C2 ventral ramus sends a branch to the hypoglossal nerve (CN XII), not the glossopharyngeal nerve (CN IX). Fibers from this branch later form the superior root of the ansa cervicalis. The phrenic nerve is formed by ventral rami branches form C3, C4, and C5 (C3, C4, C5...keeps you alive). The supraclavicular trunk is formed by branches from the C3 and C4 ventral rami.

4) c – The afferent nerve of Hering is a sensory nerve carrying information to the brain from baroreceptors of the carotid artery sinus and chemoreceptors of the carotid body.

5) c – The hypoglossal nerve is cranial nerve twelve. It is a motor nerve that supplies the intrinsic muscles (chondroglossus, longitudinalis superior linguae, longitudinalis inferior linguae, transversus linguae, verticalis linguae) and extrinsic muscles (genioglossus, hyoglossus, and styloglossus) of the tongue.

6) c – Auricular branches are sensory branches originating from the vagus (CN X) and facial (CN VII) nerves. The glossopharyngeal nerve (CN IX) may also contribute fibers. These branches supply tissue of the inferior and posterior external meatus of the ear.

7) a – The trapezius muscle is supplied by the spinal accessory nerve (component of CN XI). The omohyoid muscle is supplied by the ansa cervicalis nerve loop. The hyoglossus muscle is innervated by the hypoglossal nerve (CN XII).

8) c – The levator veli palatini muscle is supplied by vagus nerve (CN X) fibers from the pharyngeal plexus.

9) c – The supraclavicular trunk is formed by branches from the C3 and C4 ventral rami. The supraclavicular trunk is a sensory nerve. It usually gives off three supraclavicular nerves, which supply skin of the anterior chest over the first two ribs.

10) b – The glossopharyngeal nerve (CN IX) is the origin of a tympanic branch, the fibers of which contribute to the tympanic plexus and form the lesser petrosal nerve. The lesser petrosal travels to the otic ganglion and innervates the parotid gland.

11) a – The ansa cervicalis is a motor nerve that innervates the sternohyoid, sternothyroid, and omohyoid muscles.

12) d – Both the glossopharyngeal (CN IX) and vagus (CN X) nerves are mixed nerves, providing motor and sensory functions. The glossopharyngeal nerve is the primary sensory nerve of the pharynx. The vagus nerve is the primary motor nerve of the pharynx.

13) e – The phrenic nerve innervates the diaphragm. The phrenic nerve is formed by ventral rami branches from C3, C4, and C5 (C3, C4, C5...keeps you alive).

14) a – Muscles are frequently named with reference to their origins and/or insertion. The origin is the fixed point of attachment of a muscle. The insertion is the attachment to the bone (or other structure) it moves. In many of the small, intricate muscles of the neck, the origin is referred to in the first part of the muscle name. The insertion is referred to in the second part of the name.

15) c – The greater occipital nerve is a mixed nerve, supplying both skin and muscle of the posterior head and neck. The third occipital nerve is a sensory nerve that supplies skin on the back of the upper neck and lower head. The suboccipital nerve is a motor nerve.

16) a – The palatoglossus muscle is supplied by vagus nerve (CN X) fibers from the pharyngeal plexus.

17) e – The third occipital nerve is formed from the C3 dorsal ramus. The third occipital nerve is a sensory nerve that supplies skin on the back of the upper neck and lower head. The rectus capitis posterior major muscle is innervated by the suboccipital and greater occipital nerves. The sternocleidomastoid muscle is supplied by a nerve formed by branches from the C2 ventral ramus and spinal accessory nerve (component of CN XI). The omohyoid muscle is supplied by the ansa cervicalis nerve loop. The genioglossus muscle is innervated by the hypoglossal nerve (CN XII).

18) b – See #10 answer explanation.

19) d – The spinal accessory nerve (component of CN XI) is a motor nerve formed by branches from C1-C5 spinal segments. The spinal accessory nerve innervates the trapezius muscle and gives a branch that combines with a C2 ventral ramus branch to innervate the sternocleidomastoid muscle.

20) b – The inferior laryngeal nerve is the terminal branch or distal continuation of the recurrent laryngeal nerve.

21) c – The ansa cervicalis is a motor nerve that innervates infrahyoid muscles, including the sternohyoid, sternothyroid, and omohyoid muscles. The stylohyoid muscle is innervated by the facial nerve (CN VII). The cricothyroid muscle is innervated by the external laryngeal nerve (external branch of superior laryngeal nerve).

22) b – The carotid artery sinus is the dilated area of the common carotid artery that bifurcates into the internal and external carotid arteries. The carotid body is an area of chemoreceptors at the fork of the common carotid artery. These chemoreceptors detect changes in blood oxygen, carbon dioxide, and pH and function in regulation of respiration. Baroceptors are stretch receptors that are located in the wall of the carotid sinus and function in blood pressure regulation.

23) a – The semispinalis capitis muscle is innervated by the suboccipital and greater occipital nerves. The 3rd occipital nerve is formed from the C3 dorsal ramus. It is a sensory nerve that supplies skin of the posterior upper neck and lower head. The lesser occipital nerve is a branch of the C2 ventral ramus. The lesser occipital nerve is a sensory nerve supplying skin behind the ear.

24) e – Taste sensation to the anterior 2/3 of the tongue is provided by facial nerve fibers (CN VII) that travel with the lingual nerve, a trigeminal nerve (CN V) branch. Trigeminal fibers provide general sensation to the anterior 2/3 of the tongue. The glossopharyngeal nerve (CN IX) supplies taste and general sensation to the posterior 1/3 of the tongue.

25) d – All are supplied by vagus nerve (CN X) fibers. The cricothyroid is innervated by the external laryngeal nerve. This is the external branch of the superior laryngeal nerve, a vagus nerve branch. The palatoglossus is supplied by vagus fibers from the pharyngeal plexus. The posterior cricoarytenoid, like all intrinsic laryngeal muscles, is innervated by the inferior laryngeal nerve. This is the distal continuation of the recurrent laryngeal nerve, another vagus nerve branch.

26) a – The spinal accessory nerve is a division of the accessory nerve, CN XI. The spinal accessory nerve is formed by ventral rami branches from C1-C5. It is a motor nerve that innervates the trapezius muscle and gives a branch that combines with a C2 ventral ramus branch to innervate the sternocleidomastoid muscle. The sternothyroid muscle is supplied by the ansa cervicalis nerve loop. The semispinalis capitis muscle is innervated by the suboccipital and greater occipital nerves.

27) b – The glossopharyngeal nerve (CN IX) is the origin of tonsillar branches. These are sensory nerves that supply the mucosa near the tonsil.

28) c – The superior root of the ansa cervicalis is formed by a branch of the hypoglossal nerve (CN XII) composed of C1 and C2 ventral rami nerve fibers that previously joined the hypoglossal by way of a C2 ventral ramus

branch. After the superior root branches from the hypoglossal, the remaining C1 and C2 fibers continue with the hypoglossal to innervate the geniohyoid and thyrohyoid muscles.

29) e – All three scalene muscles (anterior, middle, and posterior) are supplied by *ventral* rami branches from C2-C7.

30) a – The parasympathetic cranial nerves include the oculomotor (CN III), facial (CN VII), glossopharyngeal (CN IX), and vagus (CN X) nerves.

31) d – See #11 answer explanation.

32) c – The middle constrictor muscle of pharynx is supplied by vagus (CN X) and glossopharyngeal (CN IX) nerve fibers from the pharyngeal plexus.

33) e – See #28 answer explanation. Both the styloglossus and hyoglossus are extrinsic muscles of the tongue innervated by the hypoglossal nerve (CN XII). The cricothyroid muscle is innervated by the external laryngeal nerve (external branch of superior laryngeal nerve).

34) b – See #24 answer explanation.

35) c – The rectus capitis posterior major muscle is innervated by the suboccipital and greater occipital nerves.

36) b – See #10 answer explanation. Tympanic branches may also originate from the facial nerve (CN VII) and internal carotid plexus.

37) e – The suboccipital nerve supplies the semispinalis capitis, rectus capitis posterior major, rectus capitis posterior minor, obliquus capitis superior, and obliquus capitis inferior muscles. The palatopharyngeal muscle is supplied by vagus nerve (CN X) fibers from the pharyngeal plexus. The hyoglossus muscle is innervated by the hypoglossal nerve (CN XII). The trapezius muscle is supplied by the spinal accessory nerve (component of CN XI). The cricothyroid muscle is innervated by the external laryngeal nerve (external branch of superior laryngeal nerve).

38) c – See #14 answer explanation.

39) c – The palatoglossus muscle is supplied by vagus nerve (CN X) fibers from the pharyngeal plexus. The stylohyoid muscle is innervated by the facial nerve (CN VII). The sternothyroid muscle is supplied by the ansa cervicalis nerve loop.

40) c – The oblique arytenoid muscle, like all intrinsic muscles of the larynx, is supplied by the recurrent laryngeal nerve (via the inferior laryngeal nerve).

41) e – See #19 answer explanation. The spinal accessory nerve (component of CN XI) is a motor nerve. It has no cutaneous innervations.

42) d – The rectus capitis *anterior* muscle is supplied by the *ventral* rami branches from C1 and C2. Coincidently, the rectus capitis *posterior* muscles (major and minor) are supplied by both the suboccipital nerve (C1 *dorsal* ramus) and greater occipital nerve (C2 *dorsal* ramus).

43) c – See #28 answer explanation.

44) c – See #24 answer explanation.

45) e – The phrenic nerve innervates the diaphragm. The palatopharyngeal muscle is supplied by vagus nerve (CN X) fibers from the pharyngeal plexus. The sternohyoid muscle is supplied by the ansa cervicalis nerve loop. The cricothyroid muscle is innervated by the external laryngeal nerve (external branch of superior laryngeal nerve). The thyroarytenoid muscle is supplied by the recurrent laryngeal nerve (via the inferior laryngeal nerve).

46) b – See #4 answer explanation.

47) a – The great auricular nerve is a sensory nerve that supplies skin of the ear and anterior to the ear. The great auricular and transversus colli nerves arise from a common trunk formed by ventral rami branches from C2 and C3. The transversus colli is a sensory nerve that supplies skin across the front of the neck. The suboccipital nerve is a motor nerve.

48) c – The cricothyroid muscle is innervated by the

external laryngeal nerve (external branch of superior laryngeal nerve).

49) c – The greater occipital nerve is a mixed nerve, supplying both skin and muscle of the posterior head and neck. The C1 dorsal ramus forms the suboccipital nerve.

50) e – The pharyngeal plexus is formed by pharyngeal branches from the vagus (CN X) and glossopharyngeal (CN IX) nerves.

51) e – See #9 answer explanation. The trapezius muscle is supplied by the spinal accessory nerve (component of CN XI). The mylohyoid muscle is supplied by a trigeminal nerve (CN V) branch (inferior alveolar nerve). The palatopharyngeal muscle is supplied by vagus nerve (CN X) fibers from the pharyngeal plexus. The thyroarytenoid muscle is supplied by the recurrent laryngeal nerve (via the inferior laryngeal nerve).

52) b – The glossopharyngeal nerve (CN IX) is the origin of a tympanic branch. This branch, along with possible input from the facial nerve (CN VII) and internal carotid plexus, contributes to the tympanic plexus.

53) c – The ansa cervicalis is a motor nerve that innervates the sternohyoid, sternothyroid, and omohyoid muscles. The inferior root is formed by branches from the C2 and C3 ventral rami. The superior root is formed by a branch of the hypoglossal nerve (CN XII) composed of C1 and C2 ventral rami nerve fibers that previously joined the hypoglossal by way of a C2 ventral ramus branch. After the takeoff of the superior root, the remaining C1 and C2 fibers travel with the hypoglossal nerve to supply the thyrohyoid and geniohyoid muscles.

54) a – See #5 answer explanation. The palatoglossus muscle is supplied by vagus nerve (CN X) fibers from the pharyngeal plexus.

55) b – The suboccipital nerve innervates muscles of the posterior triangle of the neck. The ansa cervicalis innervates infrahyoid muscles, including the sternohyoid, sternothyroid, and omohyoid muscles.

56) a – The inferior laryngeal nerve is the terminal branch or distal continuation of the recurrent laryngeal nerve. The internal laryngeal nerve is the internal branch of the superior laryngeal nerve.

57) a – The phrenic nerve is formed by ventral rami branches from C3, C4, and C5 (C3, C4, C5... keeps you alive). The spinal accessory nerve (component of CN XI) is formed by branches from the C1-C5 spinal segments. The C5 ventral ramus is a contributor to the brachial plexus. The supraclavicular trunk is formed by branches from the C3 and C4 ventral rami.

58) d – The inferior laryngeal nerve is the terminal branch or distal continuation of the recurrent laryngeal nerve. It supplies the intrinsic muscles of the larynx. The transversus linguae muscle is innervated by the hypoglossal nerve. The cricothyroid muscle is innervated by the external laryngeal nerve (external branch of superior laryngeal nerve). The palatopharyngeal muscle is supplied by vagus nerve (CN X) fibers from the pharyngeal plexus.

59) a – The transversus colli nerve, along with the great auricular nerve, branches from a trunk formed by ventral rami branches from C2 and C3. The transversus colli is a sensory nerve that supplies skin across the front of the neck.

60) b – Both the stylohyoid muscle and posterior belly of the digastric muscle are supplied by the facial nerve (CN VII).

61) b – See #19 answer explanation. The omohyoid muscle is supplied by the ansa cervicalis nerve loop.

62) c – Both the palatopharyngeal muscle and superior constrictor muscle of pharynx are supplied by vagus nerve (CN X) fibers from the pharyngeal plexus.

63) b – The suboccipital nerve is formed by the C1 dorsal ramus. The third occipital nerve is formed from the C3 dorsal ramus. The lesser occipital nerve is a branch of the C2 ventral ramus. The spinal accessory nerve (component of CN XI) is formed by branches that originate

directly from the C1-C5 spinal segments, not their dorsal rami.

64) c – The internal laryngeal nerve is the internal branch of the superior laryngeal nerve. It is a sensory nerve that supplies the inner mucous membrane of the larynx. The inferior laryngeal nerve supplies the intrinsic muscles of the larynx. It is the terminal branch, or distal continuation of the recurrent layrngeal nerve.

65) d – See #53 answer explanation.

66) d – See #24 answer explanation.

67) d – See #53 answer explanation.

68) d – The rectus capitis anterior muscle is supplied by the ventral rami branches from C1 and C2. All three scalene muscles (anterior, middle, and posterior) are supplied by ventral rami branches from C2-C7. The longus colli muscle is supplied in a variable fashion by cervical ventral rami branches.

69) a – See #53 answer explanation. The transversus colli nerve, along with the great auricular nerve, branches from a trunk formed by ventral rami branches from C2 and C3. The suboccipital nerve is formed by the C1 dorsal ramus.

70) c – The inferior laryngeal nerve is the terminal branch or distal continuation of the recurrent laryngeal nerve. It supplies the intrinsic muscles of the larynx, including the aryepiglottic, oblique arytenoid, transverse arytenoid, posterior cricoarytenoid, lateral cricoarytenoid, thyroarytenoid, thyroepiglottic, and vocalis muscles. The cricothyroid is an extrinsic muscle of the larynx and is supplied by the external laryngeal nerve (external branch of superior laryngeal nerve). The internal laryngeal nerve (internal branch of superior laryngeal nerve) is a sensory nerve supplying the inner mucous membrane of the larynx.

71) b – The greater occipital nerve is a mixed nerve, supplying both skin and muscles of the posterior head and upper neck. The transversus colli is a sensory nerve that supplies skin across the front of the neck.

72) b – The afferent nerve of Hering is the carotid branch of the glossopharyngeal nerve (CN IX). The lingual nerve is a branch of the trigeminal nerve (CN V) and provides general sensation to the anterior 2/3 of the tongue. The inferior laryngeal nerve is the terminal branch or distal continuation of the recurrent laryngeal nerve, a branch of the vagus nerve (CN X).

73) e – The spinal accessory nerve (component of CN XI) is formed by branches from the C1-C5 spinal segments. The supraclavicular trunk is formed by branches from the C3 and C4 ventral rami. The phrenic nerve is formed by ventral rami branches from C3, C4, and C5 (C3, C4, C5...keeps you alive). The brachial plexus may receive input from the C4 ventral ramus by way of a branch of communication with the C5 ventral ramus.

74) b – The vagus nerve (CN X) is the origin of the superior cervical cardiac branch, which contributes parasympathetic input to the cardiac plexus. The lesser petrosal nerve and nerve to the carotid sinus are branches of the glossopharyngeal nerve (CN IX).

75) d – See #53 answer explanation.

76) e – The hypoglossal nerve (CN XII) is a motor nerve that supplies the intrinsic and extrinsic muscles of the tongue. Taste sensation to the anterior 2/3 of the tongue is transmitted by facial nerve fibers (CN VII). General sensation to the anterior 2/3 is by way of the trigeminal nerve (CN V). The glossopharyngeal nerve (CN IX) supplies taste and general sensation to the posterior 1/3 of the tongue.

77) a – The superior root of the ansa cervicalis is formed by a branch of the hypoglossal nerve (CN XII) composed of C1 and C2 ventral rami nerve fibers that previously joined the hypoglossal by way of a C2 ventral ramus branch. The spinal accessory nerve (component of CN XI) is formed by branches from the C1-C5 spinal segments. The suboccipital nerve is formed by the C1 dorsal ramus. The phrenic nerve is formed by ventral rami branches from C3, C4, and C5.

78) d – The ansa cervicalis innervates infrahyoid muscles, including the sternohyoid, sternothyroid, and omohyoid muscles. The lesser occipital nerve is a sensory nerve supplying skin behind the ear. The third occipital nerve is another sensory nerve and supplies skin on the back of the upper neck and lower head.

79) d – See #53 answer explanation. The thyroepiglottic, like other intrinsic muscles of the larynx, is supplied by the inferior laryngeal nerve (distal continuation of recurrent laryngeal nerve).

80) c – The transversus colli nerve, along with the great auricular nerve, branches from a trunk formed by ventral rami branches from C2 and C3. The supraclavicular trunk is formed by branches from the C3 and C4 ventral rami. The superior root of the ansa cervicalis is formed by a branch of the hypoglossal nerve (CN XII) composed of C1 and C2 ventral rami nerve fibers, which previously joined the hypoglossal by way of a C2 ventral ramus branch. The third occipital nerve is formed from the C3 dorsal ramus.

"Nothing in the world can take the place of persistence. Talent will not; nothing is more common than unsuccessful men with talent. Genius will not: unrewarded genius is almost a proverb. Education will not; the world is full of educated derelicts. Persistence and determination alone are omnipotent."

– Calvin Coolidge

CHAPTER TEN

BRACHIAL PLEXUS AND NERVES OF THE UPPER EXTREMITY

The brachial plexus is the group of nerves providing innervation to the upper extremity. The word *brachial* pertains to the arm. These nerves supply structures of the free limb of the upper extremity. Some nerves supply muscles of the torso that are associated with the pectoral (shoulder) girdle and function in movement of the upper extremity. The brachial plexus is formed by ventral rami branches of the lower four cervical nerves (C5-C8) and first thoracic nerve (T1).

The first of the lower four cervical nerves (C5) contributes to the dorsal scapular and long thoracic nerves. Although dorsal rami branches also exist for the C5-T1 spinal segments, they consist of various unnamed muscular and cutaneous branches. Their description is limited to their mention here.

LOWER FOUR CERVICAL VENTRAL RAMI BRANCHES

Two nerves formed by branches of the C5 spinal segment were described in the prior chapter. The **spinal accessory nerve** (26) is formed by branches of the C1-C5 spinal segments. The **phrenic nerve** (**47, 234, 235, 238, 239**) is formed by ventral rami branches of C3, C4, and C5. The C5 ventral ramus contributes to three other nerve structures. These are the dorsal scapular nerve, long thoracic nerve, and upper trunk of the brachial plexus.

> The **C5** spinal segment has **5** significant branches. They are the branch to the spinal accessory nerve, branch to the phrenic nerve, the dorsal scapular nerve, branch to the long thoracic nerve, and branch to the upper trunk of the brachial plexus. The last four branches originate from the ventral ramus.
>
> **C5 = 5 named branches**

The **dorsal scapular nerve** (203) is a direct branch of the C5 ventral ramus. It arises very close to the vertebrae and travels deep to innervate the rhomboid muscles of the back. This includes the greater and smaller rhomboid muscles on each side of the spinal column. They originate from the spinous processes of the C7-T5 vertebrae and insert on the vertebral margin of the scapula, the side of the scapula closest to the vertebral column. The

rhomboids are named for their shape. A rhomboid is a rectangle with sides off center so that one pair of parallel sides appears to make an oblique course. The rhomboids function to laterally rotate the scapula. This occurs when the arm is pulled toward the torso from a forward extended position. In some people, the dorsal scapular nerve also innervates the levator muscle of the scapula (levator scapulae), which lifts the scapula superiorly.

FIGURE 10.1
POSTERIOR MUSCLES OF THE SHOULDER GIRDLE
The overlying trapezius, latissimus dorsi, and deltoid muscles have been removed on the subject's right.

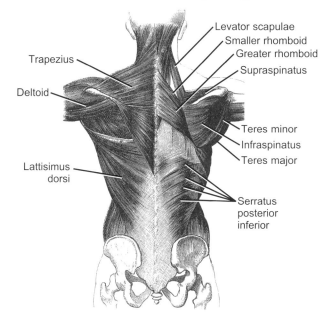

The **long thoracic nerve** (177) is formed from ventral rami branches from the fifth, sixth, and seventh cervical nerves. It runs posterior to the brachial plexus and down the lateral chest wall to supply the serratus anterior muscle. This muscle originates from the first eight ribs and inserts on the vertebral border of the scapula. It is named for its serrated or sawtooth appearance over the anterior and lateral aspects of the chest wall. There are also serratus posterior superior and serratus posterior inferior muscles of the posterior chest wall. Upon contraction, the serratus anterior moves the scapula anteriorly while turning it to raise the shoulder and abduct the arm.

FIGURE 10.2
**RIGHT SERRATUS
ANTERIOR MUSCLE**
Anterolateral view

To help remember the ventral rami contribution to the long thoracic nerve, imagine a child lying in the snow on his or her back making a snow angel. The arms are flapping up and down while the legs are moving in and out. The serratus anterior is functioning to move the scapula anteriorly while turning it to abduct the arms (raise the arms up as the child "flaps his or her wings"):

C5, C6, C7 are angels in heaven

The long thoracic nerve certainly is well-named. It is long because it comes all the way from the lower cervical spinal segments to supply the serratus anterior muscle over the first eight ribs of the thorax. It truly is the *"long"* **thoracic nerve**.

BRACHIAL PLEXUS

Attention will now turn to the brachial plexus. At first, learning the plexus appears a daunting task for the beginning student. With a little patience, diligence, and hard work, it will soon be mastered.

The **roots** of the brachial plexus are formed from the ventral rami of the fifth through eighth cervical nerves and first thoracic nerve. The ventral ramus of C4 may also contribute via a **C4 branch of communication with the C5 ventral ramus** (15). The roots join in specific combinations to form the three **trunks** (198-200) of the brachial plexus. The emergence of these roots (ventral rami) from their spinal cord segment of origin and subsequent contribution to the trunks of the brachial plexus is depicted in Figure 2 of the poster. Branches from the ventral rami of the fifth and sixth cervical nerves combine to make the **upper trunk** (200). The **middle trunk** (199) is formed singly by the ventral ramus of the seventh cervical nerve. The **lower trunk** (198) is formed by the combination of ventral rami branches from the eighth cervical and first thoracic nerves.

Each trunk travels distally and subsequently divides into an **anterior and posterior division** (192-197). These divisions then recombine in various ways to form the three **cords** (189-191) of the brachial plexus. The **anterior division of the upper trunk** (197) combines with the **anterior division of the middle trunk** (195) to form the **lateral cord** (189). The **posterior divisions of the upper** (196), **middle** (194), **and lower** (192) **trunks** combine to form the **posterior cord** (190). Finally, the **medial cord** (191)

is formed solely by the **anterior division of the lower trunk** (193).

The medial cord is the only cord formed by only one division, the anterior division of the lower trunk. This can be remembered because the transition stays in immediate alphabetical order.

L ➜ M

Ant. Division **L**ower trunk ➜ **M**edial cord

The brachial plexus is formed by ventral rami of C5 - T1, with possible contribution from C4. Every trunk is formed by ventral rami from two spinal segments except the middle trunk. The upper trunk is formed from C5 and C6. Likewise, the lower trunk is formed by C8 and T1 (remember…**up and down** = upper and lower = 2 spinal segments each). The middle trunk receives only C7 contribution. Next, consider the cords of the plexus and memorize the following numbering system:

1 = medial cord   2 = lateral   3 = posterior cord

These numbers coincide with the number of trunk divisions (branches) each cord receives. The medial cord only gets the anterior division of the lower trunk. The lateral cord receives the anterior divisions of the upper and middle trunks. Note also that these two cords receive only anterior divisions from the trunks. By contrast, the posterior cord receives three posterior divisions, one from each trunk. Again, remember **up and down**. The *up* cord (lateral cord) and the ***down*** cord (medial cord) are the two cords which only receive anterior divisions from the trunks. The posterior cord (it is posterior, it is neither up or down) receives only posterior divisions from the trunks. It receives one posterior division from each of the three trunks. In other words, the **posterior cord receives all the posterior divisions**.

An aid to remembering the names of the trunks and cords is to visualize an individual in an upright position. Hence, the names of the upper, middle, and lower trunks make perfect sense. Now imagine the individual's arm is down against the side of the body. The structures which were higher or more superior (upper trunk) are now more lateral (lateral cord) as they travel distally down the arm. The posterior cord is simply located more posterior in the arm. In actuality, the cords of the brachial plexus are named based on their anatomic position relative to the axillary artery.

Of final note, the **m**iddle trunk is formed by only **one root**, C7. Likewise the **m**edial cord is formed by only **one division**, the anterior division of the lower trunk.

FIGURE 10.3
ROOTS, TRUNKS, DIVISIONS, CORDS, AND BRANCHES OF BRACHIAL PLEXUS
Note relationship to axillary artery. The intercostobrachial nerve is not shown in this diagram.

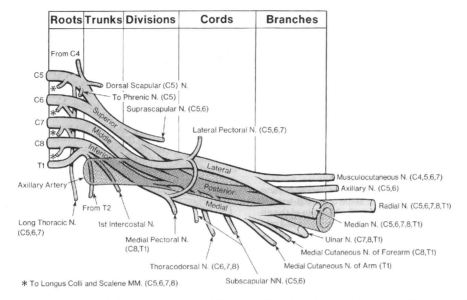

(Reproduced and modified with permission from Cousins, M.J., Bridenbaugh, P.O.: Neural Blockade in Clinical Anesthesia and Management of Pain, 2nd ed. Philadelphia, Lippincott, 1988)

<u>R</u>EAL <u>T</u>EXANS <u>D</u>RINK <u>C</u>OLD <u>B</u>EER!

This is a way to remember the order in which the brachial plexus evolves from the spinal cord.

<u>R</u>oots ➜ <u>T</u>runks ➜ <u>D</u>ivisions ➜ <u>C</u>ords ➜ <u>B</u>ranches

---

Although it does not take much time to cover the basic structure of the brachial plexus, care should be taken to ensure that it is actually learned before proceeding to the brachial plexus branches. *It is suggested that the student go no further until the plexus is successfully drawn and labeled without the aid of a reference.*

BRANCHES OF THE BRACHIAL PLEXUS

The brachial plexus is the immediate origin of multiple nerves that supply structures of the shoulder girdle and upper extremity. Some originate from the trunks, some from the cords, and some from the terminal branches of the cords. As mentioned earlier, the brachial plexus and its nerve system innervate muscles of both the torso and free limb. Those of the torso are associated with the shoulder girdle. Innervation of skin is confined to that of the free limb.

BRANCHES OF THE TRUNKS

Each trunk of the brachial plexus divides into an anterior and posterior division. Before dividing, the upper trunk serves as the origin of two nerves, the nerve to subclavius and suprascapular nerve.

The **nerve to subclavius** (202) innervates the subclavius muscle. The subclavius muscle can be seen in Figure 10.11. This small muscle originates from the anterior aspect of the first rib and inserts on the inferior side of the clavicle. Upon contraction, it pulls the outer end of the clavicle down. In addition, the nerve to subclavius usually supplies the sternoclavicular joint, the articulation between the sternum and clavicle.

The **suprascapular nerve** (201) travels toward the scapula to supply the acromioclavicular joint, shoulder joint, and the supraspinatus and infraspinatus muscles. The acromion is a lateral structure of the scapula and the highest, most superior part of the shoulder. It is the non-moving "bump" on top of the shoulder which can be felt as the arm is rotated. The acromioclavicular joint is the articulation between the acromion (scapula) and clavicle. The shoulder joint is the junction of the clavicle, scapula, and humerus of the upper arm.

The posterior aspect of the scapula has an elevated ridge of bone known as the spine of the scapula. The supraspinatus muscle is so named because of its location superior to the spine. It originates from this area of the scapula, known as the supraspinatus fossa, and inserts on the proximal humerus. The supraspinatus muscle functions to abduct the arm. The infraspinatus muscle is located inferior to the spine. It originates from the infraspinatus fossa of the scapula. The infraspinatus muscle inserts on the proximal humerus and functions to turn the arm laterally. Both muscles can be seen in Figure 10.1. Other than the anterior and posterior divisions of the trunks, the nerve to subclavius and the suprascapular nerve are the *only* branches of *any* trunk of the brachial plexus.

The **<u>supra</u>scapular nerve** is a branch of the **<u>upper</u>** trunk.

QUIZ 1
Brachial Plexus and Nerves of the Upper Extremity

Time for Quiz = 23 minutes.
For questions 1-14, choose the single best answer.

_____1) Which of the following neurological struc-
tures directly contribute to the formation of
the medial cord of the brachial plexus?
   a) C8 ventral ramus
   b) T1 ventral ramus
   c) both a and b
   d) anterior division of the middle trunk
   e) none of the above

_____2) Which nerve is formed by branches of the
ventral rami of C5, C6, and C7?
   a) phrenic nerve
   b) spinal accessory nerve
   c) dorsal scapular nerve
   d) long thoracic nerve
   e) upper trunk of the brachial plexus

_____3) Which of the following is a branch of the
upper trunk of the brachial plexus?
   a) anterior division to the posterior cord
   b) posterior division to the lateral cord
   c) anterior division to the lateral cord
   d) anterior division to the medial cord
   e) none of the above

_____4) Contributors to the lower trunk of the
brachial plexus include the
   a) C7 ventral ramus
   b) C8 ventral ramus
   c) T1 ventral ramus
   d) both a and b
   e) both b and c

_____5) Which of the following contribute a direct
branch to the lateral cord of the brachial
plexus?
   a) C5 ventral ramus
   b) C6 ventral ramus
   c) both a and b
   d) the anterior division of the middle
      trunk
   e) none of the above

_____6) The dorsal scapular nerve is a direct branch
of the
   a) upper trunk of the brachial plexus
   b) middle trunk of the brachial plexus
   c) C5 ventral ramus
   d) C7 ventral ramus
   e) none of the above

_____7) Which of the following is a branch of the
middle trunk of the brachial plexus?
   a) posterior division to the lateral cord
   b) anterior division to the medial cord
   c) anterior division to the lateral cord
   d) anterior division to the posterior cord
   e) none of the above

_____8) Contributors to the formation of the upper
trunk of the brachial plexus include the
   a) anterior division of the lateral cord
   b) anterior division of the medial cord
   c) both a and b
   d) C5 ventral ramus
   e) none of the above

_____9) Which of the following is true regarding the
long thoracic nerve?
   a) It is formed by the dorsal rami of C5-C7.
   b) It innervates the pectoralis major muscle.
   c) It innervates the supraspinous muscle.
   d) It innervates the serratus anterior muscle.
   e) None of the above

_____10) Which of the following neurological struc-
tures directly contribute to the formation of
the posterior cord of the brachial plexus?
   a) posterior division of the lateral cord
   b) posterior division of the medial cord
   c) both a and b
   d) branch of the C7 ventral ramus
   e) none of the above

_____11) The middle trunk of the brachial plexus is
formed by the
   a) anterior division of lower cord
   b) C6 ventral ramus
   c) C8 ventral ramus
   d) anterior division of lateral cord
   e) none of the above

_____12) Which of the following serve as a direct branch of the lower trunk of the brachial plexus?
      a) anterior division to the lateral cord
      b) anterior division to the posterior cord
      c) posterior division to the medial cord
      d) anterior division to the medial cord
      e) none of the above

_____13) The suprascapular nerve is a branch of the
      a) C5 ventral ramus
      b) upper trunk
      c) middle trunk
      d) posterior cord
      e) none of the above

_____14) Which of the following is true concerning the dorsal scapular nerve?
      a) It innervates the supraspinous muscle.
      b) It is a branch of the upper trunk of the brachial plexus.
      c) It innervates the rhomboid muscles.
      d) It is a branch of the posterior cord of the brachial plexus.
      e) None of the above

For questions 15-23, use the following directions:
    a.......1,2,3 are correct
    b.......1,3 are correct
    c.......2,4 are correct
    d.......only 4 is correct
    e.......all are correct

_____15) Which of the following directly contribute to the formation of the posterior cord of the brachial plexus?
    1. posterior division of upper cord
    2. posterior division of middle cord
    3. posterior division of lower cord
    4. posterior division of middle trunk

_____16) Direct branches of the upper trunk of the brachial plexus include
    1. the suprascapular nerve
    2. the anterior division to the anterior cord
    3. the posterior division to the posterior cord
    4. the dorsal scapular nerve

_____17) Which of the following are true concerning the dorsal scapular nerve?
    1. It innervates the rhomboid muscles.
    2. It is a direct branch of the C5 ventral ramus.
    3. Its innervation causes the scapula to move back and turn laterally.
    4. It innervates the supraspinatus muscle.

_____18) The lateral cord of the brachial plexus is formed by the
    1. anterior division of upper trunk
    2. posterior division of middle trunk
    3. anterior division of middle trunk
    4. anterior division of lower trunk

_____19) Which of the following directly contribute to the formation of the medial cord of the brachial plexus?
    1. anterior division of the upper trunk
    2. C7 ventral ramus
    3. anterior division of middle trunk
    4. anterior division of lower trunk

_____20) Direct branches of the C5 dorsal ramus include
    1. a branch to the spinal accessory nerve
    2. a branch to the phrenic nerve
    3. the dorsal scapular nerve
    4. muscular branches

_____21) Direct branches of the middle trunk of the brachial plexus include the
    1. anterior division to the lateral cord
    2. anterior division to the medial cord
    3. posterior division to the posterior cord
    4. posterior division to the posterior trunk

_____22) Contributors to the middle trunk include the
    1. C5 ventral ramus
    2. C8 ventral ramus
    3. C6 ventral ramus
    4. C7 ventral ramus

_____23) Which of the following statements concerning the suprascapular nerve are true?
    1. It innervates the supraspinatus muscle.
    2. It innervates the acromioclavicular joint.
    3. It innervates the infraspinatus muscle.
    4. It originates from the upper cord of the brachial plexus.

QUIZ 1: Brachial Plexus Answers and Explanations

1) e – The medial cord of the brachial plexus is formed solely from the anterior division of the lower trunk. Branches from the ventral rami of C8 and T1 combine to form the lower trunk of the brachial plexus. The anterior division of the middle trunk combines with the anterior division of the upper trunk to form the lateral cord. Argument could be made that the ventral rami of C8 and T1 are contributors to the medial cord by way of the anterior division of the lower trunk. However, the question asks for *direct* contributors.

2) d – The phrenic nerve is formed by the ventral rami branches of C3, C4, C5. The spinal accessory nerve is formed by branches from C1-C5. The dorsal scapular nerve arises directly from the C5 ventral ramus. Finally, the upper trunk is formed by ventral rami branches from only C5 and C6. The middle trunk is formed by a branch from the C7 ventral ramus.

3) c – The upper trunk serves as the origin of the nerve to subclavius and the suprascapular nerve before it divides into the anterior division to the lateral cord and posterior division to the posterior cord.

4) e – The lower trunk is formed by ventral rami branches from C8 and T1.

5) d – The lateral cord is formed by the anterior divisions of the upper and middle trunks. Branches from the C5 ventral ramus and C6 ventral ramus combine to form the upper trunk.

6) c – In addition to the dorsal scapular nerve, the C5 ventral ramus also gives branches to the phrenic nerve, long thoracic nerve, spinal accessory nerve, and the upper trunk of the brachial plexus.

7) c – The middle trunk divides into an anterior division to the lateral cord and a posterior division to the posterior cord. The anterior division combines with the anterior division of the upper trunk to form the lateral cord. The pos-

terior division combines with the posterior divisions of the upper and lower trunks to form the posterior cord.

8) d – The upper trunk is formed by branches from the ventral rami of C5 and C6. The upper trunk, in turn, serves as the origin of four nerve structures: the nerve to subclavius, the suprascapular nerve, the anterior division to the lateral cord, and the posterior division to the posterior cord.

9) d – The long thoracic nerve is formed by contribution from the C5-C7 ventral rami. It innervates the serratus anterior muscle of the chest. This muscle functions to move the scapula forward and twist it in order to abduct the arm. Remember children making snow angels: C5, C6, C7 are angels in heaven. The pectoralis major muscle is supplied by both the medial and lateral pectoral nerves. The supraspinous muscle is innervated by the suprascapular nerve.

10) e – The posterior cord of the brachial plexus is formed by the combination of the posterior divisions from each of the three trunks. This includes the upper, middle, and lower trunks. The lateral cord and medial cord don't divide into anterior and posterior divisions. A branch of the C7 ventral ramus solely forms the middle trunk of the brachial plexus. The middle trunk, in turn, contributes one of the three previously-mentioned posterior divisions to the posterior cord. One could argue that the C7 ventral ramus is a contributor to the posterior cord, but it is not a *direct* contributor.

11) e – The middle trunk is formed solely by a ventral ramus branch from C7.

12) d – The lower trunk divides into an anterior and posterior division. The anterior division serves as the lone contributor to the medial cord. The posterior division combines with posterior divisions from the upper and middle trunks to form the posterior cord.

13) b – In addition to divisions to cords, the upper

trunk is also the origin of two nerves. The nerve to subclavius and suprascapular nerve branch directly from it. The upper trunk then divides into the anterior division to the lateral cord and posterior division to the posterior cord. The middle trunk gives no branches before dividing into the anterior division to the lateral cord and posterior division to the posterior cord. Finally, the lower trunk gives no branches before dividing into the anterior division to the medial cord and posterior division to the posterior cord.

14) c – The dorsal scapular nerve is a branch of the C5 ventral ramus. The rhomboid muscles function to pull the scapula back and laterally. The supraspinous muscle is innervated by the suprascapular nerve, which originates from the upper trunk.

15) d – The posterior cord is formed by the posterior divisions from the upper, middle and lower *trunks*.

16) b – The dorsal scapular nerve is a direct branch of the C5 ventral ramus. The upper trunk is formed by ventral rami branches from C5 and C6. The upper trunk serves as the origin of four nerve structures: the nerve to subclavius, the suprascapular nerve, the anterior division to the lateral cord, and the posterior division to the posterior cord. There is no anterior cord.

17) a – Both the supraspinatus and infraspinatus muscles are supplied by the suprascapular nerve, a branch of the upper trunk of the brachial plexus.

18) b – The lateral cord is formed by the anterior divisions of the upper trunk and middle trunk. Each of the three trunks gives off posterior divisions that combine to form the posterior cord. Finally, the medial cord is formed solely by the anterior division of the lower trunk.

19) d – The medial cord is formed solely from the anterior division of the lower trunk. The anterior divisions of the upper and middle trunks combine to form the lateral cord. The C7 ventral ramus is the sole contributor to the middle trunk.

20) d – The C5 *dorsal* ramus, like most of the cervical, thoracic, and lumbar dorsal rami, gives rise to various unnamed muscular and cutaneous branches. These branches are so varied in origination and innervation that they are unnamed. The spinal accessory nerve is formed by branches from the C1-C5 spinal cord segments. The phrenic nerve and dorsal scapular nerve both receive contribution from the C5 *ventral* ramus.

21) b – The two branches of the middle trunk are the anterior division to the lateral cord and posterior division to the posterior cord. The medial cord is formed solely by the anterior division of the lower trunk. There is no posterior *trunk*, only a posterior *cord*.

22) d – The middle trunk is formed solely from a branch of the C7 ventral ramus. Branches from the C5 and C6 ventral rami form the upper trunk. Branches from the C8 and T1 ventral rami form the lower trunk.

23) a – In addition to the first three answers, the supraclavicular nerve also innervates the shoulder joint. Sorry about the last answer. Unfortunately, trickery is fair game to some instructors during test time. The suprascapular nerve is a branch of the upper *trunk*. There is no upper *cord*.

LATERAL AND POSTERIOR CORD BRANCHES

BRANCHES OF THE LATERAL CORD

The lateral cord gives off one motor nerve prior to dividing into its two terminal branches. The **lateral pectoral nerve** (181) branches from the lateral cord to supply the pectoralis major muscle. This muscle originates from the sternum and upper six costal cartilages, clavicle, and fascia sheath of the external oblique muscle of the abdomen. It inserts on the humerus. The pectoralis major functions to adduct the arm and turn it medially. The two terminal branches of the lateral cord are the musculocutaneous nerve and the lateral root of the median nerve.

The **musculocutaneous nerve (169,** 187) is a mixed nerve, having both motor and cutaneous responsibilities. Soon after branching from the lateral cord, the musculocutaneous nerve disappears into the substance of the coracobrachialis muscle to supply the three muscles of the anterior compartment of the arm. This includes the coracobrachialis, brachialis, and biceps brachii muscles. These three muscles constitute what many consider "the biceps." The coracobrachialis is the deep muscle of the proximal aspect of the anterior arm. The brachialis is the deep muscle of the distal aspect of the anterior arm. The biceps brachii is the anterior, overlying muscle of the three. The primary effect of musculocutaneous stimulation is flexion of the arm and/or forearm. Flexion of the arm occurs at the shoulder joint, where the angle of the joint is decreased. Flexion of the forearm is by way of the elbow joint. The elbow is bent, pulling the forearm closer to the arm.

> Flexion of both the arm and forearm moves the component distal to the joint in a forward or anterior direction from the anatomic position. Flexion of the arm at the shoulder joint moves the humerus forward. Flexion of the forearm at the elbow joint moves the radius and ulna forward.

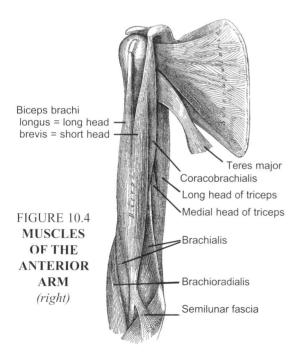

Biceps brachi
longus = long head
brevis = short head

Teres major
Coracobrachialis
Long head of triceps
Medial head of triceps

Brachialis

Brachioradialis

Semilunar fascia

FIGURE 10.4
MUSCLES OF THE ANTERIOR ARM
(right)

The coracobrachialis adducts and flexes the arm. Like many muscles, the coracobrachialis is named for its origin and insertion. It originates from the coracoid process of the scapula and inserts on the medial shaft of the humerus (humerus = long bone of arm = brachial). It works by way of the shoulder joint to flex and adduct the arm. Because of its insertion on the humerus, the coracobrachialis is limited to moving the arm. It has no direct role in forearm movement. This is in contrast to the brachialis and biceps brachii muscles, which insert on long bones of the forearm and function in forearm movement.

The brachialis originates from the anterior humerus and inserts on the proximal ulna. By crossing the elbow joint, the brachialis exerts its effect on the forearm. Brachialis contraction causes forearm flexion.

The word *biceps* describes a muscle with two heads. *Bi-* is a Greek combining form meaning *two*. The second component of the name is derived from the Latin word root *cephal(o)* meaning *head*. It may be recalled from the second chapter that the word *cephalic* describes the head. In anatomic structures, a head usually refers to an upper or proximal part of a structure. With muscles, a two-headed muscle has two points of origination. The long head of the biceps brachii originates from the supraglenoid tubercle of scapula. It forms the lateral aspect of the muscle and has a longer tendon as compared to the short head. Like the coracobrachialis, the short head originates from the coracoid process of the scapula. Both heads insert on the radius and ulna at the elbow. The word *brachii* is a derivation of the word *brachial* and distinguishes the two-headed biceps brachii muscle of the arm from the two-headed biceps femoris muscle of the thigh. In addition to flexing the forearm, the biceps brachii also supinates the forearm.

FIGURE 10.5
BRACHIALIS MUSCLE

Head

Greater tubercle
Lesser tubercle

Deltoid

R U

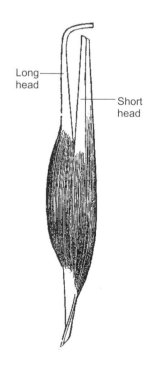

FIGURE 10.6
BICEPS BRACHII MUSCLE

Long head

Short head

Anterior Arm = Flexion

Coracobrachialis: The only anterior arm muscle that does not start with a *B*. It starts with a *C* because it originates on the coracoid process of the scapula. It has *brachialis* in its name because it inserts on the humerus, the long bone of the *brachium* (arm). It is also the only anterior arm muscle that exerts its force on the arm as opposed to the forearm. To match the 2 parts to its name ("coraco" and "brachialis"), it also has two actions. It flexes and adducts the arm.

Brachialis and Biceps Brachii: Both start with a *B*. Both insert on long bones of forearm and cause forearm flexion. Brachialis is one word. It inserts on one bone, the ulna. It has one action, forearm flexion. Biceps Brachii is two words. It inserts on two bones, the radius and ulna. It has two actions: forearm flexion and supination

The musculocutaneous nerve reappears from the substance of the biceps brachii muscle just above the elbow and is then known as the **lateral antebrachial cutaneous nerve** (165). Like many anatomic structures, an evaluation of this nerve's name reveals its function. *Antebrachial* is another word for *forearm* and *cutaneous* means *skin*. This nerve supplies the skin on the anterior and lateral (radial) part of the forearm. In Figure 2 of the poster, the musculocutaneous nerve is drawn dotted in a certain area to represent its travel through the substance of the coracobrachialis muscle. When it emerges from the biceps brachii (solid line), it is known as the lateral antebrachial cutaneous nerve.

Musculocutaneous Nerve is Well-Named

Although it may seem a bit "long-winded," the musculocutaneous nerve may have the most accurate of all nerve names.

At its more *proximal* location (in the arm), the nerve is *muscular*. It supplies the coracobrachialis, brachialis, and biceps brachii muscles. In the *proximal* aspect of its name, it is also muscular (*"musculo-"*).

In its *distal* location (in the forearm), the nerve is *cutaneous* and is known as the lateral antebrachial cutaneous nerve. The *distal* aspect of its name is also *"-cutaneous."*

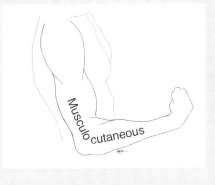

The **lateral root of the median nerve** (185) is the other terminal branch of the lateral cord. It combines with a terminal branch of the medial cord, the medial root of the median nerve (183) to form the median nerve. The median nerve will be described in more detail later.

Lateral Cord has *Lateral* Branches

The *lateral* cord is the origin of the *lateral* pectoral nerve before dividing into terminal branches. The musculocutaneous nerve is a terminal branch of the *lateral* cord and becomes the *lateral* antebrachial cutaneous nerve. The *lateral* root of median nerve is the other terminal branch of the *lateral* cord.

BRANCHES OF THE POSTERIOR CORD

The posterior cord gives off three nerves before it divides into its two terminal branches. The first nerve to branch off is the **upper subscapular nerve** (180). This nerve supplies the subscapularis and teres major muscles. The subscapularis muscle is located over the anterior surface of the scapula bone. Since the scapula is located near the posterior surface of the torso, the subscapularis is below the scapula when viewed from the back. Hence, it is named the *sub*scapularis muscle. It inserts on the humerus and functions to turn the arm medially. The teres major muscle, along with the soon-to-be-discussed teres minor muscle, is named for its shape. The word *teres* describes a structure with a long, round shape. Like the subscapularis, the teres major originates on the scapula and inserts on the humerus, but at a more distal location. The teres major adducts the arm and also turns it medially.

FIGURE 10.7
DEEP MUSCLES OF LEFT SHOULDER
Anterior view

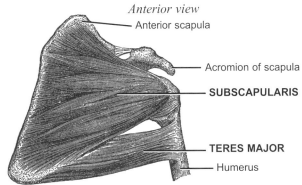

POSTERIOR CORD = PURPLE

To facilitate learning, the **posterior cord** (190) and all of its branches are colored purple in Figure 2 of the poster. Like the use of this color with dorsal rami branches, *p*urple denotes *p*osterior. Coincidently, many nerves of the posterior cord innervate structures on the *p*osterior aspect of the arm.

Next, the **thoracodorsal nerve** (179) runs from the posterior cord to innervate the latissimus dorsi muscle. This is the large muscle of the back that functions to adduct and turn the arm medially.

> The thoraco**dorsal** nerve innervates
> the latissimus **dorsi** muscle.

The third nerve to come off the posterior cord is the **lower subscapular nerve** (178). Like the upper subscapular nerve, this nerve also supplies the subscapularis and teres major muscles.

4 "Scapular" Nerves

There are four "scapular" nerves. Effort should be made not to get them confused. All are named with reference to the scapula. The *dorsal* scapular nerve is a direct branch of the C5 ventral ramus and travels *dorsally* to innervate the rhomboid muscles of the *back* and, in some individuals, the levator scapulae muscle. Because the rhomboids originate from the vertebral column, the dorsal scapular nerve does not have to travel far to reach them. The nerve is therefore a direct branch of the C5 ventral ramus. The **supra**scapular nerve originates from the **upper** trunk and innervates the **supra**spinous and infraspinous muscles and the two **upper** extremity joints located in the **upper** torso, the acromioclavicular and shoulder joints. Both the upper **SUB**scapular and lower **SUB**scapular nerves originate from the **POSTERIOR** cord and innervate the **SUB**scapularis and teres major muscles. Of the four scapular nerves, there are one "dorsal," one "supra," and two "subs." All of these descriptive terms are made with reference to the scapula. One nerve is a direct ventral ramus branch (C5), one is a branch of a trunk (upper trunk), and two are branches of a cord (posterior cord).

After serving as the origin of these three nerves, the posterior cord divides into two terminal branches: the axillary nerve and

radial nerve. The **axillary nerve** (**171,** 188) travels out to supply the teres minor and deltoid muscles. Like its big brother, the teres major, the teres minor also originates from the scapula and inserts on the humerus, although on a more proximal and posterior location. The teres minor functions to move the arm laterally. The deltoid muscle originates from both bones of the shoulder girdle. This includes the spine and acromion of the scapula and the lateral clavicle. The deltoid inserts on the lateral aspect of the humerus and abducts the arm. Before ending, the axillary nerve serves as the origin of the **superior (upper) lateral brachial cutaneous nerve** (170). This sensory nerve supplies an area of skin on the lateral aspect of the shoulder.

The **radial nerve** (**166,** 186) is the other terminal branch of the posterior cord. It provides several cutaneous branches and supplies five muscles before dividing into its two terminal branches, the superficial and deep radial nerves. The radial nerve and its branches supply skin and muscles on the posterior side of the arm, forearm, and hand. The muscles it innervates are used to extend and adduct the arm (via the shoulder), extend the forearm (straighten the elbow), flex the forearm (bend the elbow), extend the wrist (dorsiflex the hand), and extend (straighten) the digits. It also has branches which supinate the hand, abduct the thumb, and adduct the thumb.

By and large, the radial nerve functions in extension. This includes extension of the arm, forearm, wrist, and digits. One notable exception is radial innervation of the brachioradialis muscle, which flexes the forearm.

Soon after its origination from the posterior cord, the radial nerve gives muscular branches that supply all three heads of the triceps brachii muscle. As it approaches the elbow, other muscular branches supply the anconeus muscle and extensor muscles of the forearm.

Similar to the biceps brachii, the triceps brachii is named for its three heads. The specification of brachii differentiates this

FIGURE 10.8
SUPERFICIAL MUSCLES OF THE BACK

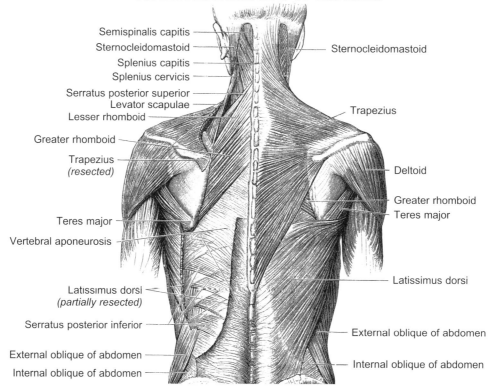

Semispinalis capitis
Sternocleidomastoid
Splenius capitis
Splenius cervicis
Serratus posterior superior
Levator scapulae
Lesser rhomboid
Greater rhomboid
Trapezius *(resected)*
Teres major
Vertebral aponeurosis
Latissimus dorsi *(partially resected)*
Serratus posterior inferior
External oblique of abdomen
Internal oblique of abdomen

Sternocleidomastoid
Trapezius
Deltoid
Greater rhomboid
Teres major
Latissimus dorsi
External oblique of abdomen
Internal oblique of abdomen

muscle from the triceps surae of the calf. The long head of the triceps brachii originates from the lateral scapula, just beneath the shoulder joint. Both the medial and lateral heads originate from the posterior humerus; the medial head originates from a more distal location. All three heads insert on the olecranon of the proximal ulna and extend the forearm. Because the long head originates from the scapula, it also extends and adducts the arm by way of the shoulder joint.

"Oh you elbow"
O   U
The **O**lecranon is the prominent posterior "bump"
of the elbow and is on the proximal **U**lna.

The anconeus muscle is located in the distal arm. It originates from the back of the lateral epicondyle of the distal humerus. The anconeus inserts on the posterior aspect of the olecranon and proximal ulna. Like the triceps, it extends the forearm. Named for its close proximity to the soon-to-be-described ulnar nerve, the radial nerve branch that innervates the medial head of the triceps and anconeus muscle is often called the **ulnar collateral nerve** (not drawn on poster).

In addition to supplying muscles of the posterior compartment, the radial nerve is the origin of several sensory branches in the arm. The two most notable are the posterior brachial and posterior antebrachial cutaneous nerves. The **posterior brachial cutaneous nerve** (168) arises from the radial in the axilla and supplies skin of the posterior arm. This includes posterior skin that is inferior to that supplied by the superior (upper) lateral brachial cutaneous nerve. As described in the second chapter, the arm extends from the shoulder to elbow. The distal edge of innervated skin is thereby limited to the approximate level of the elbow. The **posterior antebrachial cutaneous nerve** (167) arises from the radial farther down the arm. It continues distally to supply skin of the posterior forearm.

As the radial nerve travels distally, it gives muscular branches that supply three muscles of the forearm: the brachioradialis, extensor carpi radialis longus, and extensor carpi radialis brevis. The brachioradialis is named for its origin and insertion. It originates from the lateral aspect of the distal humerus (humerus = long bone of arm = brachial) and inserts on the inner part of the distal radius. Again, this muscle is an exception to the rule that the radial nerve innervates "extensors." The brachioradialis causes forearm flexion upon contraction. The extensor carpi radialis longus originates on the lateral humerus just distal to the origination of the brachioradialis. It inserts on the back of the second metacarpal bone. The extensor carpi radialis brevis originates from an even more distal location at the end of the lateral humerus, the lateral epicondyle. It inserts on the back of the second and third metacarpal bones. Both muscles extend the wrist joint (dorsiflex the hand) and deviate the hand in a radial direction.

Radial deviation is "sideways" movement of the hand toward the side of the radius bone (thumb). Ulnar deviation is movement of the hand toward the side of the ulna bone (little finger).

Muscle names often give clues to their function
Longus is Latin for *long*. *Brevis* means *short*. In addition, the word *superficialis* inherently describes a structure which is superficial. *Profundus* describes a deep structure. The word *carpi* refers to the carpus or the wrist joint. Muscles with the word *carpi* in their name often insert on carpal or metacarpal bones of the wrist and hand, respectively. Their contraction will thus move the wrist joint. The word *radialis* refers to the radius bone. A muscle may have *radialis* in its name because it attaches to the radius or it may cause movement toward the radius. Below are some of the descriptive words which may appear in anatomic names. Each is paired with its associated structure.

brachialis/brachio- = brachium (arm or humerus)
radialis = radius
ulnaris = ulna
carpi = wrist
digitorum/digiti = digits (fingers and toes)
pollicis = thumb
indicis = index finger
minimi = small finger
manus = hand

Soon after entering the forearm, the radial nerve divides into two terminal branches: the superficial and deep radial nerves. The **superficial radial nerve** (164) is a sensory branch that continues distally to wind around the radial side of the wrist. It supplies skin of the radial side of the dorsal hand. Cutaneous innervation extends to the proximal aspect of digits one (thumb), two (index finger), three (long finger), and inner half of four (ring finger). The median nerve provides cutaneous innervation to the dorsal fingertips of these digits. A discussion of the median nerve is provided in the next section.

The **deep radial nerve** (151) gives branches innervating the supinator, extensor digitorum, extensor digiti minimi, and extensor carpi ulnaris muscles. The supinator is named for the action obtained by its contraction. It originates from the lateral epicondyle of the humerus and inserts on the proximal 1/3 of the lateral radius. As evidenced by its name, it supinates the forearm. The extensor digitorum also originates from the lateral epicondyle of the

FIGURE 10.9
MUSCLES SUPPLIED BY RADIAL NERVE SYSTEM
Most are extensors. The supinator is also supplied by the radial system, but is not visible in this image.

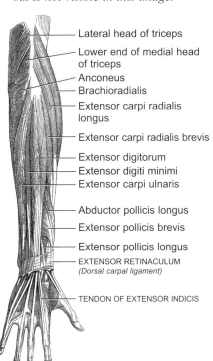

- Lateral head of triceps
- Lower end of medial head of triceps
- Anconeus
- Brachioradialis
- Extensor carpi radialis longus
- Extensor carpi radialis brevis
- Extensor digitorum
- Extensor digiti minimi
- Extensor carpi ulnaris
- Abductor pollicis longus
- Extensor pollicis brevis
- Extensor pollicis longus
- EXTENSOR RETINACULUM (Dorsal carpal ligament)
- TENDON OF EXTENSOR INDICIS

humerus. The muscle inserts on the extensor aponeurosis (or tendon expansion) over the dorsal side of the four fingers. Upon contraction, it extends the wrist and phalanges of the fingers. The extensor digiti minimi originates from the same location and inserts on the extensor aponeurosis of digit five, extending it upon contraction. The extensor carpi ulnaris has two heads. The humeral head originates from the same location as the other muscles, the lateral epicondyle of the humerus. The ulnar head originates from the posterior border of the ulna. Both heads insert on the proximal segment of the fifth metacarpal bone. The extensor carpi ulnaris extends the wrist joint and deviates the hand in the ulnar direction.

> The **extensor** **carpi** **ulnar**is **extends** the **wrist**
> and also deviates it in the **ulnar** direction.

As the deep radial nerve continues distally, it comes to travel between the two long bones of the forearm, the radius and ulna. At this point it is known as the **posterior interosseus nerve** (151). Interosseus denotes that the nerve is traveling "between bone."

> Do not confuse the posterior interosseus nerve with the soon-to-be-discussed median nerve branch, the anterior interosseus nerve. The **posterior** interosseus nerve comes from the radial nerve, which comes from the **posterior** cord and innervates **posterior** structures.

The posterior interosseus nerve supplies muscles that extend (straighten) the thumb and index finger and abduct and adduct the thumb. Specific muscles innervated include the abductor pollicis longus (abducts and extends thumb), extensor pollicis brevis (extends thumb), extensor pollicis longus (adducts and extends thumb), and extensor indicis (extends digit two = index finger) muscles.

In overview, the radial nerve gives several muscular branches before dividing into its two terminal branches, the superficial (sensory) and deep (motor) radial nerves. The radial nerve prop-

FIGURE 10.10
DEEPER MUSCLES OF POSTERIOR FOREARM

Superficial muscles have been removed, including triceps, anconeus, brachioradialis, extensor carpi radialis longus, extensor carpi radialis brevis, extensor digitorum, extensor digiti minimi, and extensor carpi ulnaris. All muscles, including both removed and depicted, are supplied by radial nerve system.

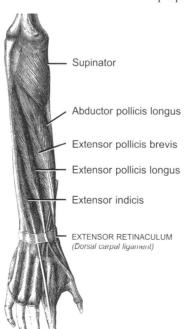

Supinator

Abductor pollicis longus

Extensor pollicis brevis

Extensor pollicis longus

Extensor indicis

EXTENSOR RETINACULUM
(Dorsal carpal ligament)

er innervates muscles that adduct and extend the arm (long head of triceps), extend the forearm (medial and lateral heads of triceps, anconeus), flex the forearm (brachioradialis), and extend and radial deviate the wrist (extensor carpi radialis longus, extensor carpi radialis brevis). The deep radial supplies four muscles and continues distally as the posterior interosseus nerve. Theses four muscles function to supinate the forearm (supinator), extend the wrist and phalanges of the fingers (extensor digitorum), extend the little finger (extensor digiti minimi), and extend and ulnar deviate the wrist joint (extensor carpi ulnaris). Finally, the posterior interosseus nerve is responsible for abducting and extending the thumb (abductor pollicis longus), extending the thumb (extensor pollicis brevis), adducting and extending the thumb (extensor pollicis longus), and extending the index finger (extensor indicis).

To summarize, the radial nerve proper innervates five muscles. The deep radial branch of the radial nerve supplies four muscles before continuing as the posterior interosseus nerve. Like the deep branch of the radial nerve, the posterior interosseus nerve also innervates four muscles.

> **Radial Nerve Supplies the Most Muscles of any Posterior Cord Branch**
>
> | 5 | + | 4 | + | 4 | = | 13 | Radial |
> |---|---|---|---|---|---|---|---|
> | radial proper | | deep branch | | posterior interosseus | | nerve muscles | supplied by the |
>
> **P O S T E R I O R   C O R D**
> 1 2 3 4 5 6 7 8 9   10 11 12 **13**
>
> Although this mnemonic may help to remember muscles supplied by the radial nerve, it is important to remember that there are additional muscles supplied by other posterior cord branches.

Obviously, there is a great deal of variation in which nerve innervates which muscle. As long as the student realizes there is such variation, this material will serve as an effective template to work from. The important point is that these particular muscles, most of which are extensors, are supplied by the radial nerve system.

> **Posterior Cord = 3**
>
> There are 3 cords. The posterior cord was earlier assigned the #3 because it was formed by the coalition of **3** divisions (3 posterior divisions, one from each of the 3 trunks). In addition, the posterior cord serves as the origin of **3** nerves (upper subscapular, thoracodorsal, and lower subscapular nerves) prior to separating into its two terminal branches. These 3 nerves supply **3** muscles (subscapularis, teres major, and latissimus dorsi). One of the terminal branches, the axillary nerve, has **3** main responsibilities: 1) innervation of deltoid 2) innervation of teres minor 3) origin of superior (upper) lateral brachial cutaneous nerve. Finally, the other terminal branch, the radial nerve, innervates 13 muscles and is the origin of **3** named cutaneous nerves (posterior brachial cutaneous nerve, posterior antebrachial cutaneous nerve, superficial radial nerve).

QUIZ 2
Brachial Plexus and Nerves of the Upper Extremity

Time for Quiz = 32 minutes.
For questions 1-27, choose the single best answer.

_____1) The axillary nerve is a direct branch of the
  a) radial nerve
  b) lateral cord of the brachial plexus
  c) posterior cord of the brachial plexus
  d) upper trunk of the brachial plexus
  e) none of the above

_____2) The lower subscapular nerve innervates
  which muscle?
  a) teres minor muscle
  b) supraspinous muscle
  c) teres major muscle
  d) pectoralis minor muscle
  e) none of the above

_____3) Which nerve is a branch of the radial nerve?
  a) anterior interosseous nerve
  b) ulnar collateral nerve
  c) both a and b
  d) superior lateral brachial cutaneous
    nerve
  e) none of the above

_____4) Direct branches of the lateral cord of the
  brachial plexus include the
  a) axillary nerve
  b) suprascapular nerve
  c) lateral pectoral nerve
  d) upper subscapular nerve
  e) none of the above

_____5) Which muscle is supplied by the deep
  branch of the radial nerve?
  a) supinator
  b) extensor digitorum
  c) extensor digiti minimi
  d) all of the above
  e) none of the above

_____6) All of the following are terminal branches
  of brachial plexus cords except the
  a) axillary nerve
  b) lateral root of median nerve
  c) lateral pectoral nerve
  d) musculocutaneous nerve
  e) all the above are terminal branches
    of brachial plexus cords

_____7) The thoracodorsal nerve innervates which
  muscle?
  a) teres major muscle
  b) teres minor muscle
  c) supraspinous muscle
  d) pectoralis minor muscle
  e) none of the above

_____8) Which of the following is a direct branch of
  the posterior cord of the brachial plexus?
  a) musculocutaneous nerve
  b) upper subscapular nerve
  c) suprascapular nerve
  d) dorsal scapular nerve
  e) none of the above

_____9) The posterior brachial cutaneous nerve is a
  branch of which nerve structure?
  a) upper trunk
  b) lateral cord of the brachial plexus
  c) radial nerve
  d) axillary nerve
  e) none of the above

_____10) The axillary nerve innervates which muscle?
  a) teres major muscle
  b) teres minor muscle
  c) both a and b
  d) pectoralis minor muscle
  e) none of the above

_____11) The upper subscapular nerve is a direct
  branch of the
  a) lateral cord of the brachial plexus
  b) posterior cord of the brachial plexus
  c) upper trunk of the brachial plexus
  d) axillary nerve
  e) none of the above

_____12) The lateral pectoral nerve innervates which muscle?
    a) pectoralis minor
    b) supraspinous
    c) teres major
    d) latissimus dorsi
    e) none of the above

_____13) The lateral antebrachial cutaneous nerve is derived from which structure?
    a) deep radial nerve
    b) posterior cord of the brachial plexus
    c) axillary nerve
    d) superficial radial nerve
    e) none of the above

_____14) Which nerve serves as a terminal branch of the posterior cord of the brachial plexus?
    a) axillary nerve
    b) lateral root of median nerve
    c) both a and b
    d) musculocutaneous nerve
    e) none of the above

_____15) Which muscle is innervated by the radial nerve or one of its branches?
    a) brachioradialis
    b) brachialis
    c) pectoralis major
    d) deltoid
    e) none of the above

_____16) The thoracodorsal nerve is a direct branch of the
    a) C5 ventral ramus
    b) upper trunk of the brachial plexus
    c) posterior cord of the brachial plexus
    d) lateral cord of the brachial plexus
    e) none of the above

_____17) All of the following are branches of the posterior cord of the brachial plexus except the
    a) dorsal scapular nerve
    b) thoracodorsal nerve
    c) axillary
    d) lower subscapular nerve
    e) none of the above

_____18) The musculocutaneous nerve innervates which muscle?
    a) brachioradialis muscle
    b) brachialis muscle
    c) supinator
    d) all of the above
    e) none of the above

_____19) What is the name of the sensory branch of the axillary nerve?
    a) medial brachial cutaneous nerve
    b) medial antebrachial cutaneous nerve
    c) posterior brachial cutaneous nerve
    d) superior lateral brachial cutaneous nerve
    e) none of the above

_____20) Which nerve serves as a terminal branch of the radial nerve?
    a) ulnar collateral nerve
    b) branch to long head of triceps
    c) posterior brachial cutaneous nerve
    d) anterior interosseous nerve
    e) none of the above

_____21) The posterior interosseous nerve is the distal continuation of which nerve?
    a) superficial radial nerve
    b) deep radial nerve
    c) musculocutaneous nerve
    d) ulnar collateral nerve
    e) none of the above

_____22) The upper subscapular nerve innervates which muscle?
    a) supraspinous muscle
    b) subscapularis muscle
    c) teres minor
    d) pectoralis major
    e) none of the above

_____23) The radial nerve is a direct branch of the
    a) upper trunk of the brachial plexus
    b) lateral cord of the brachial plexus
    c) medial cord of the brachial plexus
    d) axillary nerve
    e) none of the above

____24) Which of the following is a terminal branch of the lateral cord of the brachial plexus?
    a) anterior division to upper trunk
    b) lateral root of the median nerve
    c) lateral pectoral nerve
    d) axillary nerve
    e) none of the above

____25) The continuation of the musculocutaneous nerve into the forearm is known as the
    a) medial antebrachial cutaneous nerve
    b) lateral antebrachial cutaneous nerve
    c) posterior antebrachial cutaneous nerve
    d) posterior brachial cutaneous nerve
    e) none of the above

____26) The lower subscapular nerve is a direct branch of the
    a) C5 ventral ramus
    b) upper trunk of the brachial plexus
    c) radial nerve
    d) lateral cord of the brachial plexus
    e) none of the above

____27) The lateral pectoral nerve is a branch of the
    a) upper trunk of the brachial plexus
    b) lower trunk of the brachial plexus
    c) medial cord of the brachial plexus
    d) posterior cord of the brachial plexus
    e) none of the above

For questions 28-32, use the following directions:
  a.......1,2,3 are correct
  b.......1,3 are correct
  c.......2,4 are correct
  d.......only 4 is correct
  e.......all are correct

____28) Which statements about the posterior cord of the brachial plexus are true?
    1. The thoracodorsal nerve is a direct branch.
    2. The anterior division of the upper trunk contributes to its formation.
    3. The latissimus dorsi muscle is innervated by one of its branches.
    4. The brachialis muscle is innervated by one of its branches.

____29) Which muscles are supplied by the lateral cord of the brachial plexus or one of its branches?
    1. brachialis
    2. brachioradialis
    3. coracobrachialis
    4. pectoralis minor

____30) Which nerves are eventual branches of the posterior cord system?
    1. ulnar collateral nerve
    2. anterior interosseous nerve
    3. superior lateral brachial cutaneous nerve
    4. lateral antebrachial cutaneous nerve

____31) Injury to the lateral cord may result in decreased
    1. ability to flex arm
    2. ability to flex forearm
    3. ability to supinate forearm
    4. cutaneous sensation over the lateral aspect of the proximal forearm

____32) Which muscles are innervated by a branch of the posterior cord system of the brachial plexus?
    1. coracobrachialis
    2. pectoralis major
    3. brachialis
    4. deltoid

QUIZ 2: Brachial Plexus Answers and Explanations

1) c – The posterior cord is the origin of the upper subscapular, thoracodorsal, and lower subscapular nerves prior to dividing into two terminal branches: the radial and axillary nerves.

2) c – The lower subscapular nerve also provides innervation to the subscapularis muscle. The teres minor muscle is supplied by the axillary nerve. The supraspinous muscle is innervated by the suprascapular nerve. The pectoralis minor muscle is supplied by the medial pectoral nerve.

3) b – The anterior interosseous nerve is a branch of the median nerve. The superior lateral brachial cutaneous nerve is a branch of the axillary nerve.

4) c – The axillary nerve is a terminal branch of the posterior cord of the brachial plexus. The suprascapular nerve is a branch of the upper trunk of the plexus. The upper subscapular nerve is a branch of the posterior cord.

5) d – The deep radial nerve usually supplies four muscles. These include the supinator, extensor digitorum, extensor digiti minimi, and extensor carpi ulnaris.

6) c – The musculocutaneous nerve and lateral root of the median nerve are the two terminal branches of the lateral cord. The ulnar nerve and medial root of the median nerve are the two terminal branches of the medial cord. The axillary nerve and radial nerve are the two terminal branches of the posterior cord. The lateral pectoral nerve is a branch of the lateral cord of the brachial plexus, but it is not a terminal branch.

7) e – The thoracodorsal nerve innervates the latissimus dorsi muscle of the back. The teres major muscle is innervated by the upper and lower subscapular nerves. The teres minor muscle is supplied by the axillary nerve. The supraspinous muscle is supplied by the suprascapular nerve. Finally, the pectoralis minor muscle is innervated by the medial pectoral nerve.

8) b – The musculocutaneous nerve is a branch of the lateral cord of the brachial plexus. The suprascapular nerve is a branch of the upper trunk of the plexus. The dorsal scapular nerve is a direct branch of the C5 ventral ramus.

9) c – The posterior brachial cutaneous nerve, like all "posterior" cutaneous nerves of the upper extremity, is a radial nerve branch.

10) b – The axillary nerve also innervates the deltoid muscle. The teres major muscle is innervated by both the upper and lower subscapular nerves. The pectoralis minor muscle is supplied by the medial pectoral nerve.

11) b – See #1 answer explanation.

12) e – The lateral pectoral nerve innervates the pectoralis major muscle. The pectoralis minor is innervated by the medial pectoral nerve, which supplies both the pectoralis major and pectoralis minor muscles. The supraspinous is supplied by the suprascapular nerve of the upper trunk. The teres major is supplied by the upper and lower subscapular nerves of the posterior cord. The latissimus dorsi is innervated by way of the thoracodorsal nerve, also of the posterior cord.

13) e – The lateral antebrachial cutaneous nerve is the continuation of the musculocutaneous nerve once this nerve emerges from the biceps brachii muscle just above the elbow.

14) a – The radial nerve is the other posterior cord terminal branch. The lateral root of the median nerve and the musculocutaneous nerve are the two terminal branches of the lateral cord.

15) a – The brachioradialis flexes the forearm (bends the elbow). The brachialis is supplied by the musculocutaneous nerve. The pectoralis major is supplied by both the lateral and medial pectoral nerves. The deltoid is innervated by the axillary nerve.

16) c – See #1 answer explanation.

17) a – The dorsal scapular nerve is a direct branch of the C5 ventral ramus.

18) b – The musculocutaneous nerve also innervates the coracobrachialis and biceps brachii muscles. Both the brachioradialis and supinator muscles are innervated by the radial nerve.

19) d – Both the medial brachial and medial antebrachial cutaneous nerves are sensory branches that arise from the medial cord of the brachial plexus. The posterior brachial cutaneous nerve is a sensory branch of the radial nerve.

20) e – The terminal branches of the radial nerve are the superficial and deep radial nerves. The superficial radial is sensory. The deep radial is motor. The first three answers are radial nerve branches. The anterior interosseous nerve is a branch of the median nerve.

21) b – As the deep radial nerve courses distally, it travels between the two long bones of the forearm. At this point it is known as the posterior interosseous nerve. It supplies muscles that extend the thumb and index finger and abduct and adduct the thumb.

22) b – The upper subscapular nerve also innervates the teres major muscle. The supraspinous muscle is supplied by the suprascapular nerve. The teres minor muscle is supplied by the axillary nerve. The pectoralis major muscle is supplied by both the lateral and medial pectoral nerves.

23) e – The radial nerve is a direct branch of the posterior cord of the brachial plexus.

24) b – The other terminal branch of the lateral cord is the musculocutaneous nerve. The lateral cord is formed by the combination of the anterior divisions from the upper and middle trunks. The lateral pectoral nerve is a branch of the lateral cord, but not a terminal branch. The axillary nerve is a terminal branch of the posterior cord.

25) b – The medial antebrachial cutaneous nerve is a branch of the medial cord of the brachial plexus. Both the posterior antebrachial cutaneous nerve and posterior brachial cutaneous nerve are branches of the radial nerve.

26) e – The lower subscapular nerve is a direct branch of the posterior cord of the brachial plexus.

27) e – The lateral pectoral nerve is a branch of the lateral cord of the brachial plexus.

28) b – The thoracodorsal nerve is direct branch of the posterior cord and innervates the latissimus dorsi muscle. The posterior cord is formed by the combination of the posterior divisions of the upper, middle and lower trunks. The brachialis muscle is innervated by the musculocutaneous nerve, which is a branch of the lateral cord.

29) b – The musculocutaneous nerve is a terminal branch of the lateral cord. It innervates the brachialis, coracobrachialis, and biceps brachii muscles before continuing on as the lateral antebrachial cutaneous nerve. The brachioradialis is a muscle of the forearm that is supplied by a terminal branch of the posterior cord, the radial nerve. The medial pectoral nerve is a medial cord branch that supplies the pectoralis minor muscle.

30) b – The ulnar collateral nerve is a branch of one of the posterior cord terminal branches, the radial nerve. It supplies the anconeus muscle and the medial head of the triceps brachii muscle. The superior lateral brachial cutaneous nerve is a branch of the other posterior cord terminal branch, the axillary nerve. The anterior interosseous nerve is a branch of the median nerve. The lateral antebrachial cutaneous nerve is the continuation of the musculocutaneous nerve into the forearm. The musculocutaneous nerve is a terminal branch of the lateral cord.

31) e – The musculocutaneous nerve is a terminal branch of the lateral cord. It innervates three muscles of the arm before continuing into the forearm as the lateral antebrachial cutaneous nerve. The coracobrachialis muscle flexes and adducts the arm. The brachialis muscle flexes the forearm. The biceps brachii muscle both flexes and supinates the forearm.

32) d – The deltoid muscle is supplied by one of the terminal branches of the posterior cord, the axillary nerve. The coracobrachialis and brachialis muscles are innervated by the musculocutaneous nerve, a terminal branch of the lateral cord. The pectoralis major is supplied by both the lateral and medial pectoral nerves. These nerves branch from the lateral and medial cords, respectively.

MEDIAL CORD BRANCHES, MEDIAN NERVE, AND CHAPTER OVERVIEW

BRANCHES OF THE MEDIAL CORD

The medial cord, like the posterior cord, gives off three nerves before it divides into its two terminal branches, the ulnar nerve and medial branch to the median nerve. The three nerves include the medial pectoral, medial brachial cutaneous and medial antebrachial cutaneous nerves.

The **medial pectoral nerve** (175) supplies both the pectoralis minor and pectoralis major muscles. The pectoralis minor originates from the coracoid process of the scapula and inserts on the superior border of the costal cartilage of ribs #3 - #5. It raises the third, fourth, and fifth ribs while pulling the shoulder down during inspiration. The pectoralis major originates from the sternum, upper six costal cartilages, clavicle, and fascia sheath of the external oblique muscle of the abdomen. It inserts on the humerus and adducts the arm and turns it medially upon contraction. The previously-described lateral pectoral nerve (181) is a branch of the lateral cord and also innervates the pectoralis major muscle. It has no role in supplying the pectoralis minor muscle.

An alternative way to remember the innervation of the pectoralis muscles is to note that the medial cord is closest to both muscles. The medial pectoral nerve thereby participates in the innervation of both muscles. The lateral pectoral nerve only participates in the innervation of the larger pectoralis major, which extends close enough for the nerve to reach.

The **medial brachial cutaneous nerve** (**147,** 173) comes off the medial cord and is easily identified due to its relationship with the intercostobrachial nerve. The **intercostobrachial nerve** (176) originates from the second and third intercostal nerves. The intercostal nerves are described in the next chapter. They are thoracic ventral rami that course parallel to the ribs and supply tissues of the chest wall and abdomen. The intercostobrachial nerve runs from the second intercostal space (the space between rib #2 and #3) and combines with the medial brachial cutaneous nerve to form a nerve which innervates skin of the medial and posterior arm. The **medial antebrachial cutaneous nerve** (**148,** 174) is the third branch to come off the medial cord. It continues down the arm to supply sensory innervation to the skin of the medial forearm.

The pectoralis major is larger than the pectoralis minor. It extends across a larger area of the torso. The pectoralis major requires innervation from two nerves, the medial and lateral pectoral nerves. The pectoralis minor only requires one nerve. Because this muscle is *medial* to the brachial plexus, it utilizes the closest nerve, the *medial* pectoral nerve, which is a branch of the *medial* cord.

Note that the *medial* antebrachial cutaneous nerve comes off the *medial* cord. Likewise, the previously mentioned, *lateral* antebrachial cutaneous nerve comes off the *lateral* cord (as the musculocutaneous nerve).

FIGURE 10.11
MUSCLES OF THE UPPER ANTERIOR TORSO AND UPPER EXTREMITY

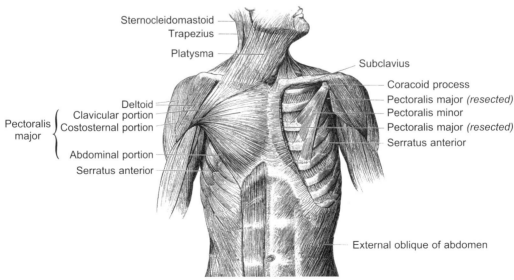

The medial cord then divides into its terminal branches: the medial root of the median nerve and the ulnar nerve. The median nerve is formed by the combination of the lateral root from the lateral cord and the medial root from the medial cord. It will be discussed in more detail shortly.

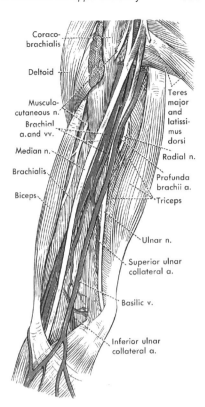

FIGURE 10.12
**CHIEF NERVES
AND VESSELS
OF THE ARM**

(Reproduced with permission from Hollinshead, W.H., Rosse, C.: Textbook of Anatomy, 4th ed. Philadelphia, Harper & Row, 1985)

---

14 Branches of Brachial Plexus

The brachial plexus consists of three trunks and three cords. Each trunk divides into an anterior and posterior division. Likewise, each cord divides into its two respective terminal branches. Outside of this, there are nine other brachial plexus branches. There are two branches that originate directly from a trunk. Both the nerve to subclavius and suprascapular nerve come off the upper trunk. Thus, the upper trunk is the only trunk serving as the direct origin of a nerve (other than a division). The lateral cord has only one branch, the lateral pectoral nerve. Both the posterior cord and the medial cord have three branches each. The posterior cord is the origin of the upper subscapular, thoracodorsal, and lower subscapular nerves. The medial cord produces the medial pectoral, medial brachial cutaneous, and medial antebrachial cutaneous nerves. $2 + 1 + 3 + 3 = 9$

Although there are three cords and each divides into two terminal branches, only five terminal nerves continue down the arm. This is because the median nerve is formed by two terminal branches of cords, the lateral root of the median nerve and the medial root of the median nerve. The terminal branches of the lateral cord are the musculocutaneous nerve and the lateral root of the median nerve. The terminal branches of the posterior cord are the radial nerve and axillary nerve. Finally, the terminal branches of the medial cord are the medial root of the median nerve and the ulnar nerve. It makes sense for the musculocutaneous nerve to come off the *lateral* cord because it later becomes the *lateral* antebrachial cutaneous nerve. It also makes sense that the ulnar nerve comes off the *medial* cord, as it provides innervation on the ulnar or *medial* side of the forearm. **9** (plexus branches) + **5** (terminal branches) = **14**

There are **fourteen (14) nerves** that are direct branches of the **brachial plexus**.

B_1 R_2 A_3 C_4 H_5 I_6 A_7 L_8 P_9 L_{10} E_{11} X_{12} U_{13} S_{14}

1. nerve to subclavius	8. medial brachial nerve
2. suprascapular nerve	9. medial antebrachial nerve
3. lateral pectoral nerve	10. musculocutaneous nerve
4. upper subscapular nerve	11. axillary nerve
5. thoracodorsal nerve	12. radial nerve
6. lower subscapular nerve	13. median nerve
7. medial pectoral nerve	14. ulnar nerve

The **ulnar nerve (149,** 182) comes off the medial cord and travels to the hand. It supplies skin of the ulnar or medial aspect of the hand and flexor muscles of the elbow joint, forearm, and hand. The muscular function provided by the ulnar nerve is similar to the muscular function of the median nerve, flexion of the forearm and/or hand. One difference is that the ulnar nerve is responsible for flexion toward the ulnar or little finger direction. The median nerve provides flexion in the radial or thumb direction.

The ulnar nerve leaves the medial cord and travels down the arm without providing any branches. As it enters the forearm, it supplies two muscles before continuing toward the hand to divide into deep and superficial branches. Like the radial nerve, the deep branch is a motor branch and the superficial is sensory. The deep branch supplies muscles of the hand. The superficial branch supplies skin of the ulnar or medial aspect of the hand.

The two muscles supplied in the forearm include the flexor carpi ulnaris and the ulnar portion of the flexor digitorum profundus. The flexor carpi ulnaris has two heads. The humeral head originates from the medial epicondyle of the humerus. The ulnar head originates from the olecranon and posterior ulna. Both insert on the pisiform and hamate bones of the carpus and proximal aspect of the fifth metacarpal bone. The flexor carpi ulnaris flexes the wrist (palmar flexion of the hand) and deviates the hand in an ulnar direction.

The flexor digitorum profundus originates from the shaft of the ulna and inserts on the proximal portion of the distal phalange of each of the four fingers. Upon contraction, it flexes the distal phalanges of the four fingers. This muscle is innervated by two nerves, the ulnar and median nerves. The portion innervated by the ulnar nerve is closer to the ulna bone. Hence, it is known as the ulnar portion of the flexor digitorum profundus. It is only coincidental that the ulnar nerve, which is also named for its proximity to the ulna bone, provides the innervation. The other portion of this muscle is closer to the radius bone and is therefore known as the radial portion of the flexor digitorum profundus. It is innervated by a branch of the median nerve, the anterior interosseus nerve. The word *profundus* means deep. This would imply the presence of a superficial muscle as well. Indeed, like the radial portion of the flexor digitorum profundus, the flexor digitorum superficialis is also innervated by the median nerve. It flexes the middle phalanges of the fingers and will be discussed later.

As the ulnar nerve approaches the hand, it divides into its two terminal branches, the deep and superficial branches of the ulnar nerve. The **deep branch of the ulnar nerve** (154) travels down, supplying several muscles as it travels across the palm of the hand toward the thumb. It innervates three hypothenar muscles, all seven interosseous muscles, two of four lumbrical muscles, the adductor pollicis muscle, and the deep head of the flexor pollicis brevis muscle.

The three hypothenar muscles collectively form the hypothenar eminence, the prominence of the ulnar side of the palm proximal to the little finger. These three muscles include the abductor digiti minimi manus, flexor digiti minimi brevis manus, and opponens digiti minimi manus. The word *manus* denotes hand. This is to differentiate these muscles from those of the foot. For instance, the abductor digiti minimi pedis abducts the little toe. By their location proximal to the little finger in the anterior and medial side of the hand, it seems intuitive that the hypothenar muscles should abduct and flex the little finger. Both the abductor digiti minimi manus and flexor digiti minimi brevis manus insert on the base of the proximal phalanx of the little finger. The abductor digiti minimi manus abducts the little finger. The flexor digiti minimi brevis manus is the short flexor muscle of the little finger. The opponens digiti minimi manus inserts on the lateral part of the fifth metacarpal bone, just proximal to the little finger. It abducts and flexes the fifth metacarpal, just as the other two muscles abduct and flex the little finger, respectively.

> The **ulnar** nerve is responsible for flexion, especially in the **ulnar** or little finger direction. Abduction or "spreading" of the little finger away from the hand and digits is movement in the **ulnar** direction. Two of the three hypothenar muscles, the abductor digiti minimi manus and the flexor digiti minimi brevis manus, insert on the proximal phalanx of the little finger. They thereby exert their forces of abduction and flexion, respectively, on the little finger. As **opposed** to the other two hypothenar muscles, the **opponens** digiti minimi manus inserts on the lateral aspect of the fifth metacarpal bone. It therefore exerts its forces of abduction and flexion on the bone which is just proximal to the little finger.

There are seven interosseus muscles (interossei) of the hand. As with the word's use in the naming of other anatomic structures, the word *interosseus* denotes that these muscles are "between bone." The interosseus muscles are located in the spaces of the hand between the metacarpal bones of the digits. Because each hand contains five metacarpal bones, there are four metacarpal spaces. Four dorsal interossei are located in these spaces in the dorsal side of the hand, and three palmar interossei are located in the palmar side. The deep branch of the ulnar nerve innervates all seven interossei.

Each of the four dorsal interossei originates from the two adjacent metacarpal bones bordering its metacarpal space. Each muscle is therefore considered to have two heads. Because there are four interosseus spaces, there are also four dorsal interossei. Every metacarpal bone serves as an origin for at least one dorsal interosseous muscle. The middle three metacarpal bones are the

origin of two muscles each, one muscle on each side. The four dorsal interossei insert on the outer aspect of the extensor tendons of the middle three fingers. The extensor tendon of digit #3 (middle finger) receives two insertions, one on each side. There is no dorsal interossei insertion on the extensor tendon of the thumb or little finger. Each finger has three phalanges: a proximal, middle, and distal phalanx. The dorsal interosseus muscles abduct and flex the proximal phalanges and extend the middle and distal phalanges.

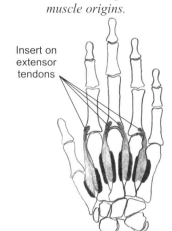

FIGURE 10.13
DORSAL INTEROSSEI
Posterior (Dorsal) view
Right Hand
Darkened areas represent muscle origins.

Insert on extensor tendons

> Both dorsal and palmar interosseus muscles (interossei) flex the proximal phalanges and extend the middle and distal phalanges. In other words, they cause flexion of the metacarpophalangeal joints (the joints between the metacarpal bones of the hand and proximal phalanges of the digits, where each digit attaches to the hand) and extension of the two interphalangeal joints (the joints between the phalanges of each digit). This action can be reproduced when the fingers are kept straight while flexed forward or down at the knuckle (metacarpophalangeal joint).
>
> Each finger has 3 bones…
> All interossei **Flex Once** then **Extend Twice.**

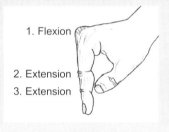

1. Flexion
2. Extension
3. Extension

The three palmar interossei are also located in metacarpal spaces and are found on the palmar side of the dorsal interossei. Each originates from the inner side of one metacarpal bone. This includes the ulnar side of the second and the radial side of the fourth and fifth metacarpal bones. The metacarpal bones of the thumb and middle finger do not participate. Each muscle extends distally and dorsally to insert on the extensor tendon of the same digit as the metacarpal bone from which it originated. The pal-

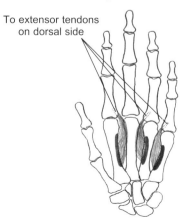

FIGURE 10.14
PALMAR INTEROSSEI
Anterior (Palmar) view
Right Hand
Darkened areas represent muscle origins.

To extensor tendons on dorsal side

The **d**orsal interossei **ab**duct = **DAB**   The **p**almar interossei **ad**duct = **PAD**

The location and attachments of the interossei may seem irregular. An evaluation of the functional differences between the two interosseous groups may make their attachments seem more logical, and hence, easier to remember.

The dorsal interossei abduct: The thumb and little finger have their own abducting muscles located at the outer sides of the hand (abductor pollicis longus*/abductor pollicis brevis* and abductor digiti minimi manus, respectively). There is therefore no dorsal interosseous insertion on either of these digits. To abduct (or spread) the other three digits, there is insertion on the outer side of each digit's extensor tendon. This includes the radial side of digit #2, both sides of digit #3, and ulnar side of digit #4. Because digit #3 is in the midline of the extremity, it must be able to "abduct" in either direction. To provide this function, a dorsal interosseous inserts on each side of the middle finger. Four dorsal interossei are required.

The palmar interossei adduct: The thumb has its own adductor (adductor pollicis*), which allows the thumb to be brought against the side of the hand. The middle finger is already midline. There is no way for it to "adduct." For these reasons, palmar interossei do not insert on either of these two digits. Only three palmar interossei are required.

Note: Neither group of muscles inserts on the thumb. The thumb has its own abductors and adductors. Although all fingers are supplied, each group inserts on only 3 of 4 fingers. There are 4 dorsal muscles, so 2 must insert on one finger (middle) in order to skip one finger (the little finger, which has its own abductor). There are 3 palmar muscles. Because they adduct, they skip the middle finger and insert on each of the other 3 fingers.

* Pollicis muscles will be described shortly.

---

mar interosseus muscles adduct and flex the proximal phalanges while also extending the middle and distal phalanges.

The deep branch of the ulnar nerve also innervates two of the four lumbrical muscles of the hand. The lumbrical muscles are named for their "worm-like" appearance. A *lumbricus* is an earthworm or ascaris (intestinal parasitic worm). Each of the four lumbrical muscles originates from a particular finger's flexor digitorum profundus tendon sheath. The tendon of each lumbrical muscle passes around the radial aspect the metacarpophalangeal joint to insert on the extensor tendon of the same digit. Phrased differently, each of the four fingers is associated with a lumbrical muscle. This muscle originates from its flexor tendon, curves around the radial aspect or thumb-side of the digit, and inserts on its extensor tendon on the dorsal aspect of the digit. The numbering of the lumbrical muscles is similar to that of the digits, starting on the radial side and moving in an ulnar direction. Since the thumb is not associated with a lumbrical muscle, the first lumbrical is associated with the sec-ond digit (index finger). Likewise, the second lumbrical is associated with the third digit (middle finger), the third with the fourth digit (ring finger), and the fourth with the fifth digit (little finger). The deep branch of the ulnar nerve innervates the third and fourth lumbrical muscles, the two on the ulnar side of the hand. The median nerve supplies the first and second lumbricals. Like the interosseus muscles, the lumbrical muscles flex the metacarpophalangeal joints and extend the middle and distal phalanges.

Lumbrical Muscles are "Wormy!"

Not only do they have the appearance of worms, but they don't have the "muscle" to attach to bones. Instead they attach to tendons. Each originates from the flexor tendon and inserts on the extensor tendon of a particular finger.

FIGURE 10.15
MUSCLES AND TENDONS OF THE HAND
Anterior view

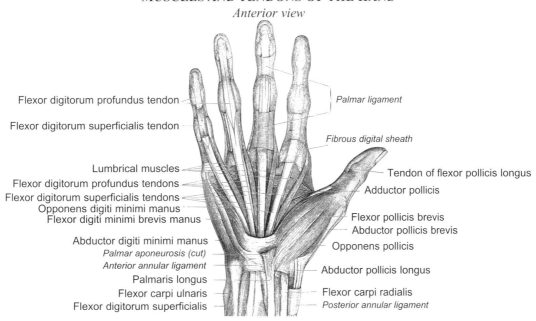

Flexor digitorum profundus tendon
Flexor digitorum superficialis tendon
Lumbrical muscles
Flexor digitorum profundus tendons
Flexor digitorum superficialis tendons
Opponens digiti minimi manus
Flexor digiti minimi brevis manus
Abductor digiti minimi manus
Palmar aponeurosis (cut)
Anterior annular ligament
Palmaris longus
Flexor carpi ulnaris
Flexor digitorum superficialis

Palmar ligament
Fibrous digital sheath
Tendon of flexor pollicis longus
Adductor pollicis
Flexor pollicis brevis
Abductor pollicis brevis
Opponens pollicis
Abductor pollicis longus
Flexor carpi radialis
Posterior annular ligament

Finally, as the deep branch of the ulnar nerve approaches the thumb, it gives branches to innervate the adductor pollicis muscle and deep head of the flexor pollicis brevis muscle. The adductor pollicis muscle originates from the capitate, trapezoid, and second and third metacarpal bones. It inserts on the medial side of the proximal phalanx of the thumb. The adductor pollicis adducts and opposes the thumb. Adduction occurs when the thumb is brought against the side of the hand and index finger. Opposition occurs when the thumb is brought across the palm toward the little finger, as if to grasp an object with only the thumb and little finger.

The flexor pollicis brevis muscle has two heads. The deep portion originates from the trapezium bone and is supplied by the ulnar nerve. The superficial head is the more substantial portion and originates from the flexor retinaculum. It is supplied by the median nerve. Both portions insert on lateral side of the proximal phalanx of the thumb. The flexor pollicis brevis muscle flexes and adducts the thumb.

The **superficial branch of the ulnar nerve** (155) is the sensory branch of the ulnar nerve. In addition, it supplies a small muscle of the palm, the palmaris brevis. The palmaris brevis originates in the aponeurosis of the palm and inserts on skin of the ulnar or little finger side of the hand. Its stimulation causes an increase in the crater of the palm.

After supplying the palmaris brevis, the superficial branch divides into three sensory branches. The **digital branch of the ulnar** (156) supplies the skin of the outer half of the little finger (digit #5). The **common digital branch** (157) divides into two **proper digital nerves** (158) that supply the adjacent sides of the little (digit #5) and ring (digit #4) fingers. The ulnar also often gives a **communicating branch** (159) to the last common digital nerve arising from the median nerve.

As mentioned earlier, the general muscular function of the ulnar nerve is similar to that of the median nerve, that is, flexion

FIGURE 10.16
NERVES AND ASSOCIATED STRUCTURES OF HAND
Anterior view

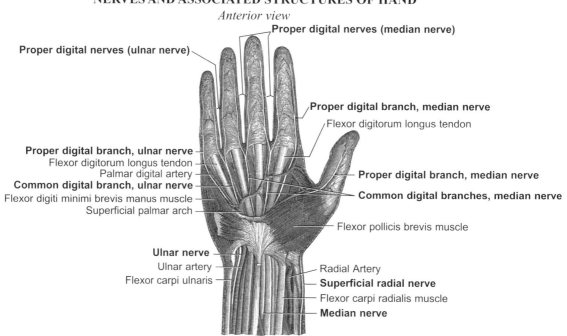

FIGURE 10.17
NERVES AND ASSOCIATED STRUCTURES OF HAND, DEEPER DISSECTION

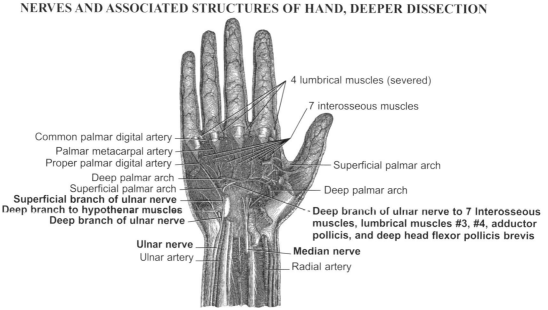

of the wrist and digits. The ulnar nerve favors flexion toward the ulnar side of the arm. This includes ulnar deviation of the wrist (flexor carpi ulnaris) and adduction of the thumb (adductor pollicis and deep head of flexor pollicis brevis). It also includes abducting or "spreading" of the little finger (abductor digiti minimi manus). The median nerve is responsible for the majority of the flexion of the wrist, hand, and digits. It is also responsible for movement toward the radial or thumb side of the hand.

In summary, the ulnar nerve supplies seventeen muscles and skin of the ulnar aspect of both sides of the hand. It gives no branches in the arm. In the forearm, it supplies two muscles, the flexor carpi ulnaris and ulnar portion of the flexor digitorum profundus. It continues to the hand and divides into deep and superficial branches. The deep branch supplies three hypothenar muscles (the abductor, short flexor, and opposing muscles of the little finger), all seven interossei, two lumbrical muscles, and two thumb muscles (adductor pollicis muscle and the deep head of the flexor pollicis brevis muscle). The superficial branch innervates the palmaris brevis muscle and gives branches that supply skin of both the palmar and dorsal side of the ulnar aspect of the hand, including the medial 1½ fingers. In other words, the ulnar nerve supplies skin of both the ulnar and radial sides of the little finger (digit #5) and the adjacent ulnar side of the ring finger (digit #4).

Ulnar Nerve is Well-Named

The nerve is named for its proximity to the *ulna*, a long bone of the forearm, not arm. Likewise, the ulnar nerve gives no branches in the arm. In the forearm, it supplies the flexor carpi *ulnaris* and *ulnar* portion of the flexor digitorum profundus. In the hand, the deep branch supplies the three hypothenar muscles (on the *ulnar* side of the hand), all seven interossei, two lumbrical muscles on the *ulnar* side of the hand (#4, #5), and two thumb muscles which move the thumb in the *ulnar* direction. The superficial branch supplies the palmaris brevis, a superficial muscle on the *ulnar* side of the palm, and skin on both sides (palmar and dorsal) of the *ulnar* aspect of the hand and *ulnar* 1½ fingers.

Muscles supplied = 1½ forearm muscles + 3 hypothenar + 7 interossei + 2 lumbricals + 1½ pollicis muscles + palmaris brevis

---

MEDIAN NERVE

Attention will be directed to the last major nerve of the upper extremity to be described, the median nerve. The **median nerve (150,** 184) is formed by a terminal branch of the lateral cord (the lateral root of median nerve [185]) combined with a terminal branch of the medial cord (the medial root of median nerve [183]). The median nerve is colored green in the main illustration as if to represent a green grassy highway "median." The median nerve supplies many of the flexor muscles of the elbow joint, anterior forearm, and hand. It also supplies skin on the anterior and lateral aspect of the hand and dorsal finger tips of digits one, two, three, and the radial half of four. A review of the anatomic position, with the palms facing forward, demonstrates that the anterior aspect of the hand is the palm side. The lateral aspect is the radial or thumb side. Hence, the median nerve supplies skin on the thumb side of the palm.

To remember how the branches of the brachial plexus arise, envision the capital letter, "M" being formed by the branches of the lateral and medial cords of the brachial plexus. The **m**edian nerve starts with the letter "M" and is in the **m**iddle. The nerve is appropriately named. The musculocutaneous nerve also starts with the letter "M" and is located at the top. The ulnar nerve is the only one which does not start with an "M" and is therefore left with the lowest position. The **u**lnar nerve is **u**nder the two "M" nerves.

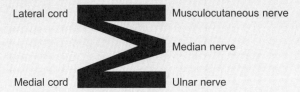

Lateral cord / Musculocutaneous nerve
Median nerve
Medial cord / Ulnar nerve

Behind the capital "M" is the posterior cord. The posterior cord gives off the axillary and radial nerves.

"M" = Mnemonic for Brachial Plexus

In addition to the shape of formation of the **m**usculocutaneous, **m**edian, and ulnar nerves, there are other roles the letter "M" plays as a learning tool. The **m**usculocutaneous nerve is the flexor nerve of the arm. The **m**edian nerve is the **m**ain flexor nerve of the forearm (ulna nerve also contributes). The radial nerve is from the posterior cord, travels down the posterior aspect of the arm and innervates the extensor muscles of the arm, forearm, and wrist.

Furthermore, the **m**iddle trunk is the only trunk that is formed by only one spinal segment ventral ramus (C7). Likewise, the **m**edial cord is the only cord that is formed by only one trunk division (anterior division of the lower trunk).

FIGURE 10.18

The brachial plexus and its branches in a dissection of the axilla and neck. In this specimen, the lateral pectoral nerve arises rather high, above the clavicle instead of from the lateral cord in the axilla.

(Reproduced with permission from Hollinshead, W.H., Rosse, C.: Textbook of Anatomy, 4th ed. Philadelphia, Harper & Row, 1985)

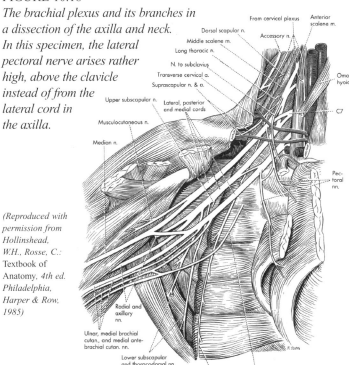

Like the ulnar nerve, the median nerve travels down the arm (shoulder to elbow) producing no branches. At the approximate level of the elbow, the median nerve sends branches to supply four muscles. These include the pronator teres, flexor carpi radialis, palmaris longus, and flexor digitorum superficialis muscles.

The pronator teres muscle is named for its function and shape. It has two heads. The humeral head originates from the medial epicondyle of the humerus. The ulnar head originates from the coronoid process of the ulna. Both heads insert on the lateral or outer side of the radius. Upon contraction, the muscle functions to pronate and flex the forearm. Just as the word *teres* is used to designate the long, round shape of the teres major and teres minor muscles, its presence in the name of the pronator teres refers to the similar shape of the muscle.

The flexor carpi radialis muscle originates from the medial epicondyle of the humerus and inserts on the proximal aspect of the second and third metacarpal bones. The muscle functions in flexion and radial deviation of the wrist joint.

The palmaris longus muscle also originates from the medial epicondyle of the humerus. It inserts on the flexor retinaculum and palmar aponeurosis. A retinaculum is a structure which keeps a tissue in place. In this case, the flexor retinaculum is the fibrous strap binding the flexor tendons as they pass through the carpus en route to the hand and digits. An aponeurosis is a broadened tendon sheet that connects a muscle to the structures it moves. The palmar aponeurosis is associated with flexor muscles acting on structures of the hand and digits. Upon contraction, the palmaris longus increases the tension on the palmar aponeurosis; thereby favoring flexion of the hand and digits.

The flexor digitorum superficialis has two heads. The humeroulnar head originates from the medial epicondyle of the humerus and coronoid process of the ulna. The radial head originates from the front or anterior side of the radius. The muscle inserts on the medial phalanx of each of the four fingers. As may be surmised, the flexor digitorum superficialis flexes the middle phalanges of the four fingers upon contraction.

While supplying these four muscles, the median nerve continues distally and gives a motor branch known as the **anterior interosseous nerve** (152). The anterior interosseus nerve dives deep to travel distally between the radius and ulna bones. Effort should be made not to confuse this nerve with the posterior interosseus nerve, a radial nerve branch described earlier. The anterior interosseous nerve

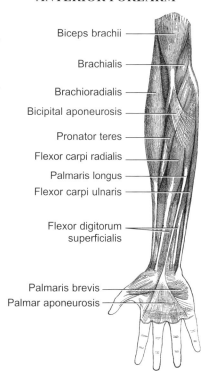

FIGURE 10.19
SUPERFICIAL MUSCLES OF ANTERIOR FOREARM

Biceps brachii

Brachialis

Brachioradialis

Bicipital aponeurosis

Pronator teres

Flexor carpi radialis

Palmaris longus

Flexor carpi ulnaris

Flexor digitorum superficialis

Palmaris brevis

Palmar aponeurosis

supplies three additional muscles, including the radial portion of the flexor digitorum profundus, flexor pollicis longus, and pronator quadratus.

The flexor digitorum profundus is composed of an ulnar and radial portion. The ulnar portion was previously described. It is named for its proximity to the ulna bone and coincidently, is innervated by the ulnar nerve. The radial portion is named for its location near the radius and is supplied by the anterior interosseous nerve. The flexor digitorum profundus originates from the coronoid process and shaft of the ulna to insert on the distal phalanx of each of the four fingers. Upon contraction, it flexes the distal phalanges of the fingers. It should be noted that the median nerve supplies both the flexor digitorum superficialis, which flexes the middle phalanges of the fingers, and the radial portion of the flexor digitorum profundus, which flexes the distal phalanges.

> The word *profundus* means *deep*. The flexor digitorum profundus is the muscle that has an ulnar and radial portion because it is the muscle located in a *deep* position, near the ulna and radius, respectively.

The flexor pollicis longus muscle originates from the medial epicondyle of the humerus, coronoid process of the ulna and front or anterior side of the radius. It inserts on the proximal phalanx of the thumb to flex the thumb upon contraction.

Similar to the other "pronator," the pronator teres, the pronator quadratus is also named for its function and structure. Whereas the pronator teres is a long, round muscle, the pronator quadratus is a rather flattened, four-sided muscle. The word *quadrate* refers to a square or square-shaped structure. The pronator quadratus is nearer to the wrist than the pronator teres, which is closer to the elbow. The pronator quadratus originates from the front or anterior side of the distal third of the ulna and inserts on the same area of the radius to pronate the forearm.

After the takeoff of the anterior interosseous nerve, the median nerve proceeds distally to give off a **palmar branch** (153) at the approximate level of the wrist. The palmar branch supplies skin of the radial or thumb-side of the palm. The median nerve then continues forward to produce six nerves of the hand. Included are the recurrent branch of the median nerve, three digital nerves, and two common digital nerves.

The **recurrent branch of the median nerve** (163) supplies three thenar muscles, which manipulate the thumb. The thenar

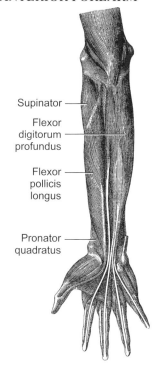

FIGURE 10.20
DEEP MUSCLES OF ANTERIOR FOREARM

Supinator

Flexor digitorum profundus

Flexor pollicis longus

Pronator quadratus

eminence is the thick area of the palm just proximal to, or at the base of, the thumb. These three thenar muscles include the abductor pollicis brevis, superficial head of flexor pollicis brevis, and opponens pollicis muscles.

Two Eminences of Palm:

Thenar eminence is at base of **Th**umb
Hypothenar eminence is **Below** thenar eminence (when in anatomic position, with palms facing forward)

Each eminence contains 3 muscles that act on one of the two outer digits (thumb and little finger). Each set of 3 contains muscles that are similar in function to the other set of 3, although each set exerts its force on its respective digit

---

By now, based on its name, it should be apparent that the abductor pollicis brevis muscle abducts the thumb. It originates from the trapezium and scaphoid bones of the carpus and flexor retinaculum of the hand. It inserts on the lateral or outer side of the proximal phalanx of the thumb.

The flexor pollicis brevis muscle flexes and adducts the thumb. This muscle has two heads. The superficial head originates from the flexor retinaculum, is larger, and is innervated by the recurrent branch of the median nerve. The smaller, deep head was previously described. It originates from the trapezium bone of the carpus and is supplied by the deep branch of the ulnar nerve. Like

the abductor pollicis brevis, the flexor pollicis brevis inserts on the lateral or outer side of the proximal phalanx of the thumb.

The opponens pollicis muscle opposes and flexes the thumb. Opposition occurs when the thumb is moved inward across the front of the palm, as if to grasp an object with the little finger. Similar to the flexor pollicis brevis, the opponens pollicis originates from the trapezium bone and flexor retinaculum. It inserts on the lateral or outer side of the first metacarpal bone, the metacarpal of the thumb.

After giving off the recurrent branch, the median nerve continues distally and supplies the first and second lumbrical muscles. The four lumbrical muscles were previously described. The median nerve supplies the two muscles located on the radial side of the hand. The ulnar nerve supplies the two muscles of the ulnar side.

<u>All</u> Muscles in Hand (4 groups) are Supplied by Median and Ulnar Nerves

1) **Thenar muscles:** (3) Median
2) **Hypothenar muscles:** (3) Ulnar
3) **Lumbrical muscles:** (4) #1 and #2 = Median, #3 and #4 = Ulnar
4) **Interosseous muscles:** (7) both palmar and dorsal via Ulnar

No other nerve supplies a muscle located in the hand.

FIGURE 10.21
FLEXOR NERVES OF HAND AND DIGITS

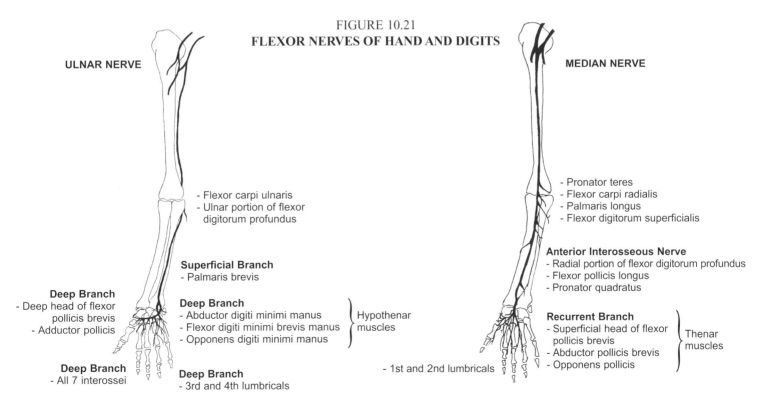

ULNAR NERVE

- Flexor carpi ulnaris
- Ulnar portion of flexor digitorum profundus

Superficial Branch
- Palmaris brevis

Deep Branch
- Deep head of flexor pollicis brevis
- Adductor pollicis

Deep Branch
- Abductor digiti minimi manus
- Flexor digiti minimi brevis manus } Hypothenar muscles
- Opponens digiti minimi manus

Deep Branch
- All 7 interossei

Deep Branch
- 3rd and 4th lumbricals

MEDIAN NERVE

- Pronator teres
- Flexor carpi radialis
- Palmaris longus
- Flexor digitorum superficialis

Anterior Interosseous Nerve
- Radial portion of flexor digitorum profundus
- Flexor pollicis longus
- Pronator quadratus

Recurrent Branch
- Superficial head of flexor pollicis brevis
- Abductor pollicis brevis } Thenar muscles
- Opponens pollicis

- 1st and 2nd lumbricals

Median vs. Ulnar in the Hand

Both nerves give off a motor branch as they travel distally to provide cutaneous innervation to the hand/digits (via proper and common digital branches). In addition to cutaneous branches, the median nerve also supplies the first and second lumbrical muscles (located on the radial side of the hand) after the motor branch separates. The superficial ulnar nerve also supplies the palmaris brevis muscle (located on the ulnar side of the hand) after the takeoff of its motor branch.

The motor branch of the median is the **recurrent br. of median nerve**. The median nerve is responsible for flexion, especially in the radial direction. The recurrent br. supplies the three thenar muscles. These are located on the radial side of the palm, the region supplied by the median nerve. They flex and abduct the thumb. Thumb abduction is movement in the radial direction. There is one portion of a thenar muscle that is not supplied by the median nerve. The deep head of the flexor pollicis brevis is innervated by the ulnar nerve. This follows the common theme of innervation responsibility, as this muscle flexes and *adducts* the thumb. Adduction moves the thumb in an ulnar direction. The other, larger portion of the flexor pollicis brevis, the superficial head, is innervated by the median nerve.

The motor branch of the ulnar is the **deep br. of ulnar nerve**. The ulnar nerve is responsible for flexion, especially in the ulnar direction. The deep br. supplies the three hypothenar muscles. These are located on the ulnar side of the palm, the region supplied by the ulnar nerve. Furthermore, they flex and abduct the little finger. Little finger abduction is movement in the ulnar direction. In addition to the hypothenar muscles, the deep br. of the ulnar nerve also supplies all seven interosseous muscles, the two lumbrical muscles on the ulnar side (#4, #5), adductor pollicis (moves thumb in ulnar direction), and the deep portion of the flexor pollicis brevis (moves thumb in ulnar direction).

Thenar vs. Hypothenar Muscles (each set composed of 3 similar muscles)

MUSCLE	INSERTION
abductor pollicis brevis	lateral/outer side, proximal phalanx thumb
abductor digiti minimi manus	medial/outer side, proximal phalanx little finger
flexor pollicis brevis (median and ulnar)	lateral/outer side, proximal phalanx thumb
flexor digiti minimi brevis manus	medial/outer side, proximal phalanx little finger
opponens pollicis	lateral/outer side, first metacarpal bone
opponens digiti minimi manus	medial/outer side, fifth metacarpal bone

As *opposed* to the other thenar and hypothenar muscles, which insert on the outer side of the base of the first phalanx of their respective digit, the two "*opponens*" muscles insert on the outer side of the metacarpal bone of their respective digit.

As the median nerve approaches the digits, it gives off three digital and two common digital branches. These are sensory branches that ultimately supply skin on the sides of the digits.

The **first digital nerve** (162) supplies the radial or outer side of the thumb. The **second digital nerve** (162) supplies the ulnar or inner side of the thumb. Finally, the **third digital nerve** (162) supplies the adjacent radial or thumb-side of the index finger.

Each common digital nerve courses distally to divide into two proper digital nerves, each of which supplies the skin on one side of a digit (finger). In other words, each common digital nerve is responsible for innervating skin of two adjacent fingers. It does so by dividing into two proper digital nerves. Each proper digital nerve supplies the skin on the side of one digit.

The **first common digital nerve** (161) comes off the median nerve and courses toward the space between the index (digit #2) and middle (digit #3) fingers. It then divides into two **proper digital nerves** (160). One supplies the ulnar side of digit #2, while the other supplies the radial side of digit #3. The **second common digital nerve** (161) travels toward the space between the middle (digit #3) and ring (digit #4) fingers. It divides into two **proper digital nerves** (160) that supply the ulnar side of digit #3 and radial side of digit #4, respectively. As described earlier, the ulnar side of digit #4 and both sides of digit #5 are innervated by the ulnar nerve. The second common digital nerve often receives a **communicating branch from the ulnar nerve** (159).

The innervation responsibilities of the median nerve will now be reviewed. Like the ulnar nerve, the only cutaneous or sensory innervation provided by the median nerve is isolated to the hand. It supplies the lateral or radial 3½ digits. The median nerve is responsible for the majority of innervation that results in flexion of the forearm, wrist, hand, and digits. This is especially true for flexion in the radial direction. Like the ulnar nerve, the median nerve travels through the arm without producing any branches. In the forearm, its only responsibility is motor. The forearm muscular innervation starts and ends with pronators, the pronator teres and pronator quadratus, respectively. In between are five flexors: flexor carpi radialis, palmaris longus, flexor digitorum superficialis, radial portion of flexor digitorum profundus, and flexor pollicis longus. Of the seven forearm muscles supplied by the median nerve, the last three are actually innervated by a branch of the median nerve, the anterior interosseus nerve. This includes the radial portion of flexor digitorum profundus, flexor pollicis longus, and pronator quadratus. The median nerve continues toward the hand and gives off the recurrent branch of the median nerve. The recurrent branch supplies three thenar muscles, including the abductor pollicis brevis, superficial head of flexor pollicis brevis, and opponens pollicis. Finally, the median nerve continues on to innervate the first and second lumbrical muscles of the hand.

Both named motor branches of median nerve (anterior interosseous nerve and recurrent branch) supply three muscles each.

**12 Muscles and Lateral 3¼ Fingers (palmar side)
Supplied by Median Nerve**

7 forearm (pronator, 5 flexors, pronator) + **3 thenar**
+ 2 lumbrical = 12 muscles

The opposing thumb is a unique appendage that gives primates a distinct advantage in the animal kingdom. The thumb provides the ability to grip more effectively and pick up objects more deliberately and efficiently. The complex muscular structure of the thumb enables it to move in a variety of directions. This complexity also makes it easy to get all the "pollicis" muscles confused.

There are eight "pollicis" muscles. Three are innervated by the radial nerve, three by the median nerve, and one by the ulnar nerve. One muscle, the flexor pollicis brevis, has one head supplied by the median nerve and another by the ulnar nerve. It could therefore be said that the median nerve supplies three and a half pollicis muscles and the ulnar supplies one and a half. By considering the basic function of each of these nerves, their muscular innervation to the thumb seems appropriate.

The radial nerve supplies three pollicis muscles. This nerve is the extensor nerve of the forearm and hand. Hence, it supplies the only two "extensor" muscles of the thumb, the extensor pollicis brevis and extensor pollicis longus. In order to move the thumb away from the palm and digits, when the thumb is extended, it is often also abducted. The radial nerve also innervates the abductor pollicis longus muscle.

Again, the median nerve carries most of the flexion responsibility for the wrist, hand, and digits. It is especially responsible for flexion in the radial direction. The median nerve innervates four thumb muscles. There are only two pollicis "flexor" muscles and the median nerve innervates both. It supplies the flexor pollicis longus and the superficial head of the flexor pollicis brevis muscles. The other two median-supplied pollicis muscles include the abductor pollicis brevis and opponens pollicis. Abduction of the thumb can be considered movement in the radial direction. It should be noted that the last three muscles mentioned – the superficial head of the flexor pollicis brevis, abductor pollicis brevis, and opponens pollicis – are the three thenar muscles innervated by the recurrent branch of the median nerve.

Maintaining its job description as a flexor, especially in the ulnar direction, the ulnar nerve innervates part of one muscle that flexes the thumb and one muscle that moves it in an ulnar direction. The ulnar nerve supplies the deep head of the flexor pollicis brevis. The larger superficial head of this muscle is supplied by the median nerve. Since adduction is movement in the ulnar direction, it is no surprise that the ulnar nerve innervates the only "adductor" muscle of the thumb, the adductor pollicis muscle.

In summary, each of these three nerves remains consistent in its basic function as it innervates the muscles of the thumb. The radial nerve innervates the two extensors. The median nerve supplies one flexor in its entirety and splits the innervation of another flexor with the ulnar nerve. The ulnar nerve innervates the one adductor. The radial nerve and median nerve split the responsibility of abduction. The radial nerve supplies the abductor pollicis longus, as it is consistent with extension. The median nerve innervates the abductor pollicis brevis because it moves the thumb in a radial direction. Additionally, the median nerve supplies the opponens pollicis, which also theoretically acts to move the thumb in a radial direction.

There are eight (8) "pollicis" muscles:

P_1 O_2 L_3 L_4 I_5 C_6 I_7 S_8

Radial
  { 1. abductor pollicis longus
  { 2. extensor pollicis brevis
  { 3. extensor pollicis longus

Median
  { 4. flexor pollicis longus
  { 5. abductor pollicis brevis
  { 6. opponens pollicis
  { 7. flexor pollicis brevis
      - superficial head (larger): median nerve
      - deep head (smaller): ulnar nerve

Ulnar
  { 8. adductor pollicis

The brachial plexus and its branches present a significant challenge to the beginning student. It is easy to feel overwhelmed by information overload. The following synopsis should provide the basic foundation from which more specific material can later be learned. Perseverance, time, and repetition are the instruments needed to master this information.

There are three cords of the brachial plexus. Each divides into two terminal branches. Six terminal branches therefore exist, yet only five nerves continue on to provide innervation to the arm. This is because the median nerve is formed by the combination of two brachial plexus terminal branches, the lateral and medial roots of the median nerve. The five nerves include the axillary and radial nerves (posterior cord), musculocutaneous nerve (lateral cord), ulnar nerve (medial cord), and median nerve (lateral and medial cords). Each of these nerves innervates both muscles and skin of the upper extremity. In fact, there is not a muscle located in the upper extremity which is supplied by any nerve other than one of these five brachial plexus terminal branches.

FIGURE 10.22
**MAJOR NERVES
OF UPPER EXTREMITY**

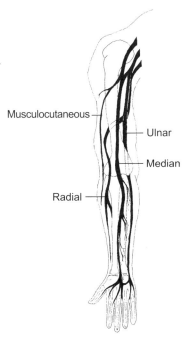

Musculocutaneous

Ulnar

Median

Radial

As previously mentioned, all five nerves also provide sensory innervation to the skin of the upper extremity. This innervation is confined to the free limb. By way of the superior lateral brachial cutaneous nerve, the axillary nerve innervates an area on the lateral aspect of the shoulder and upper arm. The musculocutaneous nerve supplies skin on the lateral forearm as the lateral antebrachial cutaneous nerve. The radial nerve serves as the origin of the posterior brachial and posterior antebrachial cutaneous nerves. These innervate skin of the posterior arm and forearm, respectively. The superficial radial nerve continues distally to wrap around the radial aspect of the wrist and supply skin of the radial side of the dorsal hand and lateral (radial) 3½ digits. This includes the proximal two-thirds of digits one, two, three, and the radial half of four. Just as they share a common function in serving as flexion nerves of the wrist, hand, and digits, the median and ulnar nerves also possess similarities in their distribution of sensory innervation. Both travel through the arm while furnishing no branches. It is not until they get to the forearm that they give off motor branches and continue on to supply skin of the hand and digits. The median nerve supplies the palmar aspect of the radial side of the hand, including digits one, two, three, and the radial half of four. It also supplies the dorsal fingertips of these same digits. As described, the superficial radial nerve supplies the proximal aspect of the dorsal surface of these digits. The ulnar nerve supplies both the palmar and dorsal surface of the ulnar side of the hand and digits. This includes both sides of digit five and the adjacent, ulnar half of digit four.

Three nerves provide cutaneous innervation in the hand:

RADIAL SIDE
{ **Radial** – dorsal hand, radial 3½ digits (except fingertips). In addition to hand, radial supplies back of arm and forearm
Medial – palmar hand, radial 3½ digits (and dorsal fingertips of same digits)

ULNAR SIDE
{ **Ulnar** – both sides of hand, ulnar 1½ digits

FIGURE 10.23
CUTANEOUS INNERVATION OF HAND

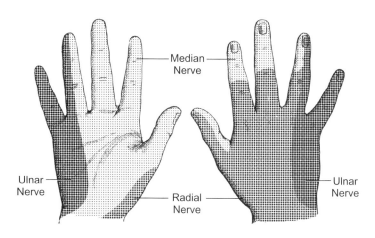

The medial aspect of the arm and forearm are the only cutaneous areas of the upper extremity not supplied by one of the five terminal branches of the brachial plexus. This medial area is innervated by two branches of the medial cord, the medial brachial and medial antebrachial cutaneous nerves. In addition, the second and third intercostal nerves contribute by way of the intercostobrachial nerve, which combines with the medial brachial cutaneous nerve.

The motor responsibilities of the five terminal branches will be reviewed next. The muscles of the arm are bigger and less numerous than those of the forearm. The motion of flexing and extending the arm and forearm may require strength; hence, the muscles of the arm are bigger. Further-more, these muscles exert their effects by way of the shoulder joint (to move the arm) and elbow joint (to move the forearm). The elbow only allows for flexion, extension, sup-ination, and pronation. This limits the required number of muscles. The wrist and digits, by contrast, must allow for very intricate, detailed movements. The wrist and metacarpophalangeal joints, for instance, can move in virtually any direction. This requires numerous small muscles in the forearm and hand.

FIGURE 10.24
SENSORY NERVES
OF UPPER EXTREMITY

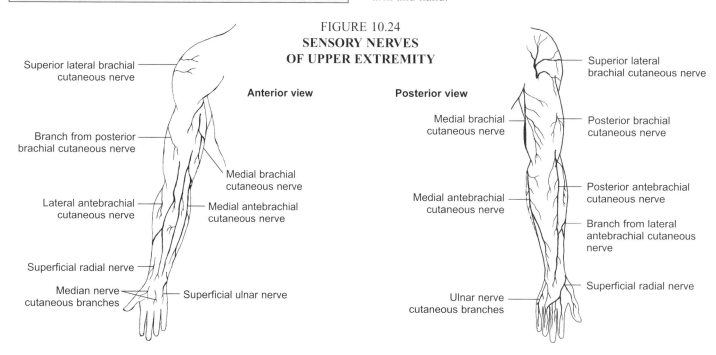

FIGURE 10.25
CHIEF NERVES AND VESSELS OF THE ANTERIOR ASPECT OF THE FOREARM

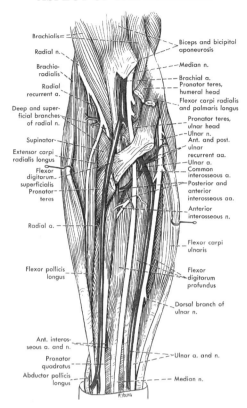

(Reproduced with permission from Hollinshead, W.H., Rosse, C.: Textbook of Anatomy, 4th ed. Philadelphia, Harper & Row, 1985)

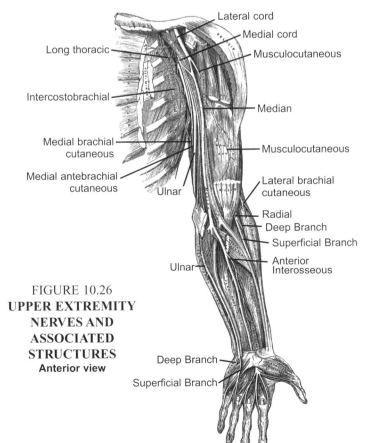

FIGURE 10.26
UPPER EXTREMITY NERVES AND ASSOCIATED STRUCTURES
Anterior view

Each of the five terminal nerves possesses basic motor responsibilities. Although exceptions may exist, the general action of a particular nerve should be learned. One nerve abducts the arm (shoulder) and rotates it laterally (shoulder). One nerve is responsible for flexion of the arm (shoulder) and forearm (elbow). Because of the higher complexity of the musculature of the forearm and hand, two nerves are responsible for flexion of the wrist and digits. Finally, one nerve is responsible for extension of the entire upper extremity, including arm (shoulder), forearm (elbow), wrist, and digits. In addition to these basic functions, some of these same nerves also pronate or supinate the forearm.

The axillary nerve serves to abduct the arm and rotate it laterally via the deltoid and teres minor muscles. These muscles exert their influence by way of the shoulder joint.

The musculocutaneous nerve innervates the coracobrachialis, brachialis, and biceps brachii muscles. The coracobrachialis flexes and adducts the arm via the shoulder joint. Both the brachialis and biceps brachii flex the forearm by way of the elbow. In addition, the biceps brachii also supinates the forearm.

By supplying numerous flexor muscles, both the median nerve and ulnar nerve flex the wrist, hand, and digits. The median nerve is responsible for the majority of this action and provides for flexion in the radial direction. This includes radial deviation of the wrist and thumb abduction. The ulnar nerve provides for flexion in an ulnar direction, including ulnar deviation of the wrist and little finger abduction. By innervating the pronator teres and pronator quadratus, the median nerve is also responsible for pronation of the forearm.

Finally, the radial nerve is the extensor nerve. It innervates the triceps muscle, which extends the arm and forearm. Additionally, it supplies numerous extensor muscles that extend the wrist and hand. It also innervates the supinator muscle, which along with the biceps brachii muscle, supinates the forearm.

Terminal Branches of Brachial Plexus

Axillary	*- abducts arm; rotates arm laterally*
Musculocutaneous	*- adducts arm; flexes arm, forearm; supinates forearm*
Median	*- flexes forearm, wrist, digits; pronates forearm*
Ulnar	*- flexes forearm, wrist, digits*
Radial	*- adducts arm; extends arm, forearm, wrist, digits; supinates forearm; flexes forearm via brachioradialis muscle*

Of the five brachial plexus terminal branches, there is only one that abducts the arm, the axillary nerve. There are two nerves that adduct the arm: the musculocutaneous and radial nerves. By coincidence, these are also the same two that supinate the forearm. The median nerve pronates the forearm.

To mechanically exert its force to accomplish supination, the supinator must be on the back of the forearm. This is the area supplied by the radial nerve.

To mechanically exert their forces to accomplish pronation, the pronators must be on the front of the forearm. This is the area supplied by the median and ulnar nerves. The median nerve is responsible for the majority of innervation to the flexors of the anterior forearm. Maintaining its role as the dominant nerve of the area, the median nerve also supplies the pronators.

Once the basic function of each nerve is learned, it is much easier to tell which muscles are innervated by which nerves by simply evaluating the name of the muscle. A helpful hint is to use yourself as a "working model." What nerve causes supination? Supinate your forearm against resistance. Feel the muscle on the **posterior** aspect of the forearm contract. Hence, the radial nerve would be a good guess. Feel your biceps also contract during supination. You should know that the three flexor muscles of the upper arm are all innervated by the musculocutaneous nerve (it is actually the biceps brachii muscle that is active in supination). Now pronate your forearm and feel the muscles of the **anterior** forearm contract. The two "flexing" nerves of the forearm muscles are the median nerve and ulnar nerve. Because the median nerve is responsible for most of the muscular function of this area, it would be an excellent guess.

FIGURE 10.27

Some characteristic movements of fingers, wrist, and elbow in response to nerve stimulation.

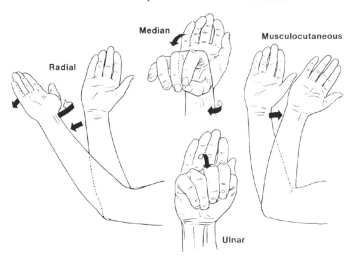

(Reproduced with permission from Cousins, M.J., Bridenbaugh, P.O.: Neural Blockade in Clinical Anesthesia and Management of Pain, 2nd ed. Philadelphia, Lippincott, 1988)

QUIZ 3
Brachial Plexus and Nerves of the Upper Extremity

Time for Quiz = 33 minutes.
For questions 1-28, choose the single best answer.

_____1) Sensory innervation to the skin of the posterior aspect of the arm is provided by which nerve structure?
   a) axillary nerve
   b) radial nerve
   c) medial cord of brachial plexus
   d) musculocutaneous nerve
   e) none of the above

_____2) Which of the following nerves is a direct branch of the medial cord of the brachial plexus?
   a) musculocutaneous nerve
   b) radial nerve
   c) medial pectoral nerve
   d) suprascapular nerve
   e) none of the above

_____3) Which nerve provides innervation to the radial side of digit #4?
   a) median nerve
   b) ulnar nerve
   c) radial nerve
   d) musculocutaneous nerve
   e) none of the above

_____4) Which muscle is supplied by the anterior interosseous nerve?
   a) pronator teres
   b) flexor pollicis longus
   c) flexor carpi radialis
   d) adductor pollicis
   e) none of the above

_____5) The superior lateral brachial cutaneous nerve is derived from which nerve structure?
   a) axillary nerve
   b) musculocutaneous nerve
   c) radial nerve
   d) medial cord of the brachial plexus
   e) none of the above

_____6) Sensory innervation to the skin of the lateral aspect of the forearm is provided by which nerve structure?
   a) ulnar nerve
   b) axillary nerve
   c) musculocutaneous nerve
   d) radial nerve
   e) none of the above

_____7) Which muscle is supplied by the ulnar nerve or one of its branches?
   a) second lumbrical
   b) extensor digiti minimi
   c) flexor pollicis longus
   d) palmaris longus
   e) none of the above

_____8) Concerning the number and type of digital nerves that come directly off the median nerve, which of the following is true?
   a) There are three proper digital nerves.
   b) There are three common digital nerves.
   c) Both a and b
   d) There is one common digital nerve.
   e) None of the above

_____9) Which nerve serves as a terminal branch of the medial cord?
   a) radial nerve
   b) axillary nerve
   c) both a and b
   d) musculocutaneous nerve
   e) none of the above

_____10) Sensory innervation to the skin of the lateral aspect of the shoulder is provided by which nerve structure?
   a) axillary nerve
   b) lateral cord of the brachial plexus
   c) radial nerve
   d) intercostobrachial nerve
   e) none of the above

_____11) The posterior interosseous nerve is a branch of which nerve structure?
  a) radial nerve
  b) axillary nerve
  c) median nerve
  d) ulnar nerve
  e) none of the above

_____12) Which muscle is supplied by the median nerve or one of its branches?
  a) pronator quadratus
  b) supinator
  c) palmaris brevis
  d) adductor pollicis
  e) none of the above

_____13) Which nerve does the intercostobrachial nerve combine with?
  a) posterior brachial cutaneous nerve
  b) medial pectoral nerve
  c) medial brachial cutaneous nerve
  d) medial antebrachial cutaneous nerve
  e) none of the above

_____14) Sensory innervation of the skin of the dorsal aspect of the radial side of the hand is provided by which nerve structure?
  a) superficial branch of ulnar nerve
  b) deep branch of ulnar nerve
  c) digital branch of ulnar nerve
  d) median nerve
  e) none of the above

_____15) Stimulation by the axillary nerve serves to
  a) abduct the arm
  b) rotate the arm laterally
  c) both a and b
  d) adduct the arm
  e) none of the above

_____16) Which muscle is supplied by the posterior interosseous nerve?
  a) flexor digitorum profundus
  b) extensor indicis
  c) extensor carpi radialis brevis
  d) pronator quadratus
  e) nonc of the above

_____17) The medial brachial cutaneous nerve is branch of which nerve structure?
  a) posterior cord of brachial plexus
  b) radial nerve
  c) musculocutaneous nerve
  d) medial cord of brachial plexus
  e) none of the above

_____18) Sensory innervation of the skin of the palmar aspect of the radial side of the hand is provided by which nerve structure?
  a) median nerve
  b) radial nerve
  c) superficial branch ulnar nerve
  d) deep branch of ulnar nerve
  e) none of the above

_____19) Concerning the number and type of digital nerves that come directly off the ulnar nerve, which of the following is true?
  a) There is one proper digital nerve.
  b) There is one common digital nerve.
  c) Both a and b
  d) There are two common digital nerves.
  e) None of the above

_____20) The ulnar collateral nerve is a branch of which nerve structure?
  a) ulnar nerve
  b) median nerve
  c) anterior interosseous nerve
  d) medial trunk of the brachial plexus
  e) none of the above

_____21) Which muscle is supplied by the recurrent branch of the median nerve?
  a) superficial head of flexor pollicis brevis
  b) adductor pollicis
  c) both a and b
  d) deep head of the flexor pollicis brevis
  e) none of the above

_____22) The anterior interosseous nerve is a branch of which nerve?
  a) posterior interosseous nerve
  b) deep radial nerve
  c) ulnar nerve
  d) median nerve
  e) none of the above

_____23) To which muscular motion does the radial nerve contribute?
- a) extension of forearm
- b) pronation of forearm
- c) both a and b
- d) palmar flexion of hand
- e) none of the above

_____24) The medial antebrachial cutaneous nerve is derived from which nerve structure?
- a) radial nerve
- b) musculocutaneous nerve
- c) posterior cord of brachial plexus
- d) axillary nerve
- e) none of the above

_____25) Sensory innervation of the skin of the dorsal aspect of the ulnar side of the hand is provided by which nerve structure?
- a) superficial radial nerve
- b) deep radial nerve
- c) median nerve
- d) ulnar nerve
- e) none of the above

_____26) Which muscle is supplied by the deep branch of the ulnar nerve?
- a) flexor carpi ulnaris
- b) ulnar portion of flexor digitorum profundus
- c) abductor digiti minimi manus
- d) extensor digiti minimi
- e) none of the above

_____27) Which nerve innervates the two lateral sides of digit three?
- a) median nerve
- b) ulnar nerve
- c) both a and b
- d) radial nerve
- e) none of the above

_____28) Sensory innervation to the skin of the medial aspect of the forearm is provided by which nerve structure?
- a) ulnar nerve
- b) medial cord of brachial plexus
- c) radial nerve
- d) musculocutaneous nerve
- e) none of the above

For questions 29-33, use the following directions:
- a.......1,2,3 are correct
- b.......1,3 are correct
- c.......2,4 are correct
- d.......only 4 is correct
- e.......all are correct

_____29) Which of the following muscles are innervated by a nerve branch of the posterior cord system of the brachial plexus?
1. extensor pollicis brevis
2. extensor pollicis longus
3. extensor indicis
4. abductor pollicis longus

_____30) The median nerve is responsible for which of the following functions in the hand?
1. innervation to the 3rd and 4th lumbrical muscles
2. innervation to the dorsal skin of the fingertips of digits 1, 2, 3
3. innervation to the skin of the ulnar side of digit 4
4. innervation to the palmar skin of the fingertips of digits 1, 2, 3

_____31) Which of the following muscles are innervated by a branch of the medial cord system of the brachial plexus?
1. anconeus
2. adductor pollicis
3. supinator
4. pectoralis major

_____32) The ulnar nerve is responsible for which of the following functions in the hand?
1. cutaneous innervation to the radial side of digit five
2. cutaneous innervation to the radial side of digit four
3. cutaneous innervation to the ulnar side of the dorsal hand
4. innervation to the 1st and 2nd lumbrical muscles

_____33) An injury to the posterior cord may be associated with which of the following clinical signs?
1. numbness over the medial portion of the forearm
2. difficulty supinating the forearm
3. difficulty flexing the wrist
4. numbness over the radial aspect of the dorsal surface of the hand

QUIZ 3: Brachial Plexus Answers and Explanations

1) b – The radial nerve should initially be considered any time the word *posterior* is associated with structures of the upper extremity. The posterior brachial cutaneous nerve is a radial nerve branch.

2) c – The musculocutaneous nerve is a terminal branch of the lateral cord of the brachial plexus. The radial nerve is a terminal branch of the posterior cord. The suprascapular nerve is a branch of the upper trunk of the brachial plexus.

3) a – The ulnar nerve provides innervation to the ulnar side of this same digit.

4) b – The anterior interosseous is a branch of the median nerve. It routinely innervates three muscles, including the radial portion of flexor digitorum profundus, flexor pollicis longus, and pronator quadratus. The pronator teres is supplied by the median nerve, but not via the anterior interosseous nerve. The flexor carpi radialis is also supplied by the median nerve, but again, not by way of the anterior interosseous nerve. The adductor pollicis is innervated by the ulnar nerve.

5) a – The superior lateral brachial cutaneous nerve supplies skin of the lateral shoulder and lateral upper arm.

6) c – The musculocutaneous nerve becomes the lateral antebrachial cutaneous nerve as it emerges from the substance of the biceps brachii muscle.

7) e – The first and second lumbrical muscles are innervated by the median nerve. The third and fourth lumbrical muscles are innervated by the ulnar nerve. The extensor digiti minimi is supplied by the radial nerve. It is the only "digiti minimi" (little finger) muscle that is not innervated by the ulnar nerve. Remember, the little finger is on the *ulnar* side of the hand. Also remember that the radial nerve supplies all the "extensors." The flexor pollicis longus and palmaris longus are both sup-

plied by the median nerve. The ulnar nerve primarily supplies small, short muscles involved in flexion of the wrist and digits. The ulnar nerve innervates no "longus" muscles.

8) a – The median nerve supplies three digital branches. One goes to one side of digit 1 (thumb), one goes to the other side of digit 1, and one goes to the adjacent, radial side of digit 2 (index finger). The median nerve also supplies two common digital nerves. Each common digital nerve divides into two proper digital nerves that supplies adjacent sides of adjoining fingers. One common digital supplies the ulnar side of digit two (index finger) and the adjacent, radial side of digit three (middle finger). The other common digital supplies the ulnar side of digit three and the adjacent, radial side of digit four (ring finger). Ultimately, there are seven proper digital nerves of median nerve origin. The ulnar side of digit four and both sides of digit five are supplied by the ulnar nerve.

9) e – The terminal branches of the medial cord of the brachial plexus are the ulnar nerve and medial root of median nerve. The terminal branches of the posterior cord are the radial and axillary nerves. The terminal branches of the lateral cord are the musculocutaneous nerve and lateral root of median nerve.

10) a – This is by way of the superior lateral brachial cutaneous nerve.

11) a – The posterior interosseous nerve is a branch of the radial nerve. In the upper extremity, nerve names containing the word *posterior* should be associated with the radial nerve. The anterior interosseous nerve is a branch of the median nerve.

12) a – The two "pronator" muscles, pronator teres and pronator quadratus, are supplied by the median nerve. The supinator is supplied by the radial nerve. Both the palmaris brevis and adductor pollicis muscles are supplied by the ulnar nerve.

13) c – The combination supplies sensory innervation to the medial aspect of the upper arm.

14) e – This area of skin is supplied by the superficial radial nerve.

15) c – The axillary nerve innervates two muscles. The deltoid muscle abducts the arm. The teres minor muscle laterally rotates the arm.

16) b – The posterior interosseous nerve is a branch of the deep radial nerve that travels distally between the two long bones of the forearm. It usually supplies four muscles: the abductor pollicis longus, extensor pollicis brevis, extensor pollicis longus, and extensor indicis. Both the radial portion of flexor digitorum profundus and pronator quadratus are innervated by a median nerve branch, the anterior interosseous nerve. The ulnar portion of flexor digitorum profundus is supplied by the ulnar nerve. The extensor carpi radialis brevis is innervated by the radial nerve, but not by way of the posterior interosseous nerve.

17) d – The medial antebrachial cutaneous nerve is also a direct branch of the medial cord of the brachial plexus.

18) a – The median nerve supplies the palmar aspect of the radial side of the hand. The superficial radial nerve supplies the approximate same area on the dorsal side of the hand. The ulnar nerve supplies both the dorsal and palmar surfaces of the ulnar side of the hand.

19) c – The ulnar nerve supplies one digital branch that innervates the outer, ulnar side of the little finger (digit 5). It also provides one common digital nerve that divides into two proper digital nerves. One of these proper digital nerves supplies the inner, radial side of digit 5. The other supplies the adjacent, ulnar side of digit 4 (ring finger). Ultimately, there are three proper digital nerves of ulnar nerve origin.

20) e – The ulnar collateral nerve branches off the radial nerve in the arm. It is named *ulnar collateral* because it travels in close proximity to the ulnar nerve. It innervates the medial head of the triceps muscle and anconeus muscle. Both serve to extend the forearm.

21) a – The recurrent branch of the median nerve, supplies the three thenar muscles. These manipulate the thumb and include the abductor pollicis brevis, superficial head of flexor pollicis brevis, and opponens pollicis. Both the adductor pollicis and deep head of flexor pollicis brevis are supplied by the ulnar nerve.

22) d – The anterior interosseous nerve is a branch of the median nerve. It usually innervates three muscles, including the radial portion of the flexor digitorum profundus, the flexor pollicis longus, and the pronator quadratus muscles. This nerve should not be confused with the posterior interosseous nerve, which is a radial nerve branch.

23) a – The radial nerve extends and adducts the arm (via the shoulder joint), extends and supinates the forearm (via the elbow joint), extends (dorsiflexes) the hand (via the wrist joint), and extends the digits (via the metacorpophalangeal and interphalangeal joints). In the arm, the radial nerve innervates all three heads of the triceps muscle. The long head adducts and extends the arm. The medial and lateral heads of triceps, along with the anconeus muscle, extend the forearm. In the forearm, the radial nerve innervates multiple extensor muscles which extend the wrist and digits. The radial nerve also innervates the supinator muscle of the forearm, which supinates the forearm.

24) e – Both the medial brachial and medial antebrachial cutaneous nerves are direct branches of the medial cord of the brachial plexus.

25) d – See #18 answer explanation.

26) c – The deep branch of the ulnar nerve innervates the three hypothenar muscles. These muscles are located at the base of the small finger along the radial aspect of the palm. They function to manipulate the little finger and include the abductor digiti minimi manus, flexor digiti minimi brevis manus, and opponens digiti minimi manus. The flexor carpi ulnaris and ulnar portion flexor digitorum profundus are both innervated by the ulnar nerve, but not specifically by the *deep branch* of the ulnar nerve. The extensor digiti minimi, like all

forearm muscles with the word *extensor* in their name, is innervated by the radial nerve.

27) a – The median nerve innervates both the radial and ulnar sides of digit three. With digit four, the median nerve supplies the radial side; the ulnar nerve supplies the ulnar side.

28) b – The medial antebrachial cutaneous nerve is a direct branch of the medial cord of the brachial plexus. The medial brachial cutaneous nerve is also a direct branch of the cord.

29) e – All are innervated by the posterior interosseous nerve. This nerve is the continuation of the deep radial nerve as it runs distally between the two long bones of the forearm.

30) c – The median nerve is responsible for cutaneous innervation of the radial (thumb) aspect of the palm and the palmar surface of digits one, two, three and half of four. It also supplies both sides of digits one, two, three, and the radial side of digit four. Sensation to the ulnar side of digit four is provided by the ulnar nerve. In addition, the median nerve also supplies skin of the dorsal surface of the distal ends of digits one, two, three, and usually, half of four. The median nerve innervates the 1st and 2nd lumbrical muscles. It is the ulnar nerve that supplies the 3rd and 4th lumbrical muscles.

31) c – The adductor pollicis muscle is innervated by a terminal branch of the medial cord, the ulnar nerve. The medial pectoral nerve originates directly from the medial cord and supplies both the pectoralis major and pectoralis minor muscles. The anconeus muscle is supplied by a terminal branch of the posterior cord, the radial nerve. The supinator muscle is supplied by one of its subsequent terminal branches, the deep radial nerve.

32) b – The ulnar nerve provides cutaneous innervation to both the palmar and dorsal surfaces of the ulnar side of the hand. This includes the ulnar half of digit four and both the radial and ulnar sides of digit five. The lumbrical muscles are located in the hand between each of the digits. The first and second lumbricals are supplied by the median nerve The third and fourth lumbricals are supplied by the ulnar nerve.

33) c – The radial nerve is a terminal branch of the posterior cord. It travels distally down the arm and divides into two terminal branches: the deep and superficial radial nerves. The deep radial is a motor branch innervating several muscles, including the supinator. The superficial radial is a sensory branch that continues distally, eventually winding around the radial (thumb) side of the wrist to supply skin on the radial aspect of the dorsum of the hand. The skin over the medial portion of the forearm is supplied by a branch of the medial cord, the medial antebrachial cutaneous nerve. Flexion of the wrist occurs via multiple flexor muscles supplied by both the median and ulnar nerves.

"It has been my experience that folks who have no vices have very few virtues."

– Abraham Lincoln

CLINICAL CORRELATION

Nerve damage occurs as a result of both acute and chronic processes. Acute nerve damage can follow traumatic injuries, infection, or tumor growth. Chronic damage can occur with chronic compression states or coexisting disease processes.

Chronic nerve compression can be associated with either musculoskeletal or soft tissue abnormalities. For instance, a herniated intervertebral disc may chronically compress a spinal nerve root, eventually causing permanent nerve damage if untreated. Likewise, a particular nerve may be chronically compressed by soft tissue structures as it travels distally. Such damage can also lead to permanent injury, with loss of sensory and/or motor function of the tissues supplied by the damaged nerve.

A multitude of coexisting disease states can lead to chronic nerve damage. A common example is diabetes mellitus. Diabetes is frequently accompanied by arteriosclerosis, which chronically impedes microvascular blood flow. This blood flow impediment can involve the small vessels that supply nerves. Over time, the decreased blood and oxygen supply leads to neuropathy, or chronic nerve dysfunction. Peripheral neuropathy is a common problem in poorly-controlled or long-term diabetic patients.

Despite the cause, nerve damage leads to sensory loss and paralysis in the distribution of the affected nerve. *Palsy* is a word meaning *paralysis*. There are a number of specific palsies that are due to damage to particular nerves. These palsies may result from acute or chronic nerve injury. Although paralysis infers motor deficit, many palsies involve a sensory loss as well.

To appropriately manage nerve injury, the motor and sensory innervation of each of the major nerves must be known. Should a sensory or motor deficit occur, a prior knowledge of peripheral nerve responsibilities allows the identification of the nerve most likely involved. From the clinical location of the motor of sensory deficit, the affected nerve can be back tracked to the causative agent. This search may extend all the way to the spinal segments from which the nerve originates. Certain diagnostic tests may be needed, but a prior knowledge of nerve anatomy gets the treatment plan going down the right path from the onset. The sooner the diagnosis is made, the sooner treatment options are determined.

PUSH, PULL, PINCH, PINCH

This clinical exam can be performed in seconds and specifically identifies the major upper extremity nerves affected by an acute injury.

PUSH
evaluates *radial nerve* by testing triceps muscle function

PULL
evaluates *musculocutaneous nerve* by testing function of upper arm flexor muscles (brachialis and biceps brachii muscles)

PINCH
pinch of radial side of palm evaluates *median nerve* function

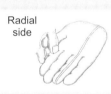

Radial side

PINCH
pinch of ulnar side of palm evaluates *ulnar nerve* function

Ulnar side

With distal upper extremity injuries, function of the three nerves active in hand movement may additionally be evaluated by these movements:
1) flexion of the thumb against mild resistance...**median nerve**
2) abduction (spreading) of little finger against mild resistance...**ulnar nerve**
3) dorsiflexion of hand and/or extension of digits against mild resistance...**radial nerve**

Regardless of whether the cause was an acute injury or chronic disease process, once significant nerve damage occurs, permanent changes develop in the tissues supplied by the affected nerve. Certain upper extremity nerve injuries have clinical signs and symptoms which are consistent in their pattern of manifestation. Many of these palsies have stereotypical descriptions and names that should be learned. The motor, sensory, and physical changes seen with damage to the long thoracic nerve and the five terminal branches of the cords of the brachial plexus are as follows:

LONG THORACIC NERVE (C5-C7)
"winging of the scapula"

Motor – the serratus anterior muscle originates from the eight upper ribs and inserts on the vertebral border of the scapula. It functions to pull the scapula anteriorly and twist it in order to lift the shoulder and abduct the arm. The person therefore has difficulty abducting the arm. Because the long thoracic nerve has no sensory responsibilities, there is no sensory deficit with injury.

Physical – the scapula droops inferiorly, as if the person is "winged."

MUSCULOCUTANEOUS NERVE (C5-C6)
"can't make a muscle"

Motor – difficulty flexing the arm at the shoulder (coracobrachialis), the forearm at the elbow (brachialis, biceps brachii), and supinating the forearm (biceps).

Sensory – skin on the radial or lateral aspect of the forearm via the lateral antebrachial cutaneous nerve.

Physical – atrophy (wasting) of the anterior arm, the location of the supplied muscles.

MEDIAN NERVE (C6-T1)

Motor – difficulty bending the wrist toward the radial (thumb) side, difficulty flexing the wrist, and difficulty flexing digits one (thumb), two (index finger), and three (long finger). There is also difficulty in pronation of the forearm.

Sensory – skin on the radial (thumb) side of the palm and palmar surface of digits one (thumb), two (index finger), three (long finger), and the radial half of four (ring finger).

Physical – atrophy (wasting) of the thenar eminence, the prominence of the palm just proximal to the thumb. The thenar muscles are supplied by the recurrent branch of the median nerve.

Carpal tunnel syndrome – this is a fairly common syndrome caused by chronic compression of the median nerve as it travels within the wrist, in close approximation to the flexor tendons of the hand and digits. The syndrome is named with reference to the carpus, the wrist joint. Usually, there is tingling, numbness, and burning pain in the median nerve distribution of the hand, although the entire hand may be involved. The pain and numbness is most common at night or during periods of inactivity. The symptoms are often improved by shaking the hands. There may be motor deficits of the median nerve distribution. Carpal tunnel syndrome is frequently associated with excessive, repetitive use of the hands. Because of this, certain occupations have an increased incidence of the syndrome. Examples include keyboard operators, typists, and instrumental musicians. Median nerve compression can also occur after an unaccustomed activity is repetitively performed. When a weekend warrior gets off the couch to rake the yard, he or she may notice the subsequent development of hand weakness or numbness. Arthritis, tenosynovitis,

and obesity are coexisting conditions which can predispose to the development of carpal tunnel syndrome. Diagnosis is by clinical signs and confirmed by nerve conduction studies. Treatment includes decreasing hand activity, anti-inflammatory medications, steroid injections, and splinting the wrist in an effort to decrease movement. Surgical decompression (carpal tunnel release) may be required. If untreated, the neurological deficits, including sensory, motor, and physical impairment, may become permanent.

ULNAR NERVE (C8-T1)
"claw hand"

Motor – difficulty flexing the wrist and digits four (ring finger) and five (little finger). There is also difficulty flexing the wrist toward the ulnar (little finger) side. There is difficulty abducting and adducting the fingers. A specific clinical test for ulnar nerve injury is to check for the ability to abduct or spread the little finger against mild resistance.

Sensory – the skin on the medial (ulnar) side of both the palmar and dorsal surfaces of the hand. This includes digit five (little finger) and the adjacent half of the digit four (ring finger).

Physical – atrophy (wasting) of the hypothenar eminence, the prominence of the palm just proximal to digit five. The hypothenar muscles are supplied by the deep branch of the ulnar nerve. Eventually, the atrophy and weakness produces a *claw hand*. Because there is inability to flex digits four and five at the metacarpophalangeal joints, they become chronically extended from the hand. The interphalangeal joints of these two fingers are chronically flexed. This gives the appearance of a claw. In addition to flexor muscles, the ulnar nerve supplies the fourth lumbrical, fifth lumbrical, and interosseous muscles. These paralyzed muscles would otherwise flex the metacarpophalangeal joint and extend the two interphalangeal joints of the ring and little fingers.

Injury of the ulnar nerve often occurs at the elbow. This may follow an acute dislocation or fracture. Milder cases may involve compression of the ulnar nerve as it travels in the shallow ulnar groove of the elbow. This can occur while resting the weight of the upper body on the elbows for prolonged periods of time. More commonly, it happens while sleeping with the elbows resting on the sleeping surface. Awakening with a hand "asleep" is often due to ulnar nerve compression at the elbow. This can be established by noting numbness or tingling in the little finger and adjacent half of the ring finger. The other digits are unaffected. When the ulnar nerve is injured in the palm, as seen with **cycle-racing palsy,** the deficits are usually confined to motor deficits.

RADIAL NERVE (C5-C8)
"wrist drop"

Motor – difficulty extending the arm, forearm, hand, and fingers

Sensory – proximal injury (above the origin of the posterior brachial and antebrachial cutaneous nerves) affects skin of the posterior and lateral aspects of the lower arm, forearm, and radial half of the dorsal surface of the hand. With distal injury, only the skin of the dorsal hand is affected.

Physical – atrophy of the posterior arm and forearm. The inability to dorsiflex the hand causes *wrist drop.*

Radial nerve palsy is associated with consistent motor deficits such as finger and wrist drop. The sensory deficits are more varied. Injuries occur with fractures and dislocations. In addition, the radial nerve may be injured as it is compressed against the humerus. **Bridegroom's palsy** is an example. This

occurs when a partner rests his or her head on the upper arm of an individual for prolonged periods of time as they sleep. **Saturday night palsy** occurs when the radial nerve is compressed following excessive sedation associated with the use of alcohol or drugs.

AXILLARY NERVE (C5, C6)
Motor – difficulty abducting the upper arm (deltoid muscle)

Sensory – a "patch" of skin along the lateral aspect of the upper arm via the superior lateral brachial cutaneous nerve

Physical – atrophy of the lateral shoulder

SUMMARY OF CHAPTER BOXES

1) C**5** = **5** named branches

2) Long thoracic nerve = C5, C6, C7 are angels in heaven

3) L ➜ M...Ant. Division **L**ower trunk ➜ **M**edial cord

4) The # of trunk divisions each cord receives: 1 = medial, 2 = lateral, 3 = posterior. **up and down**: *up* cord (lateral cord) and *down* cord (medial cord) are the two cords receiving anterior trunk divisions. Posterior cord (neither up or down) receives all 3 posterior divisions from the trunks.

5) **R**EAL **T**EXANS **D**RINK **C**OLD **B**EER!
Roots ➜ **T**runks ➜ **D**ivisions ➜ **C**ords ➜ **B**ranches

6) **Supra**scapular nerve is a branch of the **upper** trunk

7) Flexion of arm via shoulder joint moves humerus forward from anatomic position. Flexion of forearm via elbow joint moves radius and ulna forward from anatomic position.

8) Anterior Arm = Flexion: coracobrachialis = arm, brachialis and biceps brachii = forearm

9) Musculocutaneous nerve is well-named: motor in arm, cutaneous in forearm

10) **Lateral cord has *lateral* branches**...origin of lateral pectoral nerve before terminal branches: Musculocutaneous nerve (becomes *lateral* antebrachial cutaneous nerve) and *lateral* root of median nerve.

11) **p**osterior cord = **p**urple

12) Thoraco**dorsal** nerve innervates latissimus **dorsi** muscle

13) 4 "scapular" nerves: dorsal scapular (C5), suprascapular (upper trunk), upper and lower subscapular (posterior cord)

14) "Oh you elbow" (OU): **O**lecranon process is on **U**lna and forms posterior "bump" of elbow

15) Radial deviation – movement of hand toward radius bone or thumb. Ulnar deviation – movement toward ulna bone or little finger.

16) Descriptive terms in upper extremity anatomic names: brachialis/brachio, ulnaris, radialis, carpi, digitorum/digiti, pollicis, indicis, minimi, manus

17) extensor carpi ulnaris *extends wrist* and deviates it in an *ulnar* direction

18) posterior interosseus nerve (radial nerve) vs. anterior interosseus nerve (median nerve)

19) **5** (radial) + **4** (deep branch) + **4** (post. Interosseous) = **13** Radial nerve muscles supplied by the **P₁O₂S₃T₄E₅R₆I₇O₈R₉ C₁₀O₁₁R₁₂D₁₃**

20) **Posterior Cord = 3:** formed by <u>3</u> divisions, gives off <u>3</u> brs. before terminal branches: axillary n. (<u>3</u> responsibilities) and radial n. (supplies 1<u>3</u> muscles and has <u>3</u> named cutaneous branches)

21) Pectoralis major supplied by medial and lateral pectoral nerves. Pectoralis minor supplied by medial pectoral nerve only.

22) *medial* antebrachial cutaneous nerve comes off *medial* cord.
lateral antebrachial cutaneous nerve comes off *lateral* cord (as musculocutaneous nerve).

23) **14 nerves** are direct branches of
$B_1R_2A_3C_4H_5I_6A_7L_8$ $P_9L_{10}E_{11}X_{12}U_{13}S_{14}$
(upper trunk = 2, lateral cord = 2½, posterior cord = 5, medial cord = 4½)

24) Ulnar nerve: flexion in ulnar direction, including little finger abduction (hypothenar muscles)

25) All 7 interossei and 4 lumbrical muscles flex once then extend twice

26) <u>d</u>orsal interossei <u>ab</u>duct = **DAB**
The <u>p</u>almar interossei <u>ad</u>duct = **PAD**

27) Lumbrical muscles are "wormy." Originate from flexor tendon and insert on extensor tendon

28) Ulnar nerve is well-named: supplies palmar and dorsal skin of ulnar side of hand and innervates **1½** forearm muscles + **3** hypothenar + **7** interossei + **2** lumbricals + **1½** pollicis + **palmaris brevis**

29) "M" = <u>M</u>nemonic for Brachial Plexus: "M" shape of formation of <u>m</u>usculocutaneous, <u>m</u>edian, and ulnar nerves, <u>m</u>usculocutaneous = flexor of arm, <u>m</u>edian nerve = <u>m</u>ain flexor nerve of forearm, <u>m</u>iddle trunk = only trunk formed by only one spinal segment (C7), <u>m</u>edial cord = only cord formed by only one trunk division (anterior division of lower trunk).

30) Flexor digitorum profundus is deep: (*profundus* means deep) so it is near the radius and ulna bones. Radial portion innervated by median nerve. Ulnar portion innervated by ulnar nerve

31) Two Eminences of Palm: **th**enar (= **th**umb) and hypothenar. Each eminence is composed of 3 muscles of similar functions as those of the other eminence, but they contract on different digits. 3 thenar muscles via median nerve 3 hypothenar muscles via ulnar nerve.

32) **All** muscles in hand (4 groups) supplied by median or ulnar nerve: 1) Thenar = median; 2) Hypothenar = ulnar; 3) lumbrical: #1-#2 = median, #3-#4 = ulnar; 4) interosseous = ulnar

33) **median vs. ulnar nerve in the hand**
median: motor branch = recurrent branch ➜ thenar muscles
ulnar: motor branch = deep branch ➜ hypothenar muscles
Both thenar and hypothenar muscle groups consist of 3 "similar" muscles. Each group works on one of the outer digits.

34) Both named motor branches of median nerve (anterior interosseous nerve and recurrent branch) supply three muscles each.

35) **12 muscles via median n.**: **7** forearm (pronator, 5 flexors, pronator) + **3** thenar + **2** lumbrical

36) Eight $P_1O_2L_3L_4I_5C_6I_7S_8$ muscles of thumb: Radial n. (2 extensors, 1 abductor), Median n. (1½ flexors, 1 abductor, 1 opponens), Ulnar n. (½ flexor, 1 adductor)

37) Cutaneous nerves of hand: **radial nerve** = radial (lateral) 3½ digits of dorsal hand, except fingertips, **median nerve** = radial (lateral) 3½ digits of palm and dorsal fingertips of same digits, **ulnar nerve** = both palmar and dorsal sides of ulnar (medial) 1½ digits

38) **5 Terminal Branches**: **Axillary** (abducts, rotates arm laterally), **Musculocutaneous** (adducts arm; flexes arm, forearm; supinates forearm), **Median** (flexes forearm, wrist, digits; pronates forearm), **Ulnar** (flexes forearm, wrist, digits) **Radial** (adducts arm, extends forearm, wrist, digits; supinates forearm; flexes forearm via brachioradialis). Note: the two that adduct the arm, also supinate the forearm (musculocutaneous and radial). All terminal branches supply both skin and muscles isolated to the upper extremity. Every muscle located in the upper extremity is supplied by one of these 5 terminal branches.

39) Use yourself as a working model to determine the location of muscles that contract during certain movements…feel the muscle on the ***back*** of the forearm contract during supination (***radial n.***); ***front*** of the forearm during pronation (***median n.***); ***biceps*** during supination (***musculocutaneous n.***).

40) To mechanically exert its force to accomplish supination, the supinator must be on the back of the forearm. The muscles of the back of the forearm are supplied by the radial nerve. The "pronators" must be on the front of the forearm, the region where the median nerve provides the majority of motor innervation.

41) **CLINICAL CORRELATION: Push, Pull, Pinch, Pinch** is a clinical exam which tests the integrity of 4 major upper extremity nerves: **Push** = radial, **Pull** = musculocutaneous, **Pinch** of radial palm = median, **Pinch** of ulnar palm = ulnar. Additionally, for evaluation of distal injuries, ulnar abduction (spreading) of little finger against light resistance = ulnar, flexion of thumb against light resistance = median, dorsiflexion of hand and/or extension of digits = radial.

END OF CHAPTER TEST

Time for Exam = 80 minutes.
For questions 1-61, choose the single best answer.

_____1) Concerning the number and type of digital nerves that come directly off the ulnar nerve, which of the following are true?
    a) There are two proper digital nerves.
    b) There is one common digital nerve.
    c) Both a and b
    d) There are four proper digital nerves.
    e) None of the above

_____2) Which muscle is innervated by the radial nerve or one of its branches?
    a) supinator
    b) extensor digitorum
    c) both a and b
    d) opponens pollicis
    e) none of the above

_____3) Which neurological structures directly contribute to the formation of the posterior cord of the brachial plexus?
    a) posterior division of upper trunk
    b) anterior division of upper trunk
    c) posterior division of medial trunk
    d) both a and c
    e) none of the above

_____4) Sensory innervation of the skin of the dorsal aspect of the radial side of the hand is provided by which nerve structure?
    a) superficial radial nerve
    b) deep radial nerve
    c) median nerve
    d) ulnar nerve
    e) none of the above

_____5) The upper subscapular nerve is a direct branch of the
    a) C5 ventral ramus
    b) upper trunk of the brachial plexus
    c) lateral cord of the brachial plexus
    d) medial cord of the brachial plexus
    e) none of the above

_____6) Concerning the long thoracic nerve, which of the following are true?
    a) It is formed by the dorsal rami of C5-C7.
    b) It is formed by the ventral rami of C7-T1.
    c) It is formed by the ventral rami of C5-C7.
    d) It innervates the pectoralis minor muscle.
    e) None of the above

_____7) Which muscle is supplied by the deep branch of the ulnar nerve?
    a) abductor pollicis brevis
    b) abductor pollicis longus
    c) flexor digiti minimi brevis manus
    d) flexor carpi ulnaris
    e) none of the above

_____8) The thoracodorsal nerve innervates which muscle?
    a) teres minor muscle
    b) latissimus dorsi muscle
    c) teres major muscle
    d) subscapularis muscle
    e) none of the above

_____9) The lateral pectoral nerve is a branch of the
    a) upper trunk of the brachial plexus
    b) lower trunk of the brachial plexus
    c) lateral cord of the brachial plexus
    d) posterior cord of the brachial plexus
    e) none of the above

_____10) The posterior antebrachial cutaneous nerve is a branch of which nerve structure?
    a) medial cord of the brachial plexus
    b) median nerve
    c) musculocutaneous nerve
    d) ulnar nerve
    e) none of the above

_____11) Which of the following contribute to the formation of the middle trunk of the brachial plexus?
    a) C6 ventral ramus
    b) C7 ventral ramus
    c) C8 ventral ramus
    d) anterior division of lower trunk
    e) none of the above

_____12) The suprascapular nerve is a branch of the
      a) upper trunk
      b) middle trunk
      c) lower trunk
      d) C5 ventral ramus
      e) none of the above

_____13) Which muscle is supplied by the recurrent
branch of the median nerve?
      a) opponens digiti minimi manus
      b) abductor pollicis brevis
      c) abductor pollicis longus
      d) palmaris brevis
      e) none of the above

_____14) Which of the following is a direct branch of
the posterior cord of the brachial plexus?
      a) suprascapular nerve
      b) dorsal scapular nerve
      c) thoracodorsal nerve
      d) medial pectoral nerve
      e) none of the above

_____15) Which nerve does the intercostobrachial
nerve combine with?
      a) medial antebrachial cutaneous nerve
      b) medial brachial cutaneous nerve
      c) medial pectoral nerve
      d) lateral pectoral nerve
      e) none of the above

_____16) Stimulation by the axillary nerve serves to
      a) adduct the arm
      b) rotate the arm medially
      c) both a and b
      d) extend the forearm
      e) none of the above

_____17) Which of the following is a terminal branch
of the lateral cord of the brachial plexus?
      a) musculocutaneous nerve
      b) lateral antebrachial cutaneous nerve
      c) both a and b
      d) ulnar nerve
      e) none of the above

_____18) Which muscle is supplied by the deep
branch of the radial nerve?
      a) extensor carpi radialis longus
      b) extensor carpi radialis brevis
      c) extensor digitorum
      d) all of the above
      e) none of the above

_____19) The lateral antebrachial cutaneous nerve is
derived from which structure?
      a) posterior cord of the brachial plexus
      b) medial cord of the brachial plexus
      c) musculocutaneous nerve
      d) axillary nerve
      e) none of the above

_____20) The lower subscapular nerve is a direct
branch of the
      a) posterior cord of the brachial plexus
      b) lateral cord of the brachial plexus
      c) upper trunk of the brachial plexus
      d) medial cord of the brachial plexus
      e) none of the above

_____21) Sensory innervation of the skin of the pal-
mar aspect of the radial side of the hand is
provided by which nerve structure?
      a) superficial branch of ulnar nerve
      b) deep branch of ulnar nerve
      c) superficial radial nerve
      d) deep radial nerve
      e) none of the above

_____22) To which muscular motion does the radial
nerve contribute?
      a) supinating of forearm
      b) dorsiflexion of wrist
      c) both a and b
      d) abduction of arm
      e) none of the above

_____23) Which of the following contribute to the
upper trunk of the brachial plexus?
      a) C6 ventral ramus
      b) C7 ventral ramus
      c) both a and b
      d) anterior division of the lateral cord
      e) none of the above

____24) All of the following are terminal branches of brachial plexus cords except the
      a) ulnar nerve
      b) radial nerve
      c) medial root of musculocutaneous nerve
      d) axillary nerve
      e) all of the above are terminal branches of brachial plexus cords

____25) The axillary nerve innervates which muscle?
      a) deltoid muscle
      b) teres major muscle
      c) both a and b
      d) subscapularis muscle
      e) none of the above

____26) Which nerve serves as a terminal branch of the medial cord?
      a) ulnar nerve
      b) musculocutaneous nerve
      c) axillary nerve
      d) lateral root of the median nerve
      e) none of the above

____27) Which muscle is supplied by the ulnar nerve or one of its branches?
      a) anconeus
      b) flexor carpi ulnaris
      c) flexor digitorum superficialis
      d) radial portion of flexor digitorum profundus
      e) none of the above

____28) The axillary nerve is a direct branch of the
      a) medial cord of the brachial plexus
      b) lateral cord of the brachial plexus
      c) ulnar nerve
      d) median nerve
      e) none of the above

____29) Which of the following is a branch of the upper trunk of the brachial plexus?
      a) posterior division to the posterior cord
      b) anterior division to the upper cord
      c) both a and b
      d) anterior division to the medial cord
      e) none of the above

____30) Sensory innervation to the skin of the posterior aspect of the arm is provided by which nerve structure?
      a) median nerve
      b) ulnar nerve
      c) median cord of brachial plexus
      d) radial nerve
      e) none of the above

____31) Which nerve is formed by the ventral rami of C5, C6, and C7 and innervates the serratus anterior muscle?
      a) dorsal scapular nerve
      b) suprascapular nerve
      c) intercostobrachial nerve
      d) medial pectoral nerve
      e) none of the above

____32) Which of the following is a branch of the middle trunk of the brachial plexus?
      a) posterior division to the lateral cord
      b) anterior division to the posterior cord
      c) anterior division to the lateral trunk
      d) anterior division to the medial cord
      e) none of the above

____33) The upper subscapular nerve innervates which muscle?
      a) teres major muscle
      b) teres minor muscle
      c) infraspinatus muscle
      d) pectoralis minor muscle
      e) none of the above

____34) What is the name of the sensory branch of the axillary nerve?
      a) superior lateral brachial cutaneous nerve
      b) medial brachial cutaneous nerve
      c) posterior brachial cutaneous nerve
      d) lateral antebrachial cutaneous nerve
      e) none of the above

____35) The ulnar collateral nerve is a branch of which nerve structure?
      a) median nerve
      b) radial nerve
      c) ulnar nerve
      d) musculocutaneous nerve
      e) none of the above

_____36) Which nerve serves as a terminal branch of the radial nerve?
    a) anterior interosseous nerve
    b) branch to long head of triceps
    c) deep radial nerve
    d) ulnar collateral nerve
    e) none of the above

_____37) The musculocutaneous nerve innervates which muscle?
    a) pronator teres muscle
    b) deltoid muscle
    c) teres minor muscle
    d) brachioradialis muscle
    e) none of the above

_____38) The posterior interosseous nerve is the distal continuation of which nerve?
    a) deep branch of ulnar nerve
    b) ulnar collateral nerve
    c) deep radial nerve
    d) recurrent branch of median nerve
    e) none of the above

_____39) Which of the following is a branch of the lateral cord of the brachial plexus?
    a) anterior division to the upper trunk
    b) musculocutaneous nerve
    c) suprascapular nerve
    d) ulnar nerve
    e) none of the above

_____40) Which nerves serve as a terminal branch of the posterior cord of the brachial plexus?
    a) upper subscapular nerve
    b) ulnar nerve
    c) axillary nerve
    d) musculocutaneous nerve
    e) none of the above

_____41) Concerning the number and type of digital nerves that come directly off the median nerve, which of the following is true?
    a) There are three proper digital nerves.
    b) There are two common digital nerves.
    c) Both a and b
    d) Thcrc are two proper digital nerves.
    e) None of the above

_____42) The lower subscapular nerve innervates which muscle?
    a) supraspinatus muscle
    b) latissimus dorsi muscle
    c) teres minor muscle
    d) pectoralis minor muscle
    e) none of the above

_____43) Which neurological structures contribute a direct branch to the lateral cord of the brachial plexus?
    a) anterior division of the upper trunk
    b) anterior division of the medial cord
    c) Both a and b
    d) C5 ventral ramus
    e) none of the above

_____44) Which nerve is a branch of the radial nerve?
    a) lateral antebrachial cutaneous nerve
    b) anterior interosseous nerve
    c) posterior interosseous nerve
    d) medial brachial cutaneous nerve
    e) none of the above

_____45) Sensory innervation to the skin of the lateral aspect of the forearm is provided by which nerve structure?
    a) superior lateral brachial cutaneous nerve
    b) musculocutaneous nerve
    c) radial nerve
    d) medial trunk of brachial plexus
    e) none of the above

_____46) Which of the following serve as a direct branch of the lower trunk of the brachial plexus?
    a) ulnar nerve
    b) musculocutaneous nerve
    c) radial nerve
    d) anterior division to the lateral cord
    e) none of the above

_____47) Which muscle is supplied by the anterior interosseous nerve?
    a) abductor pollicis longus
    b) extensor pollicis brevis
    c) palmaris longus
    d) pronator quadratus
    e) none of the above

_____48) The continuation of the musculocutaneous nerve into the forearm is known as the
    a) anterior antebrachial cutaneous nerve
    b) medial antebrachial cutaneous nerve
    c) lateral antebrachial cutaneous nerve
    d) posterior antebrachial cutaneous nerve
    e) none of the above

_____49) The thoracodorsal nerve is directly formed from what nerve structure(s)?
    a) branches from the ventral rami of C5, C6, C7
    b) branches from the second and third intercostal nerves
    c) the upper trunk of the ventral plexus
    d) the lateral cord of the brachial plexus
    e) none of the above

_____50) Which neurological structures directly contribute to the formation of the medial cord of the brachial plexus?
    a) anterior division of lower trunk
    b) C7 ventral ramus
    c) anterior division of middle trunk
    d) both a and c
    e) none of the above

_____51) The medial brachial cutaneous nerve is a branch of which nerve structure?
    a) radial nerve
    b) musculocutaneous nerve
    c) posterior cord of brachial plexus
    d) axillary nerve
    e) none of the above

_____52) The anterior interosseous nerve is a branch of which nerve?
    a) median nerve
    b) musculocutaneous nerve
    c) ulnar nerve
    d) radial nerve
    e) none of the above

_____53) Which muscle is supplied by the median nerve or one of its branches?
    a) 4th lumbrical
    b) palmar interosseous muscles
    c) abductor pollicis longus
    d) adductor pollicis
    e) none of the above

_____54) The radial nerve is a direct branch of the
    a) lateral cord of the brachial plexus
    b) medial cord of the brachial plexus
    c) posterior cord of the brachial plexus
    d) anterior cord of the brachial plexus
    e) none of the above

_____55) The lateral pectoral nerve innervates which muscle?
    a) latissimus dorsi
    b) pectoralis major
    c) teres major
    d) teres minor
    e) none of the above

_____56) The superior lateral brachial cutaneous nerve is derived from which nerve structure?
    a) lateral cord of the brachial plexus
    b) musculocutaneous nerve
    c) radial nerve
    d) axillary nerve
    e) none of the above

_____57) In which digit is the radial and ulnar side of the digit innervated by different nerves?
    a) one
    b) two
    c) three
    d) four
    e) none of the above

_____58) Which nerve is a direct branch of the medial cord of the brachial plexus?
    a) medial pectoral nerve
    b) ulnar nerve
    c) both a and b
    d) musculocutaneous nerve
    e) none of the above

_____59) Which muscle is supplied by the posterior interosseous nerve?
    a) abductor pollicis longus
    b) abductor pollicis brevis
    c) superficial head of flexor pollicis brevis
    d) opponens pollicis
    e) none of the above

____60) Which of the following contribute to the formation of the lower trunk of the brachial plexus?
      a) C6 ventral ramus
      b) C7 ventral ramus
      c) T1 ventral ramus
      d) anterior division of the medial cord
      e) none of the above

____61) All of the following are branches of the posterior cord of the brachial plexus except the
      a) thoracodorsal nerve
      b) axillary nerve
      c) upper subscapular nerve
      d) suprascapular nerve
      e) all are branches of the posterior cord

For questions 62-80, use the following directions:
    a.......1,2,3 are correct
    b.......1,3 are correct
    c.......2,4 are correct
    d.......only 4 is correct
    e.......all are correct

____62) Direct branches of the C5 ventral ramus include the
    1. suprascapular nerve
    2. dorsal scapular nerve
    3. branch to the middle trunk of the brachial plexus
    4. branch to the phrenic nerve

____63) Which of the following directly contribute to the formation of the posterior cord of the brachial plexus?
    1. anterior division of upper trunk
    2. posterior division of middle trunk
    3. anterior division of middle trunk
    4. posterior division of lower trunk

____64) The median nerve is responsible for which of the following functions in the hand?
    1. innervation to the skin of the dorsal fingertip of digit three
    2. innervation to the radial side of the palm
    3. innervation to the first and second lumbrical muscles
    4. innervation to the skin of the radial side of digit four

____65) Which of the following contribute to the formation of the lateral cord of the brachial plexus?
    1. anterior division of anterior trunk
    2. anterior division of upper cord
    3. anterior division of posterior trunk
    4. anterior division of middle trunk

____66) Which statements concerning the dorsal scapular nerve are true?
    1. It supplies the shoulder joint.
    2. It innervates the supraspinatus muscle.
    3. It is branch of the upper trunk of the brachial plexus.
    4. It innervates the rhomboid muscles.

____67) Which muscles are innervated by a branch of the posterior cord system of the brachial plexus?
    1. teres major
    2. teres minor
    3. extensor digiti minimi
    4. opponens digiti minimi manus

____68) Branches of the upper trunk of the brachial plexus include the
    1. anterior division to the lateral cord
    2. suprascapular nerve
    3. posterior division to the posterior cord
    4. nerve to subclavius

____69) Which statements concerning the lateral cord of the brachial plexus are true?
    1. The posterior division of the upper trunk contributes to its formation.
    2. The ulnar nerve is a terminal branch.
    3. The deltoid muscle is supplied by one of its branches.
    4. The pectoralis major is supplied by one of its branches.

____70) Eventual branches of the posterior cord system include the
    1. ulnar collateral nerve
    2. posterior interosseous nerve
    3. posterior brachial cutaneous nerve
    4. superior lateral brachial cutaneous nerve

____71) Which of the following contribute to the formation of the middle trunk of the brachial plexus?
   1. anterior division of lateral cord
   2. C6 ventral ramus
   3. anterior division of medial cord
   4. C7 ventral ramus

____72) The ulnar nerve is responsible for which of the following functions in the hand?
   1. cutaneous innervation to the ulnar side of digit three
   2. cutaneous innervation to the radial side of digit five
   3. cutaneous innervation to the radial side of the dorsal hand
   4. cutaneous innervation to the ulnar half of the dorsal fingertip of digit four

____73) Direct branches of the lower trunk of the brachial plexus include the
   1. medial pectoral nerve
   2. anterior division to the middle cord
   3. ulnar nerve
   4. posterior division to the posterior cord

____74) An injury to the posterior cord may be associated with which of the following clinical signs?
   1. numbness over the lateral aspect of the shoulder
   2. difficulty with pronation of the forearm
   3. difficulty with dorsiflexion of the wrist
   4. difficulty with abduction of the little finger

____75) Which muscles are innervated by a branch of the medial cord system of the brachial plexus?
   1. supinator
   2. pectoralis minor
   3. abductor pollicis longus
   4. flexor carpi ulnaris

____76) Which statements concerning the suprascapular nerve are true?
   1. It originates from the upper trunk of the brachial plexus.
   2. It innervates the subscapularis muscle.
   3. It innervates the acromioclavicular joint.
   4. It provides sensory innervation to skin over the anterior aspect of the first two ribs.

____77) Direct branches of the middle trunk of the brachial plexus include the
   1. anterior division to the lateral trunk
   2. medial brachial cutaneous nerve
   3. posterior division to the posterior trunk
   4. anterior division to the lateral cord

____78) Which statements concerning the posterior cord of the brachial plexus are true?
   1. The posterior division of the upper trunk contributes to its formation.
   2. The posterior division of the middle cord contributes to its formation.
   3. The posterior division of the lower trunk contributes to its formation.
   4. The adductor pollicis muscle is innervated by one of its eventual branches.

____79) Which of the following directly contribute to the formation of the medial cord of the brachial plexus?
   1. C8 ventral ramus
   2. posterior division of lower trunk
   3. T1 ventral ramus
   4. anterior division of lower trunk

____80) Which muscles are supplied by branches of the lateral cord?
   1. coracobrachialis
   2. brachioradialis
   3. brachialis
   4. pectoralis minor

END OF CHAPTER TEST: Answers and Explanations

1) b – The ulnar nerve supplies one proper digital branch that innervates the outer, ulnar side of the little finger (digit 5). It also provides one common digital nerve, which divides into two proper digital nerves. One of these proper digital nerves supplies the inner, radial side of digit 5. The other supplies the adjacent, ulnar side of digit 4 (ring finger). Ultimately, there are three proper digital nerves of ulnar nerve origin.

2) c – All of the "extensors" are innervated by the radial nerve. The radial nerve supinates, whereas the median nerve pronates. The opponens pollicis is supplied by the median nerve.

3) a – The posterior cord is formed by the combinations of the posterior divisions from each of the three trunks of the brachial plexus: the upper, middle, and lower trunks. There is no medial trunk. There is a middle trunk and a medial cord.

4) a – The deep radial nerve is a motor branch. The median nerve supplies the palmar aspect of the approximate same area of the hand. The ulnar nerve supplies both the dorsal and palmar surfaces of the ulnar side of the hand.

5) e – The upper subscapular nerve is a branch of the posterior cord of the brachial plexus.

6) c – The long thoracic nerve is formed by contribution from the C5-C7 ventral rami. It innervates the serratus anterior muscle of the chest. This muscle functions to move the scapula forward and twist it in order to abduct the arm. Remember children making snow angels: C5, C6, C7 are angels in heaven.

7) c – The deep branch of the ulnar nerve innervates the three hypothenar muscles. These muscles are located at the base of the small finger along the radial aspect of the palm. They function to manipulate the little finger and include the abductor digiti minimi manus, flexor digiti minimi brevis manus, and opponens digiti minimi manus. The abductor pollicis brevis is one of three thenar muscles which manipulate the thumb and is supplied by the recurrent branch of median nerve. The abductor pollicis longus is supplied by the radial nerve. The flexor carpi ulnaris is supplied by the ulnar nerve, but not specifically by the *deep branch* of the ulnar nerve.

8) b – The teres minor muscle is innervated by the axillary nerve. Both the teres major and subscapularis muscles are innervated by the upper and lower subscapular nerves.

9) c – The *lateral* pectoral nerve is the sole branch of the *lateral* cord prior to its division into two terminal branches: the musculocutaneous nerve and lateral root of the median nerve. Coincidently, the *medial* pectoral nerve is a branch of the *medial* cord.

10) e – The posterior antebrachial cutaneous nerve, like all "posterior" cutaneous nerves of the upper extremity, is a radial nerve branch.

11) b – The middle trunk is formed solely by a ventral ramus branch from C7.

12) a – In addition to divisions to cords, the upper trunk is also the origin of two nerves. The nerve to subclavius and suprascapular nerve branch directly from it. The upper trunk then divides into the anterior division to the lateral cord and posterior division to the posterior cord. The middle trunk gives no branches before dividing into the anterior division to the lateral cord and posterior division to the posterior cord. Finally, the lower trunk gives no branches before dividing into the anterior division to the medial cord and posterior division to the posterior cord.

13) b – The recurrent branch of median nerve supplies the three thenar muscles, all of which manipulate the thumb. They are the abductor pollicis brevis, superficial head of flexor pollicis brevis, and the opponens pollicis. The superficial head of flexor pollicis brevis is the larger portion of this muscle. The smaller deep head is supplied by the ulnar nerve. The opponens dig-

iti minimi manus is one of the three hypothenar muscles, which manipulate the little finger and are innervated by the deep branch of ulnar nerve. The abductor pollicis longus is innervated by the radial nerve. The palmaris brevis is supplied by the ulnar nerve.

14) c – The suprascapular nerve is a branch of the upper trunk of the brachial plexus. The dorsal scapular is a direct branch of the C5 ventral ramus. The medial pectoral nerve is a branch of the medial cord of the brachial plexus.

15) b – The combination supplies sensory innervation to the medial aspect of the upper arm.

16) e – The axillary nerve innervates two muscles. The deltoid muscle abducts the arm. The teres minor muscle laterally rotates the arm

17) c – Sorry! Trick question. The lateral antebrachial cutaneous nerve is the continuation of the musculocutaneous nerve as the musculocutaneous emerges from the lateral aspect of the biceps tendon. They are the same nerve. Some people would therefore consider the lateral antebrachial cutaneous nerve as a terminal branch of the lateral cord. It all depends on how one views it. The ulnar nerve is a terminal branch of the medial cord.

18) c – The deep radial nerve usually supplies four muscles. These include the supinator, extensor digitorum, extensor digiti minimi, and extensor carpi ulnaris. Both the extensor carpi radialis longus and extensor carpi radialis brevis are innervated by the radial nerve, but not by way of the deep radial nerve.

19) c – The lateral antebrachial cutaneous nerve is the continuation of the musculocutaneous nerve once this nerve emerges from the biceps brachii muscle just above the elbow.

20) a – The posterior cord is the origin of the upper subscapular, thoracodorsal, and lower subscapular nerves prior to dividing into its two terminal branches: the radial and axillary nerves.

21) e – The median nerve innervates this area of the hand.

22) c – The radial nerve extends and adducts the arm (via the shoulder joint), extends and supinates the forearm (via the elbow joint), extends (dorsiflexes) the hand (via the wrist joint), and extends the digits (via the metacorpophalangeal and interphalangeal joints). In the arm, the radial nerve innervates all three heads of the triceps muscle. The long head adducts and extends the arm. The medial and lateral heads of triceps, along with the anconeus muscle, extend the forearm. In the forearm, the radial nerve innervates multiple extensor muscles which extend the wrist and digits. The radial nerve also innervates the supinator muscle of the forearm, which supinates the forearm.

23) a – The upper trunk is formed by ventral rami branches from C5 and C6. This trunk is the origin of four nerve structures: the nerve to subclavius, the suprascapular nerve, the anterior division to the lateral cord, and the posterior division to the posterior cord. The C7 ventral ramus is the sole contributor to the middle trunk.

24) c – The musculocutaneous nerve and lateral root of the median nerve are the two terminal branches of the lateral cord. The ulnar nerve and medial root of the median nerve are the two terminal branches of the medial cord. The axillary nerve and radial nerve are the two terminal branches of the posterior cord.

25) a – The axillary nerve also innervates the teres minor muscle. Both the teres major and subscapularis muscles are innervated by the upper and lower subscapular nerves.

26) a – See #24 answer explanation.

27) b – This muscle flexes and ulnar abducts the wrist. The word *ulnaris* should give a clue. The ulnar nerve innervates muscles that flex the wrist, especially toward the ulnar side. The anconeus is supplied by the radial nerve. The other two answers (c and d) are muscles supplied by the median nerve.

28) e – The axillary nerve is a direct branch of the posterior cord of the brachial plexus.

29) a – See #12 answer explanation. There is no upper *cord*, only an upper *trunk*.

30) d – The radial nerve should be considered any time the word *posterior* is associated with structures of the upper extremity. The posterior brachial cutaneous nerve is a radial nerve branch.

31) e – The long thoracic nerve is formed by contribution from the C5-C7 ventral rami. It innervates the serratus anterior muscle of the chest. This muscle functions to move the scapula forward and twist it in order to abduct the arm. The dorsal scapular nerve is a branch of the C5 ventral ramus. It innervates the rhomboid muscles of the back. The suprascapular nerve is a branch of the upper trunk of the brachial plexus. It provides innervation to the acromioclavicular and shoulder joints and the supraspinatus and infraspinatus muscles. The intercostobrachial nerve is a branch of the second and third intercostal nerves and combines with the medial brachial cutaneous nerve to provide sensory innervation to the skin of the medial arm. Finally, the medial pectoral nerve is a branch of the medial cord of the brachial plexus. It innervates both the pectoralis minor and pectoralis major muscles.

32) e – The middle trunk divides into an anterior division to the lateral cord and a posterior division to the posterior cord. The anterior division combines with the anterior division of the upper trunk to form the lateral cord. The posterior division combines with the posterior divisions of the upper and lower trunks to form the posterior cord. There is no lateral *trunk*.

33) a – The upper subscapular nerve also innervates the subscapularis muscle. The teres minor is supplied by the axillary nerve. The infraspinatus muscle is innervated by the suprascapular nerve. The pectoralis minor muscle is innervated by the medial pectoral nerve.

34) a – The medial brachial cutaneous nerve is a sensory branch of the medial cord of the brachial plexus. The posterior brachial cutaneous nerve is a sensory branch of the radial nerve. The lateral antebrachial cutaneous nerve is simply the continuation of the musculocutaneous nerve once this nerve emerges from the biceps brachii muscle.

35) b – The ulnar collateral nerve branches off the radial nerve in the arm. It is named ulnar collateral because it travels in close proximity to the ulnar nerve. It innervates the medial head of the triceps muscle and anconeus muscle. Both serve to extend the forearm.

36) c – The terminal branches of the radial nerve are the superficial and deep radial nerves. The superficial radial is sensory. The deep radial is motor. The anterior interosseous nerve is a branch of the median nerve. The branch to the long head of triceps and ulnar collateral nerve are both radial nerve branches that originate in the arm.

37) e – The musculocutaneous nerve innervates the coracobrachialis, biceps brachii, and brachialis muscles. The pronator teres muscle is supplied by the median nerve. Both the deltoid and teres minor muscles are innervated by the axillary nerve. The brachioradialis is innervated by the radial nerve.

38) c – As the deep radial nerve courses distally, it travels between the two long bones of the forearm. At this point it is known as the posterior interosseous nerve. It supplies muscles that extend the thumb and index finger and abduct and adduct the thumb.

39) b – The lateral cord is formed by the combination of the anterior divisions from the upper and middle trunks of the brachial plexus. The suprascapular nerve is a branch of the upper trunk of the plexus. The ulnar nerve is a terminal branch of the medial cord of the brachial plexus.

40) c – The upper subscapular nerve branches from the posterior cord before the cord divides into its two terminal branches, the axillary and radial nerves. The ulnar nerve is a terminal branch of the medial cord. The musculocutaneous nerve is a terminal branch of the lateral cord.

41) c – The median nerve supplies three proper digital branches. One goes to one side of digit 1 (thumb), one goes to the other side of digit 1, and one goes to the adjacent, radial side of digit 2 (index finger). The median nerve also

supplies two common digital nerves. Each common digital nerve divides into two proper digital nerves that supply adjacent sides of adjoining fingers. One common digital supplies the ulnar side digit two (index finger) and the adjacent, radial side of digit three (middle finger). The other common digital supplies the ulnar side of digit three and the adjacent, radial side of digit four (ring finger). Ultimately, there are seven digital nerves of median nerve origin. The ulnar side of digit four and both sides of digit five are supplied by the ulnar nerve.

42) e – Along with the upper subscapular nerve, the lower subscapular nerve provides innervation to both the subscapularis and teres major muscles. The supraspinatus muscle is supplied by the suprascapular nerve. The latissimus dorsi muscle is supplied by the thoracodorsal nerve. The teres minor muscle is supplied by the axillary nerve. The pectoralis minor muscle is supplied by the medial pectoral nerve.

43) a – The lateral cord of the brachial plexus is formed by the combination of anterior divisions from both the upper and middle trunks of the brachial plexus. The medial cord is a *cord* formed solely from the anterior division of the lower trunk. A branch of the C5 ventral ramus combines with a branch of the C6 ventral ramus to form the upper trunk.

44) c – The posterior interosseous nerve is a branch of the radial nerve. The anterior interosseous nerve is a branch of the median nerve. The lateral antebrachial cutaneous nerve is the continuation of the musculocutaneous nerve into the forearm. The medial brachial cutaneous nerve is a direct branch of the medial cord of the brachial plexus.

45) b – The musculocutaneous nerve becomes the lateral antebrachial cutaneous nerve as it emerges from the substance of the biceps muscle.

46) e – The lower trunk gives off an anterior division, which serves as the lone contributor to the medial cord. The posterior division of the lower trunk combines with posterior divisions of the upper and middle trunks to form the

posterior cord. The ulnar nerve is a terminal branch of the medial cord. The musculocutaneous nerve is a terminal branch of the lateral cord. The radial nerve is a terminal branch of the posterior cord.

47) d – The anterior interosseous is a branch of the median nerve. It routinely innervates three muscles: the radial portion of flexor digitorum profundus, flexor pollicis longus, and pronator quadratus. Both the abductor pollicis longus and extensor pollicis brevis are supplied by a branch of the radial nerve, the posterior interosseous nerve. These are two of the four muscles this nerve routinely supplies. The palmaris longus is supplied by the median nerve, but not by way of the anterior interosseous nerve.

48) c – There is no anterior antebrachial cutaneous nerve. There is only a medial, lateral, and posterior antebrachial cutaneous nerve. The medial antebrachial cutaneous nerve is a branch of the medial cord of the brachial plexus. The posterior antebrachial cutaneous nerve is a branch of the radial nerve.

49) e – The thoracodorsal nerve is a branch of the posterior cord of the brachial plexus. Ventral rami branches from C5, C6, and C7 combine to form the long thoracic nerve. The second and third intercostal nerves give branches that combine to form the intercostobrachial nerve. The upper trunk of the brachial plexus serves as the origin of the nerve to subclavius and suprascapular nerve before it divides into the anterior division to the lateral cord and the posterior division to the posterior cord. The lateral cord of the brachial plexus serves as the origin of the lateral pectoral nerve before it divides into its two terminal branches: the musculocutaneous nerve and lateral root of the median nerve.

50) a – The medial cord is formed solely by the anterior division of the lower trunk. The C7 ventral ramus is the sole contributor to the middle trunk. The anterior division of the middle trunk combines with the anterior division of the upper trunk to form the lateral cord of the brachial plexus.

51) e – Both the medial brachial and medial antebrachial cutaneous nerves are direct branches of the medial cord of the brachial plexus.

52) a – See #47 answer explanation. The anterior interosseous nerve should not be confused with the posterior interosseous nerve, which is a radial nerve branch.

53) e – The median nerve innervates the 1st and 2nd lumbrical muscles. These are located between digit one (thumb) and digit two (index finger) and between digit two (index finger) and digit three (middle finger), respectively. The ulnar nerve innervates the 3rd and 4th lumbrical muscles. All dorsal and all palmar interosseous muscles of the hand are supplied by the ulnar nerve. The abductor pollicis longus is supplied by the radial nerve. In addition, the radial nerve also supplies the extensor pollicis brevis and extensor pollicis longus. Remember, all muscles of the forearm with the word *extensor* in their name are supplied by the radial nerve. The adductor pollicis, like the deep head of flexor pollicis brevis, is supplied by the ulnar nerve. All other muscles that have the word *pollicis* in their name (and hence, manipulate the thumb) are innervated by the median nerve.

54) c – See #20 answer explanation. There is no anterior cord of the brachial plexus.

55) b – The latissimus dorsi is innervated by the thoracodorsal nerve, which is a branch of the posterior cord. The teres major is supplied by the upper and lower subscapular nerves, which are also branches of the posterior cord. The teres minor is supplied by the axillary nerve. This nerve is a terminal branch of the posterior cord.

56) d – The superior lateral brachial cutaneous nerve supplies skin of the lateral shoulder/upper arm.

57) d – The radial side of digit four is innervated by the median nerve. The ulnar side of this same digit is innervated by the ulnar nerve.

58) c – The *medial* cord is the origin of the *medial* pectoral, *medial* brachial cutaneous, and *medial* antebrachial cutaneous nerves before dividing into its two terminal branches: the *medial* root of the median nerve and ulnar nerve. The musculocutaneous nerve is a terminal branch of the lateral cord.

59) a – The posterior interosseous nerve is a branch of the deep radial nerve that travels distally between the two long bones of the forearm. It usually supplies four muscles: the abductor pollicis longus, extensor pollicis brevis, extensor pollicis longus, and extensor indicis. The abductor pollicis brevis, superficial head of flexor pollicis brevis and opponens pollicis are the three thenar muscles and are innervated by the recurrent branch of the median nerve.

60) c – The lower trunk is formed by ventral rami branches from C8 and T1.

61) d – The suprascapular nerve is a branch of the upper trunk of the brachial plexus.

62) c – The suprascapular nerve is a branch of the upper trunk of the brachial plexus. Although this could be considered a potential subsequent branch of the C5 ventral ramus, it is not a *direct* branch. The middle trunk of the brachial plexus is formed by a ventral rami branch from C7. The phrenic nerve is formed by ventral rami branches from C3, C4, and C5.

63) c – The posterior cord is formed by the combination of three posterior divisions, one from each of the three trunks. This includes the upper, middle, and lower trunks of the brachial plexus. The anterior divisions of the upper and middle trunks combine to form the lateral cord.

64) e – The median nerve provides cutaneous innervation to the radial aspect of the palm. The superficial radial nerve provides cutaneous innervation to the radial aspect of the dorsal hand. The median nerve also provides innervation to the skin of the dorsal fingertips of digits one, two, three, and the radial half of digit four. The ulnar nerve provides cutaneous innervation to both the palmar and dorsal surfaces of the ulnar side of the hand. This includes the ulnar half of digit four and both the radial and ulnar sides of digit five. The median nerve innervates the skin of both the radial and ulnar sides

of digits one, two, and three. It also supplies the skin on the radial side of digit four. The lumbrical muscles are located in the hand between each of the digits. The first and second lumbricals are supplied by the median nerve. The third and fourth lumbricals are supplied by the ulnar nerve.

65) d – The lateral cord is formed by the anterior divisions of the upper trunk and middle trunk. Each of the three trunks gives off posterior divisions that combine to form the posterior cord. Finally, the medial cord is formed solely by the anterior division of the lower trunk. There is no anterior trunk, upper cord, or posterior trunk.

66) d – The dorsal scapular nerve is a direct branch of the C5 ventral ramus. The first three answers describe the suprascapular nerve.

67) a – The teres major muscle, along with the subscapularis muscle, is innervated by both the upper and lower subscapular nerves. These are direct nerve branches of the posterior cord. The teres minor is supplied by the axillary nerve. The extensor digiti minimi muscle is a supplied by the deep radial nerve. The opponens digiti minimi manus is one of the three hypothenar muscles and is supplied by the deep branch of the ulnar nerve. The ulnar nerve is a terminal branch of the medial cord.

68) e – These are the four nerve structures that originate from the upper trunk.

69) d – The lateral cord is formed by the combination of the anterior divisions of the upper and middle trunks. Other than its two terminal branches, the musculocutaneous nerve and lateral root of median nerve, the lateral pectoral nerve is the only direct branch of the lateral cord. The lateral pectoral nerve provides innervation to the pectoralis major muscle. The medial pectoral nerve is a branch of the medial cord and provides innervation to both the pectoralis major and pectoralis minor muscles. The ulnar nerve is a terminal branch of the medial cord. The deltoid muscle is supplied by a terminal branch of the posterior cord, the axillary nerve.

70) e – The first three answers are all branches of the radial nerve. The superior lateral brachial cutaneous nerve is a branch of the axillary nerve.

71) d – The middle trunk is formed solely by a branch of the C7 ventral ramus. Cords are formed by trunk divisions. There is no anterior division of the lateral or medial cord.

72) c – See #64 answer explanation.

73) d – The two branches of the lower trunk are the anterior division to the medial cord and posterior division to the posterior cord. The medial pectoral nerve and ulnar nerve are both branches of the medial cord. There is no middle cord. There is a middle trunk and a medial cord.

74) b – The superior lateral brachial cutaneous nerve is a branch of the axillary nerve, which is a terminal branch of the posterior cord. The other terminal branch of the posterior cord, the radial nerve, innervates multiple extensor muscles of the forearm. Some of these dorsiflex the wrist. A clinical sign know as "wrist drop" occurs with radial nerve injury. Both the pronator teres and pronator quadratus muscles are supplied by median nerve branches. Finally, difficulty with abduction of the little finger is indicative of an ulnar nerve injury.

75) c – The medial pectoral nerve is a direct branch of the medial cord. This nerve innervates both the pectoralis major and pectoralis minor muscles. The ulnar nerve is a terminal branch of the medial cord and innervates multiple flexor muscles of the forearm, including the flexor carpi ulnaris. The supinator muscle is innervated by a terminal branch of the posterior cord, the radial nerve. The abductor pollicis longus muscle is supplied by the posterior interosseous nerve, which is a branch of the radial nerve system.

76) b – The suprascapular nerve innervates the acromioclavicular and shoulder joints as well as the supraspinatus and infraspinatus muscles. The subscapularis muscle is supplied by the upper and lower subscapular nerves, both of which are branches of the posterior cord of

the brachial plexus. The skin over the anterior aspect of the first two ribs is innervated by the supraclavicular nerves. These nerves are branches of the supraclavicular trunk of the cervical plexus.

77) d – The two branches of the middle trunk are the anterior division to the lateral cord and posterior division to the posterior cord. The medial brachial cutaneous nerve is a direct branch of the medial cord. There is no lateral *trunk* or posterior *trunk*, only lateral and posterior *cords*.

78) b – There is no middle *cord*. The posterior cord is formed by the combination of the posterior divisions of the upper, middle, and lower *trunks*. The adductor pollicis muscle is innervated by the ulnar nerve, which is a terminal branch medial cord.

79) d – The medial cord is formed solely from the anterior division of the lower trunk. The posterior division of the lower trunk, like the other two posterior divisions of brachial plexus trunks, contributes to the formation of the posterior cord. The C8 and T1 ventral rami send branches which combine to form the lower trunk of the brachial plexus.

80) b – Both the coracobrachialis and brachialis are supplied by a terminal branch of the lateral cord, the musculocutaneous nerve. The brachioradialis is supplied by a terminal branch of the posterior cord, the radial nerve. The pectoralis minor is supplied by a medial cord branch, the medial pectoral nerve. The pectoralis major receives innervation from both the medial pectoral nerve and a branch of the lateral cord, the lateral pectoral nerve.

"Simplicity is the ultimate sophistication."

– Leonardo Da Vinci

CHAPTER ELEVEN

THORACIC NERVES

The peripheral nerves of the thorax will now be described. This includes the thoracic spinal nerves and the thoracic course of the vagus and phrenic nerves.

THORACIC SPINAL NERVES

The thoracic spinal nerves are the only group of spinal nerves that do not participate in the formation of a large nerve plexus. Because the majority of space in the thorax is occupied by visceral organs, the structure of nerve innervation is more generalized than that of other body regions. The smooth muscle of the visceral organs is under control of the autonomic nervous system; the nerve plexuses that innervate these organs come from the sympathetic and parasympathetic nervous systems. The majority of space in the neck, arm, and leg, by contrast, is occupied by somatic or body wall structures. Providing a unique, specific movement upon contraction, each skeletal muscle requires an individualized nerve supply. The complexity of nerve innervations necessitates the formation of nerve plexuses. The thoracic skeletal muscle that does exist is confined to the chest wall. The chest wall is formed by the bony sternum, ribs, accompanying cartilage, muscles, and their supporting structures. It serves two main purposes: protection of vital organs and provision of structure to enable respiration.

The thoracic spinal nerves are often used as the quintessential example to explain spinal nerves to beginning students. This is because the dorsal rami of these nerves course *dorsally,* or posteriorly, to innervate muscles and skin of the back. The ventral rami do not participate in confusing plexuses, but instead course *ventrally,* or anteriorly, to supply muscles and skin of the anterolateral torso.

FIGURE 11.1
CROSS-SECTION OF THORACIC SPINAL NERVE

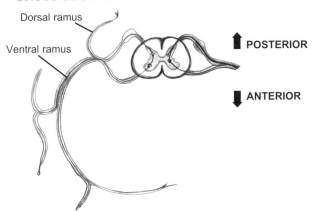

Dorsal ramus

Ventral ramus

▲ **POSTERIOR**

▼ **ANTERIOR**

THORACIC DORSAL RAMI

Like the lower cervical and lumbar spinal nerve dorsal rami, the dorsal rami of thoracic spinal nerves innervate muscles and skin of the back. The thoracic dorsal rami innervate back muscles and skin of the thoracic and upper lumbar areas. Each dorsal ramus usually provides innervation to an area of tissue that is below the level of origination of the spinal nerve from the spinal cord. Because of the high degree of variability in the origin and innervation of these nerves, none of the thoracic dorsal rami have specific nerve names. They are merely known as the dorsal ramus of whichever thoracic spinal nerve they came from (e.g. T4 dorsal ramus).

In addition to muscular innervations, each thoracic dorsal ramus usually also provides a **posterior cutaneous branch,** which supplies skin of the medial back. Like the general theme of spinal nerve innervation, the area of supplied skin is usually below the level or origination of the spinal nerve from the spinal cord. There is often seen a repetitive "back and forth" pattern in which one nerve supplies skin in a medial area, the next lowest nerve supplies a relatively lateral area, and the next lowest a medial area.

THORACIC VENTRAL RAMI

After the takeoff of the dorsal ramus from the thoracic spinal nerve, the thoracic ventral ramus continues laterally from the vertebrae. The thoracic ventral rami form the **intercostal nerves (51,** 55, 58, 172). The combining form *inter* means *between.* *Costa* means *rib.* The intercostal nerves travel in the spaces between the ribs, parallel to the ribs. They innervate muscles and skin of the chest and abdominal walls. The first six (T1-T6) intercostal nerves remain confined to the thorax. The last six (T6-T12) continue down to also innervate muscles and skin of the anterior abdomen.

Each intercostal nerve is located immediately below its respective rib. The seventh intercostal nerve, for instance, travels below the seventh rib, in the intercostal space between the seventh and eighth ribs. The twelfth intercostal nerve travels below the twelfth rib. There is no rib below it. By the truest sense of the name, it is not an *inter*costal nerve. It shares other attributes of intercostal nerves and is named the **subcostal nerve** (146).

Because they innervate muscles that function in respiration, oxygenating the blood and keeping it *"red,"* the intercostal nerves are colored red in Figure 2 of the poster. There are twelve pairs of thoracic ventral rami, consisting of eleven pairs of intercostal nerves and one pair of subcostal nerves. Although there are twelve pairs, only six single nerves are drawn. Each intercostal nerve depicted in the poster represents a pair, consisting of a right and left nerve. Four intercostal nerves are depicted on the subject's left (146, 172). These nerves possess differences from other intercostal nerves. The two intercostals depicted on the subject's right (51, 55, 58) are used to represent "typical" intercostals. They include the fourth and seventh intercostal nerves. The **fourth intercostal nerve (51,** 55) represents the upper six thoracic intercostals. These nerves remain confined to the thorax. With one exception, their innervation is also confined to the thorax. The exception is the innervation of inner arm skin by the intercostobrachial nerve. The **seventh intercostal nerve** (58) is used to represent the lower six intercostals, each of which eventually leaves the thorax to provide muscular and cutaneous innervation to the anterior abdomen. The seventh thoracic intercostal nerve is drawn because it is the first intercostal to leave the thorax to supply the abdominal wall in most individuals.

The intercostal nerves supply muscles which assist in respiration. They are colored red on the poster because they help to oxygenate the blood and keep it red.

All the intercostal nerves are initially drawn as a dotted line as they leave the vertebral column to travel laterally in the posterior thorax. This dotted line becomes solid as the nerve travels around the lateral thorax to supply muscles and skin of the anterolateral torso.

Before discussing the intercostal nerves in greater detail, the muscles of the chest wall should be described. These muscles function in respiration and are innervated by the intercostal nerves. They are described starting with the more superficial muscles and progressing deeper.

There are two posterior serratus muscles supplied by intercostal nerves. These include the serratus posterior superior and serratus posterior inferior. The serratus anterior muscle was described in the previous chapter and is innervated by the long thoracic nerve. The word *serratus* refers to the serrated or sawtooth appearance these muscles possess. The serratus posterior superior muscle originates from the spinous processes of the upper thoracic vertebrae and inserts on ribs two through five. It functions to lift the ribs in inspiration. This muscle is usually innervated by the upper four intercostal nerves. The serratus posterior inferior originates on the spinous processes of the lower thoracic and upper lumbar vertebrae and inserts on the lower four ribs. It functions to lower the ribs in inspiration. This muscle is innervated by the lower four intercostal nerves. Both serratus posterior muscles are located in the medial section of the back, superficial to the external intercostal muscles and ribs. They can be seen in Figure 10.8 of the previous chapter.

The levatores costarum are a group of muscles usually innervated by intercostal nerves, although dorsal rami branches may supply them in certain individuals. The levatores costarum originate from the transverse processes of the last cervical and first eleven thoracic vertebrae. There are both short and long levatores costarum muscles. As the short muscles travel inferiorly, they slant laterally to insert on the rib immediately below their vertebrae of origination. The long muscles "skip" a rib and insert on the second rib below their vertebrae of origination. The levatores costarum are also known as the levator muscles of the ribs and are named for their lifting of the ribs during inspiration.

FIGURE 11.2
LEVATORES COSTARUM

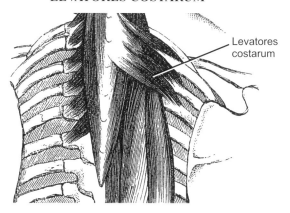

Levatores costarum

The intercostal muscles are located between the ribs and function in respiration. There are three layers of intercostal muscles. All are innervated by intercostal nerves.

The external intercostal muscles originate on the inferior side of a rib and insert on the superior side of the rib immediately below. Their fibers travel in a slight posterior to anterior (back to front) direction as they travel from one rib down to the next. The external intercostal muscles begin just lateral to the vertebrae and follow the ribs around the chest wall to end just beyond the junction of the ribs and costal cartilage. From this point, the external intercostal membrane continues to the sternum or costal cartilage, depending on whether the involved ribs are true or false ribs. Muscle tissue is present in the posterior 4/5 of the upper thorax. No external intercostal muscle tissue is present in the medial area of the anterior thorax. In the lower thorax, the fibers of the external intercostal muscles blend with the fibers of the external oblique muscle of the abdominal wall. The external intercostal muscles are predominately active in inspiration.

The internal intercostal muscles originate from the inferior side of a rib and/or its costal cartilage. It travels down to insert on the superior side of the rib or costal cartilage immediately below it. In contrast to the external intercostals, the fibers of the internal intercostals travel in a slight anterior to posterior (front to back) direction as they travel to the rib below. Another difference is their presence in the anterior 4/5 of the upper thorax. They are present from the sternum to the lateral aspect of the posterior thorax. From this point, the internal intercostal membrane extends to the lateral edge of the vertebral column. The fibers of the internal intercostal muscles of the lower thorax blend with fibers of the internal oblique muscle of the abdomen. The internal intercostals predominately function in forced expiration. Both external and internal intercostals also function in actions such as coughing, sneezing, sucking, blowing, and talking.

FIGURE 11.3
MUSCLES OF CHEST AND ABDOMINAL WALLS

Fibers of the internal intercostal muscles blend with those of the internal oblique. In the upper abdomen, internal oblique fibers are running in the same direction as those of the internal intercostals.

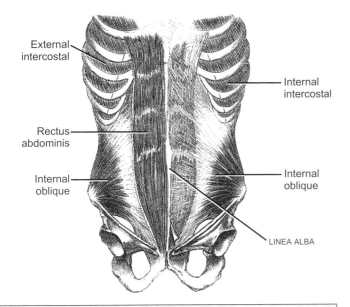

The external and internal intercostals can be thought of as opposites. The external fibers run back to front as they travel down the intercostal space. (This is the same direction as a downhill snow skier (down and forward). One must be outside *(external)* to snow ski.) The internal fibers run front to back as they travel down. This fiber orientation can be remembered by pairing it with the coincidence that the external intercostals are located in a more posterior location in the thorax. The internal muscles are in a more anterior location. Finally, the *ex*ternal intercostals function in *in*spiration. The *in*ternal intercostals function in *ex*piration.

EX = IN   and   IN = EX

The third layer of intercostal muscle is actually formed by three individual muscles which share a common membrane. This innermost muscle layer lies deep to the internal intercostal muscles. It is formed by the subcostal muscles, innermost intercostal muscles, and transversus thoracis muscle. The subcostal muscles are located in the posterior thorax, the innermost intercostals in the lateral thorax, and the transversus thoracis in the anterior thorax. These muscles are not continuous, but are separated from one another by the common membrane they share. The fibers of the three muscles are thought to be of the same origin as those of the transversus abdominis muscle of the abdominal wall.

The subcostal muscles are located in the posterior thorax, near the vertebral column. They originate on the lower surface of a rib and travel down to insert on the upper surface of the second or third rib below. In other words, they "skip" one or two ribs. They function to elevate the ribs during inspiration.

The innermost intercostal muscles are located in the approximate lateral half of the thorax. They originate on the lower surface of a rib and travel down to insert on the upper surface of the

rib immediately below it. Like the internal intercostal muscles, the fibers run in an anterior to posterior direction as they travel down the intercostal space. The function of these muscles is thereby similar to that of the internal intercostals – forced expiration.

The transversus thoracis muscle originates from the posterior surface of the lower sternum and xyphoid process. The muscle travels out in different directions to insert on the costal cartilages of the second through sixth ribs. Stimulation of this muscle narrows the chest in forced expiration.

FIGURE 11.4
TRANSVERSUS THORACIS
Internal View

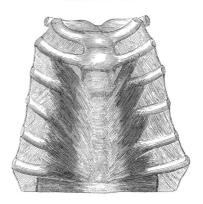

Because the aforementioned muscles function in respiration, a brief review of the basic mechanics of respiration is in order. Inspiration is active. Nonexertional expiration is mostly passive. During the active phase of inspiration, muscles contract to expand the rib cage and lungs. This creates a negative pressure or vacuum within the lungs that pulls air in. Upon expiration, the muscles simply relax. The thorax passively returns to its previous size, similar to elastic recoil. The decrease in lung volume creates a positive pressure within the lungs, which forces air out.

Approximately 2/3 of the active thoracic expansion during inspiration is due to the contraction of the diaphragm. The other 1/3 of thoracic expansion is provided by muscles of the chest wall. Upon contraction, most cause expansion of the rib cage. In extreme circumstances of respiratory distress, accessory muscles may be recruited to further increase thoracic expansion during inspiration. Examples of such accessory muscles include the sternocleidomastoid and scalene muscles of the neck and muscles of the shoulder.

Individuals in respiratory distress often rest their upper body weight on their elbows, arms, or hands. This serves to fixate the upper extremity. Because the upper extremity is immobilized, the shoulder muscles are allowed to "work backwards" and function in expansion of the rib cage instead of arm movement. Consider the body position an exhausted runner assumes: the knees are bent with the hands or arms placed on the knees, the upper torso is leaned forward, resting the weight of the upper body on the knees and fixating the upper extremities while the person frantically pants.

Although expiration is largely passive in a relaxed state, forced expiration becomes more evident during exertion. Muscles of the chest wall and abdomen are used to hasten expiration so the next breath can be taken. Certain muscles of the chest wall contract to actually decrease the size of the rib cage. As the diaphragm relaxes during expiration, muscles of the abdominal wall contract to increase intraabdominal pressure and push abdominal contents up against the diaphragm. The diaphragm, in turn, pushes up against the lungs and promotes their emptying. Forced expiration also occurs with actions such as talking, singing, sneezing, and coughing. Although expiration is largely passive during relaxed breathing, these same chest and abdominal wall muscles may provide some contribution to resting expiration.

Each intercostal nerve, along with an intercostal artery and vein, travels in the costal groove under the inferior border of the superior rib of each intercostal space. For example, the first intercostal space is between the first and second ribs. The first intercostal nerve travels in the first intercostal space, just below the costal groove of the first rib.

The **first intercostal nerve** (172) is small. This is for two reasons. First, and more simplistically, the first rib is small. More importantly, most of the T1 ventral ramus contributes to the formation of the brachial plexus. Ventral rami from C8 and T1 combine to form the lower trunk of the brachial plexus.

The formation of the intercostobrachial nerve was mentioned in the previous chapter. The **second intercostal nerve** (172) and **third intercostal nerve** (172) contribute branches that form the **intercostobrachial nerve** (176). This nerve travels laterally and combines with a branch of the medial cord, the medial brachial cutaneous nerve (**147,** 173), to provide sensory innervation to skin of the medial aspect of the upper arm.

Intercostal nerves located below the third intercostal contribute **lateral cutaneous branches** (54). These branches provide innervation to the skin of the thorax and anterior abdomen. The lateral cutaneous branches and their sub-branches will be described in more detail shortly.

Because the first intercostal is small and the second and third contribute to the intercostobrachial nerve, the skin of the first two or three intercostal spaces requires the assistance of the cervical plexus. The supraclavicular trunk descends to provide three supraclavicular nerves that innervate the skin of the first two to three intercostal spaces of the anterior chest.

The "typical" intercostal nerve is depicted in Figure 2 as the **fourth thoracic intercostal nerve (51,** 55). Any difference an intercostal nerve of a different level may possess from this description will subsequently be covered.

Remember the "atypical" or "different" intercostal nerves are shown on the subject's left in Figure 2 of the poster. This includes the first intercostal (small, noncontributory), second and third intercostals (contribution to intercostobrachial nerve instead of lateral cutaneous branches), and the twelfth thoracic or subcostal nerve (*sub*costal, not true *inter*costal nerve). The "typical" intercostal nerves are depicted on the subject's right. This includes the T4 intercostal nerve (representing the first 6 intercostals – remain confined to the thorax) and T7 intercostal nerve (representing the last 6 intercostals – leave the thorax to also innervate muscle and skin of the anterior abdominal wall).

As each intercostal nerve emerges from the vertebral column, it travels on the internal surface of the internal intercostal membrane. As previously discussed, the internal intercostal muscle does not extend all the way to the vertebral column. Near the vertebra, the intercostal nerve quickly communicates with a sympathetic chain ganglion via two small nerves, a **white ramus communicans** (52) and **gray ramus communicans** (53).

The sympathetic nervous system is also known as the thoracolumbar system because the preganglionic sympathetic cell bodies are located in the spinal cord at the T1-L2 levels. Preganglionic sympathetic fibers from these cell bodies leave the spinal cord with spinal nerves. In this case, the spinal nerve is an intercostal nerve. These fibers then leave the spinal nerve (intercostal nerve) in a small nerve, the white ramus communicans, to enter the sympathetic chain. It is the white ramus communicans that supplies sympathetic input to the sympathetic chain. They carry preganglionic sympathetic fibers that are leaving the intercostal nerve (spinal nerve) and entering the sympathetic chain. Because the preganglionic cell bodies are only located at the T1-L2 spinal levels of the spinal cord, white rami communicans are only associated with spinal nerves that originate from the spinal cord at these levels. This includes all twelve intercostal nerves and the L1 and L2 spinal nerves. By contrast, gray rami communicans carry sympathetic fibers that may have previously traveled a variable distance up or down the sympathetic chain and are now leaving the chain to enter a spinal nerve. Because these fibers are able to travel up and down the sympathetic chain before leaving it, gray rami communicans are associated with spinal nerves throughout most of the length of the spinal cord. They are not confined to the T1-L2 levels. It is through this communication with the sympathetic chain via a gray ramus communicans that the intercostal nerve, like other spinal nerves, obtains sympathetic fibers. These fibers provide sympathetic innervation to peripheral tissues supplied by the spinal nerve.

FIGURE 11.5
LEFT SYMPATHETIC CHAIN

The sympathetic chain can be considered a *"Sympathetic Freeway."* A spinal nerve would therefore be a road which crossed the freeway.
The **white rami communicans** is the **on-ramp.**
The **gray rami communicans** is the **off-ramp.**

After communicating with the sympathetic chain ganglion, the intercostal nerve continues laterally on the inner surface of the internal intercostal muscle until the innermost intercostal muscle is reached. At this point, the intercostal nerve, along with an intercostal artery and intercostal vein, enters the plane between these two muscles. Again, they travel between the innermost and internal intercostal muscles. This combination of a nerve traveling with an artery and vein is not uncommon in anatomy. The three collectively make up what is known as a **neurovascular bundle**. This neurovascular bundle continues laterally and then anteriorly, parallel to the rib it is accompanying. It travels just beneath the costal groove of the lower border of the upper rib of an intercostal space. Phrased differently, the neurovascular bundle travels just beneath the inferior border of the superior rib of each intercostal space.

> While traveling beneath the inferior border of the superior rib of an intercostal space, an intercostal nerve innervates the muscles and skin of the intercostal space located immediately *below* it. This follows the "rule" that spinal nerves supply tissues located *below* their level of origination.

> In the neurovascular bundle, the <u>v</u>ein is most superior. The <u>a</u>rtery is in the middle, and the <u>n</u>erve is most inferior. A VAN is a shortened form of the word *caravan*. Think of the neurovascular bundle as a caravan of structures traveling across the body. This same relative relationship of vein, artery, and nerve occurs with other neurovascular bundles in other areas of the body.
>
> <u>V</u>ein
> <u>A</u>rtery
> <u>N</u>erve

FIGURE 11.6
INTERCOSTAL NEUROVASCULAR BUNDLE

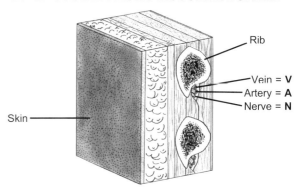

At the approximate level of the mid-axillary line, the intercostal nerve gives off a **lateral cutaneous branch** (54). Since the axilla is the armpit, the mid-axillary line runs from the middle of the armpit downward. It represents the most lateral aspect of the torso. To reach the surface of the chest wall, the lateral cutaneous branch must pierce both the internal and external intercostal muscles. It then divides into anterior and posterior sub-branches. The **anterior sub-branch of the lateral cutaneous branch** (**57,** 59) travels anterior, innervating skin to the level of innervation provided by the anterior cutaneous branch. The **posterior sub-branch of the lateral cutaneous branch** (50) runs posteriorly, innervating skin to the level of innervation of thoracic dorsal rami.

The intercostal nerve continues anterior and turns medial around the side of the chest wall. Slightly lateral to the midline of the anterior torso, the intercostal nerve gives off the **anterior cutaneous branch** (56). This nerve pierces the musculature to innervate skin of the anterior and medial thorax. With each of the lower six intercostal nerves, it innervates skin of the anterior abdomen.

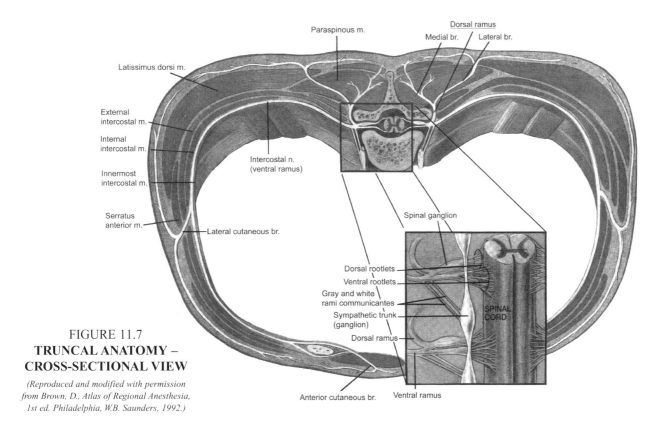

FIGURE 11.7
TRUNCAL ANATOMY –
CROSS-SECTIONAL VIEW

(Reproduced and modified with permission from Brown, D., Atlas of Regional Anesthesia, 1st ed. Philadelphia, W.B. Saunders, 1992.)

As mentioned earlier, the presence of the **seventh intercostal nerve** (58) in Figure 2 serves as a reminder that the lower six intercostal nerves leave the thorax to innervate muscles and skin of the anterior abdominal wall. Since the first six intercostal nerves are confined to the thorax (except for T2 and T3 contributions to the intercostobrachial nerve), the seventh intercostal is the first of the lower six intercostals to leave the thorax.

As with the other intercostal nerves, the **lateral cutaneous branch of each of the lower 6 intercostal nerves** branches off the intercostal at the approximate level of the mid-axillary line. It also branches into an anterior and posterior sub-branch. The **anterior sub-branch of the lateral cutaneous nerve** (59) travels anterior and inferior to supply skin over the lateral aspects of the abdominal wall. The area of supplied skin is bordered medially by skin innervated by branches of the anterior cutaneous nerve of the same intercostal. In Figure 2 of the poster, the nerve is drawn with an arrow at its end to denote that it, along with the intercostal nerve it came from, continues forward to supply tissue of the abdominal wall. The **posterior sub-branch of the lateral cutaneous nerve** travels posterior and inferior to supply skin over the posterior thorax and back. The area of supplied skin is bordered medially by skin innervated by thoracic dorsal rami branches.

After giving off the lateral cutaneous nerve, each of the lower six intercostal nerves continues anterior and medial to cross the costal arch and leave the intercostal space. As each nerve leaves the thorax, it travels in the same muscle plane as in the intercostal space. Instead of traveling between the innermost and internal intercostal muscles, it now travels between the transversus abdominis and internal oblique muscles of the abdominal wall. Fibers of the transversus abdominis are from the same embryologic derivation as the innermost intercostal muscles. Fibers of the internal oblique muscles blend with those of the internal intercostals. The transversus abdominis and internal oblique muscles – as well as the external oblique, rectus abdominis, and pyramidalis muscles – are innervated by the lower six intercostal nerves.

Like the upper six intercostals, each of the lower six nerves ends in an **anterior cutaneous branch**. This branch pierces the musculature of the anterior abdominal wall to innervate skin of the medial abdomen. The area of skin innervated by this branch is bound laterally on both sides by skin innervated by the anterior sub-branch of the lateral cutaneous nerve that originated from the same intercostal nerve.

Finally, the twelfth thoracic ventral ramus, the **subcostal nerve** (146), is named for its location in the costal groove below the last rib. It is not in an intercostal space. Other than the lack of a rib and accompanying intercostal muscles below it, the subcostal nerve has the same basic characteristics and innervation responsibilities as the lower five intercostal nerves.

Before discussing the protective properties of the abdominal wall, a review of the basic structure of the rib cage is in order. Each of the first ten ribs travels in a slight inferior direction as it leaves the vertebral column to curve around the chest wall. In the anterior aspect of the chest wall, they make a superior turn to reach the sternum (true ribs, #1-7) or costal cartilage of the superior rib (false ribs, #8-10). The floating ribs (#11,12) simply travel out laterally and inferiorly. Because the first ten ribs extend inferiorly and then return superiorly, the rib cage extends significantly more inferior at the lateral aspects of the chest wall. This structure provides the optimal balance of protection and flexibility. In the back, the vertebral column and floating ribs provide protection from traumatic injuries. In the front, there is an absence of bone. The protection here is provided by the anterior abdominal wall. The protective presence of muscle instead of bone enhances flexibility. Not only is flexibility important in speed and agility, but it greatly facilitates the ability to withstand a blow; it is better to bend than break.

FIGURE 11.8
ASSOCIATION OF RIB CAGE TO INTERNAL ORGANS

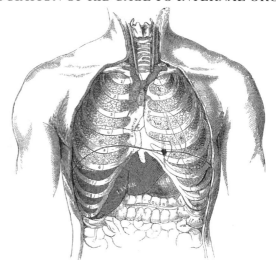

The transversus abdominis is the deepest muscle of the abdominal wall. It originates from the costal cartilage of the lower six ribs and iliac crest. It inserts on a midline tendinous sheath of the abdomen, the linea alba. The transversus abdominis functions to tighten or "squeeze" the viscera of the abdomen. This causes an increase in intra-abdominal pressure which is transferred to the diaphragm, and subsequently to the lungs. This promotes forced expiration of air that is used for actions such as coughing, blowing, sneezing, or exertional breathing. Increased intra-abdominal pressure is also utilized for forced expulsion of gastric contents during regurgitation or "bearing down" to empty the bladder, empty the rectum, or push a baby out of the birth canal.

The internal oblique muscle is external to the transversus abdominis. It originates from the anterior iliac crest and fascia of the iliac, thoracolumbar, and inguinal regions. It inserts on the lower edge of costal cartilage of the last three or four ribs and the linea alba. Like the transversus abdominis, this muscle also tightens or squeezes the abdominal viscera to increase intra-abdominal pressure. In addition, it rotates and flexes the vertebral column. By flexing the vertebral column, the ribs are pulled toward the pelvis, as if performing a sit-up.

The external oblique muscle is external to the internal oblique. It shares the same functions as the internal oblique: tightening of the abdominal contents and rotation and flexion of the vertebral column. The external oblique originates from the costal cartilages of the lower eight ribs and inserts on the iliac crest and linea alba. These three muscles, the transversus abdominis, internal oblique, and external oblique, are also known as the three flat muscles of the abdomen. The aponeuroses of these muscles enclose the rectus abdominis muscle.

FIGURE 11.9
MUSCLES OF ANTERIOR TORSO
Muscles on the subjects left are deep to those on the right. The transversus abdominis is deep to all.

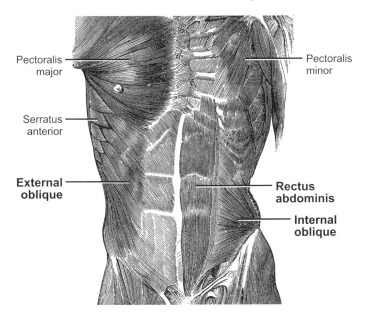

The rectus abdominis muscle originates at the pubic crest and pubic symphysis, the anterior portion of the pelvic bone. It inserts on the costal cartilage of the fifth, sixth, and seventh ribs and xyphoid process of the sternum. The rectus abdominis functions to support the abdomen and flex the vertebral column. It is the rectus abdominis muscle which is responsible for the "6-pack abs" seen on very thin or muscular individuals.

Finally, the pyramidalis is a small, midline muscle of the lower abdominal wall. It is superficial to the rectus abdominis muscle and immediately above the pubis. It originates from the body of the pubis and inserts on the linea alba. The pyramidalis is named for it's pyramid-like triangle shape. Upon contraction it functions to tighten the lower abdominal wall.

FIGURE 11.10
ANTERIOR ABDOMINAL WALL

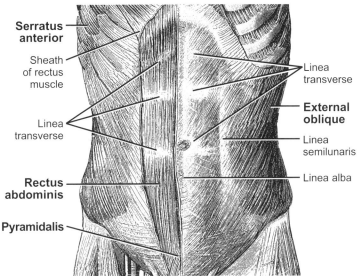

There are three basic functions of abdominal wall muscles: increasing intra-abdominal pressure, support of abdominal contents, and flexion/rotation of the spine. Each muscle may be grouped according to their general function. The three flat muscles tighten abdominal contents and increase intra-abdominal pressure. The rectus abdominis has little involvement in increasing intra-abdominal pressure. A second function is support of abdominal contents. Again, it is the flat muscles that are also responsible for support. The third function is movement of the trunk. This includes flexion and/or rotation of the vertebral column. This function is primarily provided by both obliques and the rectus abdominis muscles. The transversus abdominis has little involvement in movement of the trunk.

↑ intra-abdominal pressure	support contents	flexion/rotation of spine
• Transversus abdominis	• Transversus abdominis	• Rectus abdominis
• Obliques	• Obliques	• Obliques

QUIZ 1
Thoracic Nerves

Time for Quiz = 25 minutes.
For questions 1-16, choose the single best answer.

_____1) To reach the surface of the torso, what muscles must the lateral cutaneous branch of an intercostal nerve travel through?
   a) innermost intercostal
   b) subcostal muscle
   c) both a and b
   d) transversus thoracis
   e) none of the above

_____2) Which of the following is true concerning the relative anatomic relationship between the three structures of the intercostal neurovascular bundle?
   a) The artery is most superior.
   b) The vein is intermediate in location.
   c) The nerve is most inferior.
   d) All of the above
   e) None of the above

_____3) Which nerve does the intercostobrachial nerve combine with?
   a) musculocutaneous nerve
   b) medial brachial cutaneous nerve
   c) medial antebrachial cutaneous nerve
   d) medial pectoral nerve
   e) none of the above

_____4) Which muscles primarily function during inspiration?
   a) levatores costarum
   b) internal intercostals
   c) innermost intercostals
   d) all of the above
   e) none of the above

_____5) Which nerves could supply the transversus abdominis muscle?
   a) subcostal nerve
   b) dorsal rami branches
   c) intercostobrachial nerve
   d) thoracodorsal nerve
   e) none of the above

_____6) Which statements concerning gray rami communicans are true?
   a) They carry fibers which are entering the sympathetic chain.
   b) They carry fibers which are leaving the intercostal nerve.
   c) Both a and b
   d) They are associated with spinal nerves throughout the length of the spinal cord.
   e) None of the above

_____7) Within a particular intercostal space, where is the neurovascular bundle located?
   a) behind the superior border of the inferior rib
   b) superficial to the superior border of the inferior rib
   c) behind the inferior border of the superior rib
   d) superficial to the inferior border of the inferior rib
   e) none of the above

_____8) Which muscles share a common membrane with the subcostal muscles to form the most internal layer of intercostal muscle?
   a) transversus thoracis muscle
   b) internal intercostal muscles
   c) internal oblique muscles
   d) transversus abdominis muscle
   e) none of the above

_____9) Of the following, which nerve is the first branch of a typical intercostal nerve?
   a) gray ramus communicans
   b) anterior cutaneous branch
   c) lateral cutaneous branch
   d) posterior sub-branch
   e) none of the above

_____10) Which statements about the T1 ventral ramus are true?
   a) Most of it contributes to the brachial plexus.
   b) It is responsible for the second intercostal nerve.
   c) Both a and b
   d) Its branches contribute to the intercostobrachial nerve.
   e) None of the above

_____11) The serratus posterior superior muscle is innervated by the
   a) intercostal nerves
   b) thoracic ventral rami branches
   c) both a and b
   d) long thoracic nerve
   e) none of the above

_____12) Which muscles have fibers which merge with those of the internal intercostal muscles?
   a) transversus abdominis muscle
   b) internal oblique muscles
   c) external oblique muscles
   d) serratus posterior superior muscles
   e) none of the above

_____13) Which intercostal nerves usually contribute branches to form the intercostobrachial nerve?
   a) fourth
   b) fifth
   c) both a and b
   d) first
   e) none of the above

_____14) The levatores costarum muscles are innervated by the
   a) intercostal nerves
   b) dorsal rami branches
   c) both a and b
   d) thoracodorsal nerve
   e) none of the above

_____15) Intercostal nerves travel between which two muscles?
   a) internal and external intercostal muscles
   b) transversus thoracis and innermost intercostal muscles
   c) internal and innermost intercostal muscles
   d) internal and external oblique muscles
   e) none of the above

_____16) Which muscles have fibers of the same embryonic derivation as the innermost intercostal muscles?
   a) internal intercostal muscles
   b) transversus thoracis muscle
   c) transversus abdominis muscle
   d) internal oblique muscles
   e) none of the above

_____

For questions 17-25, use the following directions:
   a.......1,2,3 are correct
   b.......1,3 are correct
   c.......2,4 are correct
   d.......only 4 is correct
   e.......all are correct

_____17) Which statements about internal intercostal muscles are true?
   1. They predominately function in forced expiration.
   2. They are innervated by intercostal nerves.
   3. They slant posterior as they travel from one rib to the rib below.
   4. They are innervated by thoracic ventral rami.

_____18) Which statements concerning white rami communicans are true?
   1. They carry fibers which are leaving the intercostal nerve.
   2. They carry fibers which are entering the sympathetic chain.
   3. They are one of the first branches of an intercostal nerve.
   4. They are associated with spinal nerves throughout the length of the spinal cord.

_____19) Which of the following tissues may be supplied by intercostal nerves?
    1. chest wall musculature
    2. abdominal wall musculature
    3. skin over the abdominal wall
    4. skin over the medial arm

_____20) Which statements about the intercosto-brachial nerve are true?
    1. It supplies skin of the posterior chest wall.
    2. The first intercostal nerve frequently contributes to its formation.
    3. It combines with the medial ante-brachial cutaneous nerve.
    4. It is formed by branches equivalent to the lateral cutaneous branches of the lower intercostal nerves.

_____21) Muscles innervated by intercostal nerves include the
    1. internal obliques
    2. transversus thoracis
    3. subcostal muscles
    4. transversus abdominis

_____22) Which statements about the first intercostal nerve are true?
    1. Most if its vental ramus of origin contributes to the brachial plexus.
    2. It is superior to the first intercostal artery in the costal groove.
    3. It is small relative to other intercostal nerves.
    4. It is responsible for innervating skin of the first intercostal space.

_____23) Which muscles share a common membrane, forming the deepest layer of intercostal muscle?
    1. transversus thoracis
    2. internal intercostal muscles
    3. subcostal muscles
    4. external intercostal muscles

_____24) Which statements about external intercostal muscles are true?
    1. In the lower thorax, fibers blend with those of the transversus abdominis muscle.
    2. They are innervated by thoracic dorsal rami.
    3. They are present in the anterior 4/5 of the upper thorax.
    4. They predominately function in inspiration.

_____25) Which statements about typical branches of the lower nine intercostal nerves are true?
    1. The lateral cutaneous branch is the origin of the anterior sub-branch.
    2. The lateral cutaneous branch is the origin of the posterior sub-branch.
    3. The anterior cutaneous branch is the distal continuation of the intercostal nerve.
    4. Cutaneous innervation borders that of dorsal rami branches.

QUIZ 1: Thoracic Nerves Answers and Explanations

1) e – The most internal layer of intercostal muscle is comprised of three separate muscles that share a common membrane: the transversus thoracis, innermost intercostal, and subcostal muscles. In the thorax, intercostal nerves travel between the innermost intercostal muscle on the deep side and internal intercostal muscle on the superficial side. To reach the surface and supply skin of the chest wall, the lateral cutaneous branch must pierce both the internal and external intercostal muscles.

2) c – A neurovascular bundle is formed by a vein, artery, and nerve. These structures often have a consistent anatomic relationship relative to one another. An intercostal neurovascular bundle is no exception. From superior to inferior, the *v*ein is most superior, the *a*rtery is in an intermediate position, and the *n*erve is most inferior. Thus, from superior to inferior, the word *VAN* is spelled out. This may be remembered by considering a neurovascular bundle as a *caravan* traveling in different regions of the body. The shortened form of the word *caravan* is van. Instead of the superior and inferior directions, the relative relationships may involve the medial and lateral directions in neurovascular bundles of other regions of the body. Nevertheless, the same relative relationships exist: the vein is on one side, the artery is in an intermediate position, and the nerve is on the other side.

3) b – The intercostobrachial nerve is formed by what is the equivalent to the lateral cutaneous branch from both the second and third intercostal nerves. The second intercostal nerve is more consistent in this contribution, but the third intercostal frequently participates. The intercostobrachial nerve combines with a branch of the medial cord of the brachial plexus, the medial brachial cutaneous nerve, to supply skin of the medial arm.

4) a – The levatores costarum originate from the transverse processes of the last cervical and first eleven thoracic vertebrae. They insert on ribs located one or two levels below their origination. Upon contraction, they lift the ribs during inspiration. Both the internal and innermost intercostals primarily function during forced expiration.

5) a – The subcostal nerve could be considered the twelfth intercostal nerve. Because it is located behind the inferior border of the twelfth rib, it does not have a rib below it. It therefore is called the *sub*costal nerve as opposed to an *inter*costal nerve. The lower six intercostal nerves, including the subcostal nerve, eventually leave the thorax to also supply skin and muscles of the anterior abdominal wall. This includes the transversus abdominis muscle. The intercostobrachial nerve is formed by branches of the second and third intercostal nerves. It combines with the medial brachial cutaneous nerve to supply skin of the medial arm. The thoracodorsal nerve is a branch of the posterior cord of the brachial plexus. It supplies the latissimus dorsi muscle.

6) d – Preganglionic sympathetic cell bodies are located in the spinal cord at the T1-L2 levels. Preganglionic sympathetic fibers from these cell bodies exit the spinal cord with spinal nerves. In this case, the spinal nerve is an intercostal nerve. These fibers then leave the spinal nerve (intercostal nerve) in small nerves known as white rami communicans to enter the sympathetic chain. The sympathetic chain is not directly connected to the brain or spinal cord and must obtain its sympathetic input by some means. It is the white rami communicans that provide sympathetic input to the sympathetic chain. Again, white rami communicans carry preganglionic sympathetic fibers that are leaving the intercostal nerve (spinal nerve) to enter the sympathetic chain. Because the preganglionic cell bodies are only located at the T1-L2 spinal cord levels, white rami communicans are only associated with spinal nerves that originate from the spinal cord at these levels. This includes all twelve intercostal nerves and the L1 and L2 spinal nerves. By contrast, gray rami communicans carry sympathetic fibers that may have previously traveled a variable distance up or down the sympathetic chain and are now leaving the sympathetic chain to enter a

spinal nerve. Because these fibers are capable of traveling up or down the sympathetic chain before leaving it, gray rami communicans are associated with spinal nerves throughout most of the length of the spinal cord. They are not confined to spinal nerves of the T1-L2 levels. It is the gray rami communicans that actually provide the sympathetic innervation to the spinal nerve (intercostal nerve) and subsequently, the tissues supplied by the spinal nerve.

7) c – The neurovascular bundle is composed of an intercostal nerve, artery, and vein. An intercostal neurovascular bundle travels in the costal groove behind the inferior border of the superior rib of a particular intercostal space. This can be remembered by considering that most spinal nerves supply tissues which are located *below* their level of origination. The intercostal nerves follow this rule. By traveling behind the inferior border of the superior rib, an intercostal nerve supplies tissues located in the intercostal space *below* it.

8) a – There are three layers of intercostal muscle. The innermost layer is formed by three separate muscles that share a common membrane. These include the transversus thoracis, innermost intercostal, and subcostal muscles. The next layer of muscle is formed by the internal intercostal muscles. The third and outer layer is formed by the external intercostal muscles.

9) a – Branches with the sympathetic chain via gray and white rami communicans are usually the first branches of intercostal nerves. They are the routes of communication between spinal nerves and the sympathetic chain. White and gray rami are found proximally, soon after the formation of the intercostal nerve.

10) a – The first intercostal nerve is small because the first rib is small. More importantly, the majority of the T1 ventral ramus contributes to the brachial plexus. The lower trunk of the brachial plexus is formed by ventral rami roots from C8 and T1. The intercostobrachial nerve is formed by what is the equivalent to the lateral cutaneous branch from both the second and third intercostal nerves. The second intercostal nerve is more consistent in this contribution, but the third intercostal frequently participates. The

intercostobrachial nerve combines with the medial brachial cutaneous nerve to supply skin of the medial arm.

11) c – The intercostal nerves are thoracic ventral rami branches. The serratus posterior superior muscle is supplied by the upper four intercostal nerves. The serratus posterior inferior muscle is supplied by the lower four intercostal nerves. The long thoracic nerve is formed by ventral rami branches from C5, C6, C7 and supplies the serratus anterior muscle.

12) b – While in the thorax, intercostal nerves travel between the innermost and internal intercostal muscles. The lower six intercostal nerves, which eventually leave the thorax to supply the abdominal wall, travel between the transversus abdominis and internal oblique while in the abdomen. Muscle fibers of the innermost intercostal and transversus abdominis are of the same embryonic derivation. Fibers of the internal intercostal and internal oblique merge with one another. Thus, by traveling between the innermost and internal intercostal muscles, and subse-quently, the transversus abdominis and internal oblique muscles, the lower six intercostal nerves are able to remain in the same muscle plane. Coincidently, muscle fibers of the external intercostals blend with those of the external oblique muscles.

13) e – See #10 answer explanation.

14) c – The intercostal nerves are thoracic ventral rami branches. The levatores costarum are supplied by intercostal nerves in the majority of people. In some individuals, they are instead supplied by dorsal rami branches. Some individuals may actually have a combination of both intercostal nerves (ventral rami) and dorsal rami branches providing innervation. The thoracodorsal nerve is a branch of the posterior cord of the brachial plexus and supplies the latissimus dorsi muscle.

15) c – Because the innermost intercostal muscles do not extend as posterior as the internal intercostal muscles, an intercostal nerve initially travels on the internal membrane of an internal intercostal muscle as the nerve emerges from the spine. The nerve courses outward to reach the innermost intercostal muscle. It then continues distal-

ly between the internal and innermost inter-costal muscles. The lower six intercostal nerves eventually leave the thorax to supply skin and muscles of the abdominal wall. These nerves travel across the abdomen between the transversus abdominis and internal oblique muscles.

16) c – See #12 answer explanation.

17) e – The intercostal nerves are the thoracic ventral rami. The predominant function of the *in*ternal intercostal muscles is forced *ex*piration. The predominant function of the *ex*ternal inter-costal muscles is *in*spiration. IN = EX and EX = IN

18) a – See #6 answer explanation.

19) e – Intercostal nerves supply the serratus posterior superior, serratus posterior inferior, levators costarium, and all three layers of intercostal muscles. The most internal layer of intercostal muscle is formed by the transversus thoracis, subcostal, and innermost intercostal muscles. The internal intercostal muscles form the next layer. Finally, the external intercostal muscles form the most superficial layer. The lower six intercostal nerves eventually leave the thorax to supply skin and muscles of the abdominal wall. Included are the transversus abdominis, internal oblique, external oblique, rectus abdominis, and pyramidalis muscles. The intercostobrachial nerve is formed by what is the equivalent to the lateral cutaneous branch from both the second and third intercostal nerves. The intercostobrachial nerve combines with a branch of the medial cord of the brachial plexus, the medial brachial cutaneous nerve, to supply skin of the medial arm.

20) d – See #3 answer explanation.

21) e – Along with the innermost intercostal muscles, the transversus thoracis and subcostal muscles share a common membrane, forming the most internal layer of intercostal muscles. The lower six intercostal nerves eventually leave the thorax to supply muscles and skin of the abdominal wall. This includes the internal oblique and transversus abdominis muscles.

22) b – The first intercostal nerve is small because the first rib is small. More importantly, the majority of the T1 ventral ramus contributes to the brachial plexus. The lower trunk of the brachial plexus is formed by ventral rami roots from C8 and T1. The order of structures of the intercostal neurovascular bundle, from superior to inferior, is VAN: the *v*ein is most superior, *a*rtery is intermediate in location, and the *n*erve is most inferior. The nerve is closest to the intercostal space. The skin over the first two or three intercostal spaces is largely supplied by supraclavicular nerves, which branch from the supraclavicular trunk of the cervical plexus.

23) b – See #8 answer explanation.

24) d – Fibers of the external intercostal muscles blend with those of the external oblique. Intercostal muscles are supplied by intercostal nerves, which are thoracic ventral rami. The predominant function of the *in*ternal intercostal muscles is forced *ex*piration. The predominant function of the *ex*ternal inter-costal muscles is *in*spiration. IN = EX and EX = IN.

25) e – The lateral cutaneous branch originates from an intercostal nerve at the approximate level of the mid-axillary line. This represents the most lateral aspect of the torso. The lateral cutaneous nerve pierces the internal and external intercostal nerves to reach the subcutaneous tissue and divide into anterior and posterior sub-branches. The anterior sub-branch travels anterior and supplies skin that borders skin supplied by the anterior cutaneous nerve, the distal continuation of the intercostal nerve after the lateral cutaneous nerve is given off. The posterior sub-branch travels posterior to supply skin bordering skin supplied by dorsal rami branches.

PHRENIC AND VAGUS NERVES

The vagus nerve and phrenic nerve were discussed in previous chapters. As they travel down the thorax, each nerve has specific anatomic relationships with the heart and great vessels. These relationships will now be described. As the course of each nerve is discussed, it will be necessary to follow the anatomic relationships on Figure 4 of the poster. A review of the basic anatomy of the heart and great vessels may be beneficial.

Each phrenic nerve (47) is formed from ventral rami branches of the C3, C4, and C5 spinal nerves. The two phrenic nerves course inferiorly through the thorax to supply the diaphragm. Although they are known for innervating the diaphragm, the phrenic nerves also carry somatic afferent information. Pain sensation is transmitted from the diaphragm, peritoneum, pleura, and pericardium. Signals associated with proprioception are transmitted from the diaphragm. As they travel through the thorax, the two phrenic nerves are generally anterior to the two vagus nerves.

Entering the thorax from above, the **right (R.) phrenic nerve** (**47**, 234, 235) travels lateral to and in close proximity with the R. internal jugular vein. This is depicted in Figure 4 of the poster. It passes anterior to the R. subclavian artery, posterior to the right brachiocephalic vein, and emerges lateral to the superior vena cava. As it continues inferiorly, it crosses the right lateral surface of the pericardium to enter the diaphragm with the inferior vena cava.

The **left (L.) phrenic nerve** (238, **239**) enters the thorax positioned between the L. common carotid artery medially and the L. subclavian artery laterally. As it courses down the neck and upper thorax, it travels behind the L. internal jugular vein. Similar to its counterpart, the L. phrenic crosses anterior to the L. subclavian artery and posterior to the L. brachiocephalic vein. Alternatively, it may pass behind the L. subclavian vein if this vessel had not yet converged with the L. internal jugular vein to form the L. brachiocephalic. The L. phrenic then passes anterior to the arch of the aorta, L. vagus nerve, and L. pulmonary artery/pulmonary trunk. It crosses the surface of the left lateral pericardium and enters the diaphragm near the apex of the heart.

The two **PHRENIC** nerves pass **ANTERIOR** to **ALL** structures associated with the heart and great vessels **EXCEPT** the proximal **VENOUS** structures. The right phrenic passes behind the right brachiocephalic v. (or right subclavian v.) Likewise, the left phrenic passes behind the left brachiocephalic v. (or left subclavian v.)

The vagus nerve is cranial nerve #10 and provides the majority of the body's parasympathetic innervation. This includes parasympathetic input to virtually all thoracic viscera and abdominal viscera to the level of the left (splenic) flexure of the large colon. Like the two phrenic nerves, the two vagus nerves have specific anatomic relationships to the heart and great vessels as they pass through the thorax.

The **R. vagus nerve** (**29**, 49, 232, 236, 244) descends the neck between the R. common carotid artery medially and R. internal jugular vein laterally. It serves as the origin of three named nerves and continues inferiorly to supply structures of the abdomen. After the last of the three branches is given off, the R.

vagus continues downward, posterior to the R. brachiocephalic vein and superior vena cava.

The **superior cervical cardiac branch of the R. vagus** (**37**, 245) is formed by the coalition of a number of R. vagus branches that arise in the neck. Figure 5 of the poster is a view of the medial thorax, after removal of the heart and great vessels. The superior cervical cardiac branch (245) is drawn as a dotted line to signify that it travels down the neck deep or posterior to the R. vagus nerve. The superior cervical cardiac branch contributes parasympathetic innervation to the **cardiac plexus** (253), the autonomic plexus which supplies the heart.

As the R. vagus continues distally, it passes anterior to the R. subclavian artery and gives off the **recurrent branch of the right vagus**, also known as the **R. recurrent laryngeal nerve** (**46**, 233, 242). The recurrent laryngeal is named for its recurrent trip up the neck to reach and supply intrinsic muscles of the larynx. After leaving the R. vagus, the R. recurrent travels inferiorly and posteriorly to pass under the cover of the brachiocephalic (innominate) artery. It turns upward and begins its trek back up the neck behind this artery.

The Brachiocephalic (innominate) artery can be remembered because there is only one, and it is on the right. It "carries" the R. common carotid and R. subclavian arteries from the left-curving aortic arch to supply the externally symmetrical right side of the body. As it leaves the aortic arch, the brachiocephalic artery should be envisioned as a side view of a horse's neck. The R. common carotid artery represents the horse's ears and the R. subclavian artery represents the snout. Obviously, this requires quite an imagination!

The R. vagus seems to be infatuated with the brachiocephalic artery. First, it travels down the neck just lateral to one of its two branches, the R. common carotid artery. It then passes anterior to the other branch, the R. subclavian artery. Finally, it lassos the brachiocephalic with the R. recurrent nerve, similar to a lasso around a horse's neck. It is as if the R. vagus was attempting to keep the brachiocephalic from going anywhere.

The R. recurrent emerges from behind the R. common carotid artery and continues up the neck, medial to this vessel. It supplies sensation to the tracheal mucosa up to the level of the vocal cords. It also innervates intrinsic laryngeal muscles, which function in vocalization. After giving off the R. recurrent, the R. vagus continues down the thorax posterior to the R. brachiocephalic vein and superior vena cava.

While looking in the mirror, the student should attempt to identify the external jugular vein of the neck. This gives a crude, generalized representation of how lateral in the neck the deeper-located internal jugular vein is. Next, the carotid pulse should be felt. The carotid is medial to the jugular. The most medial structure is the trachea and therefore, the larynx. Identifying these structures will help learning the anatomic relationships of the R. vagus and R. recurrent laryngeal nerves.

(continued)

The R. vagus descends the neck between the R. internal jugular vein (laterally) and R. common carotid artery (medially). In other words, it descends lateral to the common carotid artery. As the R. recurrent laryngeal ascends the neck, it is heading toward the medially-located larynx. It therefore travels medial to the common carotid artery. The R. vagus descends on the lateral side of the common carotid. The R. recurrent laryngeal ascends on the medial side of the common carotid.

The third and final R. vagus branch of thoracic significance is the **inferior cardiac branch of the R. vagus (48,** 246). It arises from the vagus soon after the takeoff of the recurrent laryngeal. Like the superior cardiac branch, the inferior cardiac branch contributes parasympathetic input to the cardiac plexus (253).

After giving off these three branches, the R. vagus continues inferiorly traveling behind the R. brachiocephalic vein and superior vena cava. It passes posterior to the right bronchus of the trachea and gives branches that contribute to the **esophageal plexus** (248), the thin meshwork of autonomic nerves covering and supplying the esophagus. At this point, the right vagus forms the **posterior vagal trunk (249,** 259), which continues down the esophagus, through the esophageal hiatus of the diaphragm, and ends in the **celiac plexus** (260) of the upper abdomen.

From a superior location, the **vagus nerves** can be thought to travel down the thorax while rotating in a *clock*wise direction, similar to a **screw** being screwed into a piece of wood. The R. vagus becomes the posterior vagal trunk and the L. vagus becomes the anterior vagal trunk.

V a g u s = C l o c k = S c r e w
1 2 3 4 5   1 2 3 4 5   1 2 3 4 5

Similar, to its right counterpart, the **L. vagus nerve (241,** 237, 255) travels down the neck between the L. common carotid artery medially and the L. internal jugular vein laterally. It also gives off the same three branches as the R. vagus, but because the anatomy of the great vessels is different on the left side, the anatomic relationships of the L. recurrent laryngeal are different from those of the R. recurrent laryngeal nerve.

The **superior cervical cardiac branch of the L. vagus** (254) is formed by a coalition of L. vagus branches that arise in the neck. It is drawn dotted in Figure 5 to signify that it is deep or posterior to the L. vagus as it travels down the neck and enters the thorax. The superior cervical cardiac branch contributes parasympathetic input to the cardiac plexus (253).

The L. vagus enters the thorax between the L. common carotid artery and L. internal jugular vein. It descends posterior to the L. brachiocephalic vein and across the front of the aortic arch

to give off the **recurrent branch of the L. vagus** or **L. recurrent laryngeal nerve (240,** 257). This branch continues down the front of the arch of the aorta and curves backward, traveling inferior and posterior. It passes under the aortic arch and travels between the aortic arch and pulmonary trunk. The L. recurrent laryngeal then begins its ascent back up the neck to the larynx, traveling posterior to aortic arch and emerging between the L. common carotid and brachiocephalic arteries. Like the R. recurrent, the L. recurrent travels up the neck medial to the common carotid artery of its respective side.

Not to be outdone by its right-sided sibling, the L. vagus decided to lasso more than just an artery. Whereas the R. vagus lassos the brachiocephalic artery with the R. recurrent, the L. vagus lassos the whole aortic arch with its L. recurrent!

The **inferior cardiac branch of the left vagus** (252) branches from the vagus after the takeoff of the recurrent laryngeal nerve. Like the superior cardiac branch, it contributes parasympathetic innervation to the **cardiac plexus** (253).

As it descends the thorax, the L. vagus travels posterior to the L. brachiocephalic vein and anterior to the aortic arch. After giving off the L. recurrent laryngeal nerve and inferior cardiac branch, the L. vagus disappears behind the pulmonary trunk. It travels down the thorax posterior to the pulmonary trunk and left tracheal bronchus to reach the **esophageal plexus** (248). Here, it forms the **anterior vagal trunk (250,** 258), which continues through the esophageal hiatus of the diaphragm to supply the **celiac plexus** (260) with parasympathetic innervation. It is from the anterior and posterior vagal trunks that parasympathetic innervation is provided to abdominal viscera to the level of the left (splenic) flexure of the colon.

The phrenic nerves are "in a hurry" to reach and supply the diaphragm. They don't have time to dilly-dally around the heart and great vessels. In fact, the only structures they travel posterior to are the brachiocephalic veins.

Although the vagus nerves are passing through as well, they must also provide parasympathetic innervation to the thoracic structures. They therefore must get much more involved with the heart, great vessels, and lungs. They venture much deeper, traveling posterior to more structures than the phrenic nerves.

The R. vagus travels posterior to the R. brachiocephalic vein, superior vena cava, and R. tracheal bronchus. The L. vagus is posterior to the L. brachiocephalic vein, pulmonary trunk, and L. tracheal bronchus.

QUIZ 2
Thoracic Nerves

Time for Quiz = 19 minutes.
For questions 1-12, choose the single best answer.

_____1) Which thoracic structures are immediately posterior to the course of the right phrenic nerve?
     a) aorta
     b) right subclavian artery
     c) right brachiocephalic vein
     d) left common carotid artery
     e) none of the above

_____2) Around which blood vessel does the left recurrent laryngeal nerve loop beneath prior to its ascent up the neck?
     a) brachiocephalic artery
     b) L. brachiocephalic vein
     c) arch of aorta
     d) L. internal jugular vein
     e) none of the above

_____3) While in the chest, the left vagus nerve passes posterior to the
     a) brachiocephalic artery
     b) L. subclavian artery
     c) pulmonary trunk and/or L. pulmonary vein
     d) arch of aorta
     e) none of the above

_____4) As it descends the thorax, the left phrenic nerve passes posterior to the
     a) aorta
     b) left subclavian artery
     c) left pulmonary artery
     d) left vagus nerve
     e) none of the above

_____5) Vagus nerve branches that supply thoracic structures include the
     a) recurrent laryngeal nerve
     b) inferior cardiac branch
     c) superior cervical cardiac branch
     d) all the above
     e) none of the above

_____6) While in the neck, the right vagus nerve is lateral to which structure?
     a) R. common carotid artery
     b) R. subclavian artery
     c) R. internal jugular vein
     d) R. brachiocephalic vein
     e) none of the above

_____7) While in the chest, the left phrenic nerve passes anterior to the
     a) aorta
     b) left vagus nerve
     c) left pulmonary artery
     d) all the above
     e) none of the above

_____8) Around which blood vessel does the right recurrent laryngeal nerve loop beneath prior to its ascent up the neck?
     a) brachiocephalic artery
     b) R. brachiocephalic vein
     c) arch of aorta
     d) R. internal jugular vein
     e) none of the above

_____9) As it descends the thorax, the right vagus nerve passes posterior to the
     a) R. tracheal bronchus
     b) R. brachiocephalic vein
     c) superior vena cava
     d) all the above
     e) none of the above

_____10) The left vagus nerve passes anterior to which of the following thoracic structures?
     a) brachiocephalic artery
     b) L. brachiocephalic vein
     c) L. tracheal bronchus
     d) all the above
     e) none of the above

_____11) Which thoracic structures are anterior to the course of the right phrenic nerve?
     a) aorta
     b) right subclavian artery
     c) right brachiocephalic vein
     d) left common carotid artery
     e) none of the above

_____12) As it descends the thorax, the right vagus nerve passes immediately anterior to the
   a) arch of the aorta
   b) R. brachiocephalic vein
   c) superior vena cava
   d) R. tracheal bronchus
   e) none of the above

_____

For questions 13-19, use the following directions:
   a.......1,2,3 are correct
   b.......1,3 are correct
   c.......2,4 are correct
   d.......only 4 is correct
   e.......all are correct

_____13) Which anatomic relationships are correct concerning the phrenic and vagus nerves and their branches?
   1. The L. phrenic nerve passes posterior to the L. brachiocephalic vein.
   2. The R. vagus nerve passes anterior to arch of the aorta.
   3. The R. recurrent laryngeal nerve loops below and behind the brachiocephalic artery.
   4. The R. phrenic nerve passes posterior to the superior vena cava.

_____14) Which statements about the R. phrenic nerve are correct?
   1. It passes posterior to the R. brachiocephalic vein.
   2. It descends the neck medial to the R. common carotid artery.
   3. It passes anterior to the R. subclavian artery.
   4. It passes posterior to the superior vena cava.

_____15) Which vascular structures are located between the R. vagus and R. recurrent laryngeal nerves?
   1. the R. brachiocephalic vein
   2. the aorta
   3. the R. internal jugular vein
   4. the brachiocephalic artery

_____16) Which statements about the L. vagus nerve are true?
   1. It descends the neck lateral to the L. internal jugular vein.
   2. It becomes the posterior vagal trunk.
   3. Its recurrent laryngeal branch passes inferior and posterior to the brachiocephalic artery.
   4. It passes anterior to the L. subclavian artery.

_____17) Which vascular structures are located between the L. vagus and L. recurrent laryngeal nerves?
   1. the L. brachiocephalic vein
   2. the aorta
   3. the L. internal jugular vein
   4. the L. common carotid artery

_____18) Which statements about the R. vagus nerve are true?
   1. It becomes the posterior vagal trunk.
   2. It descends the neck lateral to the R. common carotid artery.
   3. It passes anterior to the R. subclavian artery.
   4. Its recurrent laryngeal branch passes inferior and posterior to the arch of the aorta.

_____19) Which statements about the L. phrenic nerve are correct?
   1. It descends the neck in close proximity to the L. internal jugular vein.
   2. It passes posterior to the pulmonary trunk/L. pulmonary artery.
   3. It passes anterior to the L. subclavian artery.
   4. It passes anterior to the L. brachiocephalic vein.

QUIZ 2: Thoracic Nerves Answers and Explanations

1) b – The right phrenic nerve descends the neck just behind the right internal jugular vein, passes anterior to the right subclavian artery, posterior to the right brachiocephalic vein, and crosses the anterior surface of the right lateral pericardium. The left phrenic nerve passes anterior to the arch of the aorta.

2) c – The left vagus nerve descends the neck lateral to the L. common carotid artery. It passes anterior to the arch of the aorta and gives off the L. recurrent laryngeal nerve. The L. recurrent passes inferior to the aortic arch to begin its ascent behind this vessel.

3) c – The left vagus nerve descends the neck between the L. internal jugular vein laterally and L. common carotid artery medially. It passes anterior to the arch of the aorta and posterior to the L. brachiocephalic vein, pulmonary trunk, and L. tracheal bronchus.

4) e – The left phrenic nerve descends the neck lateral to the left common carotid artery, passes anterior to the left subclavian artery, posterior to the left brachiocephalic vein, and anterior to the aortic arch, left vagus nerve, and left pulmonary artery/pulmonary trunk. It continues inferiorly across the anterior surface of the left lateral pericardium.

5) d – The superior cervical cardiac branch is formed by a coalition of vagus nerve branches that arise in the neck. It descends to contribute parasympathetic input to the cardiac plexus. The recurrent laryngeal nerve branches from the vagus in the thorax and ascends the neck to supply the larynx. On the way, it provides branches to the trachea, esophagus, and cardiac plexus. The inferior cardiac branch originates from the vagus while in the thorax. It also provides parasympathetic input to the cardiac plexus.

6) a – The right vagus nerve descends the neck between the R. internal jugular vein laterally and R. common carotid artery medially.

7) d – See #4 answer explanation.

8) a – The right vagus nerve descends the neck lateral to the R. common carotid artery. It passes anterior to the R. subclavian artery and gives off the R. recurrent laryngeal nerve. The R. recurrent passes inferior to the brachiocephalic artery to begin its ascent behind this vessel.

9) d – The right vagus nerve descends the neck between the R. internal jugular vein laterally and R. common carotid artery medially. It passes anterior to the R. subclavian artery and posterior to the R. brachiocephalic vein, superior vena cava, and R. tracheal bronchus.

10) e – See #3 answer explanation.

11) c – See #1 answer explanation.

12) e – See #9 answer explanation. The left vagus nerve passes anterior to the arch of the aorta.

13) b – The phrenic nerves travel behind the brachiocephalic veins. They pass anterior to all other major vascular structures of the thorax. The R. vagus nerve passes anterior to the R. subclavian artery.

14) b – The right phrenic nerve descends the neck lateral to the R. common carotid artery, just behind the right internal jugular vein. It passes anterior to the R. subclavian artery, posterior to the right brachiocephalic vein, and anterior to the superior vena cava. It continues inferiorly across the anterior surface of the right lateral pericardium.

15) d – The R. vagus nerve descends the neck lateral to the R. common carotid artery. It crosses anterior to the R. subclavian artery and gives off the R. recurrent laryngeal nerve. The R. recurrent laryngeal loops around the inferior aspect of the brachiocephalic artery to ascend the thorax posterior to this vessel. It then travels up the neck medial to the R. common carotid artery to reach the larynx. The L. recurrent laryngeal nerve loops around the inferior aspect of the aorta.

16) d – The L. vagus nerve descends the neck medial to the L. internal jugular vein and lateral to the

L. common carotid artery. It passes anterior to the L. subclavian artery and gives off the L. recurrent laryngeal nerve. The L. recurrent laryngeal passes inferior and then posterior to the arch of the aorta to ascend the thorax posterior to this vessel. It then travels up the neck medial to the L. common carotid artery to reach the larynx. As the L. vagus enters the abdomen, it becomes the anterior vagal trunk.

17) c – See #16 answer explanation.

18) a – See #15 answer explanation. As the R. vagus enters the abdomen, it becomes the posterior vagal trunk.

19) b – See #4 answer explanation. The left phrenic nerve descends the neck just behind the left internal jugular vein.

"Life is what happens while you are busy making other plans."

– John Lennon

CLINICAL CORRELATION

Protection of the abdominal viscera is quite a responsibility to place on the anterior abdominal musculature. Protection of the posterior abdomen is aided by the presence of bones: the vertebral column and floating ribs. In order to accomplish their protective mission, the muscles of the anterior abdominal wall are armed with certain reflexes.

When the skin of the abdomen is unexpectedly contacted, especially by a sharp object or significant blow, touch receptors of the skin are stimulated. An impulse is generated and sent via the lower intercostal and subcostal nerves. This impulse travels up the spinal cord to reach a reflex center in the brain. An efferent reflex impulse is generated and sent back down the spinal cord to the intercostal nerves. The intercostal nerves then stimulate the abdominal muscles to instantaneously contract. The contraction serves as a shield to repel the possible traumatic blow. This protective reflex and its subsequent abdominal wall contraction occur many times each day for most people. When these "false alarms" occur, the individual experiencing the abdominal contraction does not consciously realize it is happening. This abdominal reflex is a very effective mechanism for protecting the abdominal contents while permitting a high degree of flexibility. During the course of a lifetime, the average person experiences numerous traumatic blows to the abdomen. Rarely is there significant internal injury to viscera of the abdomen.

Another involuntary reflex involving the lower intercostal nerves serves to protect an already injured visceral organ. This occurs in situations where an abdominal organ is traumatically injured or becomes diseased, inflamed, or ruptured. Examples include a traumatic blow, peritonitis, appendicitis, cholangitis, or pancreatitis. The Greek suffix *-itis* signifies *inflammation.* To create a word which designates a particular inflammatory disease process, the suffix is often coupled with the word root of the tissue or structure that is inflamed. Appendicitis is inflammation of the appendix. Pharyngitis is inflammation of the pharynx. A chart of some of the more common inflammatory disease states follows this clinical correlation.

The peritoneum is the serous membrane that surrounds the abdominal and pelvic cavities. It consists of a visceral and parietal component. The visceral peritoneum lines the outer surface of the abdominal viscera and their supporting structures. It is innervated by the vagus nerve. Its innervation is thus visceral or autonomic in nature. The parietal peritoneum lines the inner surface of the abdominal wall and is innervated by branches of the lower intercostal nerves. Its innervation is somatic in nature. Visceral pain of the abdomen is frequently caused by distension or dilation of a hollow visceral organ. This is often the result of a process that halts the normal passage of consumed contents through the digestive tract. Such processes include infections, strangulated hernias, mechanical bowel obstructions, gallstones, abscesses, and tumors. The pain is dull, vague, and nonspecific. It is frequently crampy and located near the umbilicus, even though the diseased organ may be far removed from this location. As opposed to distension, there is little if any visceral pain produced by an organ as a result of surgical incisions, pinching, cold, or heat.

The parietal peritoneum, by contrast, is extremely sensitive to distension, stretch, touch, pinching, and cutting. The somatic pain relayed by the lower intercostal nerve branches can be very intense and specific in location.

Typically, the process starts with a hollow viscus that is either directly damaged or has the digestive passage distal to it blocked. As a result of the blockage, the viscus becomes distended, the visceral peritoneum becomes distended, and visceral afferent signals are conducted by autonomic afferent fibers. The patient feels a dull, crampy, generalized pain of the abdomen. As the process advances, the organ may distend further, may involve other organs, or the organ may rupture. This progression causes the parietal peritoneum in that vicinity to also distend. Afferent somatic pain is then relayed by way of the lower intercostal nerves and their branches. The patient feels a specific, localized, often intense pain.

Once these somatic pain afferents of the lower intercostal nerves are stimulated, they cause a reflexive involuntary contraction of muscles of the abdominal wall. When a particular intercostal nerve is "alerted" by somatic pain receptors of the parietal peritoneum, the nerve reflexively stimulates the abdominal muscles it supplies, causing their contraction. In some instances, the area of parietal peritoneal irritation may be localized. Inflammation of the gallbladder or appendix, for instance, may be localized to the right upper abdomen or right lower abdomen, respectively. The involved intercostal nerves cause a reflex contraction of the specific area of muscle which overlies the diseased area. This provides a protective shield over the injured viscera. In other instances, such as diffuse peritonitis, the entire anterior abdominal wall may be intensely contracted and rigid.

This involuntary abdominal muscle contraction as a result of somatic afferent stimulation of the lower intercostal nerves is called **guarding**. It may be localized or generalized, depending on the degree of severity of the disease process. In addition to its protective role, guarding serves as an important diagnostic tool. An elderly patient with fever, elevated white blood cell count, and guarding of the left lower quadrant will initially be thought to have diverticulitis. The right diagnostic tests can then be ordered to rule this in or rule this out. Knowing where to start is extremely important, as it saves

time. This could mean the difference in providing the proper treatment before the disease process is too far advanced.

In the days before widespread access to radiologic studies and lab tests, guarding was an invaluable diagnostic tool. The diagnosis of appendicitis would be made based on the presence of fever, right lower abdominal pain, and guarding. If medical facilities were available, the patient would be rushed to the operating room for a potentially life-saving appendectomy.

FIGURE 11.11

INFLAMMATION (Disease)	STRUCTURE THAT IS INFLAMED	LAGNIAPPE (A little something extra)
Appendicitis	Appendix	appendectomy is performed as soon as the diagnosis of appendicitis is made.
Arteritis	Specific for arteries	this word may be used to describe a specific artery or a generalized disease process involving all the arteries.
Arthritis	Joint	*arthr(o)-* is a combining word form that means *joint*.
Bronchitis	Bronchi of the lungs	a bronchus is a passageway in the lungs through which air travels.
Bursitis	Bursa	a bursa is a sac-like fluid-filled cavity located in areas where friction occurs, such as joints.
Cellulitis	Skin	although usually associated with inflammatory conditions of skin, *cellulitis* is actually a more generalized term describing inflammation of cells that make up the soft tissues and connective tissues of the body.
Cholangitis	Bile duct of gallbladder	*chol(o)-* is a combining word form that refers to *bile*. A cholecystectomy is surgical removal of the gallbladder.
Cystitis	Bladder	*cyst(o)-* is a combining word form that refers to the *bladder*.
Diverticulitis	A diverticulum	a diverticulum is an outward outpouching of mucosa through a defect in the outer smooth muscle layer of a visceral organ. Diverticulitis is almost always describing inflammation of diverticula of the large colon.
Encephalitis	Brain	*encephal(o)-* is a combining word form that refers to the *brain*. This can be further broken down to *en-*, which is a Greek combining word form that means *in*, and *cephal(o)-*, which is a Greek combining word form which means *head*.
Enteritis	Intestines	*enter(o)-* is a combining word form that refers to the *intestines*.
Epiglottitis	Epiglottis	life-threatening due to potential for complete airway closure.
Esophagitis	Esophagus	an inflammatory condition of the esophagus, frequently the result of acidic gastric reflux.
Fascitis	Fascia	fascia is a sheet of fibrous connective tissue which assists in holding everything together.
Gastritis	Stomach	*gastr(o)-* is a combining word form that refers to the *stomach*.
Gastroenteritis	Stomach and intestines	an inflammatory condition in which both the stomach and intestines are affected.
Glossitis	Tongue	*gloss(o)-* is a combining word form that refers to the *tongue*.
Hepatitis	Liver	*hepat(o)-* is a combining word form that refers to the *liver*. Most people equate hepatitis with a viral disease. Although many cases are viral in nature, any disease process which causes inflammation of the liver is a "hepatitis."
Laryngitis	Structures of larynx	inflammation of laryngeal muscles, vocal cords, and/or other laryngeal structures makes vocalization difficult.
Meningitis	Meninges	the *meninges* are formed by 3 membranes surrounding the brain and spinal cord: *dura mater, arachnoid, and pia mater*.
Myocarditis	Heart	*my(o)-* is a combining word form that means *muscle*; *cardi(o)* is a combining word form that means *heart*.
Nephritis	Kidneys	*nephr(o)-* is a combining word form that refers to the *kidney*.
Neuritis	Nerves	may be used to describe a specific nerve or a disease process involving all the nerves.
Ophthalmitis	Eyeball	*ophthalm(o)-* is a combining word form that refers to *eye*.
Osteitis	Bone	*oste(o)-* is a combining word form that means *bone*.
Otitis	Ear	*ot(o)-* is a combining word form that refers to the *ear*.
Pancreatitis	Pancreas	can quickly become life-threatening.
Pericarditis	Pericardium	the pericardium is the serous membrane which surrounds the heart and bases of the great vessels.
Peritonitis	Peritoneum	the peritoneum is the serous membrane which lines the abdominal and pelvic cavities.
Pharyngitis	Structures of pharynx	a common "sore throat." Like any inflammatory condition, it can become severe.
Sinusitis	Sinuses	the sinuses are open cavities found in skull bones.
Tonsillitis	Tonsils	recurrent cases may lead to *tonsillectomy*.
Vasculitis	Blood vessels	may be used to describe a specific blood vessel or generalized disease process involving all the blood vessels.

This table is by no means complete. Every living tissue in the body can become inflamed and therefore may be associated with an "itis" to describe the disease process.

SUMMARY OF CHAPTER BOXES

1) Intercostal nerves are colored red in the poster because they supply muscles that function in respiration, thus oxygenating the blood and keeping it red.

2) **EX = IN** and **IN = EX.** *Ex*ternal intercostal muscles predominantly function in *in*spiration and their fibers run *back* to front. They are located in *back* of the thorax. *In*ternal intercostals predominantly function in *ex*piration and their fibers run *front* to back. They are located in *front* of the thorax.

3) Individuals in respiratory distress fixate their upper extremities. This allows upper extremity muscles to "work backwards" as accessory muscles of respiration.

4) The "atypical" intercostal nerves are shown on subjects left in poster: 1st (small, noncontributory), 2nd and 3rd (intercostobrachial n. instead of lateral cutaneous branches), 12th (*sub*costal, not *inter*costal n.). "Typical" intercostal nerves are on subjects right: 4th (represents first 6 intercostals – except for intercostobrachial n., remain confined to thorax), 7th (represents lower 6 – eventually leave thorax to supply muscles and skin of abdominal wall).

5) Sympathetic chain = sympathetic freeway
   Spinal nerve = crossing road
   White rami communicans = on-ramp
   Gray rami communicans = off-ramp

6) An intercostal nerve travels behind the inferior border of the superior rib of an intercostal space to innervate structures of that intercostal space, which is **below** it. Spinal nerves generally supply tissues located **below** their level of origination.

7) **VAN** = vein (superior), artery (intermediate), nerve (inferior) = neurovascular bundle = cara*van* traveling through body.

8) **HALF AND HALF:** top 6 intercostal nerves confined to thorax. Bottom 6 eventually leave to supply abdominal wall.

9) Increase intra-abdominal pressure = transversus abdominis, obliques.
   Support contents = transversus abdominis, obliques.
   Flexion/rotation of spine = rectus abdominis, obliques.

10) The two **PHRENIC** nerves pass **ANTERIOR** to **ALL** structures associated with the heart and great vessels **EXCEPT** the proximal **VENOUS** structures (R. and L. brachiocephalic veins).

11) **Brachiocephalic artery** = side view of **horses neck** (R. common carotid artery = ears, R. subclavian artery = snout) R. vagus n. travels down just lateral to the ear (R. common carotid), passes anterior to the snout (R. subclavian) and lassos the neck (brachiocephalic) with the R. recurrent laryngeal n.

12) 1) Look in mirror: external jugular v. = crude representation of lateral location of internal jugular v.
    2) Feel medial location of carotid pulse.
    3) Note trachea (and larynx) is most medial. R. vagus descends the neck between R. internal jugular v. and R. common carotid a. The R. recurrent laryngeal is traveling to the larynx, so it ascends the neck medial to the R. common carotid a. (R. vagus descends on one side of common carotid [lateral], R. recurrent ascends on other side [medial]).

13) $V_1A_2G_3U_4S_5 = C_1L_2O_3C_4K_5 = S_1C_2R_3E_4W_5$ As the vagus nerves descend into the abdomen, consider them rotating in a *clock*wise fashion, similar to a *screw* being screwed into a piece of wood. The R. vagus becomes the posterior vagal trunk. The L. vagus becomes the anterior vagal trunk.

14) Not to be outdone by its right-sided sibling, the L. vagus decides to lasso more than just an artery. It lassos the whole aortic arch with its L. recurrent laryngeal nerve!

15) The phrenic nerves are "in a hurry" to reach and supply the diaphragm. The only thoracic vascular structures they pass behind are the **brachiocephalic veins.** The vagus nerves, on the other hand, must provide parasympathetic innervation to these thoracic structures. They therefore get more involved. The R. vagus travels posterior to the **R. brachiocephalic vein, superior vena cava, and R. tracheal bronchus.** The L. vagus is posterior to the **L. brachiocephalic vein, pulmonary trunk, and L. tracheal bronchus.**

END OF CHAPTER TEST

Time for Exam = 50 minutes.
For questions 1-35, choose the single best answer.

_____1) Which muscles share a common membrane with the innermost intercostal muscles to form the most internal layer of intercostal muscle?
   a) transversus thoracis muscle
   b) transversus abdominis muscle
   c) internal intercostal muscles
   d) internal oblique muscles
   e) none of the above

_____2) The subcostal muscles are innervated by the
   a) intercostal nerves
   b) phrenic nerve
   c) dorsal rami branches
   d) suprascapular nerve
   e) none of the above

_____3) As it descends the thorax, the right phrenic nerve passes immediately anterior to which vessel?
   a) aorta
   b) left subclavian artery
   c) right brachiocephalic vein
   d) left common carotid artery
   e) none of the above

_____4) Which intercostal nerves often contribute branches to form the intercostobrachial nerve?
   a) third
   b) fourth
   c) both a and b
   d) first
   e) none of the above

_____5) Within a particular intercostal space, where is the neurovascular bundle located?
   a) behind the inferior border of the inferior rib
   b) behind the superior border of the inferior rib
   c) between the internal and external intercostal muscles within the intercostal space
   d) behind the superior border of the superior rib
   e) none of the above

_____6) The left phrenic nerve courses posterior to the
   a) aorta
   b) left subclavian artery
   c) left brachiocephalic vein
   d) right common carotid artery
   e) none of the above

_____7) Which nerves innervate skin that borders skin supplied by the lateral cutaneous branch of an intercostal nerve?
   a) thoracodorsal nerve
   b) long thoracic nerve
   c) both a and b
   d) anterior cutaneous branch of intercostal nerve
   e) none of the above

_____8) Which nerves could supply the internal oblique muscle?
   a) dorsal rami branches
   b) subcostal nerve
   c) intercostobrachial nerve
   d) long thoracic nerve
   e) none of the above

_____9) Vagus nerve branches that supply thoracic structures include the
   a) recurrent laryngeal nerve
   b) superior laryngeal nerve
   c) internal laryngeal nerve
   d) all the above
   e) none of the above

_____10) Which nerve does the intercostobrachial nerve combine with?
   a) median nerve
   b) musculocutaneous nerve
   c) medial pectoral nerve
   d) medial antebrachial cutaneous nerve
   e) none of the above

_____11) The fourth intercostal nerve travels between which two muscles?
    a) internal and external intercostal muscles
    b) transversus abdominis and internal oblique muscles
    c) both a and b
    d) transversus thoracis and innermost intercostal muscles
    e) none of the above

_____12) Around which blood vessel does the right recurrent laryngeal nerve loop beneath prior to its ascent up the neck?
    a) brachiocephalic artery
    b) R. brachiocephalic vein
    c) arch of aorta
    d) R. common carotid artery
    e) none of the above

_____13) The subcostal nerve is
    a) a branch of the phrenic nerve
    b) a dorsal ramus branch
    c) a L1 ventral ramus branch
    d) the twelfth intercostal nerve
    e) none of the above

_____14) Named sub-branches of the lateral cutaneous branch of an intercostal nerve include the
    a) medial sub-branch
    b) anterior sub-branch
    c) inferior sub-branch
    d) superior sub-branch
    e) none of the above

_____15) While in the thorax, the left vagus nerve passes posterior to the
    a) brachiocephalic artery
    b) L. brachiocephalic vein
    c) arch of aorta
    d) all the above
    e) none of the above

_____16) Which nerves are directly responsible for providing sympathetic input to intercostal nerves?
    a) gray ramus communicans
    b) white ramus communicans
    c) both a and b
    d) cervical spinal nerve ventral rami
    e) none of the above

_____17) Which of the following are true concerning the relative anatomic relationship between the three structures of the intercostal neurovascular bundle?
    a) The vein is intermediate in location.
    b) The artery is most inferior.
    c) The nerve is most superior.
    d) All of the above
    e) None of the above

_____18) As it descends the thorax, the left phrenic nerve passes immediately anterior to which of the following structures?
    a) left brachiocephalic vein
    b) superior vena cava
    c) left pulmonary artery
    d) all the above
    e) none of the above

_____19) Which statements about the T1 ventral ramus are true?
    a) Most of it contributes to the cervical plexus.
    b) It is responsible for the first intercostal nerve.
    c) Both a and b
    d) Its branches contribute to the intercostobrachial nerve.
    e) None of the above

_____20) Which muscles have fibers which merge with those of the internal oblique muscle?
    a) innermost intercostal muscles
    b) internal intercostal muscles
    c) transversus thoracis muscle
    d) external intercostal muscles
    e) none of the above

_____21) In the thorax, the right vagus nerve passes anterior to the
    a) R. internal jugular vein
    b) R. brachiocephalic vein
    c) superior vena cava
    d) R. tracheal bronchus
    e) none of the above

_____22) The seventh intercostal nerve travels between which two muscles?
   a) internal and innermost intercostal muscles
   b) transversus abdominis and internal oblique muscles
   c) both a and b
   d) internal and external intercostal muscles
   e) none of the above

_____23) Which muscles have fibers of the same embryonic derivation as the transversus abdominis muscle?
   a) internal oblique muscles
   b) innermost intercostal muscles
   c) internal intercostal muscles
   d) transversus thoracis muscle
   e) none of the above

_____24) While in the neck, the left vagus nerve is medial to the
   a) L. common carotid artery
   b) L. subclavian artery
   c) L. internal jugular vein
   d) L. brachiocephalic vein
   e) none of the above

_____25) Which tissue does the intercostobrachial nerve innervate?
   a) skin of the medial arm
   b) intercostal muscles
   c) muscles of the shoulder girdle
   d) skin of the posterior chest wall
   e) none of the above

_____26) As it descends the thorax, the right vagus nerve passes posterior to which of the following structures?
   a) arch of the aorta
   b) R. tracheal bronchus
   c) R. subclavian artery
   d) all the above
   e) none of the above

_____27) Which nerve is typically the first branch of an intercostal nerve?
   a) anterior sub-branch
   b) gray ramus communicans
   c) anterior cutaneous branch
   d) lateral cutaneous branch
   e) none of the above

_____28) Which muscles have fibers which merge with those of the external intercostal muscle?
   a) external oblique muscles
   b) rectus abdominis muscle
   c) transversus abdominis muscle
   d) internal oblique muscles
   e) none of the above

_____29) The left vagus nerve courses immediately anterior to the
   a) brachiocephalic artery
   b) L. tracheal bronchus
   c) pulmonary trunk and/or L. pulmonary artery
   d) all the above
   e) none of the above

_____30) The serratus posterior inferior muscle is innervated by
   a) the long thoracic nerve
   b) dorsal rami branches
   c) the thoracodorsal nerve
   d) intercostal nerves
   e) none of the above

_____31) Which statements concerning the cutaneous innervation of thoracic dorsal rami are true?
   a) They usually supply skin which is more medial than skin supplied by the dorsal ramus of the spinal segment immediately above their spinal segment of origination.
   b) They usually supply skin which is below or inferior to their spinal segment level of origin.
   c) Both a and b
   d) They usually supply skin which is above or superior to their spinal segment level of origin.
   e) None of the above

_____32) Around which blood vessel does the left recurrent laryngeal nerve loop beneath prior to its ascent up the neck?
   a) brachiocephalic artery
   b) L. brachiocephalic vein
   c) arch of aorta
   d) L. common carotid artery
   e) none of the above

____33) To reach the surface of the torso, what muscles must the lateral cutaneous branch of an intercostal nerve travel through?
    a) innermost intercostal
    b) internal intercostal
    c) both a and b
    d) transversus thoracis
    e) none of the above

____34) The rectus abdominis muscle is innervated by the
    a) intercostobrachial nerve
    b) upper subscapular nerve
    c) dorsal rami branches
    d) intercostal nerves
    e) none of the above

____35) Which spinal nerves carry sympathetic postganglionic fibers?
    a) cervical
    b) thoracic
    c) sacral
    d) all of the above
    e) none of the above

For questions 36-50, use the following directions:
a.......1,2,3 are correct
b.......1,3 are correct
c.......2,4 are correct
d.......only 4 is correct
e.......all are correct

____36) Which statements about typical branches of the lower nine intercostal nerves are true?
1. The lateral cutaneous branch is usually the first branch.
2. Cutaneous innervation of the anterior sub-branch of the lateral cutaneous branch borders that of the anterior cutaneous nerve.
3. They supply members of the erector spinae group of muscles.
4. Cutaneous innervation of the posterior sub-branch of the lateral cutaneous branch borders that of dorsal rami branches.

____37) Which vascular structures are located between the L. vagus and L. recurrent laryngeal nerves?
1. the L. brachiocephalic vein
2. the brachiocephalic artery
3. the L. internal jugular vein
4. the L. common carotid artery

____38) Muscles innervated by intercostal nerves include the
1. serratus posterior superior
2. pyramidalis
3. subcostal muscles
4. serratus anterior

____39) Which anatomic relationships are correct concerning the phrenic and vagus nerves and their branches?
1. The L. recurrent laryngeal nerve ascends the neck medial to the L. common carotid artery.
2. The L. vagus nerve passes anterior to the brachiocephalic artery.
3. The R. phrenic nerve passes anterior of the R. subclavian artery.
4. The L. phrenic nerve passes anterior to the L. brachiocephalic vein.

____40) Which statements about external intercostal muscles are true?
1. In the lower thorax, fibers blend with those of the external oblique muscle.
2. They are innervated by thoracic ventral rami.
3. They are present in the posterior 4/5 of the upper thorax.
4. They slant anterior as they travel from one rib to the rib below.

____41) Which statements about the R. vagus nerve are true?
1. It becomes the posterior vagal trunk.
2. It descends the neck medial to the R. common carotid artery.
3. It passes anterior to the R. subclavian artery.
4. Its recurrent laryngeal branch passes inferior and posterior to the arch of the aorta.

_____42) Which statements about the intercostobrachial nerve are true?
    1. It combines with the medial brachial cutaneous nerve.
    2. It is formed by branches equivalent to the lateral cutaneous branches of the lower intercostal nerves.
    3. The second intercostal nerve frequently contributes to its formation.
    4. The third intercostal nerve frequently contributes to its formation.

_____43) Tissues which may be supplied by intercostal nerves include the
    1. skin of the abdomen
    2. abdominal wall musculature
    3. skin of the back
    4. skin of the medial forearm

_____44) Which statements about the R. phrenic nerve are correct?
    1. It passes anterior to the R. brachiocephalic vein.
    2. It descends the neck in close proximity to the R. internal jugular vein.
    3. It passes posterior to the R. subclavian artery.
    4. It passes anterior to the superior vena cava.

_____45) Which statements about internal intercostal muscles are true?
    1. They are innervated by thoracic dorsal rami.
    2. They share a common membrane with the transversus thoracis muscle.
    3. They predominately function in inspiration.
    4. They slant posterior as they travel from one rib to the rib below.

_____46) Which vascular structures are located between the R. vagus and R. recurrent laryngeal nerves?
    1. the R. brachiocephalic vein
    2. the R. common carotid artery
    3. the R. internal jugular vein
    4. the brachiocephalic artery

_____47) Which statements concerning gray rami communicans are true?
    1. They carry fibers which are leaving the sympathetic chain.
    2. They carry fibers which are entering the intercostal nerve.
    3. They are associated with spinal nerves throughout the length of the spinal cord.
    4. They are one of the first branches of an intercostal nerve.

_____48) Which statements about the L. phrenic nerve are correct?
    1. It descends the neck medial to the L. common carotid artery.
    2. It passes anterior to the pulmonary trunk/L. pulmonary artery.
    3. It passes posterior to the L. subclavian artery.
    4. It passes posterior to the L. brachiocephalic vein.

_____49) Which statements about the first intercostal nerve are true?
    1. Most if its vental ramus of origin contributes to the cervical plexus.
    2. It is responsible for innervating skin of the first intercostal space.
    3. It travels in the costal groove beneath the superior border of the second rib.
    4. In the costal groove, it is inferior to the first intercostal artery.

_____50) Which statements are correct concerning the L. vagus nerve?
    1. It descends the neck lateral to the L. internal jugular vein.
    2. It becomes the anterior vagal trunk.
    3. Its recurrent laryngeal branch passes inferior and posterior to the brachiocephalic artery.
    4. It passes anterior to the L. subclavian artery.

END OF CHAPTER TEST: Answers and Explanations

1) a – There are three layers of intercostal muscle. The innermost layer is formed by three separate muscles that share a common membrane. These include the transversus thoracis, innermost intercostal, and subcostal muscles. The next layer of muscle is formed by the internal intercostal muscles. The third and outer layer is formed by the external intercostal muscles.

2) a – The intercostal nerves are thoracic ventral rami branches. The subcostal muscles share a common membrane with the innermost intercostal and transversus thoracis muscles to form the deepest layer of intercostal muscle. The phrenic nerve (C3, C4, C5) supplies the diaphragm. The suprascapular nerve is a branch of the upper trunk of the brachial plexus. It supplies the supraspinous and infraspinous muscles.

3) e – The right phrenic nerve descends the neck just behind the right internal jugular vein, passes anterior to the right subclavian artery, posterior to the right brachiocephalic vein, and crosses the anterior surface of the right lateral pericardium. The left phrenic nerve passes anterior to the arch of the aorta.

4) a – The first intercostal nerve is small because the first rib is small. More importantly, the majority of the T1 ventral ramus contributes to the brachial plexus. The lower trunk of the brachial plexus is formed by ventral rami roots from C8 and T1. The intercostobrachial nerve is formed by what is the equivalent to the lateral cutaneous branch from both the second and third intercostal nerves. The second intercostal nerve is more consistent in this contribution to the intercostobrachial, but the third intercostal frequently also contributes. The intercostobrachial nerve combines with a branch of the medial cord of the brachial plexus, the medial brachial cutaneous nerve, to supply skin of the medial arm.

5) e – The neurovascular bundle is composed of an intercostal nerve, artery, and vein. An intercostal neurovascular bundle travels in the costal groove behind the inferior border of the superior rib of a particular intercostal space. This can be remembered by considering that most spinal nerves supply tissues that are located *below* their level of origination. The intercostal nerves follow this rule. By traveling behind the inferior border of the superior rib, an intercostal nerve supplies tissues located in the intercostal space *below* it.

6) c – The left phrenic nerve descends the neck lateral to the left common carotid artery, passes anterior to the left subclavian artery, posterior to the left brachiocephalic vein, and anterior to the aortic arch, left vagus nerve, and left pulmonary artery/pulmonary trunk. It continues inferiorly across the anterior surface of the left lateral pericardium.

7) d – The lateral cutaneous branch originates from an intercostal nerve at the approximate level of the mid-axillary line. This represents the most lateral aspect of the torso. The lateral cutaneous nerve pierces the internal and external intercostal nerves to reach the subcutaneous tissue and divide into anterior and posterior sub-branches. The anterior sub-branch travels anterior and supplies skin that borders skin supplied by the anterior cutaneous nerve, the distal continuation of the intercostal nerve after the lateral cutaneous nerve is given off. The posterior sub-branch travels posterior to supply skin bordering skin supplied by dorsal rami branches. The thoracodorsal nerve is a branch of the posterior cord of the brachial plexus and supplies the latissimus dorsi muscle. The long thoracic nerve is formed by ventral rami branches from C5, C6, C7, and supplies the serratus anterior muscle. Neither nerve has cutaneous innervation.

8) b – The subcostal nerve could be considered the twelfth intercostal nerve. Because it is located behind the inferior border of the twelfth rib, it does not have a rib below it. It therefore is called the *sub*costal nerve as opposed to an *inter*costal nerve. The lower six intercostal

nerves, including the subcostal nerve, eventually leave the thorax to also supply skin and muscles of the anterior abdominal wall. This includes the internal oblique muscle. The intercostobrachial nerve is formed by branches of the second and third intercostal nerves. It combines with the medial brachial cutaneous nerve to supply skin of the medial arm. The long thoracic nerve is formed by ventral rami branches from C5, C6, C7, and supplies the serratus anterior muscle.

9) a – There are three major branches of the vagus nerve that supply thoracic structures. The superior cervical cardiac branch is formed by a coalition of vagus nerve branches that arise in the neck. It descends to contribute parasympathetic input to the cardiac plexus. The recurrent laryngeal nerve branches from the vagus in the thorax and ascends the neck to supply the larynx. On the way, it provides branches to the trachea, esophagus, and cardiac plexus. The inferior cardiac branch originates from the vagus while the vagus is in the thorax. It also provides parasympathetic input to the cardiac plexus. The innervation of the superior and internal laryngeal nerves is confined to the larynx.

10) e – See #4 answer explanation.

11) e – Because the innermost intercostal muscles do not extend as posterior as the internal intercostal muscles, an intercostal nerve initially travels on the internal membrane of an internal intercostal muscle as the nerve emerges from the spine. The nerve courses outward to reach the innermost intercostal muscle. It then continues distally between the internal and innermost intercostal muscles. The lower six intercostal nerves eventually leave the thorax to supply skin and muscles of the abdominal wall. These nerves travel across the abdomen between the transversus abdominis and internal oblique muscles. Fibers of the innermost intercostal and transversus abdominis are of the same embryonic derivation. Fibers of the internal intercostal and internal oblique merge with one another. Thus, by traveling between the innermost and internal intercostal muscles, and subsequently, the transversus abdominis and internal oblique muscles, the lower

six intercostal nerves are able to remain in the same muscle plane. Coincidently, muscle fibers of the external intercostals blend with those of the external oblique muscles.

12) a – The right vagus nerve descends the neck lateral to the R. common carotid artery. It passes anterior to the R. subclavian artery and gives off the R. recurrent laryngeal nerve. The R. recurrent passes inferior to the brachiocephalic artery to begin its ascent behind this vessel.

13) d – The subcostal nerve is formed by the T12 ventral ramus. It would otherwise be the twelfth intercostal nerve, except it does not have a rib inferior to it. *Inter*costal nerves travel behind the inferior border of the superior rib of a particular intercostal space. The *sub*costal nerve initially travels behind the inferior border of the twelfth rib.

14) b – See #7 answer explanation.

15) b – The left vagus nerve descends the neck between the L. internal jugular vein laterally and L. common carotid artery medially. It passes anterior to the arch of the aorta and posterior to the L. brachiocephalic vein, pulmonary trunk, and L. tracheal bronchus.

16) a – Preganglionic sympathetic cell bodies are located in the spinal cord at the T1-L2 levels. Preganglionic sympathetic fibers from these cell bodies exit the spinal cord with spinal nerves. In this case, the spinal nerve is an intercostal nerve. These fibers then leave the spinal nerve (intercostal nerve) in small nerves known as white rami communicans to enter the sympathetic chain. The sympathetic chain is not directly connected to the brain or spinal cord and must obtain its sympathetic input by some means. It is the white rami communicans that provide sympathetic input to the sympathetic chain. In other words, white rami communicans carry preganglionic sympathetic fibers that are leaving the intercostal nerve (spinal nerve) to enter the sympathetic chain. Because the preganglionic cell bodies are only located at the T1-L2 spinal cord levels, white rami communicans are only associated with spinal nerves that originate from the spinal cord at these levels.

This includes all twelve intercostal nerves and the L1 and L2 spinal nerves. By contrast, gray rami communicans carry sympathetic fibers that may have previously traveled a variable distance up or down the sympathetic chain and are now leaving the sympathetic chain to enter a spinal nerve. Because these fibers are capable of traveling up or down the sympathetic chain before leaving it, gray rami communicans are associated with spinal nerves throughout most of the length of the spinal cord. They are not confined to spinal nerves of the T1-L2 levels. It is the gray rami communicans that actually provide sympathetic innervation to the spinal nerve (intercostal nerve) and subsequently, the tissues supplied by the spinal nerve.

17) e – A neurovascular bundle is formed by a vein, artery, and nerve. These structures often have a consistent anatomic relationship relative to one another. An intercostal neurovascular bundle is no exception. From superior to inferior, the *v*ein is most superior, the *a*rtery is in an intermediate position, and the *n*erve is most inferior. Thus, from superior to inferior, the word *VAN* is spelled out. This may be remembered by considering a neurovascular bundle as a cara*van* traveling in different regions of the body. Instead of the superior and inferior direction, the relative relationships may involve the medial and lateral direction in neurovascular bundles of other regions of the body. Nevertheless, the same relative relationships exist: the vein is on one side, the artery is in an intermediate position, and the nerve is on the other side.

18) c – See #6 answer explanation.

19) b – See #4 answer explanation.

20) b – See #11 answer explanation.

21) e – The right vagus nerve descends the neck between the R. internal jugular vein laterally and R. common carotid artery medially. It passes anterior to the R. subclavian artery and posterior to the R. brachiocephalic vein, superior vena cava, and R. tracheal bronchus.

22) c – See #11 answer explanation.

23) b – See #11 answer explanation.

24) c – The left vagus nerve descends the neck between the L. internal jugular vein laterally and L. common carotid artery medially.

25) a – See #4 answer explanation.

26) b – See #21 answer explanation. The left vagus nerve passes anterior to the arch of the aorta.

27) b – Gray and white rami communicans are usually the first branches of intercostal nerves. They are the routes of communication between spinal nerves and the sympathetic chain. White and gray rami are found proximally, soon after the actual formation of the intercostal nerve.

28) a – See #11 answer explanation. Muscle fibers of the external intercostals blend with those of the external oblique muscles.

29) e – See #15 answer explanation.

30) d – The intercostal nerves are thoracic ventral rami branches. The serratus posterior superior muscle is supplied by the upper four intercostal nerves. The serratus posterior inferior muscle is supplied by the lower four intercostal nerves. The long thoracic nerve is formed by ventral rami branches from C5, C6, C7 and supplies the serratus anterior muscle. The thoracodorsal nerve is a branch of the posterior cord of the brachial plexus and supplies the latissimus dorsi muscle.

31) b – Thoracic dorsal rami usually innervate skin located below their spinal cord segment of origin. Although there is often a repetitive back and forth pattern in which one nerve supplies a medial area of skin and the next lowest nerve supplies a lateral area, there is no definite order of innervation for any particular random thoracic dorsal ramus and the nerve immediately above or below it.

32) c – The left vagus nerve descends the neck lateral to the L. common carotid artery. It passes anterior to the arch of the aorta and gives off the L. recurrent laryngeal nerve. The L. recurrent passes inferior to the aortic arch to begin its ascent behind this vessel.

33) b – The most internal layer of intercostal muscle is comprised of three separate muscles which share a common membrane: the transversus thoracis, innermost intercostal, and subcostal muscles. In the thorax, intercostal nerves travel between the innermost intercostal muscle on the deep side and internal intercostal muscle on the superficial side. To reach the surface and supply skin of the chest wall, the lateral cutaneous branch must pierce both the internal and external intercostal muscles.

34) d – The intercostal nerves are thoracic ventral rami branches. The lower six intercostal nerves eventually leave the thorax to also supply skin and muscles of the anterior abdominal wall. This includes the rectus abdominis muscle. The intercostobrachial nerve is formed by branches of the second and third intercostal nerves. It combines with the medial brachial cutaneous nerve to supply skin of the medial arm. The upper subscapular nerve is a branch of the posterior cord of the brachial plexus. Along with another posterior cord branch, the lower subscapular nerve, it supplies the teres major and subscapularis muscles.

35) d – See #16 answer explanation.

36) c – See #7 answer explanation. White and gray rami communicans are usually the first branches of intercostal nerves. They occur very proximal, soon after the actual formation of the intercostal nerve. They serve as the routes of communication between a spinal nerve (and thus, the central nervous system) and the sympathetic chain. Back muscles of the erector spinae group (spinalis, longissimus, and iliocostalis) are innervated by dorsal rami branches.

37) d – The L. vagus nerve descends the neck lateral to the L. common carotid artery. It crosses anterior to the L. subclavian artery and gives off the L. recurrent laryngeal nerve. The L. recurrent laryngeal travels posteriorly to loop around the inferior aspect of the arch of the aorta and ascend the thorax posterior to this vessel. It then travels up the neck medial to the L. common carotid artery to reach the larynx. The R. recurrent laryngeal nerve loops

around the inferior aspect of the brachiocephalic artery.

38) a – The serratus posterior superior is supplied by the upper four intercostal nerves. The lower six intercostal nerves eventually leave the thorax to supply muscles and skin of the abdominal wall. This includes the pyrimadalis muscle. The subcostal muscles share a common membrane with the innermost intercostal muscles and transversus thoracis, forming the most internal layer of intercostal muscles. The serratus anterior is innervated by the long thoracic nerve (C5, C6, C7).

39) b – The L. vagus nerve passes anterior to the arch of the aorta. The R. vagus nerve passes anterior to the R. subclavian artery. The only major thoracic vascular structures which the phrenic nerves travel behind are the brachiocephalic veins. They pass anterior to all other major vascular structures.

40) e – Fibers of the internal intercostal muscles blend with those of the internal oblique. The internal intercostal muscles slant posterior as they travel from one rib to the rib below.

41) b – The R. vagus nerve descends the neck medial to the R. internal jugular vein and lateral to the R. common carotid artery. It passes anterior to the R. subclavian artery and gives off the R. recurrent laryngeal nerve. The R. recurrent laryngeal passes inferior and then posterior to the brachiocephalic artery to ascend the neck. As the R. vagus enters the abdomen, it becomes the posterior vagal trunk.

42) e – See #4 answer explanation.

43) a – An intercostal nerve gives off a lateral cutaneous branch at the lateral aspect of the torso. This branch travels to the surface and divides into anterior and posterior sub-branches, which supply skin of the anterior and posterior torso, respectively. The lower six intercostal nerves eventually leave the thorax to supply skin and muscles of the abdominal wall. The intercostobrachial nerve is formed by what is the equivalent to the lateral cutaneous branch from both the second and third intercostal nerves. The intercostobrachial nerve combines

with a branch of the medial cord of the brachial plexus, the medial brachial cutaneous nerve, to supply skin of the medial arm. Skin of the medial forearm is supplied by another medial cord branch, the medial antebrachial cutaneous nerve.

44) c – The right phrenic nerve descends the neck lateral to the R. common carotid artery, just behind the right internal jugular vein. It passes anterior to the R. subclavian artery, posterior to the right brachiocephalic vein, and anterior to the superior vena cava. It continues inferiorly across the anterior surface of the right lateral pericardium.

45) d – Intercostal muscles are supplied by intercostal nerves, which are thoracic ventral rami. The transversus thoracis, subcostal muscles, and innermost intercostal muscles share a common membrane, forming the most internal layer of intercostal muscle. The predominant function of the *in*ternal intercostal muscles is forced *ex*piration. The predominant function of the *ex*ternal intercostal muscles is *in*spiration. IN = EX and EX = IN. The internal intercostal muscles slant posterior as they travel from one rib to the rib below. The external intercostal muscles slant anterior as they travel to the rib below.

46) c – The R. vagus nerve descends the neck lateral to the R. common carotid artery. It crosses anterior to the R. subclavian artery and gives off the R. recurrent laryngeal nerve. The R. recurrent laryngeal loops around the inferior aspect of the brachiocephalic artery to ascend the thorax posterior to this vessel. It then travels up the neck medial to the R. common carotid artery to reach the larynx.

47) e – See #16 answer explanation.

48) c – See #6 answer explanation.

49) d – The first intercostal nerve is small because the first rib is small. More importantly, the majority of the T1 ventral ramus contributes to the brachial plexus. The lower trunk of the brachial plexus is formed by ventral rami roots from C8 and T1. The intercostal neurovascular bundle is located behind the inferior border of the superior rib for a particular intercostal space. In this case, it would be the inferior border of the first rib. The skin over the first two or three intercostal spaces is largely supplied by supraclavicular nerves, which branch from the supraclavicular trunk of the cervical plexus.

50) c – The L. vagus nerve descends the neck medial to the L. internal jugular vein and lateral to the L. common carotid artery. It passes anterior to the L. subclavian artery and gives off the L. recurrent laryngeal nerve. The L. recurrent laryngeal passes inferior and then posterior to the arch of the aorta to ascend the neck. As the L. vagus enters the abdomen, it becomes the anterior vagal trunk.

"Many of life's failures are people who did not realize how close they were to success when they gave up."

– Thomas Edison

CHAPTER TWELVE

LUMBOSACRAL PLEXUS AND NERVES OF THE LOWER EXTREMITY

The lumbosacral plexus is responsible for innervation of the perineum and lower extremity. It is actually comprised of two nerve plexuses, the lumbar and sacral plexuses. These are formed by ventral rami of the lumbar and sacral spinal nerves, respectively. Because there is lumbar contribution to the sacral plexus, the two plexuses are often described as one, the lumbosacral plexus.

General patterns of innervation exist for nerves from each plexus. Those from the lumbar plexus supply skin and muscles of the front or anterior thigh. In fact, except for one cutaneous nerve, all nerves of the lumbar plexus are located above the knee. Nerves from the sacral plexus supply skin and muscles of the buttocks, perineum, posterior thigh, and tissues distal to the knee. This includes all muscles and most skin below the knee.

Although both plexuses contribute several nerves to the lower extremity, each plexus is the origin of two principal nerves of the lower extremity. These nerves are mixed, supplying both muscles and skin. The lumbar plexus is the origin of the obturator and femoral nerves. The sacral plexus is the origin of the common peroneal and tibial nerves, the two terminal branches of the sciatic nerve.

Before proceeding, the color code of the lumbosacral plexus in Figure 2 of the poster should be explained. As described shortly, the L2-L4 roots of the lumbar plexus divide into anterior and posterior divisions. Like the brachial plexus, the posterior divi-

sions are colored purple (**p**urple = **p**osterior). The anterior divisions are colored green. The coloring serves as a visual aid in identifying which lumbar plexus nerves are formed by anterior divisions and which are formed by posterior divisions. As mentioned, nerves of the lumbar plexus primarily innervate skin and muscles of the anterior thigh. Nerves of the sacral plexus supply the perineum, posterior thigh and most structures below the knee. Because they supply posterior structures of the lower extremity, the sacral plexus and nerves arising from it are colored purple (purple = posterior). To differentiate these nerves from those formed by lumbar posterior divisions, the lumbar plexus nerves assume the typical nerve color of yellow as they leave the lumbar plexus.

THE LUMBAR PLEXUS

The lumbar plexus is formed by ventral rami of the L1-L4 spinal roots. In addition, the T12 ventral ramus often contributes via a branch of communication with the L1 nerve (not drawn). Much of the lumbar plexus is actually contained within the substance of a muscle of the deep back, the psoas major. Thus, in reality, many of the nerves of the lumbar plexus will only be visualized after they exit the substance of the muscle.

Similar to trunks of the brachial plexus, the L2-L4 roots of the lumbar plexus divide into anterior and posterior divisions. These divisions, however, are not quite as physically uniform as those of the brachial plexus. The anterior divisions contribute branches to two nerves: the genitofemoral and obturator nerves. Likewise, the posterior divisions contribute branches to two nerves: the lateral femoral cutaneous and femoral nerves. Two other nerves are formed by branches from the L2-L4 levels, but these branches are not designated as either anterior or posterior. The accessory obturator nerve is less consistently present and is formed by branches from the L3 and L4 ventral rami, although the L2 ventral ramus may contribute. When present, the accessory obturator originates between the obturator (anterior division) and femoral (posterior division) nerves. Because of the ambiguity of its origin, it is not considered to be part of either division with any great certainty. Finally, the L4 ventral ramus produces a nerve before it divides into anterior and posterior divisions. This nerve combines with the entire L5 ventral ramus to form the lumbosacral trunk. The lumbosacral trunk represents the only lumbar contribution to the sacral plexus and will be discussed in more detail later.

FIGURE 12.1
LOWER EXTREMITY ANATOMY – MAJOR NERVES
Lateral View

(Reproduced and modified with permission from Brown, D.L.: Atlas of Regional Anesthesia, 1st ed. Philadelphia, W.B. Saunders, 1992.)

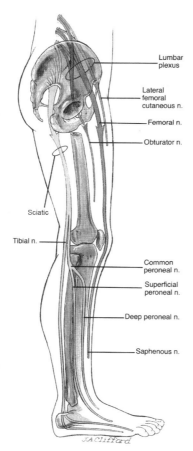

Lumbar plexus

Lateral femoral cutaneous n.

Femoral n.

Obturator n.

Sciatic

Tibial n.

Common peroneal n.

Superficial peroneal n.

Deep peroneal n.

Saphenous n.

J.A.Clifford

> **The 2 legs** are supplied by **2** lumbosacral plexuses. Each plexus is formed by **2** plexuses (lumbar and sacral). Each provides **2** primary nerves to the lower extremity (lumbar = obturator and femoral, sacral = common peroneal and tibial). Each of the L2-L4 levels of the lumbar plexus has **2** divisions (anterior and posterior). Each division supplies **2** nerves (anterior = genitofemoral and obturator, posterior = lateral femoral cutaneous and femoral). Finally there are **2** nerves that can arise from L2-L4 but are not formed by branches from anterior or posterior divisions (accessory obturator nerve and L4 branch to lumbosacral trunk).

As drawn on the subject's left in Figure 2, the ventral ramus of L1 gives several smaller branches and divides into the **iliohypogastric** (144) and **ilioinguinal** (142) **nerves**. Both of these continue around the side of the body to supply skin of the front lower abdomen and upper thigh. It should be noted that the L1 nerve is the lowest spinal nerve to supply tissue of the abdominal wall.

The iliohypogastric gives off a nerve known simply as the **lateral branch of the iliohypogastric** (143, 211). The lateral branch is drawn dotted in the main drawing to signify that the nerve runs back to supply skin of the lateral buttocks, as shown on the top right corner of Figure 3. Although it is primarily a cutaneous nerve, the iliohypogastric can provide innervation to the pyramidalis muscle of the lower abdominal wall. The **ilioinguinal nerve** (142) may give branches known as **anterior scrotal nerves** (141) that supply the skin of the anterior scrotum and adjacent thigh. In the female, these nerves are known as **anterior labial nerves** (141) and supply skin of the anterior labia majora and adjacent thigh.

The depiction of the anterior scrotal/labial nerves in Figure 2 of the poster is a good example of how the poster serves as an anatomic *chart* and not a true representation of actual anatomy. They appear to branch from the ilioinguinal nerve high in the abdomen. This is only because this is a convenient location to clearly demonstrate that these nerves do, in fact, branch from the ilioinguinal nerve. In reality, the anterior scrotal/labial nerves branch from the ilioinguinal much lower in the abdomen and/or groin.

Anterior Divisions of the Lumbar Plexus

A small **branch of the L1 ventral ramus** (145) continues down to combine with part of the **anterior division of the L2 ventral ramus** (140) to form the **genitofemoral nerve** (131). The genitofemoral travels down and gives off a genital and femoral branch.

In the male, the **genital branch of the genitofemoral nerve** (129) supplies the cremaster muscle, skin of the scrotum, and skin of the upper inner thigh bordering the scrotum. The cremaster extends from the lower aspect of the internal oblique muscle of the abdominal wall to the pubic tubercle of the pelvic bone. Its contraction elevates the testicle. In the female, the genital branch supplies skin of the labia majora and upper inner thigh. Both the anterior scrotal (labial) nerves of the ilioinguinal nerve and genital branch of the genitofemoral nerve supply skin of the same area. In some individuals, the genitofemoral may also give rise to anterior scrotal (labial) nerves.

The **femoral branch of the genitofemoral nerve** (72, **128**) follows the femoral artery and supplies skin on the upper anterior thigh. The *femoral branch* of the genitofemoral nerve should not be confused with the *femoral nerve*, which will be discussed later.

The remaining portion of the **anterior division of the L2 ventral ramus** (140) combines with the **anterior divisions of the L3** (138) and **L4** (136) **ventral rami** to form the **obturator nerve** (74, 119, **132**). The obturator travels down to supply muscles of the upper inner thigh which adduct the thigh. These muscles are collectively known as "groin muscles" by the lay public. The six muscles include the pectineus, external obturator, adductor brevis, adductor longus, gracilis, and the deep (anterior) portion of the adductor magnus muscles.

> The Function of the Obturator nerve is to **ADDUCT**.
>
> The word *adduct* has **6** letters. The obturator nerve supplies **6 muscles.**
>
> Half of these muscles have the word *adduct* in their names: adductor brevis, adductor longus, adductor magnus [deep (anterior) portion] muscles.
>
> The other half include the pectineus (shared with femoral nerve), obturator externus, and gracilis muscles.
>
> This is another example of **Half and Half.**

In addition to the obturator nerve, the pectineus muscle is also innervated by the femoral nerve. The pectineus adducts, but it also flexes the thigh. With this muscular motion, the dual nerve innervation seems logical. Just as the obturator nerve is the adduction nerve of the thigh, the femoral nerve, as later will be described, is the flexion nerve of the thigh.

The obturator externus muscle is also known as the external obturator muscle. It extends from the pubis and ischium of the pelvic bone to the top of the femur. The obturator externus turns the thigh in a lateral direction.

FIGURE 12.2
MUSCLES SUPPLIED BY OBTURATOR NERVE

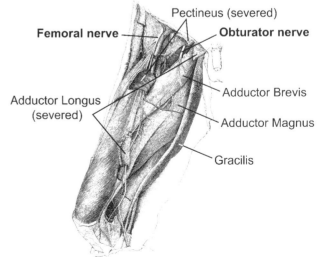

Pectineus (severed)

Femoral nerve — **Obturator nerve**

Adductor Brevis

Adductor Longus (severed)

Adductor Magnus

Gracilis

The adductor brevis and adductor longus muscles both originate on the pubis of the pelvic bone and insert on the back of the femur. The adductor longus originates higher on the pubis and inserts lower on the femur than the adductor brevis. Both muscles adduct and flex the thigh.

The gracilis muscle extends from the pubis of the pelvic bone an inserts on the medial shaft of the tibia. This muscle is named for the word *gracile,* which means *thin* or *slender.* The gracilis is indeed a long, thin muscle. It adducts the thigh. Unlike its other obturator comrades, it flexes the leg instead of the thigh.

Finally, the deep (anterior) portion of the adductor magnus muscle is innervated by the obturator nerve. It extends from the pubis and ischium of the pelvic bone and inserts on the back of the femur. The deep (anterior) portion adducts the thigh. The superficial (posterior) part of this muscle is supplied by the tibial portion of the sciatic nerve and extends the thigh. The obturator nerve may also give off **cutaneous branches** (74), which supply skin of the inner, medial thigh.

It is important to note the difference between thigh and leg. In anatomy, whenever the word *leg* is used, it is used with reference to the lower leg, below the knee. When the upper leg is referred to, it should be specified as *thigh.* It is easy to mistakenly confuse *leg* as referring to the entire lower extremity. Movements of the thigh are accomplished via the hip joint. From a standing position, flexion of the thigh would involve lifting one foot off the ground by raising the knee up and forward, toward the head. This movement is occurring by way of the hip joint. It should be remembered that flexion of a joint involves a decrease in the angle of the joint. In this case, the angle of the joint goes from 180° (full extension) to say 90° (if the thigh is raised high enough to be parallel to the ground). The thigh is then extended as the foot is lowered and the standing position is resumed. By contrast, movements of the leg are by way of the knee joint. In a standing position, flexion of the leg involves raising the heel of the foot upwards and backwards, toward the buttocks.

Although this description is not complex, effort should be made to note the difference between thigh versus leg and the joints from which they move. This is a frequent cause of confusion and missed exam questions.

In some individuals, the L3 and L4 ventral rami contribute branches that combine to form the **accessory obturator nerve** (130). The L2 ventral ramus may also contribute. When present, this nerve is formed by branches that originate between anterior division branches that form the obturator nerve and posterior division branches that form the femoral nerve. Because of the indefinite nature of the origination of these branches, they cannot reliably be said to belong to either anterior or posterior divisions. For this reason, the nerve is colored yellow in the poster instead of green or purple. When present, the accessory obturator nerve innervates the pectineus muscle. Because the pectineus is otherwise supplied by both the obturator and femoral nerves, it seems appropriate that it is alternatively innervated by a nerve that originates between fibers of these two nerves. The pectineus muscle

adducts and flexes the thigh. When the accessory obturator nerve is present, nerve innervation to the adducting muscles of the thigh can simply be considered as supplied by two smaller obturator nerves, as opposed to one larger nerve.

Posterior Divisions of the Lumbar Plexus

A portion of the **L2 posterior division** (139) combines with a portion of the **L3 posterior division** (137) to form the **lateral femoral cutaneous nerve** (134). This nerve travels down to divide into an **anterior branch** (71) and a **posterior branch** (70) that supply skin of the upper outer thigh, as depicted on the subject's right thigh in Figure 2.

Meralgia paresthetica is a condition involving numbness or burning pain in the upper outer thigh. It is due to injury or compression of the **lateral femoral cutaneous nerve**. This frequently occurs when pants or belts are worn too tight and the nerve is compressed at the waistline.

Branches from the **posterior divisions of the L2** (139), **L3** (137), and **L4** (135) roots combine to form the **femoral nerve** (120, **127**). The femoral nerve supplies eight muscles that flex the thigh and/or extend the leg. It also innervates skin of the anterior thigh and medial leg.

The general muscular motion resulting from femoral nerve stimulation is movement of the lower extremity in a forward or anterior direction. This includes flexion of the thigh at the hip and extension of the leg at the knee. The femoral nerve innervates eight muscles: the psoas major, iliacus, pectineus (shared with obturator nerve), sartorius, rectus femoris, vastus lateralis, vastus intermedius, and vastus medialis muscles.

The first four muscles function to flex the thigh. In other words, they decrease the angle of the hip, pulling the knee anteriorly and superiorly toward the head. This motion is used to lift the lower extremity off the ground when walking or running. This muscular action may also "work backwards" to lift the torso against a fixed lower extremity, as in the performance of a sit-up. While the torso is moving up during a sit-up, the angle of the hip joint is decreasing.

Collectively, the second four muscles form what is known as the quadriceps femoris muscle group. This is the large muscle mass of the anterior thigh, which is simply called the quadriceps by most people. Just as the word *biceps* denotes a two-headed muscle and the

FIGURE 12.3
ANTERIOR MUSCLES OF THIGH

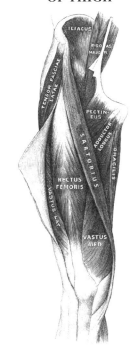

word *triceps* denotes a three-headed muscle, the word *quadriceps* denotes a four-headed muscle. The only difference is that the quadriceps femoris is actually formed by four separate muscles that share a common tendon distally. The four muscles include the rectus femoris, vastus lateralis, vastus intermedius, and vastus medialis muscles. With subtle differences, all four function to extend the leg (straighten the knee). The common tendon of the quadriceps femoris inserts on the patella and upper tibia. The word *vastus* means *great* and relates to the large size of these anterior thigh muscles. The words *lateralis, intermedius,* and *medialis* describe each muscle's location relative to the femur bone. The rectus femoris is the anterior, overlying muscle. It covers the vastus intermedius, with portions of the vastus medialis and vastus lateralis extending out from its medial and lateral border, respectively. The word *rectus* is used frequently in anatomy and means *straight*. The word *femoris* is made with reference to the femur.

Half and Half

The femoral nerve innervates 8 muscles. Half of these (4) flex the thigh. The other half (4) form the quadriceps femoris muscle group and extend the leg. Both functions move the lower extremity in an anterior or forward direction, such as occurs during a forward step.

Cutaneous responsibilities of the femoral nerve include the anterior thigh and medial leg. In the thigh, the femoral nerve gives rise to several **anterior femoral cutaneous nerves** (73). These supply skin of the anterior thigh. The femoral nerve is also the origin of another cutaneous nerve, the **saphenous nerve** (76, **92,** 103). The saphenous nerve branches from the femoral and continues inferiorly to become cutaneous at the approximate level of the knee. This is represented on the subject's right leg in Figure 2 (76). It gives off an **infrapatellar branch** (75), which supplies skin immediately below the front of the knee, and continues its descent along the inner (medial) side of the leg. Along this path, it gives several **cutaneous branches** (77). The saphenous travels distally along the medial aspect of the foot to end at the approximate level of the base of the great toe (103). The saphenous nerve, and thus, the femoral nerve, is the only nerve from the lumbar plexus that provides innervation below the knee. All other innervation of the leg, meaning below the knee, is provided by branches of the soon-to-be-discussed sciatic nerve of the sacral plexus.

The Responsibility of the Femoral Nerve is VAST

The femoral nerve innervates the vastus lateralis, vastus intermedius, and vastus medialis muscles. These three, along with the rectus femoris muscle, form the quadriceps femoris.

In addition, the femoral nerve is the only nerve of the lumbar plexus which has a branch (saphenous nerve) that travels below the knee to provide nerve innervation (cutaneous).

The final nerve of the lumbar plexus is a branch of the L4 ventral ramus that travels down to combine with the entire L5 ventral ramus. Their combination forms the **lumbosacral trunk** (133). The lumbosacral trunk descends to enter the sacral plexus. It represents the only lumbar contribution to the sacral plexus.

L5 = TRAITOR

The lowest lumbar spinal segment (L5) deserts its lumbar comrades and contributes its entire ventral ramus to the sacral plexus via the lumbosacral trunk. Because it leaves the spinal cord between the L5 vertebra and sacrum, it is no surprise that this spinal nerve was so easily recruited by its sacral counterparts. Not wanting to do it alone, this "traitor" (L5 ventral ramus) coerces a branch from the L4 ventral ramus, its nearest lumbar neighbor, to join in the formation of the lumbosacral trunk

---

FIGURE 12.4
LOWER EXTREMITY ANATOMY – MAJOR NERVES
Anterior Oblique View

(Reproduced and modified with permission from Brown, D.L.: Atlas of Regional Anesthesia, 1st ed. Philadelphia, W.B. Saunders, 1992.)

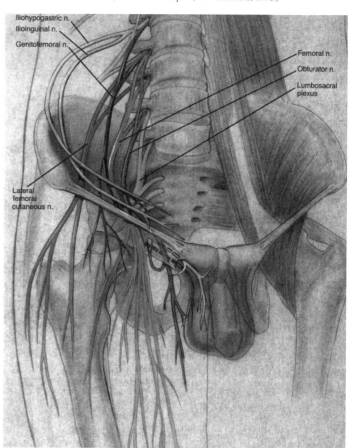

GOLF

This sport served as a helpful mnemonic in learning the bones of the carpus (wrist). It also is valuable in learning the lumbar plexus. Not only does golf require the services of the wrist, but the lumbar plexus is needed to walk out in the fairway to hit the ball.

G } anterior
O } divisions

L } posterior
F } divisions

G = genitofemoral nerve (L1, L2)

O = obturator nerve (L2, L3, L4)

L = lateral femoral cutaneous nerve (L2, L3)

F = femoral nerve (L2, L3, L4)

The obturator nerve is *the* motor nerve formed from anterior divisions (the cremaster muscle supplied by the genitofemoral nerve is not considered a voluntary muscle). The femoral nerve is *the* motor nerve created from posterior divisions. Both nerves also innervate skin. Both nerves are formed from the L2, L3, and L4 roots.

* The accessory obturator nerve may be formed by branches from the L2-L4 roots. The L4 root contributes a branch to the lumbosacral trunk. These branches are not considered anterior or posterior divisions

Lumbar Plexus = Golf plus two
1 2 3 4 5 6

GOLF + accessory obturator nerve + branch to lumbosacral trunk
1 2 3 4   5   6

FIGURE 12.5
CUTANEOUS NERVES OF LOWER ABDOMEN AND ANTERIOR THIGH

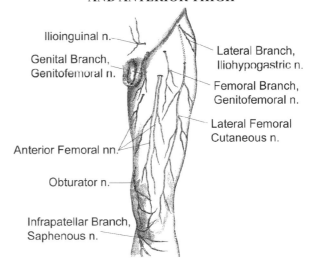

Dorsal Rami Branches

The final components of the lumbar spinal nerves that need to be discussed are the **superior cluneal nerves (63,** 212). They are cutaneous nerves which are formed by branches of the L1, L2, and L3 dorsal rami. In Figure 2 of the poster (63), the superior cluneal nerves are located on the opposite side of the spinal segments as the ventral rami branches which form the lumbar plexus. This is to signify that they are indeed branches of dorsal rami. In addition, they are colored purple. Purple equals posterior; dorsal rami travel posteriorly. The superior cluneal nerves can be seen in Figure 3 (212) as they emerge to supply skin of the upper buttock. The word *cluneal* refers to the buttocks. There are also middle and inferior cluneal nerves. The origin of these nerves will be covered shortly.

SPINAL CORD SEGMENT	VENTRAL RAMI BRANCHES *(makes up lumbar plexus)*		DORSAL RAMI BRANCHES
L1	1) iliohypogastric nerve 2) ilioinguinal nerve 3) branch to genitofemoral nerve		superior cluneal nerves
L2	**Anterior Division:**	1) branch to genitofemoral nerve 2) branch to obturator nerve	superior cluneal nerves
	Posterior Division:	1) br. to lateral femoral cutaneous n. 2) branch to femoral nerve	
	Additional:	possible br. to accessory obturator n.	
L3	**Anterior Division:**	1) branch to obturator nerve	superior cluneal nerves
	Posterior Division:	1) br. to lateral femoral cutaneous n. 2) branch to femoral nerve	
	Additional:	possible br. to accessory obturator n.	
L4	**Anterior Division:**	1) branch to obturator nerve	Unnamed dorsal rami branches
	Posterior Division:	1) branch to femoral nerve	
	Additional:	1) possible br. to accessory obturator n. 2) branch to lumbosacral trunk	

QUIZ 1
LUMBOSACRAL PLEXUS

Time for Quiz = 20 minutes.
For questions 1-12, choose the single best answer.

_____1) Muscles innervated by the obturator nerve generally function to
  a) adduct thigh
  b) extend thigh
  c) both a and b
  d) abduct thigh
  e) none of the above

_____2) Which statements are true regarding the anterior femoral cutaneous nerves?
  a) They are initially formed from branches of the posterior divisions of the L2, L3, L4 ventral rami.
  b) They supply skin of the anterior leg.
  c) Both a and b
  d) They are branches of the ilioinguinal nerve.
  e) None of the above

_____3) Which nerve innervates the psoas major muscle?
  a) femoral nerve
  b) iliohypogastric nerve
  c) obturator nerve
  d) ilioinguinal nerve
  e) none of the above

_____4) Which statements about the ilioinguinal nerve are true?
  a) It is formed by a branch of the L1 ventral ramus.
  b) It is the origin of the anterior scrotal nerves.
  c) Both a and b
  d) It supplies skin of the lateral buttocks.
  e) None of the above

_____5) Nerves that receive contribution from posterior division branches of the lumbar plexus include the
  a) lateral femoral cutaneous nerve
  b) anterior femoral cutaneous nerves
  c) both a and b
  d) posterior femoral cutaneous nerves
  e) none of the above

_____6) Which statements are true concerning the saphenous nerve?
  a) It is a branch of the obturator nerve.
  b) It supplies skin of the medial leg and foot.
  c) Both a and b
  d) It is a branch of the genitofemoral nerve.
  e) None of the above

_____7) Which nerve receives contribution from anterior division branches of the lumbar plexus roots?
  a) obturator nerve
  b) genitofemoral nerve
  c) both a and b
  d) femoral nerve
  e) none of the above

_____8) Which nerve innervates the pectineus muscle?
  a) femoral nerve
  b) obturator nerve
  c) both a and b
  d) lumbosacral trunk
  e) none of the above

_____9) Which statements are true regarding the femoral nerve?
  a) It is formed by branches of the anterior divisions of the L2, L3, L4 ventral rami.
  b) It is the origin of the posterior femoral cutaneous nerves.
  c) Both a and b
  d) It innervates the rectus femoris muscle.
  e) None of the above

_____10) Which of the following nerves are branches of the ilioinguinal nerve?
  a) femoral branch
  b) anterior scrotal nerves
  c) anterior femoral cutaneous nerves
  d) superior cluneal nerves
  e) none of the above

____11) Which nerve innervates the adductor brevis muscle?
- a) femoral nerve
- b) genitofemoral nerve
- c) obturator nerve
- d) accessory obturator nerve
- e) none of the above

____12) What is the lowest spinal nerve that supplies the abdominal wall?
- a) T11
- b) T12
- c) L1
- d) S1
- e) None of the above

For questions 13-20, use the following directions:
a.......1,2,3 are correct
b.......1,3 are correct
c.......2,4 are correct
d.......only 4 is correct
e.......all are correct

____13) Which statements are true concerning the femoral nerve?
1. It is the origin of the anterior femoral cutaneous nerves.
2. It is formed by branches of the posterior divisions of the L2, L3, and L4 ventral rami.
3. It is the origin of the saphenous nerve.
4. It is the only nerve of the lumbar plexus to supply skin of the leg.

____14) Which statements are true concerning the genitofemoral nerve?
1. It supplies the cremaster muscle.
2. It contributes sensory branches to the scrotum.
3. A branch of the L1 ventral ramus contributes to its formation.
4. A branch of the anterior division of the L2 ventral ramus contributes to its formation.

____15) Which nerves receive contribution from anterior division branches of the lumbar plexus roots?
1. femoral nerve
2. ilioinguinal nerve
3. iliohypogastric nerve
4. genitofemoral nerve

____16) Which muscles are innervated by the femoral nerve?
1. gracilis
2. cremaster
3. tensor fasciae latae
4. pectineus

____17) Which statements are true concerning the obturator nerve?
1. It supplies the gracilis muscle.
2. It supplies the obturator externus muscle.
3. It supplies the adductor brevis muscle.
4. It has no cutaneous innervation.

____18) The L1 ventral ramus contributes to which of the following nerves?
1. ilioinguinal nerve
2. genitofemoral nerve
3. iliohypogastric
4. anterior scrotal nerves

____19) Which statements concerning the saphenous nerve are true?
1. It supplies skin of the lateral side of the foot.
2. It is a branch of the femoral nerve.
3. It has both motor and sensory function.
4. It is the only lumbar plexus branch that supplies tissue of the leg.

____20) Which nerves are formed by posterior division branches of the lumbar plexus roots?
1. anterior femoral cutaneous nerves
2. lateral femoral cutaneous nerve
3. saphenous nerve
4. femoral branch of genitofemoral nerve

QUIZ 1: Lumbosacral Answers and Explanations

1) a – Muscles innervated by the obturator nerve generally function to adduct and flex the thigh.

2) a – The anterior femoral cutaneous nerves are branches of the femoral nerve. They therefore are formed by branches of the posterior divisions of the L2, L3, and L4 ventral rami. They supply skin of the anterior thigh, not the anterior leg. It should be remembered that the leg is the portion of the lower extremity between the knee and ankle. The thigh is that portion between the hip and knee. The ilioinguinal nerve serves as the origin of the anterior scrotal (labial) nerves.

3) a – The femoral nerve supplies skin of the anterior thigh and muscles that flex the thigh and extend the leg. These muscles include the psoas major, iliacus, pectineus (shared with obturator), sartorius, and the quadriceps femoris muscle group (consisting of rectus femoris, vastus lateralis, vastus intermedius, and vastus medialis muscles). In addition, the femoral nerve supplies skin of the medial leg and foot via the saphenous nerve.

4) c – It is the lateral branch of the iliohypogastric nerve that supplies skin of the lateral buttocks. The iliohypogastric is also a branch of the L1 ventral ramus.

5) c – The lateral femoral cutaneous nerve is formed by branches of the posterior divisions of the L2 and L3 ventral rami. The anterior femoral cutaneous nerves arise from the femoral nerve. They therefore are formed by branches of the posterior divisions of the L2, L3, and L4 ventral rami. The posterior femoral cutaneous nerve is formed by ventral rami branches from the S1, S2, and S3 spinal segments (sacral plexus).

6) b – The saphenous nerve is a branch of the femoral nerve. It therefore is formed by branches of the posterior divisions of the L2, L3, and L4 ventral rami. The saphenous nerve supplies skin of the medial leg and foot to the level of the great toe. The saphenous nerve is the only nerve originating from the lumbar plexus (via femoral nerve) that supplies tissue of the leg (below knee).

7) c – The obturator nerve is formed by anterior division branches of the L2, L3, and L4 ventral rami. The genitofemoral nerve is formed by a combination of a L1 ventral ramus branch and a branch of the anterior division of the L2 ventral ramus. The femoral nerve is formed by branches of the posterior divisions of the L2, L3, and L4 ventral rami.

8) c – The pectineus muscle has a dual innervation. It is innervated by the obturator nerve and the femoral nerve. When present, the accessory obturator nerve may supply it.

9) d – The femoral nerve is formed by branches of the posterior divisions of the L2, L3, and L4 ventral rami. It serves as the origin of the anterior femoral cutaneous nerves, which supply skin of the anterior thigh. The posterior femoral cutaneous nerve is formed by ventral rami branches from the S1, S2, and S3 spinal segments (sacral plexus). The femoral nerve supplies skin of the anterior thigh and muscles that flex the thigh and extend the leg. These muscles include the psoas major, iliacus, pectineus (shared with obturator or accessory obturator), sartorius, and the quadriceps femoris muscle group (consisting of rectus femoris, vastus lateralis, vastus intermedius, and vastus medialis muscles). In addition, it supplies skin of the medial leg and foot via the saphenous nerve.

10) b – The anterior scrotal (labial) nerves are branches of the ilioinguinal nerve. They therefore are derived from the L1 ventral ramus. They supply skin of the anterior scrotum (labia majora). There is no definite femoral branch of the ilioinguinal nerve. The genitofemoral nerve, on the other hand, is the origin of both genital and femoral branches. Genital branches of the genitofemoral nerve may also contribute anterior scrotal (labial) nerves. The anterior femoral cutaneous nerves arise from the femoral nerve, which is formed by branches of the posterior divisions of the L2, L3, and L4 ventral rami.

The superior cluneal nerves are formed by the L1, L2, and L3 dorsal rami.

11) c – The obturator nerve supplies muscles that adduct the thigh. Muscles innervated include the pectineus (shared with the femoral nerve), obturator externus, adductor brevis, adductor longus, gracilis, and deep (anterior) portion of adductor magnus muscles. The obturator nerve usually also supplies skin of the medial thigh. When present, the accessory obturator nerve supplies the pectineus muscle.

12) c – The L1 spinal nerve is the lowest spinal nerve to supply the abdominal wall. The L1 ventral ramus gives branches to form the ilioinguinal and iliohypogastric nerves. Both supply skin of the anterior lower abdomen and upper thigh. The L1 ventral ramus also gives a branch that combines with a L2 ventral ramus to form the genitofemoral nerve, a member of the lumbar plexus.

13) e – The saphenous nerve is a femoral nerve branch and serves as the only lumbar plexus nerve to supply skin of the leg. The leg is the portion of the lower extremity between the knee and ankle. The thigh is the portion of the lower extremity that is between the hip and knee. Obviously, there are other nerves of the lumbar plexus that supply skin of the thigh.

14) e – The genitofemoral nerve is formed by a combination of a L1 ventral ramus branch and a branch of the anterior division of the L2 ventral ramus. The genitofemoral nerve divides into a genital and femoral branch. The genital branch supplies the cremaster muscle, skin of the anterior scrotum, and skin bordering the scrotum. The femoral branch supplies skin of the upper anterior thigh. The cremaster muscle functions to raise or elevate the testis in the male.

15) d – The genitofemoral nerve is formed by the combination of a L1 ventral ramus branch and a branch of the anterior division of the L2 ventral ramus. The femoral nerve is formed by branches of the posterior divisions of the L2, L3, and L4 ventral rami. Both the ilioinguinal and iliohypogastric nerves are formed by L1 ventral ramus branches.

16) d – The femoral nerve supplies skin of the anterior thigh and muscles that flex the thigh and extend the leg. These muscles include the psoas major, iliacus, pectineus (shared with obturator), sartorius, and the quadriceps femoris muscle group (consisting of rectus femoris, vastus lateralis, vastus intermedius and vastus medialis muscles). The gracilis muscle is innervated by the obturator nerve. The cremaster muscle is innervated by the genitofemoral nerve. The tensor fasciae latae muscle is supplied by the superior gluteal nerve.

17) a – The obturator nerve is formed by branches of the anterior divisions of the L2, L3, and L4 ventral rami. It supplies muscles that adduct the thigh and skin of the medial thigh. Muscles innervated include the pectineus (shared with femoral nerve), obturator externus, adductor brevis, adductor longus, gracilis, and the deep (anterior) portion of the adductor magnus muscles.

18) e – Both the ilioinguinal and iliohypogastric nerves are formed solely from the L1 ventral ramus. The genitofemoral nerve is formed by a combination of a L1 ventral ramus branch and a branch of the anterior division of the L2 ventral ramus. The anterior scrotal (labial) nerves are branches of the ilioinguinal nerve. They therefore are derived from the L1 ventral ramus.

19) c – The saphenous nerve is the only nerve originating from the lumbar plexus (via femoral nerve) that supplies tissue of the leg (below knee). It supplies skin of the medial leg and foot to the level of the great toe. Skin of the lateral side of the foot is supplied by the sural nerve (as the lateral dorsal cutaneous nerve).

20) a – Both the anterior femoral cutaneous nerves and the saphenous nerve branch from the femoral nerve. The femoral nerve is formed by branches of the posterior divisions of the L2, L3, and L4 ventral rami. The lateral femoral cutaneous nerve is formed by branches of the posterior divisions of the L2 and L3 ventral rami. A L1 ventral ramus branch combines with a branch of the anterior division of the L2 ventral ramus to form the genitofemoral nerve.

THE SACRAL PLEXUS

Like other spinal nerves, the sacral spinal nerves consist of both ventral and dorsal rami. The ventral rami branches combine in various ways to form the sacral plexus and nerves of the perineum and lower extremity. The dorsal rami branches form the middle cluneal nerves and various unnamed nerves that supply the posterior lower trunk and upper thigh.

The **lumbosacral trunk** (133) was described earlier. It is formed by the combination of a L4 ventral ramus branch and the entire L5 ventral ramus. The lumbosacral trunk, in turn, is the origin of a branch that combines with a S1 ventral ramus branch to form the superior gluteal nerve. The **superior gluteal nerve (126, 231)** supplies three muscles and the hip joint. Supplied muscles include the gluteus medius, gluteus minimus, and tensor fasciae latae muscles.

Both the gluteus medius and gluteus minimus run from the back of the ilium of the pelvic bone to insert on the greater trochanter of the femur. This is the lateral aspect of the superior femur. Their contraction abducts the thigh and turns it medially.

The tensor fasciae latae muscle runs from the iliac crest to insert on the lateral aspect of the fascia lata, the external fascia enclosing the muscles of the thigh. The tensor fasciae latae flexes the thigh, but like the other two muscles, it also turns the thigh medially.

> The word *gluteal* refers to the buttocks (so does the word *cluneal*). The most "*superior*" aspect of the lower extremity can be considered the buttocks and hip joint. It therefore seems appropriate that tissues of the buttocks and hip are innervated by the *superior* gluteal nerve.

The **nerve to quadratus femoris** (229) is also formed from ventral rami branches from L4, L5, and S1. This nerve travels out to supply the quadratus femoris and inferior gemellus muscles. The quadratus femoris extends from the ischium of the pelvic bone to insert on the upper femur. It adducts and turns the thigh laterally.

The inferior gemellus muscle also originates on the ischium of the pelvic bone. It inserts on the soon-to-be-described obturator internus tendon. Like the quadratus femoris muscle, it turns the thigh laterally. The nerve to quadratus femoris is drawn dotted in Figure 3 to signify that, in this posterior view, it is usually covered externally by the overlying sciatic nerve as they both course downward.

> The quadratus femoris muscle should not be confused with the quadriceps femoris muscle group of the anterior thigh. The quad*ratus* femoris is named for its four-sided shape. The quad*riceps* femoris is named for its four heads, although, in actuality, it is composed of four separate muscles that share a common tendon inferiorly. Quadriceps femoris = rectus femoris, vastus lateralis, vastus intermedius, and vastus lateralis muscles.

The **nerve to obturator internus** (220) is usually formed by

ventral rami branches from L5, S1, and S2 spinal nerves. From a posterior view, it emerges from under the piriformis muscle just lateral to the pudendal nerve (216). In addition to the obturator internus muscle, this nerve also supplies the superior gemellus muscle.

The obturator internus muscle is also known as the internal obturator muscle. It stretches from an area near the obturator foramen of the hip bone to insert on the top of the femur. It, like the quadratus femoris and inferior gemellus muscles, functions to turn the thigh laterally. The obturator externus muscle was described earlier and is innervated by the obturator nerve. Like its internal cohort, the obturator externus also turns the thigh laterally.

The superior gemellus muscle originates on the spine of the ischium of the pelvic bone. Like the inferior gemellus muscle, the superior gemellus also inserts on the obturator internus tendon. Also like all of these recently-described muscles, the superior gemellus turns the thigh laterally. The gemellus muscles are named for the word *geminate,* which means *paired.*

> The inferior and superior **gem**ellus muscles are real "**GEMS**"!
>
> Both muscles go out of their way to make learning their nerve innervation difficult. First, both are innervated by nerves that are named for other muscles. The inferior gemellus is innervated by the nerve to quadratus femoris. The superior gemellus is innervated by the nerve to obturator internus. Secondly, they are named opposite to their spinal segment contribution. For instance, the nerve to quadratus femoris is formed from ventral rami branches from L4, L5, and S1. This nerve innervates the inferior gemellus muscle. The nerve to obturator internus actually originates one spinal cord segment lower (L5, S1, S2) than the nerve to quadratus femoris, yet it innervates the superior gemellus muscle.
>
> It is important to realize that each of these two nerves (nerve to quadratus femoris and nerve to obturator internus) innervates **TWO** muscles, including the muscle of the nerve name and one of the "gems." By looking at Figure 12.14, the innervation becomes more logical. The quadratus femoris is near the inferior gemellus. The obturator internus is near the superior gemellus.

> The "Nerve to Muscle" nerves have the same spinal segment makeup as the "Gluteal" nerves:
>
> Both superior gluteal nerve and nerve to quadratus femoris = L4, L5, S1
> Both inferior gluteal nerve and nerve to obturator internus = L5, S1, S2

The **inferior gluteal nerve (125, 230)** is formed by ventral rami branches from the L5 portion of the lumbosacral trunk, S1 spinal root, and S2 spinal root. The inferior gluteal nerve runs deep to supply the gluteus maximus muscle of the buttock. This muscle extends from the posterior aspect of the ilium of the pelvic bone, sacrum, and coccyx to insert on the back of the upper femur. Its contraction abducts and extends the thigh. It also turns the thigh laterally.

> The gluteus maximus thinks it is "the max." It is very high maintenance and requires a private, customized nerve supply. The inferior gluteal nerve is just that: inferior. It cowers and supplies only the gluteus maximus muscle.
>
> Gluteus **Max**imus supplied by **Inferior** Gluteal nerve

Although Figure 3 of the poster has already been referred to, it will now be briefly explained. From this view, the entire buttock is normally covered externally by the gluteus maximus muscle. The gluteus medius lies just beneath (or anterior) to the maximus. The gluteus minimus muscle lies beneath (or anterior) to the gluteus medius. In other words, there are three gluteus muscles layered on top of one another. The minimus is closest to the front of the body and the maximus to the rear. The top right of the Figure shows a view after the gluteus maximus is removed. To adequately demonstrate the nerves, the medius and minimus are considered transparent. The piriformis is depicted because it serves as a good reference for identifying nerves from this perspective. The **superior gluteal nerve** (126, **231**) emerges from the sacral plexus above the piriformis muscle and runs across the buttock between the gluteus medius and gluteus minimus muscles, both of which it supplies. It is drawn dotted to represent the fact that it is running under the cover of the gluteus medius. On the other hand, the **inferior gluteal nerve** (125, **230**) emerges from beneath the piriformis. It travels between the gluteus medius and gluteus maximus to supply the underside of the maximus. The inferior gluteal nerve travels more superficially than the superior gluteal nerve. Because the gluteus maximus is removed in this image, the inferior gluteal nerve is visible. It is therefore drawn as a solid line. All tissues remain intact on the subject's left side of Figure 3 to demonstrate cutaneous nerves.

FIGURE 12.6
NERVES AND VESSELS OF THE BUTTOCK
Posterior View

(Reproduced with permission from Hollinshead, W.H., Rosse, C.: Textbook of Anatomy, 4th ed. Philadelphia, Harper & Row, 1985.)

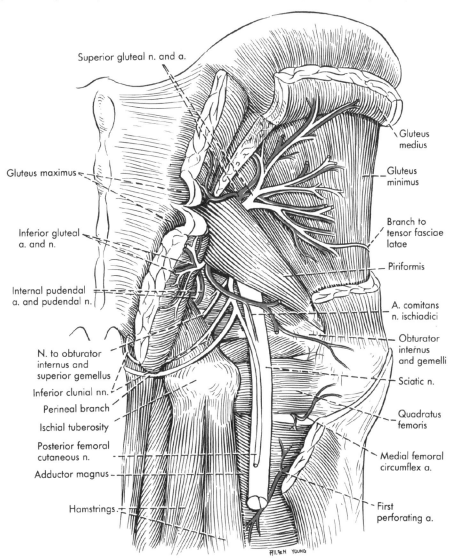

The **posterior femoral cutaneous nerve** (90, **122**, 228) is formed by ventral rami branches from the S1, S2, and S3 spinal segments. This nerve is the origin of the **inferior cluneal nerves** (89, **123**, 214, 227), which are cutaneous nerves supplying skin of the inferior buttock. The posterior femoral cutaneous nerve continues distally and gives multiple **branches** (219) that supply skin of the posterior external genitalia and posterior thigh.

The majority of skin of the thigh is supplied by the three *"femoral"* nerves.

Each is directly formed by ventral rami branches, as opposed to serving as branches of other nerves. The *femoral* nerve is formed by branches of the L2, L3, and L4 ventral rami and supplies skin of the anterior thigh. The **lateral *femoral* cutaneous nerve** is formed by branches of the L2 and L3 ventral rami and supplies skin of the lateral thigh. The **posterior *femoral* cutaneous nerve** is formed from branches of the S1, S2, and S3 ventral rami and supplies skin of the lower buttocks (inferior cluneal nerves) and posterior thigh.

In addition, the femoral branch of the genitofemoral, ilioinguinal, and iliohypogastric nerves may each supply skin of the upper anterior thigh. The genital branch of the genitofemoral, ilioinguinal, and obturator nerves may supply skin of the inner, medial thigh. Finally, the superior, middle, and inferior cluneal nerves supply skin of the buttocks and upper posterior thigh.

Originating one spinal segment lower than the posterior femoral cutaneous nerve, the **pudendal nerve** (88, 121, 216, **275**) is formed by ventral rami branches from the S2, S3, and S4 spinal cord segments. The pudendal nerve is named for the pudendum, the human external genitalia. The pudendal nerve is the primary nerve of the perineum. It supplies all perineal skeletal muscles and most perineal skin. From its origination, the pudendal nerve travels inferiorly and anteriorly to enter the perineum.

Before dividing into terminal branches, the pudendal nerve gives off **inferior rectal nerves** (215, **274**). These nerves may also be called inferior hemorrhoidal nerves. They supply the sphincter ani externus muscle (external anal sphincter) and skin around the anal opening. The internal anal sphincter is innervated by the autonomic nervous system. The pudendal nerve also gives branches that contribute to the innervation of the levator ani muscle. This muscle forms a portion of the floor of the perineum and opposes excessive intra-abdominal pressure.

The pudendal nerve is **THE** nerve of the perineum. It should be no surprise that it is the most medial of the nerves emerging from under the cover of the piriformis muscle in Fig. 3; it is closest to the perineum.

After giving off these branches, the pudendal nerve continues anteriorly and divides into its two terminal branches, the perineal nerve and dorsal nerve of the penis. The later is known as the dorsal nerve of the clitoris in the female.

The **perineal nerve** (217, **273**) continues toward the perineum while giving off several **posterior scrotal nerves** (270). These are known as **posterior labial nerves** (270) in the female. Posterior scrotal nerves supply skin of the posterior scrotum. Posterior labial nerves supply skin of the posterior labia majora. The posterior femoral cutaneous nerve may also contribute posterior scrotal (labial) nerves.

P → P → P

Pudendal → Perineal → Posterior Scrotal (Labial)

(**P**ost. Fem. Cut. n. may also give **P**ost Scrotal (labial) nn.)

The **deep perineal nerve** (271) is the continuation of the perineal nerve into the perineum after the takeoff of the posterior scrotal/labial nerves. As in the naming of other nerves, the word *deep* insinuates a muscular branch. The deep perineal nerve is the origin of muscular branches that supply the ischiocavernosus, bulbospongiosus, and superficial transverse perinei muscles. The ischiocavernosus muscle sustains an erection of the penis or clitoris. The bulbospongiosus muscle is also known as the bulbocavernosus muscle. It tightens the urethra in the male and vagina in the female. The superficial transverse perinei muscle is also known as the superficial transverse muscle of the perineum. It functions to immobilize the tendinous middle of the perineum. Along with other pudendal and sacral branches, the deep perineal nerve also contributes to the innervation of the levator ani muscle.

FIGURE 12.7
PERINEAL MUSCLES

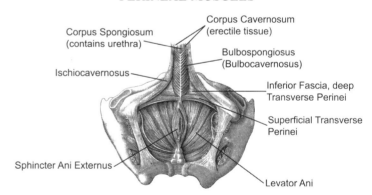

The other terminal branch of the pudendal nerve is the **dorsal nerve of the penis** or **dorsal nerve of the clitoris** (272). This nerve supplies the skin of the penis or clitoris as well as the glans, or free end, of each structure. The dorsal nerve of the penis/clitoris innervates two muscles and the corpus cavernosum. The two muscles include the sphincter muscle of the urethra and deep transverse perinei muscle. The sphincter muscle of the urethra opens and closes the urethral orifice. The deep transverse perinei muscle is also known as the deep transverse muscle of the perineum. Like the superficial counterpart innervated by the perineal nerve, the deep transverse perinei muscle serves to immobilize the tendinous middle of the perineum. Finally, the corpus cavernosum is not a muscle but a pair of erectile tissue shafts that form the anterior body of the penis in the male and clitoris in the female.

The **D**eep transverse perinei muscle is innervated by the **D**orsal nerve of penis (clitoris).

The superficial transverse perinei muscle is innervated by the perineal nerve.

Nerve Names

Male		Female
scrotal	=	labial
penis	=	clitoris

SCIATIC NERVE

After giving branches to the superior gluteal nerve, nerve to quadratus femoris, inferior gluteal nerve, and nerve to obturator internus, the lumbosacral trunk continues down to combine with branches from the S1, S2, and S3 ventral rami to form the large **sciatic nerve** (91, 118, **124,** 226). The sciatic nerve is drawn dotted in Figure 2 to represent its course in the deep core of the posterior thigh. The sciatic nerve gives several muscular branches in the thigh before dividing into its two terminal branches, the common peroneal and tibial nerves. This division occurs just above the knee. The common peroneal and tibial nerves continue distally to supply structures of the leg.

The sciatic nerve and its terminal branches appear to parallel the skeleton of the lower extremity. In the thigh there is one bone, the femur. The sciatic nerve serves as its partner in the thigh (although it divides into its terminal branches in the distal thigh). The two terminal branches parallel the two bones of the leg. The word *peroneal* refers to the fibula. The common peroneal nerve is named for its proximity to the fibula. The tibial nerve is named for its proximity to the tibia.

Although the sciatic nerve is one nerve while in the thigh, it is formed by a portion of nerve tissue that eventually becomes the peroneal nerve and a portion that eventually becomes the tibial nerve. Four thigh muscles are supplied by the sciatic nerve. Some texts describe these muscles as supplied by either the peroneal or tibial nerve, depending on which portion of the sciatic nerve provides the innervation. This is merely semantics. For purposes here, these muscles are described as innervated by the sciatic nerve. Grossly, that is what is occurring. To prevent future confusion, the specific portion of the sciatic nerve that is providing innervation will also be covered.

While in the thigh, the sciatic nerve innervates the biceps femoris, semitendinous, semimembranosus, and the superficial (posterior) portion of adductor magnus muscles. The word *biceps* refers to a muscle which has two heads. Like the biceps brachii muscle of the arm, the biceps femoris muscle has two heads. The short head is supplied by the peroneal portion of the sciatic nerve. The long head of the biceps femoris and the three other sciatic-

supplied muscles are all innervated by the tibial portion of the sciatic nerve.

Just as the fibula bone is **s**mall compared to the tibia, the innervation of the peroneal portion of the sciatic nerve in the thigh is **s**mall compared to the tibial portion. The only muscle supplied by the peroneal portion is the **s**hort head of the biceps femoris.

The short head of the biceps femoris originates on back of the femur. The long head originates from the ischium of the pelvic bone. Both heads extend down to insert on the upper aspects of the tibia and fibula. Contraction causes flexion and lateral rotation of the leg. In addition, the long head extends the thigh.

The semitendinous muscle runs from the ischium of the pelvic bone to the medial aspect of the upper tibia. Its contraction extends the thigh and flexes the leg, but as opposed to the biceps femoris, it causes medial rotation of the leg.

The semimembranosus muscle runs from the ischium of the pelvic bone to the lateral aspect of the distal femur and medial aspect of the upper tibia. It also causes extension of the thigh and flexion of the leg.

Finally, the superficial (posterior) portion of the adductor magnus stretches from the ischium of the pelvic bone to the femur. Its contraction causes extension of the thigh. The deep (anterior) portion of the adductor magnus muscle was described earlier and is innervated by the obturator muscle. The obturator portion functions to adduct the thigh.

FIGURE 12.8
POSTERIOR MUSCLES OF THIGH

S & S
The **S**ciatic nerve innervates the **S**uperficial (posterior) portion of the adductor magnus muscle.

Muscles of the thigh that are supplied by the sciatic nerve share common actions. These include extension of the thigh and flexion of the leg. To understand this motion, envision a runner in slow motion. As a runner's leg is advanced forward, the foot strikes the ground in front of the torso. At this point, the thigh is flexed forward (at the hip) and the leg is extended (at the knee). During the push-off stroke, of the same extremity, the torso travels over the contact point of the foot. As this occurs, the thigh is extended (the angle of the hip joint is increased). Furthermore, as the foot pushes off the ground, the leg is flexed back toward the posterior thigh. Hence, there is extension of the thigh and flexion of the leg.

Approximately two-thirds down the thigh, the sciatic nerve divides into its two terminal branches, the common peroneal and tibial nerves. As mentioned earlier, the word *peroneal* refers to the fibula bone. The **common peroneal nerve** (117) is named for its proximity to the fibula, the smaller, lateral bone of the leg. It travels down the posterior thigh and curves around the lateral aspect of the knee toward the front. Because it is named "common" peroneal nerve, one should assume there are subdivisions of the nerve. Indeed, the common peroneal nerve gives three named branches before dividing into its two terminal branches, the superficial and deep peroneal nerves.

Care should be taken not to confuse the common peroneal nerve or any of its branches with the perineal nerve. Only one letter separates these nerve names. Alphabetically, "I" comes before "O." The per**I**neal nerve innervates an area of the body (perineum) which is higher or more proximal than the area supplied by the per**O**neal nerve (leg). The perineal nerve is one of the terminal branches of the pudendal nerve and is named for its presence in the perineum. The peroneal nerve is a terminal branch of the sciatic nerve and is named for its location relative to the fibula bone of the leg.

The three nerve branches that leave the common peroneal prior to its separation into terminal branches include the recurrent articular branch to knee, the lateral sural cutaneous nerve, and the peroneal communicating nerve. All are sensory nerves. The **recurrent articular branch to knee** (116) is a small nerve which, along with tibial nerve branches, provides innervation to the knee joint. The **lateral sural nerve** (**115**, 221) continues down the leg supplying skin of the lateral calf. The **peroneal communicating nerve** (**114**, 222) travels distally to combine with the medial sural nerve and form the sural nerve. The medial sural nerve is a branch of the tibial nerve. Both it and the sural nerve will be discussed shortly. Maintaining the common anatomic theme of variability, the peroneal communicating nerve may branch from the lateral sural cutaneous nerve instead of the common peroneal nerve. Sura is another name for calf. The word *sural* refers to the calf of the leg.

There are **3 "sural" nerves** and all are cutaneous nerves:
1) **lateral sural nerve** branches from the common peroneal nerve (named for its proximity to the *lateral* bone of the leg, the fibula)
2) **medial sural nerve** branches from the tibial nerve (named for its proximity to the *medial* bone of the leg, the tibia)
3) the **sural nerve** is formed by the combination of the peroneal communicating and medial sural nerves. "***THE***" sural nerve requires one branch from each terminal branch of the sciatic nerve, the peroneal communicating nerve from the common peroneal nerve and the medial sural nerve from the tibial nerve.

The **superficial peroneal nerve** (**112**, 78, 108) supplies two muscles before it becomes cutaneous approximately midway between the knee and foot (78). The two muscles are the peroneus

longus and peroneus brevis. Both muscles, like the peroneal nerve, are named for their relationship with the fibula bone. The peroneus longus stretches from the top (head) of the fibula and lateral condyle of the tibia to the medial cuneiform bone of the tarsus and first metatarsal bone. In simpler words, the muscle travels along the lateral aspect of the leg, from knee to foot. The peroneus brevis extends from the lateral fibula to the fifth metatarsal bone. Both muscles plantar flex the foot ("step on the gas") and evert the foot (twist the ankle outward so the lateral aspect of the foot is superior to the medial aspect). After supplying these muscles, the superficial peroneal nerve continues distally along the lateral aspect of the leg as a cutaneous nerve. Just above the foot, it divides into a medial and lateral branch. The medial branch forms the medial dorsal cutaneous nerve. The lateral branch forms the intermediate dorsal cutaneous nerve. These nerves continue across the dorsal or top surface of the foot while supplying skin. **The medial dorsal cutaneous nerve** (79) gives off **dorsal digital nerves** (82, 83) which supply skin of the dorsal surface of the medial side of the 1st (great) toe and the dorsal surface of the adjacent sides of the 2nd & 3rd toes. The adjacent sides of the 1st & 2nd toes are skipped. They are left to the innervation of the deep peroneal nerve. The **intermediate dorsal cutaneous nerve** (80) also gives off **dorsal digital nerves** (82, 83). These supply the dorsal surface of adjacent sides of the 3rd & 4th and 4th & 5th toes. The lateral (outer) side of the 5th toe is supplied by the lateral dorsal cutaneous nerve (81). This is the distal continuation of the sural nerve and will be discussed shortly.

The "superficial" peroneal nerve supplies skin on "top" of the foot.

Once it branches from the common peroneal nerve, the **deep peroneal nerve** (**113**, 107, 85) crosses the front of the fibula to descend the leg between the fibula and tibia. It supplies five muscles, the ankle joint, the tarsal joints, and skin of the adjacent sides of the 1st (great) and 2nd toes.

Muscles innervated by the deep peroneal nerve include the tibialis anterior, extensor digitorum longus, extensor hallucis longus, peroneus tertius, and extensor digitorum brevis. The tibialis anterior muscle extends from the lateral condyle of the tibia (lateral part of the proximal tibia) to the medial cuneiform bone of the tarsus and the 1st metatarsal bone. Contraction causes dorsiflexion of the foot (raising the front foot off the ground) and inversion of the foot (twisting the ankle inward, raising the medial side of the foot higher than the lateral side).

The extensor digitorum longus muscle runs from the anterior fibula and lateral condyle of the tibia to the extensor aponeurosis of toes 2-5. Contraction causes extension of the lateral four toes.

The extensor hallucis longus runs from the front of the fibula to the distal phalanx of the great toe. It extends the great toe. Just as the word *pollicis* refers to the thumb, the word *hallucis* refers to the great toe. As opposed to other digits, both the thumb and great toe have only two phalanges, one interphalangeal joint, individualized muscles, and a specific word which refers to them.

The peroneus tertius muscle extends from the anterior fibula to the base of the 4th or 5th metatarsal bone. Like its two cousins innervated by the superficial peroneal nerve, the peroneus longus

FIGURE 12.9
NERVES OF THE PERONEAL SYSTEM

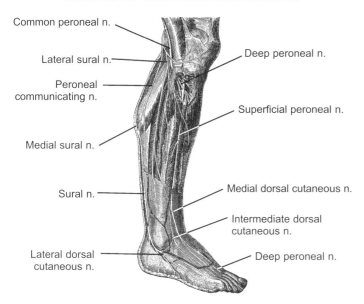

Common peroneal n.
Lateral sural n.
Peroneal communicating n.
Medial sural n.
Sural n.
Lateral dorsal cutaneous n.
Deep peroneal n.
Superficial peroneal n.
Medial dorsal cutaneous n.
Intermediate dorsal cutaneous n.
Deep peroneal n.

and peroneus brevis muscles, the peroneus tertius is named for its relationship with the fibula. Its name actually means the *third peroneus* (fibula) muscle. Like the other two peroneus muscles, the peroneus tertius everts the foot. Unlike the other two, the peroneus tertius dorsiflexes the foot. The peroneus longus and peroneus brevis both plantar flex the foot ("step on the gas").

Similar to the common, superficial, and deep peroneal nerves, the 3 peroneus muscles are named for their location relative to the fibula. Because the fibula is the lateral bone of the leg, the peroneus muscles must also be located in the lateral aspect of the leg. It is no surprise that all 3 function in eversion of the foot.

The extensor digitorum brevis stretches from the upper calcaneus bone of the tarsus to the extensor tendons of all five toes.

FIGURE 12.10
MUSCLES OF ANTERIOR LEG

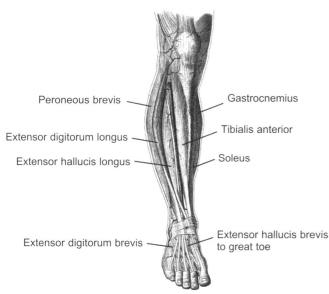

Peroneous brevis
Extensor digitorum longus
Extensor hallucis longus
Extensor digitorum brevis
Gastrocnemius
Tibialis anterior
Soleus
Extensor hallucis brevis to great toe

It extends the toes. The portion of this muscle that goes to the great toe is often treated as a separate muscle, the extensor hallucis brevis.

Not to be outdone by its brother, the superficial peroneal nerve, the deep peroneal nerve is determined to have some cutaneous innervation. The deep peroneal nerve continues distally in the foot and gives off dorsal digital nerves that supply the adjacent sides of the 1st (great) and 2nd toes. This odd cutaneous assignment is all the deep peroneal could manage, as it is busy supplying most of the muscles innervated by the peroneal system. The superficial peroneal nerve only innervates two.

The superficial and deep peroneal nerves serve as yet another example of a deep branch serving as the motor nerve and the superficial branch acting as the sensory nerve. After all, the superficial nerve is closer to the skin. The only difference with this pair is that each nerve "dabbles" in the work of the other. The superficial peroneal nerve innervates *two* muscles (peroneus longus and peroneus brevis). The deep peroneal nerve supplies skin on the sides of *two* toes (adjacent sides of 1st and 2nd toes).

2 peroneal nerves = superficial with 2 muscles, deep with 2 "toe sides"

FIGURE 12.11
CUTANEOUS NERVES OF ANTERIOR LEG AND FOOT

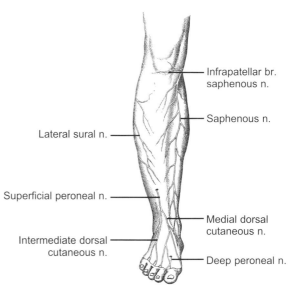

Infrapatellar br. saphenous n.
Saphenous n.
Lateral sural n.
Superficial peroneal n.
Intermediate dorsal cutaneous n.
Medial dorsal cutaneous n.
Deep peroneal n.

The **tibial nerve (93**, 99) is the other terminal branch of the sciatic nerve. It travels distally down the leg posterior to the bone it is named for, the tibia. It gives several sensory branches and innervates seven muscles of the posterior leg. In the ankle, the tibial nerve divides into its two terminal branches, the medial and lateral plantar nerves.

After leaving the sciatic nerve, the tibial nerve gives branches that contribute to the innervation of the knee joint. At the approximate level of the knee, the tibial also gives off the medial sural cutaneous nerve. The **medial sural nerve** (94) supplies skin of the posterior calf. As mentioned earlier, this nerve continues distally to receive the peroneal communicating nerve from the common peroneal nerve. The combination forms the **sural nerve** (95, 109, **224**). The sural nerve supplies skin of the posterior leg, heel, and lateral side of the foot. It continues around the lateral side of the ankle to become the lateral dorsal cutaneous nerve. The **lateral dorsal cutaneous nerve** (81, **106**, 225) supplies skin of the lateral side of the foot and fifth toe.

> There are two "S" cutaneous nerves which descend the leg and supply skin on each <u>S</u>ide of the foot. The <u>**Saphenous**</u> nerve is a branch of the femoral nerve of the lumbar plexus and represents the only contribution of this plexus below the knee. The saphenous nerve supplies the medial side of the foot. The <u>**Sural**</u> nerve supplies the lateral side of the foot (as the lateral dorsal cutaneous nerve). Alphabetically, saphenous comes before sural and saphenous is more medial than sural. Just as the toes are numbered, the more medial a structure is, the more proximal it is in "the order."

As the tibial nerve continues down the leg, it innervates seven muscles and gives off numerous sensory branches. The **interosseus nerve of leg** (96) is a sensory nerve that travels down the leg between the tibia and fibula, supplying the interosseus membrane between the two. It is a good example of a sensory nerve that travels deep. Not all deep branches are motor.

The seven muscles of the leg supplied by the tibial nerve include the plantaris, popliteus, gastrocnemius, soleus, tibialis posterior, flexor digitorum longus, and flexor hallucis longus. The plantaris muscle originates on the posterior surface of the distal femur. Its tendon runs down to join the tendons of the gastrocnemius and soleus muscles to create the Achilles tendon. The Achilles tendon continues inferiorly and attaches to the back of the calcaneus bone of the tarsus. Because these three muscles insert via a common tendon, the trio is occasionally referred to as one muscle, the triceps surae. The plantaris muscle flexes the leg (knee) and plantar flexes the foot.

> The <u>**plantar**</u>is muscle **plantar** flexes the foot.

FIGURE 12.12
POSTERIOR MUSCLES OF LEG

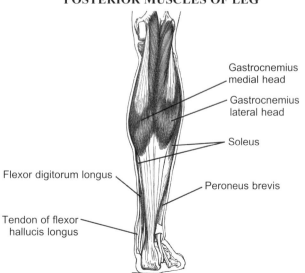

The popliteus muscle stretches from the back of the lateral condyle of the femur to the posterior tibia. The word *popliteal* refers to the area behind the knee. This muscle is named for its location behind the knee. It functions to flex and turn the leg medially.

The gastrocnemius muscle is the superior overlying muscle of the calf. It has two heads. The medial head originates on the posterior aspect of the medial condyle of the femur. The lateral head originates on the posterior aspect of the lateral condyle of the femur. Both heads travel inferiorly along the posterior leg. The gastrocnemius tendon combines with the plantaris and soleus tendons to create the Achilles tendon. Like the plantaris muscle, the gastrocnemius flexes the leg (knee) and plantar flexes the foot.

The soleus is a muscle of the calf located beneath the gastrocnemius muscle. It originates from the top of the posterior tibia and fibula. As mentioned, its tendon combines with that of the plantaris and gastrocnemius to form the Achilles tendon. Like the other two muscles, it plantar flexes the foot. Because it originates on the tibia and fibula and not the femur, it does not cross the knee joint; there is no way for it to flex the leg like the other two muscles.

> The <u>**sole**</u>us muscle solely plantar flexes the foot (it does not flex the leg). It moves the foot in the direction of the **sole**.

FIGURE 12.13
POSTERIOR MUSCLES OF LEG, DEEPER DISSECTION
*The three muscles that insert
via the Achilles tendon have been removed.*

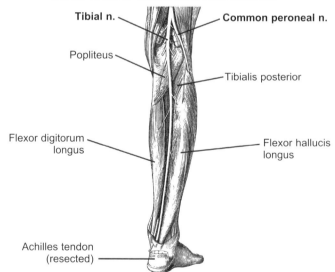

The tibialis posterior muscle stretches from the back of the tibia and fibula to the #2, #3, and #4 metatarsal bones. On the way, it also binds to most of the tarsal bones. Like many of the tibial-supplied muscles, the tibialis posterior plantar flexes the foot. In addition, it inverts the foot (medial side of foot is more superior to the lateral side).

The flexor digitorum longus originates on the posterior tibia. It travels distally to attach to the distal phalanges of toes 2-5. This muscle, as the name implies, flexes the four lateral toes.

Finally, the flexor hallucis longus originates from the back of the fibula. It inserts on the distal phalanx of the great toe. As could be surmised from the name, the muscle flexes the great toe.

The S̲ciatic S̲ystem is S̲omewhat S̲ymmetrical
with regard to each nerve dividing into two terminal branches

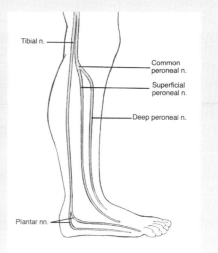

The common peroneal and tibial nerves are the two terminal branches of the huge sciatic nerve. Each of these subsequently divides into two terminal branches. These terminal branches eventually supply the foot. The only difference is the common peroneal divides early (at the approximate level of the knee) and the tibial divides late (at the approximate level of the heel). The P of **P**eroneal comes before the T of **T**ibial. The common peroneal nerve divides into its two terminal branches before the tibial.

The superficial peroneal nerve and its branches make every effort to maintain this symmetrical system. First, the superficial peroneal nerve divides into **two** terminal branches, the medial and intermediate dorsal cutaneous nerves. Each of these subsequently divides into **two** branches. The medial dorsal cutaneous nerve divides into one dorsal proper digital nerve that supplies the medial side of digit #1 (great toe) and one dorsal common digital nerve that eventually supplies dorsal skin of the adjacent sides of toes #2 and #3. The intermediate dorsal cutaneous nerve divides into two dorsal common digital nerves that eventually supply dorsal skin of the adjacent sides of toes #3 & #4, and #4 & #5, respectively.

The remainder of the cutaneous innervation of the dorsal foot is supplied by two other nerves. The deep peroneal nerve supplies the skin of the adjacent sides of toe #1 (great toe) and toe #2. The lateral dorsal cutaneous nerve supplies the skin of the lateral (outer) side of toe #5 (small toe). This nerve is the continuation of the sural nerve distally.

After completing its mission in the leg, the tibial nerve continues its trek toward the foot. Just above the ankle, it gives off **medial calcaneal branches** (98). These sensory nerves are named for the calcaneus bone of the tarsus. They travel down to innervate structures of the medial and plantar heel.

The tibial nerve divides into its two terminal branches near the heel. The terminal branches, the medial and lateral plantar nerves, travel forward across the sole of the foot. These two nerves innervate skin, muscles, and articular joints of the underside of the foot.

The **medial plantar nerve** (100) innervates four muscles and skin of the medial side of the sole. The muscles include the abductor hallucis, flexor hallucis brevis, flexor digitorum brevis, and the first lumbrical.

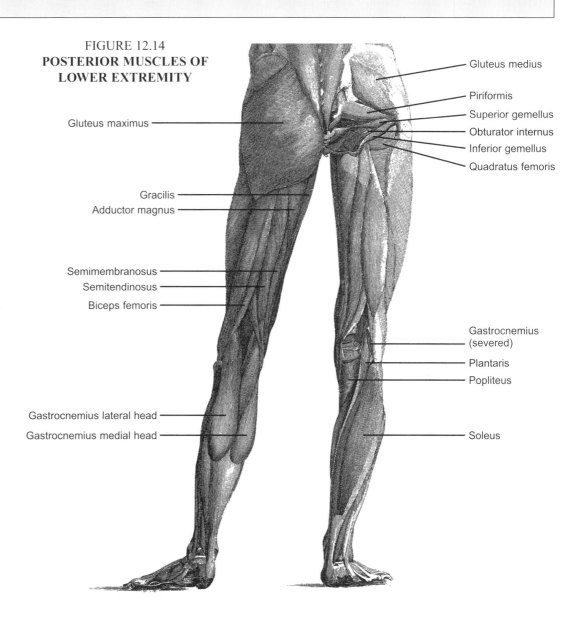

FIGURE 12.14
POSTERIOR MUSCLES OF LOWER EXTREMITY

Gluteus medius
Piriformis
Superior gemellus
Obturator internus
Inferior gemellus
Quadratus femoris

Gluteus maximus

Gracilis
Adductor magnus

Semimembranosus
Semitendinosus
Biceps femoris

Gastrocnemius (severed)
Plantaris
Popliteus

Gastrocnemius lateral head
Gastrocnemius medial head

Soleus

The abductor hallucis extends from the medial portion of the calcaneus bone of the tarsus to the medial portion of the proximal phalanx of the 1st toe. It abducts and flexes the great toe.

The flexor hallucis brevis has two portions. It originates from the inferior side of the lateral cuneiform and cuboid bones. The lateral portion inserts on the lateral side of the proximal phalanx of the great toe. The medial portion inserts on the medial side of the proximal phalanx. The flexor hallucis brevis flexes the great toe.

The flexor digitorum brevis extends from the medial calcaneus bone to the middle phalanges of toes 2-5. It flexes the lateral four toes.

FIGURE 12.15
SUPERFICIAL PLANTAR MUSCLES

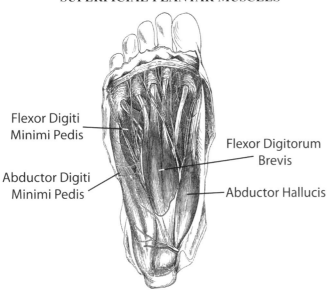

Flexor Digiti Minimi Pedis

Flexor Digitorum Brevis

Abductor Digiti Minimi Pedis

Abductor Hallucis

The first lumbrical muscle is located in the metatarsal space between the metatarsal bones of the great toe and 2nd toe. The other three lumbrical muscles are innervated by the lateral plantar nerve.

The lumbrical muscles of the foot are similar to the lumbrical muscles of the hand in that they are located between the metatarsal (metacarpal) bones. Because there are four metatarsal spaces in each foot, there are four lumbrical muscles in each foot. Each originates from two flexor digitorum longus tendons, one from each side. The muscle extends forward to insert on the medial aspect of the proximal phalanx of the toe just lateral to its metatarsal space. For instance, the fourth lumbrical inserts on the fifth toe. Each flexes the metatarsophalangeal joint and extends the distal phalanges of its respective toe. The metatarsophalangeal joint is the articulation between a metatarsal bone and the proximal phalanx of a toe. In simpler terms, it is the joint where the toes join the foot.

Lumbrical muscles flex, then extend, toes

Medial plantar sensory responsibilities include skin and articular joints of the medial sole, skin of the plantar surface of the medial 3 1/2 toes, and the nail beds of these toes. As the medial plantar nerve travels toward the front of the foot, it divides into four branches. A **proper plantar digital nerve** (104) travels medially to supply plantar skin along the medial side of the great toe. Three **common plantar digital nerves** (105) also originate from the

medial plantar nerve. The first travels forward to divide into two proper plantar digital nerves that supply the adjacent sides of toes #1 and #2. The second forms two proper plantar digital nerves that supply adjacent sides of toes #2 and #3. Finally, the third forms two proper plantar digital nerves that supply adjacent sides of toes #3 and #4. In addition to the plantar surface of the toes, these sensory nerves also supply the nail beds and articular joints.

The terms "common digital nerve" and "proper digital nerve" are used in the same context as in the description of the hand. The word *plantar* simply denotes the sole of the foot.

Like the medial plantar nerve, the lateral plantar nerve also has both sensory and motor functions. It supplies the skin and articular joints of the lateral side of the sole. This includes the plantar surface of the adjacent sides of toes #4 and #5, the plantar surface of the lateral (outer) side of the 5th (little) toe, and the nail beds of these two toes.

Again, alphabetically, the "**P**" of "**P**eroneal" comes before the "**T**" of "**T**ibial." The peroneal nerve is responsible for branches which supply the top of the foot and toes (except nail beds). The tibial nerve supplies the bottom of the foot and toes (including nail beds). The top of the lateral side of the foot is supplied by a nerve formed from branches from both the peroneal and tibial nerves, the sural nerve.

The Toes are Supplied From Above and Below
TOP *(depicted on right foot of subject in Fig. 2)* **Superficial peroneal nerve** • **medial dorsal cutaneous nerve** – medial side of great toe and adjacent sides of toes #2 and #3. It "skips" the area supplied by the deep peroneal nerve (adjacent sides of toes #1 and #2). • **intermediate dorsal cutaneous nerve** – adjacent sides of toes #3 and #4, #4 and #5. **Deep peroneal nerve** • adjacent sides of toes #1 and #2. **Sural nerve** • **lateral dorsal cutaneous nerve** – lateral side of toe #5. **BOTTOM** *(depicted on left foot of subject in Fig. 2)* **Medial plantar nerve** • medial side of toe #1, adjacent sides of toes #1 and #2, #2 and #3, and #3 and #4. **Lateral plantar nerve** • adjacent sides of toes #4 and #5, lateral side of toe #5. Unlike the palms of the hands, the soles of the feet are in almost constant contact with the ground during waking hours. This perpetual sensory input to the plantar surface can be thought to require its own nerve supply. Thus, we have the plantar nerves.

After branching from the tibial nerve, the **lateral plantar nerve** (101) travels across the sole toward the front of the foot. It gives branches that supply the quadratus plantae and abductor digiti minimi pedis muscles. The quadratus plantae muscle runs from the calcaneus bone of the tarsus to the tendon of the flexor digitorum longus. It assists this muscle in flexing the lateral four toes. The abductor digiti minimi pedis muscle extends from the calcancus bonc to the lateral aspect of the proximal phalanx of toe #5. As its name implies, this muscle abducts the little toe.

After innervating these two muscles, the lateral plantar nerve divides into a superficial and deep branch. By way of these two branches, the lateral plantar nerve is responsible for innervating all interosseous muscles of the foot. Similar to the interosseous muscles of the hand, which are located between metacarpal bones, the interosseous muscles of the foot are located between metatarsal bones. Just as there are both palmar and dorsal interossei in the hand, there are plantar and dorsal interossei in the foot. Each foot contains three plantar and four dorsal interosseous muscles. Again, this is similar to the hand.

The three plantar interossei belong to the lateral three toes. Each originates on the medial side of the lateral metatarsal bone of its respective interosseous space. The muscle travels forward to insert on the medial aspect of the proximal phalanx of the toe of the originating metatarsal bone. As with the toes, the lumbrical and interosseous muscles of the foot are numbered from medial to lateral. The first plantar interosseous muscle extends from the medial aspect of the third metatarsal bone to the proximal phalanx of the third toe. The second plantar interosseous extends from the medial aspect of the fourth metatarsal to the fourth toe. The third and final muscle extends from the medial aspect of the fifth metatarsal to the fifth toe. The plantar interossei flex and adduct the toes.

Since there are four dorsal interosseous muscles, one is found in each of the four interosseous spaces. Each dorsal interosseous muscle originates on both metatarsal bones of its respective interosseous space. The first dorsal interosseous extends forward to insert on the proximal phalanx of the toe just lateral to it, the second toe. Each of the other three muscles inserts on the proximal phalanx of the toe immediately medial to its

FIGURE 12.16
DEEPER DISSECTION OF FOOT

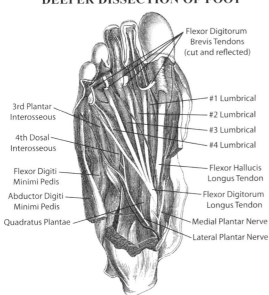

FIGURE 12.17
CUTANEOUS NERVE DISTRIBUTION OF LOWER LIMB

(Reproduced with permission from Cousins, M.J., Bridenbaugh, P.O.: Neural Blockade in Clinical Anesthesia and Management of Pain, 2nd ed. Philadelphia, J. B. Lippincott Co., 1988.)

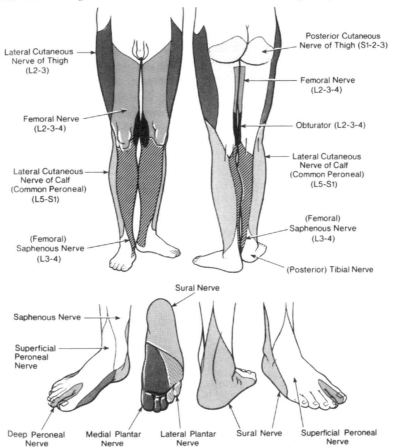

metatarsal space. The second dorsal interosseous muscle inserts on the second toe. The third dorsal interosseous inserts on the third toe. The fourth muscle inserts on the fourth toe. The proximal phalanx of the second toe is thereby bound by two dorsal interossei, one on each side. The dorsal interossei flex and abduct the toes. It should be noted that, although both plantar and dorsal interossei flex the toes, neither extends the interphalangeal joints. Interossei of the hand flex the metacarpophalangeal joint and extend the two interphalangeal joints of each finger.

> The plantar surface area that contacts the ground is relatively very small compared to the surface area of the entire body. From the ground up, the general form of the body progressively gets larger. Interossei of the foot follow this general scheme. There are three plantar interossei which are closer to the plantar surface (ground). Four dorsal interossei are further removed from the ground. Plantar interossei function similar to palmar interossei of the hand. Dorsal interossei of the foot function similar to those of the hand.
>
> **PAD** **P**lantar (and/or palmar) interossei **AD**duct
> **DAB** **D**orsal (hand and foot) interossei **AB**duct

The lateral plantar nerve divides into a superficial and deep branch at the approximate level of the metatarsal bones. The **superficial branch of the lateral plantar nerve** supplies four muscles before continuing distally to provide sensory innervation to the skin, nail beds, and articular joints of the lateral one and a half toes. This includes skin of the adjacent sides of toes #4 and #5 and the lateral side of toe #5. The four supplied muscles are the flexor digiti minimi brevis and three muscles of the fourth interosseous space: the third plantar interosseous, fourth dorsal interosseous, and fourth lumbrical muscles. The flexor digiti minimi pedis muscle runs from the tendon of the peroneus longus muscle to the proximal phalanx of the little toe. It assists in flexing the little toe.

The superficial branch of the lateral plantar nerve is the origin of one proper and one common plantar digital nerve. The proper plantar digital nerve travels laterally to innervate the plantar surface of the lateral side of the fifth toe. The common plantar digital nerve travels distally to divide into two proper plantar digital nerves that supply the plantar aspect of the adjacent sides of toes #4 and #5.

FIGURE 12.18
INTEROSSEOUS AND LUMBRICAL MUSCLES
All are located in interosseous spaces between metatarsal bones.

NAME	Plantar interossei	Dorsal interossei	Lumbrical muscles
NUMBER	3	4	4
ORIGIN	Lateral metatarsal bone of lateral 3 metatarsal spaces	Both metatarsal bones of every metatarsal space	Both flexor digitorum longus tendons
INSERTION	Lateral toe	#1=Lateral toe #2-4=Medial toe	Lateral toe
FUNCTION	Flex and adduct toe	Flex and abduct toe	Flex metatarso-phalangeal joint and extend distal phalanges

As discussed in the learning aid concerning the number of plantar and dorsal interossei, the mass of lower extremity tissue gets larger moving proximally. The thigh has more mass than the leg. There are only three plantar interosseous muscles and four dorsal interosseous muscles.

This same memory aid can be used to remember the cutaneous innervation of the feet. The plantar surface of the toes requires only two cutaneous nerves from the sciatic system, the medial and lateral plantar nerves. The dorsal surface requires four (coincidentally, this is the same number as the dorsal interosseous muscles). These include the medial dorsal cutaneous, intermediate dorsal cutaneous, lateral dorsal cutaneous, and deep peroneal nerves. In addition, a branch of the femoral nerve, the saphenous nerve, supplies skin of the medial side of the foot.

NERVES

1) medial dorsal cutaneous n.(superficial peroneal n.) –
2) deep peroneal n. –
3) intermed. dorsal cutaneous n. (superficial peroneal n.) –
4) lateral dorsal cutaneous n. (sural n.) –

1) medial plantar nerve –
2) lateral plantar nerve –

TOES

medial #1, #2 and #3
#1 and #2
#3 and #4, #4 and #5
lateral #5

medial #1, #1 and #2, #2 and #3, #3 and #4
#4 and #5, lateral #5

The **deep branch of the lateral plantar nerve** (102) travels medially and deep to supply eight muscles of the deep foot. These include the medial two plantar interossei (#1 and #2), the medial three dorsal interossei (#1, #2, and #3), the intermedially-located two lumbrical muscles (#2 and #3), and the adductor hallucis muscle. The adductor hallucis muscle originates in the plantar ligaments. It has two heads. The transverse head originates proximal to the base of the fifth toe. The oblique head originates from the mid-portion of the foot. Both travel diagonally across the foot to attach to the lateral side of the proximal phalanx of the great toe. Both heads adduct the great toe. The oblique head also flexes the great toe.

DEEP BRANCH LAT. PLANTAR =
2-3-2 + adductor hallucis
Medial **2** plantar interossei, medial **3** dorsal interossei, middle **2** lumbricals (middle, not medial)

The medial and lateral plantar nerves divide duties in the foot. The medial plantar nerve supplies fewer muscles (**four**) but relays sensory information from a greater number of toes [cutaneous innervation to the medial 3 1/2 toes (almost **four!**)]. Remember, the most <u>medial</u> toe (great toe) is the largest. The <u>medial</u> plantar nerve supplies the largest number of toes. In contrast, the lateral plantar nerve only supplies the lateral 1 1/2 toes, but innervates 14 muscles of the foot. In order to supply all these muscles, the lateral plantar nerve requires the assistance of a deep branch. The 14 muscles include 3 of the 4 lumbrical muscles and all 7 interossei. The other four muscles are the quadratus plantae, abductor digiti minimi pedis (lat. plantar n. prior to division), flexor digiti minimi brevis (superficial br.), and adductor hallucis (deep br.)

MEDIAL PLANTAR NERVE = <u>4</u> MUSCLES
(including 1 lumbrical)

LATERAL PLANTAR NERVE = <u>4</u> MUSCLES
(plus 10 = 3 lumbricals, 7 interossei) = **<u>14</u>** total

FIGURE 12.19
DEEPEST DISSECTION OF FOOT

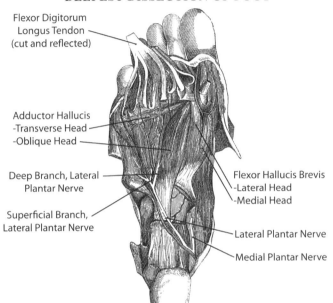

Flexor Digitorum Longus Tendon (cut and reflected)

Adductor Hallucis
-Transverse Head
-Oblique Head

Deep Branch, Lateral Plantar Nerve

Superficial Branch, Lateral Plantar Nerve

Flexor Hallucis Brevis
-Lateral Head
-Medial Head

Lateral Plantar Nerve

Medial Plantar Nerve

FIGURE 12.20
PLANTAR NERVES

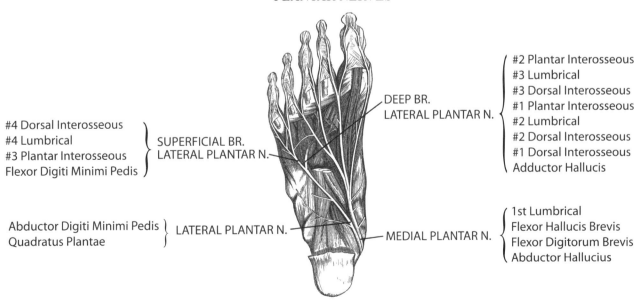

#4 Dorsal Interosseous
#4 Lumbrical
#3 Plantar Interosseous
Flexor Digiti Minimi Pedis

SUPERFICIAL BR.
LATERAL PLANTAR N.

DEEP BR.
LATERAL PLANTAR N.

#2 Plantar Interosseous
#3 Lumbrical
#3 Dorsal Interosseous
#1 Plantar Interosseous
#2 Lumbrical
#2 Dorsal Interosseous
#1 Dorsal Interosseous
Adductor Hallucis

Abductor Digiti Minimi Pedis
Quadratus Plantae

LATERAL PLANTAR N.

MEDIAL PLANTAR N.

1st Lumbrical
Flexor Hallucis Brevis
Flexor Digitorum Brevis
Abductor Hallucius

DORSAL RAMI BRANCHES

Like other spinal nerves, the sacral spinal nerves also have dorsal rami branches. Three of these are named. The dorsal rami branches of S1, S2, and S3 form the **middle cluneal nerves (67, 213)**. These cutaneous nerves supply skin of the intermediate buttock. The word *cluneal* refers to the buttocks. The superior cluneal nerves (**63**, 212) are formed by dorsal rami branches from the L1, L2, and L3 spinal nerves. The superior and middle cluneal nerves are thereby formed by dorsal rami branches from the first three spinal segments of both the lumbar and sacral spinal nerves, respectively. The inferior cluneal nerves (89, **123,** 214) are branches of the posterior femoral cutaneous nerve. Coincidently, this nerve is formed by ventral rami branches that also originate from the first three sacral spinal nerves.

THE 3 AT THE TOP AND BOTTOM

For the majority of the length of the spinal cord, the dorsal rami are represented by various unnamed muscular and cutaneous nerves. The exceptions are at the very top and bottom of the cord. The C1 dorsal ramus is small and unnamed, but both the C2 and C3 dorsal rami form named nerves. The C2 dorsal ramus forms the greater occipital nerve. The C3 dorsal ramus forms the 3rd occipital nerve. Toward the bottom of the spinal cord, dorsal rami of the top 3 lumbar spinal segments form the superior cluneal nerves. The dorsal rami of the top 3 sacral spinal segments form the middle cluneal nerves.

Gluteal and Cluneal = Buttocks

There are **two gluteal nerves** and both are **motor** nerves. The superior gluteal nerve supplies the gluteus medius, gluteus minimus, and tensor fascia latae muscles. The inferior gluteal nerve supplies the gluteus maximus muscle. By contrast, the <u>cluneal nerves</u> are <u>cutaneous</u> nerves that supply skin of the buttocks.

L1, L2, L3 ➔ dorsal rami = superior cluneal nerves ➔ skin of upper buttocks

S1, S2, S3 ➔ dorsal rami = middle cluneal nerves ➔ skin of intermediate buttocks

S1, S2, S3 ➔ ventral rami (post. femoral cut. n.) = inferior cluneal nerves ➔ skin of lower buttocks

---

GENERALIZED NERVE FUNCTIONS

Learning the specific nerve supply to individual muscles will be much easier if the general action associated with each particular nerve is known. A muscle's action upon contraction can be estimated by its location, origin, and insertion. Based upon this action, the most likely innervating nerve can be determined. As stated previously, memorization will come with time and repetition.

The hip is a ball and socket joint. This allows movement of the thigh in virtually any direction. Although the hip has a considerable range of motion, the primary action is that which is required for walking and running, flexion anteriorly and extension posteriorly. The muscles responsible for locomotion must support the weight of the body. They are large and powerful. Other muscles enable movement of the hip and thigh in various directions. These diverse movements provide the agility needed to successfully navigate and/or respond to various day-to-day occurrences. These movements are not used as consistently as those required for walking and running, and the responsible muscles are not as large.

The knee, by contrast, is a hinge joint. It moves in only two directions, flexion and extension. Like flexion and extension of the hip, flexion and extension of the knee occur against the weight of the body during locomotion. The muscles required for extension of the leg (straighten the knee) are large muscles of the anterior thigh. Muscles that flex the leg (bend the knee) are large, powerful muscles of the posterior thigh.

The ankle joint is a complex joint formed by multiple bones. Although the foot can move in multiple directions, the primary movement is dorsiflexion and plantar flexion. Injury often occurs when weight is applied to the ankle while in a position inconsistent with these two basic movements. Dorsiflexion and plantar flexion significantly increase the efficiency and strength of walking and/or running.

Plantar flexion occurs against the weight of the body while ambulating. The muscles responsible are therefore relatively large and located in the calf. By contrast, the motion of dorsiflexion is usually not against body weight but simply against the weight of the foot. The primary purpose of the motion is to lift the foot off the ground and prevent foot dragging while advancing the extremity forward to take the next step. The responsible muscles are relatively small and located in the anterior leg.

Movements of the lower limb are subconsciously harmonized with one another to provide the fluid motion necessary for coordinated locomotion. During the push-off step, the hip is extended, the leg is flexed, and the foot is plantar flexed. This all occurs at essentially the same time. Some muscles exert their contractive force on more than one segment of the lower extremity, yet these movements are coordinated in the motion of walking. The rectus femoris muscle of the anterior thigh flexes the thigh and extends the leg. Both movements are used to step forward. The biceps femoris muscle of the posterior thigh extends the thigh and flexes the leg. Both movements occur during the posteriorly-directed push-off step. Finally, the gastrocnemius muscle of the calf flexes the leg at the knee joint and plantar flexes the foot. Both movements work to propel the torso forward during the push-off step.

The femoral nerve innervates muscles that move the lower limb forward upon contraction. This involves flexion of the thigh and extension of the leg. Proximally, the femoral nerve supplies muscles that flex the thigh. This includes the psoas major, iliacus, femoral portion of the pectineus, sartorius, and rectus femoris muscles. The rectus femoris is one of the four muscles of the quadriceps femoris group. It also extends the leg. Because the other three members of the quadriceps originate on the femur and do not cross the hip, their action is limited to extension of the leg. They include the vastus lateralis, intermedius, and medialis muscles.

The sciatic nerve innervates muscles that move the lower limb posteriorly, providing the push-off step which propels the torso forward. This motion involves extension of the thigh and flexion of the leg. In the thigh, the sciatic nerve innervates three muscles that extend the thigh and flex the leg. These include the semitendinosus, semimembranosus, and biceps femoris. A fourth muscle supplied by the sciatic nerve, the superficial (posterior) portion of the adductor magnus, extends the thigh. In addition to the sciatic nerve, the inferior gluteal nerve also innervates a muscle that extends the thigh, the gluteus maximus muscle.

F = **F**emoral nerve = **F**ront **F**orward
femoral nerve supplies muscles that move the lower extremity to the front (flex thigh, extend leg)

S = **S**ciatic nerve = **S**tep off
sciatic nerve supplies muscles that are utilized during the push-off phase of a step (extend thigh, flex leg)

The tibial nerve is a terminal branch of the sciatic nerve. It supplies muscles that plantar flex the foot, an action consistent with the step-off motion provided by its parent nerve. In addition, some muscles supplied by the tibial nerve flex the leg, a motion also compatible with sciatic nerve function. These muscles originate on the femur and thus cross the posterior aspect of the knee joint. They include the popliteus, plantaris, and gastrocnemius muscles. It should be noted that the plantaris and gastrocnemius muscles also plantar flex the foot.

Continuing distally, the two terminal branches of the tibial nerve maintain the general tibial function of plantar flexion. The medial and lateral plantar nerves innervate muscles of the bottom of the foot that flex the foot and toes. Some of these may abduct or adduct toes, but the general action is flexion.

The other terminal branch of the sciatic nerve is the common peroneal nerve. It quickly divides into superficial and deep branches that supply muscles and skin of the leg.

Like the tibial nerve, the superficial peroneal nerve innervates muscles that plantar flex the foot. These two muscles, the peroneus longus and peroneus brevis, also evert the foot.

The deep peroneal nerve is responsible for the other common motions of the foot: dorsiflexion of the foot and extension of the toes. Just as flexion of the toes coincides with plantar flexion of the foot, extension of the toes coincides with dorsiflexion of the foot. In this movement, the muscles contract against the weight of the foot and/or toes instead of the weight of the body.

Inversion and eversion of the foot are accomplished by stimulation from a combination of sciatic branches. The tibial nerve innervates the tibialis posterior, which plantar flexes and inverts the foot. As mentioned, the two muscles supplied by the superficial peroneal nerve evert the foot. Finally, the deep peroneal nerve has a role in both movements. Innervation of the tibialis anterior dorsiflexes and inverts the foot. Innervation of the peroneus tertius dorsiflexes and everts the foot.

Superficial peroneal = peroneal brevis, peroneal longus
Deep peroneal = anterior muscles that extend foot and toes (dorsiflex foot)
Tibial = posterior muscles that flex foot and toes (plantar flex foot)

Propel extremity forward (after a step) –
femoral nerve, deep peroneal nerve

Propel extremity backward (during a step) –
sciatic nerve, tibial nerve, superficial peroneal nerve

The obturator nerve is the adductor nerve of the thigh. It innervates the pectineus (shared with femoral), external obturator, adductor brevis, adductor longus, gracilis, and the deep (anterior) portion of the adductor magnus muscles. Most adduct the thigh. The external obturator is the exception and rotates the thigh laterally. In addition to adduction, the pectineus, adductor brevis, and adductor longus flex the thigh. The gracilis also flexes the leg (knee joint). The superficial (posterior) portion of the adductor magnus is supplied by the sciatic nerve and extends the thigh (hip joint), an action appropriate for a sciatic-innervated muscle.

Along with other actions, the two gluteal nerves abduct the thigh (hip). The gluteus minimus and gluteus medius muscles are innervated by the superior gluteal nerve. Both muscles abduct the thigh (hip joint) and turn the thigh medially. The superior gluteal nerve also innervates the tensor fasciae latae muscle. This muscle flexes the thigh and turns the thigh medially, but does not abduct the thigh. The gluteus maximus is supplied by the inferior gluteal nerve. In addition to abducting the thigh, this muscle extends the thigh and turns the thigh laterally.

Generalized Functions

- Superior gluteal nerve – abduct thigh, turn thigh medially, flex thigh
- Inferior gluteal nerve – abduct thigh, turn thigh laterally, extend thigh
- Femoral nerve – flex thigh, extend leg
- Obturator nerve – adduct thigh, flex thigh
- Sciatic nerve – extend thigh, flex leg
- Tibial nerve – flex leg, plantar flex foot, flex toes, invert foot
- Superficial peroneal nerve – plantar flex foot, evert foot
- Deep peroneal nerve – dorsiflex foot, extend toes, invert foot, evert foot

---

QUIZ 2
LUMBOSACRAL PLEXUS

Time for Quiz = 25 minutes.
For questions 1-16, choose the single best answer.

_____1) Which statements are true concerning the pudendal nerve?
     a) It is the origin of the inferior rectal nerves.
     b) It is formed from ventral rami branches of S2, S3, S4.
     c) Both a and b
     d) It is the origin of the peroneal nerve.
     e) None of the above

_____2) Muscles innervated by the inferior gluteal nerve generally function to
     a) abduct leg
     b) extend leg
     c) both a and b
     d) flex leg
     e) none of the above

_____3) Which statements are true concerning the nerve to quadratus femoris?
     a) It innervates the superior gemellus muscle.
     b) It innervates quadriceps femoris muscle.
     c) Both a and b
     d) It innervates the inferior gemellus muscle.
     e) None of the above

_____4) Which nerve directly contributes to the formation of the sural nerve?
     a) deep peroneal nerve
     b) superficial peroneal nerve
     c) medial sural nerve
     d) lateral sural nerve
     e) none of the above

_____5) Which nerve is a direct branch of the sciatic nerve?
     a) pudendal nerve
     b) posterior femoral cutaneous nerve
     c) saphenous nerve
     d) perineal nerve
     e) none of the above

_____6) Which statements are true concerning the posterior labial nerves?
     a) In the male, they are also known as the dorsal penile nerves.
     b) They are branches of the dorsal nerve of clitoris.
     c) Both a and b
     d) They are branches of the ilioinguinal nerve.
     e) None of the above

_____7) Cutaneous innervation to which of the following areas is provided by the intermediate dorsal cutaneous nerve?
     a) superior aspect of adjacent sides of toes #3 and #4
     b) superior aspect of adjacent sides of toes #2 and #3
     c) superior aspect of adjacent sides of toes #1 and #2
     d) lateral side of toe #5
     e) none of the above

_____8) What muscle is supplied by the medial plantar nerve?
     a) quadratus plantae muscle
     b) abductor hallucis muscle
     c) adductor hallucis muscle
     d) extensor hallucis brevis muscle
     e) none of the above

_____9) Which nerve is a direct branch of the common peroneal nerve?
     a) medial sural cutaneous nerve
     b) lateral sural cutaneous nerve
     c) saphenous nerve
     d) interosseous nerve of leg
     e) none of the above

_____10) Which statements are true concerning the inferior rectal nerves?
     a) They are branches of the dorsal nerve of penis.
     b) They supply the internal anal sphincter.
     c) Both a and b
     d) They are branches of the pudendal nerve.
     e) None of the above

____11) Which muscle is directly innervated by the tibial nerve?
  a) extensor digitorum longus muscle
  b) gastrocnemius muscle
  c) peroneus brevis muscle
  d) abductor hallucis muscle
  e) none of the above

____12) Which nerves are direct branches of the superficial peroneal nerve?
  a) lateral dorsal cutaneous nerve
  b) medial sural cutaneous nerve
  c) both a and b
  d) lateral plantar nerve
  e) none of the above

____13) Muscles innervated by the deep peroneal nerve generally function to
  a) plantar flex foot
  b) extend toes
  c) both a and b
  d) flex toes
  e) none of the above

____14) Which muscle is supplied by the lateral plantar nerve?
  a) quadratus plantae muscle
  b) tibialis anterior muscle
  c) peroneus brevis muscle
  d) abductor hallucis muscle
  e) none of the above

____15) Which statements are true concerning the perineal nerve?
  a) It supplies the ischiocavernosum muscle.
  b) It supplies the superficial transverse perinei muscle.
  c) Both a and b
  d) It is the origin of the anterior scrotal nerves.
  e) None of the above

____16) Which muscle is supplied by the tibial component of the sciatic nerve?
  a) deep (anterior) portion of adductor magnus muscle
  b) gracilis muscle
  c) rectus femoris muscle
  d) semimembranosus muscle
  e) none of the above

For questions 17-25, use the following directions:
a.......1,2,3 are correct
b.......1,3 are correct
c.......2,4 are correct
d.......only 4 is correct
e.......all are correct

____17) Which statements concerning the medial dorsal cutaneous nerve are true?
  1. It is a branch of the deep peroneal nerve.
  2. It supplies skin of the medial side of toe #1.
  3. It supplies skin of the lateral side of toe #1.
  4. It supplies skin of the adjacent sides of toes #2 and #3.

____18) Which statements concerning the lateral sural nerve are true?
  1. It is the continuation of the sural nerve distal to the ankle.
  2. It combines with the medial sural nerve to form the sural nerve.
  3. It supplies skin of the lateral foot.
  4. It supplies skin of the lateral calf.

____19) Which muscles are directly innervated by the superficial peroneal nerve?
  1. peroneus brevis muscle
  2. peroneus tertius muscle
  3. peroneus longus muscle
  4. abductor hallucis muscle

____20) Which statements about the dorsal nerve of penis are true?
  1. It is a branch of the perineal nerve.
  2. It is synonymous with the dorsal labial nerve in the female.
  3. It is the origin of the posterior scrotal nerves.
  4. It innervates the corpus cavernosum.

____21) Which statements concerning the lateral plantar nerve are true?
1. The superficial branch supplies the fourth lumbrical muscle.
2. The deep branch supplies the second and third lumbrical muscles.
3. The deep branch supplies the medial two plantar interosseous muscles (#1, #2).
4. The deep branch supplies the plantar skin of the lateral side of toe #5.

____22) Which muscles are directly innervated by the sciatic nerve?
1. semitendinosus muscle
2. biceps brachii muscle
3. semimembranosus muscle
4. gluteus medius muscle

____23) Which statements concerning the deep peroneal nerve are true?
1. It supplies the extensor digitorum brevis muscle.
2. It is a terminal branch of the common peroneal nerve.
3. It supplies the extensor hallucis longus muscle.
4. It supplies skin on the medial side of toe #1.

____24) Which statements concerning the medial plantar nerve are true?
1. It is a branch of the tibial nerve.
2. It supplies the first lumbrical muscle.
3. It supplies plantar skin of the medial side of toe #1.
4. It supplies plantar skin of the medial side of toe #4.

____25) Which statements concerning the lumbosacral trunk are true?
1. A branch of the L2 ventral ramus contributes to its formation.
2. It represents the only lumbar contribution to the sacral plexus.
3. It contributes to the formation of the pudendal nerve.
4. It contributes to the formation of the superior gluteal nerve.

QUIZ 2: Lumbosacral Answers and Explanations

1) c – The pudendal nerve is formed by ventral rami branches from the S2, S3, and S4 spinal segments (sacral plexus). The pudendal nerve serves as the origin of the inferior rectal nerves before dividing into its two terminal branches, the perineal nerve and dorsal nerve of penis (clitoris). The perineal nerve should not be confused with the peroneal nerve. The common peroneal nerve is a terminal branch of the sciatic nerve.

2) e – The inferior gluteal nerve innervates the gluteus maximus muscle. This muscle functions to abduct the thigh, turn the thigh laterally, and extend the thigh. Answer C would be correct if answers A and B said *"thigh"* instead of *"leg."*

3) d – The nerve to quadratus femoris is formed from ventral rami branches from the L4, L5, and S1 spinal segments. The nerve to quadratus femoris supplies both the quadratus femoris and inferior gemellus muscles. The superior gemellus muscle is supplied by the nerve to obturator internus. The quadriceps femoris muscle group should not be confused with the quadratus femoris muscle. The quadriceps femoris is a group of four muscles of the anterior thigh that are innervated by the femoral nerve.

4) c – The sural nerve is a cutaneous nerve formed by the combination of a common peroneal nerve branch, the peroneal communicating nerve, and a tibial nerve branch, the medial sural nerve. The sural nerve supplies skin of the posterior calf and lateral side of the foot. The deep peroneal nerve supplies skin between the first and second toes. The superficial peroneal nerve is the origin of the medial and intermediate dorsal cutaneous nerves of the foot. The lateral sural nerve is a cutaneous branch of the common peroneal nerve and supplies skin of the lateral calf.

5) e – The pudendal nerve is formed by ventral rami branches from the S2, S3, and S4 spinal segments (sacral plexus). The posterior femoral cutaneous nerve is formed by ventral rami branches from the S1, S2, and S3 spinal segments (sacral plexus). The saphenous nerve is a branch of the femoral nerve. Finally, the perineal nerve, along with the dorsal nerve of penis (clitoris), is a terminal branch of the pudendal nerve.

6) e – The posterior labial nerves are branches of the perineal nerve. In the male, they are known as the posterior scrotal nerves. Remember, Pudendal → Perineal → Posterior labial (scrotal). In addition to the perineal nerve, the dorsal nerve of clitoris (penis) is a terminal branch of the pudendal nerve. Finally, the anterior labial (scrotal) nerves are branches of the ilioinguinal nerve.

7) a – The intermediate dorsal cutaneous nerve is the origin of dorsal digital nerves that supply the dorsal surface of the adjacent sides of toes #3 and #4, #4 and #5. The medial side of toe #1 and adjacent sides of toes #2 and #3 are supplied by the medial dorsal cutaneous nerve. The adjacent sides of toes #1 and #2 are supplied by the deep peroneal nerve. The lateral or outer side of the little toe, toe #5, is supplied by the lateral dorsal cutaneous nerve, which is the distal continuation of the sural nerve. The plantar surface of all toes is innervated by the plantar nerves.

8) b – The medial plantar nerve innervates the abductor hallucis, flexor hallucis brevis, flexor digitorum brevis, and first lumbrical muscles. Both the quadratus plantae and adductor hallucis muscles are supplied by the lateral plantar nerve. If the location of muscles required to abduct or adduct the great toe is considered, the innervation of the abductor hallucis by the medial plantar nerve and adductor hallucis by the lateral plantar nerve becomes more logical and easier to remember. To abduct or spread the great toe away from the other toes, the abductor hallucis must be on the *medial* side of the great toe. To adduct or pull the great toe inward, the adductor hallucis must be on the *lateral* side of the great toe. The extensor digitorum brevis muscle is supplied by the deep peroneal nerve.

The portion of this muscle which inserts on the great toe is often described as a separate muscle, the extensor hallucis brevis.

9) b – The three nerves which branch from the common peroneal prior to its separation into deep and superficial branches are the recurrent articular branch, lateral sural cutaneous nerve, and peroneal communicating nerve. The lateral sural cutaneous nerve supplies skin of the lateral calf. Both the medial sural cutaneous nerve and the interosseous nerve of leg are branches of the tibial nerve. The saphenous nerve is a branch of the femoral nerve.

10) d – The inferior rectal nerves are branches of the pudendal nerve. They supply the sphincter ani externus muscle (external anal sphincter) and skin around anal opening. The internal anal sphincter is under autonomic nervous system control. After serving as the origin of the inferior rectal nerves, the pudendal nerve divides into its two terminal branches, the perineal nerve and dorsal nerve of penis (clitoris).

11) b – The tibial nerve innervates the plantaris, popliteus, gastrocnemius, soleus, tibialis posterior, flexor digitorum longus, and flexor hallucis longus muscles. The extensor digitorum longus muscle is innervated by the deep peroneal nerve. The peroneus brevis muscle is innervated by the superficial peroneal nerve. The abductor hallucis muscle is supplied by the medial plantar nerve. Although the medial plantar nerve is a terminal branch of the tibial nerve, the question asks for muscles that are *directly* innervated by the tibial nerve.

12) e – The superficial peroneal nerve becomes a cutaneous sensory nerve approximately midway between the knee and foot. The superficial peroneal nerve divides into the medial and intermediate dorsal cutaneous nerves, which supply skin of the top or dorsum of the foot. The lateral dorsal cutaneous nerve is the continuation of the sural nerve along the lateral side of the foot. The medial sural nerve is a cutaneous branch of the tibial nerve. Finally, the lateral plantar nerve, along with the medial plantar nerve, is a terminal branch of the tibial nerve.

13) b – Muscles innervated by the deep peroneal nerve generally function to dorsiflex the foot and extend the toes.

14) a – The lateral plantar nerve is responsible for innervating 14 foot muscles. Although this may initially seem a challenge to remember, 10 of the 14 muscles are composed of lumbrical and interosseous muscles. Muscles innervated include the quadratus plantae, abductor digiti minimi pedis, flexor digiti minimi pedis, the three lateral lumbrical muscles (there are four lumbrical muscles – the medial plantar nerve innervates the first lumbrical), all four dorsal interosseous muscles, all three plantar interosseous muscles, and the adductor hallucis muscle. The tibialis anterior muscle is innervated by the deep peroneal nerve. The peroneus brevis muscle is innervated by the superficial peroneal nerve. The abductor hallucis muscle is supplied by the medial plantar nerve.

15) c – The deep branch of the perineal nerve innervates the ischiocavernosus, bulbo-spongiosus, and superficial transverse perinei muscle (superficial transverse muscle of perineum). The perineal nerve is the origin of the posterior scrotal (labial) nerves. The anterior scrotal nerves are branches of the ilioinguinal nerve, with possible contribution from the genitofemoral nerve.

16) d – The sciatic nerve is formed by a tibial and peroneal component. Each later becomes a separate nerve. The tibial component innervates the superficial (posterior) portion of the adductor magnus, semitendinosus, semimembranosus, and long head of the biceps femoris muscles. The peroneal component of the sciatic nerve innervates the short head of the biceps femoris muscle. Both the deep (anterior) portion of adductor magnus muscle and the gracilis muscle are supplied by the obturator nerve. The rectus femoris muscle is supplied by the femoral nerve.

17) c – The medial dorsal cutaneous nerve is the medial branch of the superficial peroneal nerve. The medial dorsal cutaneous nerve is the origin of dorsal digital nerves that supply the dorsal surface of the medial side of the

great toe (toe #1) and adjacent sides of toes #2 and #3. The adjacent sides of toes #1 and #2 are supplied by the deep peroneal nerve.

18) d – The lateral sural cutaneous nerve is a branch of the common peroneal nerve and supplies skin of the lateral calf. The sural nerve is formed by the combination of a common peroneal nerve branch, the peroneal communicating nerve, and a tibial nerve branch, the medial sural nerve. Skin of the lateral side of the foot is supplied by the distal continuation of the sural nerve, the lateral dorsal cutaneous nerve.

19) b – The superficial peroneal nerve innervates the peroneus longus and peroneus brevis muscles. The peroneus tertius muscle is innervated by the deep peroneal nerve. The abductor hallucis muscle is supplied by the medial plantar nerve.

20) d – The corpus cavernosum is not a muscle, but a shaft or column of erectile tissue that is innervated by the dorsal nerve of the penis (clitoris). The dorsal nerve of the penis (clitoris), along with the perineal nerve, is a terminal branch of the pudendal nerve. The posterior scrotal (labial) nerves are branches of the perineal nerve.

21) a – The lateral plantar nerve supplies the quadratus plantae and abductor digiti minimi pedis muscles before dividing into superficial and deep branches. The superficial branch supplies the flexor digiti minimi brevis, the third plantar interosseous, fourth dorsal interosseous and fourth lumbrical muscles. It also supplies the plantar skin of the lateral side of toe #5 and the adjacent sides of toes #4 and #5 (lateral 1 1/2 toes). The deep branch supplies 8 foot muscles including the medial two plantar interossei (#1 and #2), the medial three dorsal interossei (#1, #2, and #3), the intermedially located two lumbrical muscles (#2 and #3), and the adductor hallucis muscle.

22) b – The sciatic nerve supplies the semitendinosus,

semimembranosus, biceps femoris and superficial (posterior) portion of the adductor magnus muscles. The biceps brachii is an arm muscle supplied by the musculocutaneous nerve. The gluteus medius muscle is supplied by the superior gluteal nerve.

23) a – The deep peroneal nerve, along with the superficial peronial nerve, is a terminal branch of the common peroneal nerve. The deep peroneal nerve supplies five muscles and the dorsal skin of the adjacent sides of toes #1 and #2. Supplied muscles include the tibialis anterior, extensor digitorum longus, extensor hallucis longus, peroneus tertius, and extensor digitorum brevis muscles. The adjacent sides of toes #1 and #2 include the lateral side of toe #1 and medial side of toe #2. Skin on the medial side of toe #1 is innervated by the medial dorsal cutaneous nerve.

24) e – The medial plantar nerve, along with the lateral plantar nerve, is a terminal branch of the tibial nerve. The medial plantar nerve supplies four muscles, skin of the medial sole, and plantar skin of the medial 3 1/2 toes. This includes plantar skin of the medial side of toe #1 and adjacent sides of toes #1 and #2, #2 and #3, #3 and #4. The medial side of toe #4 is therefore innervated by the medial plantar nerve. The four supplied muscles include the abductor hallucis, flexor hallucis brevis, flexor digitorum brevis, and first lumbrical muscles.

25) c – A branch of the L4 ventral ramus combines with the entire L5 ventral ramus to form the lumbosacral trunk. This trunk represents the only lumbar contribution to the sacral plexus. It travels down and contributes branches that combine with sacral branches to form the superior gluteal nerve, inferior gluteal nerve, and sciatic nerve. The superior gluteal nerve is formed by a branch of the lumbosacral trunk (L4, L5) that combines with a S1 ventral ramus branch. The pudendal nerve is formed by ventral rami branches from the S2, S3, and S4 spinal segments.

"The purpose of life is a life of purpose."

– Robert Byrne

CLINICAL CORRELATION

Childbirth serves as an excellent example to demonstrate the exponential advancements made in medical care over the last century. Years ago, it was not uncommon to hear of mothers or infants who died during childbirth. Although unfortunate events continue, the incidence of perioperative mortality and morbidity is significantly less in modern times.

The reasons for the improvement are multiple. Ongoing developments and refinements in the medical training of physicians and nurses improve the quality of care. Structured training programs and licensing requirements strive to ensure that the individual taking care of a patient has a satisfactory level of competence. Technologic gains provide an ever-increasing number of better diagnostic and therapeutic tools to work with. New medicines and improved techniques provide better outcomes.

Not only are obstetrical surgical options much safer than in the past, but the diagnostic skills of practitioners are more uniformly improved. Patient access to prenatal care allows the pregnancy to be more closely monitored. Radiological imaging and laboratory studies enable the obstetrician to become aware of a potential problem earlier. Doppler ultrasound may reveal a fetus in a breech position or a uterine or placental abnormality. Laboratory studies can detect preexisting low blood counts or chemical imbalances indicative of kidney or liver disease. Once detected, a plan can be made to adequately deal with the issue at hand. This may involve admitting the mother to the hospital for bed rest and continual monitoring. Alternatively, if the fetus is viable, surgical delivery of the infant via cesarean section (C-section) may be warranted.

Although advancements in patient safety are the most significant indicator of improved patient care, much can be said about the improvement in the patient experience. This is especially apparent with childbirth. Anesthetic techniques provide the ability to almost instantaneously render the patient unconscious and pain-free with general anesthesia should emergency surgery be required. This involves administration of intravenous (IV) medications, intubation of the trachea with an endotracheal tube, and maintenance of anesthesia with inhalational gasses and other IV medications as needed. If the mother is to have a C-section and time permits, she may receive a regional anesthetic, such as an epidural or spinal. A regional anesthetic allows her to be awake during the birth of her child, yet experience little or no surgical pain. Epidural anesthesia and other techniques are also employed to significantly decrease the pain experienced by laboring patients who eventually undergo a vaginal delivery.

Understanding when and why certain pain control procedures are utilized during labor and delivery requires a basic knowledge of the etiology of labor pain and its temporal relationship to the process of labor. The stage of labor determines the type of pain experienced. This pain sensation has a certain origin and is transmitted along specific neural pathways. If the origin and routes of transmission are known, particular anatomic locations where the pain should be effectively blocked can be determined.

The process of labor is divided into three stages. The first stage begins with the onset of regular, painful uterine contractions and ends with complete cervical dilation. Most of the pain of this stage is secondary to dilation of the lower uterus, cervix, and upper vagina. These are visceral organs of the pelvis. The pain is visceral in nature and is transmitted in nerves of the sympathetic nervous system. Once initiated, these impulses travel through the paracervical ganglion. The pelvic afferent visceral fibers that carry these impulses enter the sympathetic chain at the approximate L2 and L3 vertebral levels. Subsequent to that, they travel up the chain to enter the spinal cord via white rami communicans at the T10 – L1 spinal levels. Once in the cord, these fibers synapse with other neurons to continue the signal ascent to the brain. This structure provides several analgesic or pain relief alternatives: block sympathetic transmission before it reaches the sympathetic chain, block the sympathetic chain between the L1 and L3 levels, or block the spinal cord above the T10 level. It should be noted that the first two options require that the procedure be performed on both the right and left sides. The last option may be accomplished with the use of an epidural or spinal anesthetic.

The second stage of labor lasts from complete cervical dilation to the onset of delivery. It is during this stage that the infant descends the birth canal. Although a strong visceral component to the pain remains, somatic pain becomes more prominent as perineal structures are stretched. Afferent somatic impulses of the perineum are primarily conducted in the pudendal nerve (S2, S3, S4). Somatic pain may also be transmitted via the anterior labial nerves of the ilioinguinal nerve (L1), the genital branch of the genitofemoral nerve (L1, L2), and branches of the posterior femoral cutaneous nerve (S1, S2, S3). During the second stage of labor, both visceral and somatic pain must be blocked. The requirements for preventing visceral pain were described in the previous paragraph. Somatic labor pain can be ablated by a pudendal nerve block and other local nerve blocks as needed. Alternatively, an epidural or spinal anesthetic that blocks the spinal cord at or above the T10 level would prevent both the visceral and somatic components of labor pain.

The third stage of labor includes the actual delivery of the infant and ends with the delivery of the placenta. The pain of the third stage is more somatic in nature, as structures of the body wall are stretched and dilated during delivery. If the patient arrives late in labor or has previously declined pain-relief procedures and now requests them, effort is directed towards relief of somatic pain.

Epidural anesthesia is perhaps the most familiar form of pain relief associated with modern obstetric care. The reason is simple: it is effective and provides a great deal of flexibility. The process involves placement of an epidural catheter through an epidural needle and into the epidural space. A catheter is simply a flexible tube through which fluid may pass. An epidural catheter is a very narrow tube that fits within the hollow space of an epidural needle, a relatively large-diameter needle.

Prior to placement of an epidural catheter, an epidural needle is placed between the spinous processes of two successive vertebrae and advanced toward the spine from the back. From posterior to anterior, it travels through the skin, subcutaneous tissue, supraspinous ligament, interspinous ligament, and ligamentum flavum to reach the epidural space.

FIGURE 12.21
PLACEMENT OF EPIDURAL NEEDLE
(Reproduced from Scott D.B.: Techniques of Regional Anaesthesia, Norwalk, 1989, Appleton & Lange.)

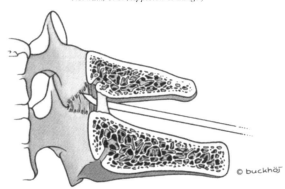

The subcutaneous tissue is the loose connective tissue found just beneath the skin. The supraspinous ligament is a layer of dense connective tissue that joins the dorsal surface of spinous processes of successive vertebrae. The infraspinous ligament connects the actual spinous processes. Finally, the ligamentum flavum is a layer of dense connective tissue that joins the laminae of successive vertebrae. Together, the anterior surface of a vertebral lamina and its associated ligamentum flavum form the posterior border of the vertebral canal.

Once the epidural space is located with the needle, an epidural catheter is threaded through the hollow needle and into the epidural space. The needle is then removed and the flexible

FIGURE 12.22
CROSS-SECTION OF SPINAL STRUCTURES
(Reproduced from Scott D.B.: Techniques of Regional Anaesthesia, Norwalk, 1989, Appleton & Lange.)

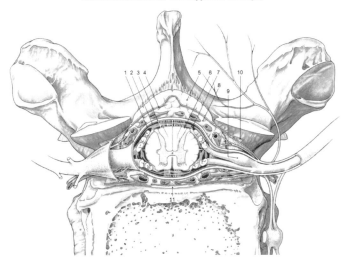

1. Arachnoid mater	5. Ligamentum flavum	9. Dorsal root ganglion
2. Subdural space	6. Pia mater	10. Periosteum
3. Dura mater (inner layer)	7. Subarachnoid space	11. Posterior longitudinal
4. Dura mater (outer layer)	8. Epidural space	ligament

catheter is secured to remain within the epidural space. The epidural space is not a true area of "space" but an area of adipose and loose connective tissue that is immediately exterior to the dura mater of the spinal canal. In other words, the epidural space is located between the dura mater, deeply, and the ligamentum flavum and vertebral laminae, superficially. There is no free fluid within the epidural space. Injected local anesthetic spreads freely to surround nerve roots emerging from the spinal canal.

As previously noted, the popularity of epidural anesthesia for management of obstetric pain is owed to its effectiveness and flexibility. Epidural anesthesia is capable of providing analgesia or pain relief during all three stages of labor. The dose can be titrated so that the mother is comfortable, yet abdominal muscular tone is maintained and she can adequately push during delivery. Furthermore, the catheter allows the medicine to be re-dosed as needed for prolonged labor. If necessary, a larger dose of local anesthetic can be delivered to provide a surgical level of anesthesia, as may be required for C-section. The patient, therefore, may undergo a surgical procedure without the additional risk of a general or spinal anesthetic. Once in place, an epidural catheter can be utilized for a wide range of indications. It is the only form of obstetric pain management that is effective for all three stages of labor, capable of re-dosing as needed for prolonged labor, and effective for C-section. In addition, a properly functioning epidural allows the mother to be awake and conscious for the birth of her child.

FIGURE 12.23
LOCATION OF EPIDURAL CATHETER
(Reproduced and modified from Scott D.B.: Techniques of Regional Anaesthesia, Norwalk, 1989, Appleton & Lange.)

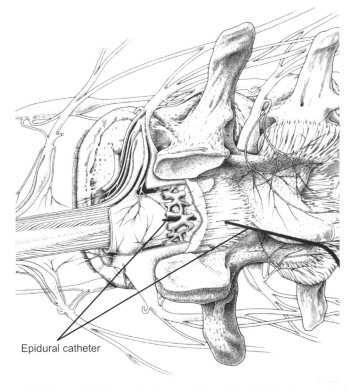

Epidural catheter

With a **spinal anesthetic** or **subarachnoid block**, a spinal needle is advanced toward the spine from the back. It takes the same route and travels through the same tissues as an epidural needle, only it goes deeper. It punctures the dura mater to reach the subarachnoid space. This is evidenced by the appearance of cerebral spinal fluid (CSF) from the needle. There is no threading of a catheter with a spinal, only a single injection of local anesthetic. A spinal needle therefore has a much smaller diameter than an epidural needle, even though it courses deeper. After the single shot is administered, the needle is removed. Depending on the type and dose of local anesthetic, the patient can lose all sensory and motor function from the upper abdomen to the toes. The duration of block is variable, but it frequently lasts one to three hours. During this time, the patient may undergo lower abdominal or lower extremity surgery without pain.

From a procedural aspect, a spinal anesthetic is very similar to a lumbar puncture (LP) or spinal tap. With a spinal, medicine is injected into the CSF to provide anesthesia or loss of sensation. With a lumbar puncture, CSF is obtained for diagnostic laboratory studies. To prevent spinal cord injury, both spinals and lumbar punctures are performed inferior to the L2 vertebral level. This is because the spinal cord ends at the approximate L1-L2 level. The dural sac, on the other hand, continues inferiorly to end at the approximate S2 level. The wall of the dural sac is formed by the dura mater and it contains CSF. Lower lumbar and sacral nerve roots branch from the conus medullaris at the L1-L2 level and travel inferiorly within the dural sac as the cauda equina. Should a spinal or lumbar puncture needle contact a descending nerve root, the needle would tend to push the root within the CSF and reflect off, as opposed to actually piercing the nerve tissue. If contact occurs, the patient may experience a sharp, "electric-like" pain that shoots to the area of the body supplied by the contacted nerve root. The pain is usually very transient, lasting only a second or two. If it persists, the needle is repositioned until the patient is pain-free.

L2 and S2
L2 = end of spinal cord   S2 = end of dural sac

Spinal anesthesia possesses specific attributes and characteristics that make it particularly attractive in certain situations. This includes providing anesthesia for a scheduled C-section. Because the procedure is scheduled and the patient is not in labor, the single shot of a spinal can be administered at just the right time to provide anesthesia for the procedure. Since the local anesthetic is delivered directly into the CSF, only a small fraction of the dose required for an epidural is needed. There is, therefore, less chance of a medication reaction or effect on the fetus. Should a medication reaction occur, its severity will likely be limited. The sensory block tends to be denser with spinal anesthesia as compared to that of epidural anesthesia for management of surgical pain. Patients are less likely to experience discomfort. Flaccid paralysis of the abdomen and lower extremities often occurs, but no pushing by the mother will be required. As compared to an epidural, the block sets up faster. This promotes its use when there is some degree of urgency to the situation, yet an epidural is not in place and a general anesthetic is not warranted.

Except for one situation, spinal anesthetics have little use with laboring patients. First and foremost, the duration of labor is unpredictable. The single shot spinal wears off after a specified period of time. The discomfort and risk to the patient would preclude its repetition. In addition, the dense motor block associated with a local anesthetic spinal is not desirable. The mother must maintain a considerable level of muscular tone to push the baby out of the birth canal.

The one exception to the use of a spinal in labor is a **saddle block**. A saddle block is a low-dose spinal that can be used to provide analgesia during the third stage of labor. During performance of a saddle block, a spinal is quickly performed with the patient in a sitting position. The dose of local anesthetic is much less than that administered in a typical spinal for C-section, usually almost half the dose. Additionally, the administered local anesthetic is hyperbaric, signifying it is "heavier" than CSF. The mother is maintained in the sitting position for a few moments after performance of the block. The "heavier" local anesthetic is pulled inferior by gravity and selectively bathes the sacral nerve roots. This results in a block specific to the perineum and lower extremity. Only the area that would otherwise contact a saddle is anesthetized. Lower abdominal muscular tone is maintained. The mother is able to successfully push the baby out of the birth canal.

There are patients for whom an epidural or spinal anesthetic is not an option. Some patients have an inherent fear of needles, especially those near the spine. It is not uncommon or unreasonable for a patient to decline the procedure for this reason. Other patients may possess preexisting spinal deformities that make needle placement difficult, if not impossible. Abnormal blood coagulation status may negate the performance of a spinal or epidural due to increased risk of local hemorrhage and subsequent blood clot formation. A blood clot could compress and injure a nerve, nerve root, or even the spinal cord within the tight confines of the vertebral canal. Although exceedingly rare, cases of permanent nerve injury and paraplegia have occurred as a result of this phenomenon. Certain coagulation abnormalities can be associated with pregnancy itself. Laboratory blood coagulation studies are obtained prior to the placement of an epidural or spinal in any obstetric patient who may be at risk. If the results reveal abnormalities, other anesthetic options may be considered. These options include general anesthesia for C-section and I.V. drug medications and/or nerve blocks for labor.

Many patients undergo labor and delivery with nothing more than I.V. pain medications. Other patients require the additional relief provided by local anesthetic nerve blockade. There are two local blocks for the relief of visceral pain associated with labor: lumbar sympathetic block and paracervical block. Somatic pain can be relieved by pudendal nerve block. This nerve block may require supplementation with additional blocks of other nerves of the area. Either a lumbar sympathetic or paracervical block is performed to relieve visceral pain associated with the first stage of labor. The pudendal and associated local blocks are performed later in the second or third stage to relieve somatic pain. Thus the patient undergoes a "dual" block; one for visceral pain (first and second stage) and one for somatic pain (second and third stage). It should again be noted that each of these local anesthetic blockades must be performed on both the right and left sides. Local anesthetic doses should be calculated and the injections separated by enough time to ensure the mother or fetus does not receive a toxic dose or undergo an adverse reaction.

Visceral pain associated with the first and second stages of labor is transmitted by sympathetic visceral afferent fibers that travel through the paracervical sympathetic ganglion on each side of the cervix. They then pass through the inferior hypogastric and pelvic plexuses to enter the sympathetic chain at the L2 and L3 vertebral levels. The fibers continue the ascent up the chain to enter the spinal cord at the T10 - L1 levels. This arrangement includes two areas where the visceral afferent fibers are tightly grouped and thus are susceptible to local anesthetic blockade: the paracervical ganglion and the sympathetic chain at the L1 - L2 levels.

A **paracervical block** is frequently used to block pain associated with the first stage of labor. The paracervical ganglion, also known as Frakenhauser's ganglion, is located just posterior and lateral to the border between the cervix and uterus. The block is performed with the patient in the dorsal lithotomy position. The patient is on her back with the legs spread and elevated. From within the vagina, the needle is placed in either the left or right vaginal fornix, the inner fold of mucosa between the cervix and vagina. The needle is advanced a few millimeters and 5-10 cc of local anesthetic is injected. The needle is removed and the patient and fetus are monitored for several minutes to ensure no adverse reaction occurs prior to repeating the block on the opposite side. Because of the close proximity of the fetal head to the point of injection, the fetus is especially susceptible to adverse drug reactions, including fetal bradycardia. For this reason, the fetal heart rate should be monitored closely during and after the performance of the block.

A **lumbar sympathetic block** is another method to block pain associated with the first stage of labor. From the back, a needle is advanced toward the spine in the lumbar region. As opposed to the midline needle approach to the subarachnoid or epidural space, the lumbar sympathetic chain is approached from a slight lateral position. This is because the sympathetic chain is located at the anterolateral surface of the bodies of the vertebrae and courses parallel to the vertebral column. The L2 spinous process is located and the needle is placed 7-8 cm to the right or left of this process. The needle is advanced in a slight anterior and medial direction until the transverse process of the L2 vertebrae is contacted. The needle is withdrawn and redirected more anteriorly until it is able to pass beneath the transverse process. It is advanced an additional 4-5 cm, at which point it should be very near the sympathetic chain at the L2 vertebral level. Approximately 10cc of local anesthetic is injected and the needle is removed. The patient is monitored several minutes for an adverse reaction prior to repeating the injection on the opposite side. The emergence of epidural anesthesia over the last several decades has significantly decreased the use of a lumbar sympathetic block as a means to control labor pain. An epidural may prove beneficial in the event of prolonged labor or C-section. Still, in unique conditions and certain situations, a lumbar sympathetic block may occasionally be used in the obstetric suite.

The final obstetric analgesic procedure to discuss is the **pudendal nerve block**. This ablates somatic pain associated with the third stage of labor. The pudendal block may be paired with a paracervical block (or rarely, lumbar sympathetic block) in a laboring patient for whom an epidural is contraindicated. More commonly, it is used in a patient who has progressed through the first stage of labor and now requires pain relief. A pudendal block

serves as an alternative to a saddle block and is especially useful if the patient cannot sit up for performance of the saddle block. The pudendal nerve supplies virtually all sensory nerves to the perineum. Possible exceptions include the innervation of the labia majora by the anterior labial nerves/genital branch of the genitofemoral nerve and areas of posterior perineal skin which may be supplied by posterior femoral cutaneous branches. If required, these other sensory branches can be blocked by injection of local anesthetic into the area of their respective innervation.

The pudendal nerve is formed by ventral rami branches from S2, S3, and S4. It exits the pelvis by way of the sciatic notch and curves around the lateral aspect of the ischial spine. It is in this location that the nerve should be blocked with local anesthetic, before it gives off the inferior rectal nerves (inferior hemorrhoidal nerves) and divides into the dorsal nerve of clitoris and perineal nerve. Blocking the nerve in this relatively proximal location ensures that all subsequent branches are also unable to transmit pain impulses.

FIGURE 12.24
NERVE SUPPLY TO PERINEUM
(Reproduced with permission from Cousins, M.J., Bridenbaugh, P.O.: Neural Blockade in Clinical Anesthesia and Management of Pain, 2nd ed. Philadelphia, J. B. Lippincott Co., 1988.)

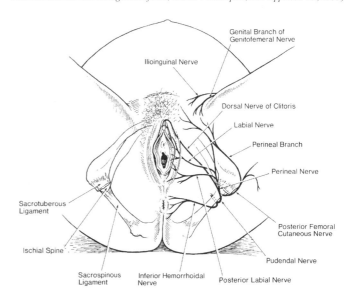

The pudendal block is performed in the dorsal lithotomy position. The patient is on her back. Legs are spread and elevated with the aid of supportive stirrups, if needed. The ischial spine is felt from within the lateral side of the vagina. Coursing posteriorly from this spine is the sacrospinous ligament. A needle is directed through the vaginal mucosa and advanced in a slight lateral direction until the sacrospinous ligament is pierced. At this point, 10-15 cc of local anesthetic is injected. The needle is then removed. After enough time has elapsed to assess the well-being of the mother and fetus, the block is repeated on the opposite side.

SUMMARY OF CHAPTER BOXES

1) The **2 legs** are supplied by **2** plexuses (lumbar and sacral). Each plexus provides **2** primary nerves to the lower extremity (lumbar = obturator and femoral, sacral = common peroneal and tibial). Each of the **L2-L4** levels of the lumbar plexus has **2** divisions (anterior and posterior). Each division supplies **2** nerves (anterior = genitofemoral and obturator, posterior = lateral femoral cutaneous and femoral). **2** nerves arise from these levels but are not formed by branches from anterior or posterior divisions (accessory obturator nerve and L4 branch to lumbosacral trunk).

2) **Half and Half:** The Function of the **Obturator** nerve is to $A_1D_2D_3U_4C_5T_6$
The obturator nerve supplies **6** muscles. Half have "adduct" in their names: adductor brevis, adductor longus, adductor magnus [deep (anterior) portion]. Half do not: pectineus (shared with femoral nerve), obturator externus, and gracilis.

3) The thigh should not be confused with the leg. Movements of **thigh** via **hip joint**. Movements of **leg** via **knee joint**.

4) **Meralgia paresthetica** = numbness/burning pain of upper outer thigh due to injury or compression of the **lateral femoral cutaneous nerve**. Often due to pants/belts that are worn too tight.

5) **Half and Half: femoral** nerve innervates 8 muscles. Half (4) flex the thigh. The other half (4) form the quadriceps femoris muscle group and extend the leg. Both functions move the lower extremity in an anterior (or forward) direction.

6) **The Responsibility of the Femoral Nerve is VAST:** femoral nerve innervates <u>vast</u>us lateralis, <u>vast</u>us intermedius, and <u>vast</u>us medialis muscles. These three, along with the rectus femoris muscle, form the quadriceps femoris. In addition, the femoral nerve is the only lumbar plexus nerve to supply tissue of the leg (below knee) via saphenous nerve.

7) **L5 = TRAITOR:** the lowest lumbar spinal segment (L5) deserts its lumbar comrades and contributes its entire ventral ramus to the sacral plexus via the lumbosacral trunk. Not wanting to do it alone, it coerces a branch from the L4 ventral ramus, its nearest lumbar neighbor, to also join in the formation of the lumbosacral trunk

8) **GOLF: GO** = anterior divisions = genitofemoral (L1,L2), obturator (L2,L3,L4)
L F = posterior divisions = lat. femoral cut. (L2,L3), femoral (L2,L3,L4)

Lumbar Plexus = **Golf plus two**
1 2 3 4 5 6

GOLF + accessory obturator nerve + branch to lumbosacral trunk
1 2 3 4   5   6

9) "gluteal" (and "cluneal") = buttocks
The most "*superior*" aspect of lower extremity = buttocks and hip joint.
It is appropriate that the hip joint is innervated by the *superior* gluteal nerve.

10) quad<u>ratus</u> (4-sided) femoris muscle vs. quad<u>riceps</u> (4-headed) femoris muscle group = rectus femoris, vastus lateralis, vastus intermedius, and vastus lateralis muscles.

11) inferior and superior <u>gem</u>ellus muscles are real "<u>GEMS</u>"!
inferior gemellus via nerve to quadratus femoris (L4, L5, S1)
superior gemellus via nerve to obturator internus (L5, S1, S2)

12) Both superior gluteal nerve and nerve to quadratus femoris = L4, L5, S1
Both inferior gluteal nerve and nerve to obturator internus = L5, S1, S2

13) The gluteus maximus thinks it is "the max." The inferior gluteal nerve is "inferior." It cowers and supplies only the gluteus maximus muscle.

14) **Most skin of the thigh** is supplied by the **three** "*femoral*" nerves.
femoral n. (L2,L3,L4) = anterior thigh
lat. *femoral* **cut. n.** (L2,L3) = lateral thigh
post. *femoral* **cut. nerve** (S1,S2,S3) = lower buttocks (inf. cluneal nerves), post. thigh
In addition: <u>upper anterior thigh</u> = fem. br. genitofemoral, ilioinguinal, and iliohypogastric
<u>inner, medial thigh</u> = genital br. genitofemoral, ilioinguinal, and obturator nerves
<u>buttocks</u> = superior and middle cluneal nerves

15) pudendal nerve = **THE** nerve of the perineum. It is the most medial nerve emerging from under the cover of the piriformis muscle in fig. 3; it is closest to the perineum.

16) P → P → P...Pudendal → Perineal → Posterior Scrotal (Labial)

17) <u>D</u>eep transverse perinei muscle via <u>D</u>orsal nerve of the penis (clitoris).
Superficial transverse perinei muscle via perineal nerve.

18) Gender differences in nerve names: scrotal = labial, penis = clitoris

19) The sciatic nerve and branches appear to parallel the skeleton of the lower extremity. **thigh** = one bone (femur) and one nerve (sciatic)
leg = two bones: common peroneal nerve with fibula, tibial nerve with tibia.

20) Just as the fibula bone is <u>s</u>mall compared to the tibia, the innervation of the peroneal portion of the sciatic nerve in the thigh is <u>s</u>mall compared to the tibial portion. The only muscle supplied by the peroneal portion is the <u>s</u>hort head of the biceps femoris.

21) S & S: <u>S</u>ciatic nerve innervates the <u>S</u>uperficial (posterior) portion of the adductor magnus muscle.

22) Muscles of the thigh that are supplied by the **sciatic nerve** share common actions, including **extension of the thigh** and **flexion of the leg**.

23) **Perineal nerve vs. Common peroneal nerve** (or branches)
"i" comes before "o." The per<u>I</u>neal nerve innervates an area of the body (perineum) that is higher or more proximal than the area supplied by the per<u>O</u>neal nerve (leg).

24) **3 "sural" nerves** and all are **cutaneous** nerves: 1) **lateral sural nerve** branches from the common peroneal nerve (named for its proximity to the *lateral* bone of the leg, the fibula) 2) **medial sural nerve** branches from the tibial nerve (named for its proximity to the *medial* bone of the leg, the tibia) 3) the **sural nerve** is formed by the combination of the peroneal communicating and medial sural nerves. "*THE*" sural nerve requires one branch from each terminal branch of the sciatic nerve, the peroneal communicating nerve from the common peroneal nerve and the medial sural nerve from the tibial nerve.

25) The "superficial" peroneal nerve supplies skin on "top" of the foot.

26) Like the common, superficial, and deep peroneal nerves, the **3 peroneus muscles** are named for their location relative to the fibula, the lateral bone of the leg. Because these muscles are located in the lateral aspect of the leg, it is no surprise that all 3 function in **eversion** of the foot.

27) The **2 peroneal nerves: superficial with 2 muscles** (peroneus longus, peroneus brevis), **deep with 2 "toe sides"** (adjacent sides of 1st and 2nd toes)
Superficial brs. are usually cutaneous and deep brs. are usually motor. The same is true with the peroneal nerves, except each "dabbles" in the work of the other.

28) Two "**S**" cutaneous nerves descend the leg and supply skin on each <u>S</u>ide of the foot:
<u>S</u>aphenous nerve (femoral nerve) = **medial** side of the foot.
<u>S</u>ural nerve (peroneal communicating n., medial sural n.) = **lateral** side of the foot (as the lateral dorsal cutaneous nerve). Alphabetically, saphenous comes before sural and saphenous is more medial than sural, just as the toes are numbered.

29) The **plantar**is muscle **plantar** flexes the foot.

30) The **sole**us muscle solely plantar flexes the foot (it does not flex the leg) ➔ foot is moved in the direction of the **sole**.

31) **The <u>S</u>ciatic <u>S</u>ystem is <u>S</u>omewhat <u>S</u>ymmetrical**: most nerves divide into two terminal branches.
<u>Sciatic</u> ➔ 1) **common peroneal**, 2) **tibial**
<u>Common peroneal</u> ➔ 1) superficial peroneal, 2) deep peroneal
<u>Superficial peroneal</u> ➔ 1) medial dorsal cut. nerve, 2) intermediate dorsal cut. nerve
<u>Medial dorsal cut. nerve</u> ➔ 1) dorsal proper digital nerve (medial side of digit one), 2) dorsal common digital nerve (adjacent sides of toes #2 and #3)
<u>Intermediate dorsal cut. nerve</u> ➔ 1) dorsal common digital nerve (adjacent sides of toes #3 & #4), 2) dorsal common digital nerve (adjacent sides of toes #4 & #5)
<u>Tibial</u> ➔ 1) medial plantar, 2) lateral plantar
<u>Lateral plantar</u> ➔ 1) superficial br. 2) deep br.
The P of <u>P</u>eroneal comes before the T of <u>T</u>ibial. The common peroneal nerve divides into its two terminal branches before the tibial.

32) Lumbrical muscles flex, then extend, toes.

33) "Common digital nerve" and "proper digital nerve" are used in the same context as in the description of the hand. The word *plantar* simply denotes the sole of the foot.

34) The P of <u>P</u>eroneal comes before the T of <u>T</u>ibial.
peroneal nerve = branches that supply the **top** of the foot and toes (except nail beds)
tibial nerve = branches that supply the **bottom** of the foot and toes (including nail beds).
• The top of the lateral side of the foot is supplied by a nerve formed from branches from both the peroneal and tibial nerves, the sural nerve.

35) The Toes are Supplied from **Above and Below**
                    TOP
Superficial peroneal nerve
• **medial dorsal cutaneous nerve** – medial side of great toe and adjacent sides of toes #2 and #3. It "skips" the area supplied by the deep peroneal nerve (adjacent sides of toes #1 and #2).
• **intermediate dorsal cutaneous nerve** – adjacent sides of toes #3 and #4, #4 and #5.
Deep peroneal nerve
• adjacent sides of toes #1 and #2.
Sural nerve
• **lateral dorsal cutaneous nerve** – lateral side of toe #5.
                    BOTTOM
Medial plantar nerve
• medial side of toe #1, adjacent sides of toes #1 and #2, #2 and #3, and #3 and #4.
Lateral plantar nerve
• adjacent sides of toes #4 and #5, lateral side of toe #5.

36) **PAD**   four **P**lantar (and/or palmar) interossei **AD**duct
DAB   three **D**orsal (hand and foot) interossei **AB**duct

37) **Mass of lower extremity gets larger from bottom to top** (thigh is bigger than leg). There are only 3 plantar interosseous muscles, but 4 dorsal interosseous muscles. The plantar surface of the toes requires only 2 cutaneous nerves from the sciatic system, the medial and lateral plantar nerves. The dorsal surface requires 4 (coincidentally, the same number as the dorsal interosseous muscles), the medial dorsal cutaneous, intermediate dorsal cutaneous, lateral dorsal cutaneous, and deep peroneal nerves. In addition, the saphenous nerve supplies skin of the medial side of the foot.

38) DEEP BRANCH LATERAL PLANTAR = **2-3-2 + adductor hallucis**
Medial **2** plantar interossei, medial **3** dorsal interossei, middle **2** lumbricals (middle, not medial!)

39) MEDIAL vs. LATERAL PLANTAR NERVES:
• Medial supplies less muscles (**four**) but sensory to a greater number of toes [cutaneous innervation to the medial 3 1/2 toes (almost **four**!)] ➔ the most medial toe (great toe) is the largest. The medial plantar nerve supplies the largest number of toes.
• Lateral supplies only the lateral 1 1/2 toes, but innervates 14 muscles of the foot ➔ requires the assistance of a deep branch. The 14 muscles include 3 of the 4 lumbrical muscles and all 7 interossei. The other four muscles are the quadratus plantae, abductor digiti minimi pedis (lat. plantar n. prior to division), flexor digiti minimi brevis (superficial br.), and adductor hallucis (deep br.)
MEDIAL PLANTAR N. = **4** muscles (including 1 lumbrical)
LATERAL PLANTAR N. = **4** muscles (plus 10 = 3 lumbricals, 7 interossei) = **14** total

40) **THE 3 AT THE TOP AND BOTTOM**
dorsal rami are unnamed, except at the very top and bottom of the cord. The C1 dorsal ramus is small and unnamed, but C2 = **greater occipital nerve**, C3 = **3rd occipital nerve**. Toward the bottom of the spinal cord, dorsal rami of the *top 3* lumbar spinal segments = **superior cluneal nerves**, dorsal rami of the *top 3* sacral spinal segments = **middle cluneal nerves.**

41) **Gluteal and Cluneal = Buttocks**
two gluteal nerves: both are motor. superior gluteal nerve (gluteus medius, gluteus minimus, and tensor fascia latae), inferior gluteal nerve (gluteus maximus)
cluneal nerves are **c**utaneous. supply skin of the buttocks.
L1, L2, L3 ➔ dorsal rami = superior cluneal nerves ➔ skin of upper buttocks
S1, S2, S3 ➔ dorsal rami = middle cluneal nerves ➔ skin of intermediate buttocks
S1, S2, S3 ➔ ventral rami (post. fem. cut. n.) = inferior cluneal nerves ➔ skin of lower buttocks

42) **F** = **F**emoral nerve = **F**ront **F**orward
(supplied muscles flex thigh, extend leg)
S = **S**ciatic nerve = **S**tep off
(supplied muscles extend thigh, flex leg)

43) **Superficial peroneal** = peroneal brevis, peroneal longus
Deep peroneal = anterior muscles that extend foot and toes (dorsiflex foot)
Tibial = posterior muscles that flex foot and toes (plantar flex foot)

44) Propel extremity forward (after a step) – femoral nerve, deep peroneal nerve
Propel extremity backward (during a step) – sciatic nerve, tibial nerve, superficial peroneal nerve

45) **Generalized Functions**
Superior gluteal nerve – abduct thigh, turn thigh medially, flex thigh
Inferior gluteal nerve – abduct thigh, turn thigh laterally, extend thigh
Femoral nerve – flex thigh, extend leg
Obturator nerve – adduct thigh, flex thigh
Sciatic nerve – extend thigh, flex leg
Tibial nerve – flex leg, plantar flex foot, flex toes, invert foot
Superficial peroneal nerve – plantar flex foot, evert foot
Deep peroneal nerve – dorsiflex foot, extend toes, invert foot, evert foot

END OF CHAPTER TEST

Time for Exam = 60 minutes.
For questions 1-37, choose the single best answer.

_____1) Which of the following is true concerning the inferior rectal nerves?
a) They supply the internal anal sphincter.
b) They are direct branches of the pudendal nerve.
c) Both a and b
d) They are branches of the perineal nerve.
e) None of the above

_____2) Which nerves receive contribution from lumbar spinal segments?
a) superior gluteal nerve
b) posterior femoral cutaneous nerve
c) middle cluneal nerves
d) inferior cluneal nerves
e) none of the above

_____3) Which statements about the plantar interosseous muscles are correct?
a) There are four of them.
b) All are innervated by the lateral plantar nerve.
c) Both a and b
d) All are innervated by the medial plantar nerve.
e) None of the above

_____4) The anterior scrotal nerves are branches of which nerve?
a) iliohypogastric nerve
b) pudendal nerve
c) perineal nerve
d) ilioinguinal nerve
e) none of the above

_____5) Which statements are true concerning the nerve to quadratus femoris?
a) It innervates skin of the lateral buttocks.
b) It innervates the superior gemellus muscle.
c) Both a and b
d) It innervates the inferior gemellus muscle.
e) None of the above

_____6) Which muscle is supplied by the medial plantar nerve?
a) fourth lumbrical muscle
b) first plantar interosseous muscle
c) first lumbrical muscle
d) first dorsal interosseous muscle
e) none of the above

_____7) Which statements are true concerning the saphenous nerve?
a) It is a branch of the femoral nerve.
b) It supplies skin of the lateral foot.
c) Both a and b
d) A branch of the tibial nerve contributes to it's formation.
e) None of the above

_____8) Which muscles are directly innervated by the sciatic nerve?
a) semitendinosus muscle
b) gracilis muscle
c) both a and b
d) deep (anterior) portion of adductor magnus muscle
e) none of the above

_____9) Which statements are true concerning the posterior scrotal nerves?
a) In the female, they are also known as the posterior clitoral nerves.
b) They are branches of the ilioinguinal nerve.
c) Both a and b
d) They are branches of the dorsal nerve of the penis.
e) None of the above

_____10) Which muscles are part of the quadratus femoris muscle group?
a) vastus medialis
b) vastus intermedius
c) rectus femoris
d) all of the above
e) none of the above

_____11) Which statements are true concerning the dorsal nerve of clitoris?
    a) It is a terminal branch of the pudendal nerve.
    b) It supplies the sphincter muscle of urethra.
    c) Both a and b
    d) It supplies the superficial transverse perinei muscle.
    e) None of the above

_____12) Which nerve is formed by posterior divisions of the lumbar plexus roots?
    a) posterior femoral cutaneous nerve
    b) femoral nerve
    c) both a and b
    d) perineal nerve
    e) none of the above

_____13) Which statements are true concerning the nerve to obturator internus?
    a) It is formed by branches from lumbar and sacral spinal nerves.
    b) It supplies the inferior gemellus muscle.
    c) Both a and b
    d) It supplies skin of the inferior buttocks.
    e) None of the above

_____14) Muscles innervated by the femoral nerve generally function to
    a) flex thigh
    b) flex leg
    c) both a and b
    d) extend thigh
    e) none of the above

_____15) Which statements are true of the genitofemoral nerve?
    a) It supplies the cremaster muscle.
    b) It supplies the skin of the upper anterior thigh.
    c) Both a and b
    d) It supplies the bulbospongiosus muscle.
    e) None of the above

_____16) Which nerve structures contribute to the formation of the sciatic nerve?
    a) lumbar plexus
    b) S2 dorsal ramus
    c) both a and b
    d) pudendal nerve
    e) none of the above

_____17) Which statements are true concerning the perineal nerve?
    a) It is the origin of the posterior labial nerves.
    b) It supplies the ischiocavernosus muscle.
    c) Both a and b
    d) It is the origin of the dorsal nerve of clitoris.
    e) None of the above

_____18) Which muscle is directly innervated by the superficial peroneal nerve?
    a) extensor hallucis longus muscle
    b) peroneus tertius muscle
    c) extensor digitorum longus muscle
    d) peroneus longus muscle
    e) none of the above

_____19) Which nerve receives contribution from anterior division branches of the lumbar plexus roots?
    a) perineal nerve
    b) lumbosacral trunk
    c) femoral nerve
    d) lateral femoral cutaneous nerve
    e) none of the above

_____20) Which statements are true concerning the pudendal nerve?
    a) It is the origin of the dorsal nerve of the penis (clitoris).
    b) It is the origin of the peroneal nerve.
    c) Both a and b
    d) It is formed by ventral root branches of the L2, L3, L4 spinal nerves.
    e) None of the above

____21) Which muscle is directly innervated by the tibial nerve?
- a) flexor hallucis longus muscle
- b) extensor hallucis longus muscle
- c) abductor hallucis muscle
- d) adductor hallucis muscle
- e) none of the above

____22) The lumbar plexus is formed by
- a) L1-L5 ventral rami
- b) L1-L5 dorsal rami
- c) L2-L5 ventral rami
- d) L1-L4 ventral rami
- e) None of the above

____23) Which nerve is a direct branch of the common peroneal nerve?
- a) medial sural cutaneous nerve
- b) saphenous nerve
- c) deep perineal nerve
- d) interosseous nerve of leg
- e) none of the above

____24) Which statements are true of the lateral femoral cutaneous nerve?
- a) It supplies skin of the lateral leg.
- b) It is formed by branches of the posterior roots of the L2 and L3 ventral rami.
- c) Both a and b
- d) It supplies the vastus lateralis muscle.
- e) None of the above

____25) Which muscle is supplied by the lateral plantar nerve?
- a) extensor digitorum brevis muscle
- b) abductor digit minimi pedis muscle
- c) peroneus brevis muscle
- d) plantaris muscle
- e) none of the above

____26) Nerves that receive contribution from posterior division branches of the lumbar plexus include the
- a) superior gluteal nerve
- b) anterior femoral cutaneous nerves
- c) both a and b
- d) obturator nerve
- e) none of the above

____27) Muscles innervated by the sciatic nerve generally function to
- a) flex thigh
- b) flex leg
- c) both a and b
- d) extend leg
- e) none of the above

____28) Which nerve is a branch of the deep peroneal nerve?
- a) medial sural nerve
- b) medial dorsal cutaneous nerve
- c) lateral plantar nerve
- d) lateral sural nerve
- e) none of the above

____29) Which nerves directly contribute to the formation of the sural nerve?
- a) peroneal communicating nerve
- b) lateral sural nerve
- c) both a and b
- d) saphenous nerve
- e) none of the above

____30) Which muscle is supplied by the peroneal component of the sciatic nerve?
- a) short head of biceps femoris muscle
- b) superficial (posterior) portion of adductor magnus muscle
- c) semitendinosus muscle
- d) gracilis muscle
- e) none of the above

____31) Which nerve is formed by branches of the lumbar plexus?
- a) posterior femoral cutaneous nerve
- b) medial sural nerve
- c) perineal nerve
- d) dorsal nerve of penis
- e) none of the above

____32) Which statements are true concerning the dorsal nerve of penis?
- a) It innervates the corpus cavernosum.
- b) It is a terminal branch of the perineal nerve.
- c) Both a and b
- d) It is the origin of the posterior scrotal nerves.
- e) None of the above

____33) Cutaneous innervation to which of the following areas is provided by the medial dorsal cutaneous nerve?
  a) superior aspect of the adjacent sides of toes #3 and #4
  b) superior aspect of the adjacent sides of toes #4 and #5
  c) superior aspect of the adjacent sides of toes #1 and #2
  d) plantar aspect of the adjacent sides of toes #1 and #2
  e) none of the above

____34) Which muscle is innervated by the genitofemoral nerve?
  a) ischiocavernosus
  b) bulbospongiosus
  c) cremaster
  d) superficial transverse perinei
  e) none of the above

____35) Muscles innervated by the tibial nerve generally function to
  a) flex leg
  b) plantar flex foot
  c) both a and b
  d) dorsiflex foot
  e) none of the above

____36) What is the lowest spinal nerve that supplies the abdominal wall?
  a) T12
  b) L1
  c) L3
  d) L5
  e) None of the above

____37) Which muscle is innervated by the deep peroneal nerve?
  a) sphincter muscle of urethra
  b) cremaster muscle
  c) bulbospongiosus muscle
  d) deep transverse perinei muscle
  e) none of the above

For questions 38-60, use the following directions:
  a.......1,2,3 are correct
  b.......1,3 are correct
  c.......2,4 are correct
  d.......only 4 is correct
  e.......all are correct

____38) Which nerves branch from the pudendal nerve system?
  1. posterior femoral cutaneous nerves
  2. anterior scrotal nerves
  3. inferior cluneal nerves
  4. dorsal nerve of penis

____39) Which statements are true concerning the accessory obturator nerve?
  1. The ventral ramus of L1 contributes to its formation.
  2. The ventral ramus of L3 contributes to its formation.
  3. It supplies the sartorius muscle.
  4. It supplies the pectineus muscle.

____40) Which statements concerning the deep peroneal nerve are true?
  1. It innervates the ischiocavernosus muscle.
  2. It is the origin of the medial dorsal cutaneous nerve.
  3. It innervates the bulbospongiosus muscle.
  4. It supplies skin of the lateral side of toe #1.

____41) Which nerves are direct branches of the tibial nerve?
  1. lateral sural nerve
  2. interosseous nerve of leg
  3. lateral dorsal cutaneous nerve
  4. medial sural nerve

____42) Which statements concerning the medial plantar nerve are true?
  1. It supplies dorsal skin of the medial side of toe #1.
  2. It is a branch of the deep peroneal nerve.
  3. It supplies dorsal skin of the lateral side of toe #2.
  4. It innervates the abductor hallucis muscle.

_____43) Which muscles are innervated the obturator nerve?
      1. adductor brevis
      2. obturator internus
      3. gracilis
      4. sartorius

_____44) Which statements about the superficial peroneal nerve are true?
      1. Its branches supply skin the adjacent sides of toes #1 and #2.
      2. Its branches supply skin of the adjacent sides of toes #2 and #3.
      3. It is the origin of the lateral dorsal cutaneous nerve.
      4. It supplies the peroneus brevis muscle.

_____45) Which muscles are innervated by the femoral nerve?
      1. adductor brevis
      2. sartorius
      3. cremaster
      4. rectus femoris

_____46) Which statements concerning the pudendal nerve are true?
      1. The dorsal nerve of penis is a terminal branch.
      2. It serves as the origin of the inferior rectal nerves.
      3. The perineal nerve is a terminal branch.
      4. One of its branches serves as the origin of the anterior scrotal nerves.

_____47) Which statements concerning the cutaneous innervation of the fourth toe are true?
      1. Plantar skin of the lateral side is supplied by the lateral plantar nerve.
      2. Plantar skin of the medial side is supplied by the lateral plantar nerve.
      3. Dorsal skin of the medial side is supplied by the intermediate dorsal cutaneous nerve.
      4. Dorsal skin of the lateral side is supplied by the lateral dorsal cutaneous nerve.

_____48) The L1 ventral ramus contributes to which of the following nerves?
      1. ilioinguinal nerve
      2. posterior scrotal nerves
      3. genitofemoral nerve
      4. femoral nerve

_____49) Which statements concerning the perineal nerve are true?
      1. It supplies the bulbospongiosus muscle.
      2. It supplies the corpus cavernosum.
      3. It supplies the ischiocavernosus muscle.
      4. It supplies the deep transverse perinei muscle.

_____50) Which statements concerning the sural nerve are true?
      1. It is a branch of the femoral nerve.
      2. The lateral sural nerve contributes to its formation.
      3. It is the origin of the medial dorsal cutaneous nerve.
      4. The peroneal communicating nerve contributes to its formation.

_____51) Which of the following are true concerning the iliohypogastric nerve?
      1. It supplies the cremaster muscle.
      2. It is the origin of the anterior scrotal nerves.
      3. It is formed by a branch of the L2 ventral ramus.
      4. It has a branch which supplies skin of the lateral buttocks.

_____52) Which muscles are innervated by the peroneal component of the sciatic nerve?
      1. adductor longus muscle
      2. semitendinosus muscle
      3. sartorius muscle
      4. short head of biceps femoris muscle

_____53) Which statements are true concerning the lumbosacral trunk?
1. It contributes to the formation of the superior gluteal nerve.
2. It contributes to the formation of the inferior gluteal nerve.
3. It contributes to the formation of the sciatic nerve.
4. The L4 ventral ramus contributes to its formation.

_____54) Which muscles are supplied by the deep peroneal nerve?
1. peroneus longus muscle
2. tibialis anterior muscle
3. abductor hallucis muscle
4. extensor hallucis brevis muscle

_____55) Which statements are true concerning the femoral nerve?
1. It is formed by branches from the anterior divisions of the L2, L3, and L4 ventral rami.
2. It is the origin of the sural nerve.
3. It innervates the gracilis muscle.
4. It is the origin of anterior femoral cutaneous nerves.

_____56) Which nerves are direct branches of the superficial peroneal nerve?
1. intermediate dorsal cutaneous nerve
2. lateral dorsal cutaneous nerve
3. medial dorsal cutaneous nerve
4. medial sural nerve

_____57) Which statements concerning the lateral plantar nerve are true?
1. It innervates the quadratus plantae muscle.
2. It innervates the abductor digiti minimi pedis muscle.
3. It is a branch of the tibial nerve.
4. It supplies plantar skin on the medial side of toe #4.

_____58) Which nerves branch from the perineal nerve?
1. inferior rectal nerves
2. deep peroneal nerve
3. dorsal nerve of penis
4. posterior scrotal nerves

_____59) Which nerves are formed by branches of the lumbar plexus?
1. posterior femoral cutaneous nerve
2. anterior femoral cutaneous nerves
3. inferior cluneal nerves
4. lateral femoral cutaneous nerve

_____60) Which statements concerning the intermediate dorsal cutaneous nerve are true?
1. It supplies skin of the adjacent sides of toes #2 and #3.
2. It supplies skin of the adjacent sides of toes #1 and #2.
3. It is a branch of the deep peroneal nerve.
4. It supplies skin of the adjacent sides of toes #3 and #4.

END OF CHAPTER TEST: Answers and Explanations

1) b – The inferior rectal nerves are branches of the pudendal nerve. They supply the sphincter ani externus muscle (external anal sphincter) and skin around anal opening. The internal anal sphincter is under autonomic nervous system control. After serving as the origin of the inferior rectal nerves, the pudendal nerve divides into its two terminal branches, the perineal nerve and dorsal nerve of the penis (clitoris).

2) a – Although the superior gluteal nerve is not considered a lumbar plexus branch, a branch of the lumbar plexus does contribute to its formation. The superior gluteal nerve is formed by a branch of the lumbosacral trunk (L4, L5) that combines with a S1 ventral ramus branch. The lumbosacral trunk is formed by the combination of a branch of the L4 ventral ramus and the entire L5 ventral ramus. The posterior femoral cutaneous nerve is formed by ventral rami branches from the S1, S2, and S3 spinal segments (sacral plexus). The middle cluneal nerves are branches of the dorsal rami of the first three sacral spinal nerves (S1, S2, S3). The inferior cluneal nerves are branches of the posterior femoral cutaneous nerve. They are therefore formed by ventral rami branches of the S1, S2, and S3 spinal nerves.

3) b – There are three plantar and four dorsal interosseous muscles in each foot. Like the toes, they are numbered from medial to lateral. All are supplied by the lateral plantar nerve.

4) d – The anterior scrotal (labial) nerves are branches of the ilioinguinal nerve, which is a branch of the L1 ventral ramus. In addition, anterior scrotal (labial) nerves may branch from the genital branch of the genitofemoral nerve.

5) d – The nerve to quadratus femoris is formed from ventral rami branches from the L4, L5, and S1 spinal segments. It supplies both the quadratus femoris and inferior gemellus muscles. The skin of the lateral buttocks is supplied by the lateral branch of the iliohypogastric nerve. The superior gemellus muscle is supplied by the nerve to obturator internus.

6) c – The medial plantar nerve innervates the abductor hallucis, flexor hallucis brevis, flexor digitorum brevis, and first lumbrical muscles. There are four lumbrical muscles, numbered from medial to lateral. The first lumbrical muscle is thereby the most *medial* and is supplied by the *medial* plantar nerve. The lateral three lumbrical muscles, all three plantar interossei, and all four dorsal interossei are supplied by the lateral plantar nerve.

7) a – The saphenous nerve is a branch of the femoral nerve. It, therefore, is formed by branches of the posterior divisions of the L2, L3, and L4 ventral rami. It supplies skin of the medial leg and foot to the level of the great toe. The saphenous nerve is the only nerve originating from the lumbar plexus that supplies tissue of the leg (below knee).

8) a – The sciatic nerve supplies the semitendinosus, semimembranosus, biceps femoris and superficial (posterior) portion of the adductor magnus muscles. Both the gracilis muscle and the deep (anterior) portion of the adductor magnus muscle are supplied by the obturator nerve.

9) e – The posterior scrotal nerves are branches of the perineal nerve. Remember, Pudendal → Perineal → Posterior scrotal (labial). In the female, they are known as the posterior labial nerves. In addition to the perineal nerve, the dorsal nerve of the penis (clitoris) is the other terminal branch of the pudendal nerve.

10) e – This is a trick question. Any student who answered it correctly was paying attention to details. Hopefully, an incorrect answer will serve to reinforce the point of the question. The quadriceps femoris muscle group should not be confused with the quadratus femoris muscle. The quadriceps femoris is a group of four muscles of the anterior thigh innervated by the femoral nerve. These muscles include the vastus lateralis, vastus intermedius, vastus medialis, and rectus femoris. The quadratus femoris is a separate muscle of the posterior lower extremity that is innervated by a nerve

named for it, the nerve to quadratus femoris.

11) c – The dorsal nerve of the clitoris (penis), along with the perineal nerve, is a terminal branch of the pudendal nerve. The dorsal nerve of clitoris innervates the skin of the clitoris, the corpus cavernosum, the sphincter muscle of urethra, and the deep transverse perinei muscle (deep transverse muscle of perineum). The superficial transverse perinei muscle is supplied by the perineal nerve.

12) b – The femoral nerve is formed by branches of the posterior divisions of the L2, L3, and L4 ventral rami. The posterior femoral cutaneous nerve is formed by ventral rami branches from the S1, S2, and S3 spinal segments (sacral plexus). The perineal nerve, along with the dorsal nerve of the penis (clitoris), is a terminal branch of the pudendal nerve. The pudendal nerve is a branch of the sacral plexus.

13) a – The nerve to obturator internus is formed by ventral rami branches from L5, S1, and S2 spinal segments. The nerve to obturator internus supplies both the obturator internus and superior gemellus muscles. The inferior gemellus muscle is supplied by the nerve to quadratus femoris. The skin of the inferior buttocks is supplied by the inferior cluneal nerves, which are branches of the posterior femoral cutaneous nerve.

14) a – Muscles innervated by the femoral nerve generally function to flex the thigh and extend the leg. <u>F</u>emoral = <u>F</u>ront <u>F</u>orward.

15) c – The genitofemoral nerve divides into a genital and femoral branch. The genital branch supplies the cremaster muscle, skin of the anterior scrotum, and skin bordering the scrotum. The femoral branch supplies skin of the upper anterior thigh. The bulbospongiosus muscle is supplied by the perineal nerve.

16) a – The sciatic nerve is formed by the combination of the lumbosacral trunk (L4, L5) and *ventral* rami branches from S1, S2, S3. The S1, S2, and S3 dorsal rami form the middle cluneal nerves. The pudendal nerve is formed by ventral rami branches from S2, S3, and S4.

17) c – The perineal nerve, along with the dorsal

nerve of the clitoris (penis), is a terminal branch of the pudendal nerve. The perineal nerve is the origin of the posterior labial (scrotal) nerves and the deep perineal nerve. The deep perineal nerve innervates the ischiocavernosus, bulbospongiosus, and superficial transverse perinei muscle (superficial transverse muscle of perineum).

18) d – The superficial peroneal nerve innervates the peroneus longus and peroneus brevis muscles. The other three muscles are supplied by the deep peroneal nerve.

19) e – The perineal nerve, along with the dorsal nerve of the penis (clitoris), is a terminal branch of the pudendal nerve. The pudendal nerve is a branch of the sacral plexus. A branch of the L4 ventral ramus combines with the entire L5 ventral ramus to form the lumbosacral trunk. The femoral nerve is formed by branches of the posterior divisions of the L2, L3, and L4 ventral rami. The lateral femoral cutaneous nerve is formed by branches of the posterior divisions of the L2 and L3 ventral rami.

20) a – The pudendal nerve is formed by ventral rami branches from the S2, S3, and S4 spinal segments (sacral plexus). The pudendal nerve serves as the origin of the inferior rectal nerves before dividing into its two terminal branches, the perineal nerve and dorsal nerve of the penis (clitoris). The perineal nerve should not be confused with the peroneal nerve. The peroneal nerve (common peroneal nerve) is a terminal branch of the sciatic nerve.

21) a – The tibial nerve innervates the plantaris, popliteus, gastrocnemius, soleus, tibialis posterior, flexor digitorum longus, and flexor hallucis longus muscles. The extensor hallucis longus muscle is innervated by the deep peroneal nerve. The abductor hallucis muscle is supplied by the medial plantar nerve. The adductor hallucis muscle is supplied by the lateral plantar nerve. Although the plantar nerves are the terminal branches of the tibial nerve, the question asks for muscles that are *directly* innervated by the tibial nerve.

22) d – The lumbar plexus is formed by the ventral rami of L1-L4 spinal cord segments. The L4

ventral ramus contributes a branch to the obturator nerve (and accessory obturator in some individuals) and femoral nerve. Both nerves are members of the lumbar plexus. Additionally, the L4 ventral ramus contributes a branch that combines with the entire L5 ventral ramus to form the lumbosacral trunk. This trunk contributes to the sacral plexus. Because of this, the L5 ventral ramus is actually not a contributor to the lumbar plexus.

23) e – The three nerves that branch from the common peroneal prior to its separation into deep and superficial branches are the recurrent articular branch, lateral sural cutaneous nerve, and peroneal communicating nerve. Both the medial sural nerve and interosseous nerve of leg are branches of the tibial nerve. The saphenous nerve is a cutaneous branch of the femoral nerve. The deep perineal nerve is a muscular branch of the perineal nerve. The perineal nerve is a terminal branch of the pudendal nerve and should not be confused with the peroneal nerve.

24) b – As difficult as it is to change a lifetime of language interpretation, the leg must now be considered that portion of the lower extremity that is between the knee and ankle. This is opposed to the entire lower extremity. The thigh is the portion of the lower extremity between the hip and knee. The lateral femoral cutaneous nerve supplies skin of the lateral thigh. Although this may be considered a trick question, its purpose is to make this point of distinction. This same point may also be made by future instructors on future exams. All 3 "vastus" muscles (vastus medialis, vastus intermedius, and vastus lateralis) are innervated by the femoral nerve.

25) b – The lateral plantar nerve is responsible for innervating 14 foot muscles. Although these initially may seem a challenge to remember, 10 of the 14 muscles are composed of lumbrical and interosseous muscles. Muscles innervated include the quadratus plantae, abductor digiti minimi pedis, flexor digiti minimi pedis, the three lateral lumbrical muscles (there are four lumbrical muscles – the medial plantar nerve innervates the first lumbrical), all four dorsal interosseous muscles, all three plantar

interosseous muscles, and the adductor hallucis muscle. The extensor digitorum brevis muscle is innervated by the deep peroneal nerve. The peroneus brevis muscle is innervated by the superficial peroneal nerve. The plantaris muscle is supplied by the tibial nerve.

26) b – The superior gluteal nerve is formed by a branch of the lumbosacral trunk (L4, L5) that combines with a S1 ventral ramus branch. The anterior femoral cutaneous nerves are branches of the femoral nerve. They therefore are formed by branches of the posterior divisions of the L2, L3, and L4 ventral rami. The obturator nerve is formed by branches of the anterior divisions of the L2, L3, and L4 ventral rami.

27) b – Muscles innervated by the sciatic nerve generally function to extend the thigh and flex the leg. Sciatic = Step off.

28) e – The deep peroneal nerve has no named branches of significance. The medial sural nerve is a branch of the tibial nerve. The medial dorsal cutaneous nerve is a branch of the superficial peroneal nerve. The lateral plantar nerve, along with the medial plantar nerve, is a terminal branch of the tibial nerve. Finally, The lateral sural nerve is a cutaneous branch of the common peroneal nerve.

29) a – The sural nerve is a cutaneous nerve formed by the combination of a common peroneal nerve branch, the peroneal communicating nerve, and a tibial nerve branch, the medial sural nerve. The sural nerve supplies skin of the posterior calf and lateral side of the foot. The lateral sural nerve is a cutaneous branch of the common peroneal nerve and supplies skin of the lateral calf. The saphenous nerve is a cutaneous branch of the femoral nerve. It supplies skin of the medial leg and foot.

30) a – The sciatic nerve is formed by a tibial and peroneal component. Each later becomes a separate nerve. The tibial component innervates the superficial (posterior) portion of the adductor magnus, semitendinosus, semimembranosus, and long head of the biceps femoris muscles. The peroneal component innervates the short head of the biceps femoris muscle. The gracilis muscle is innervated by the obturator nerve.

31) e – The posterior femoral cutaneous nerve is formed by ventral rami branches from the S1, S2, and S3 spinal segments (sacral plexus). The medial sural nerve is a cutaneous branch of the tibial nerve, one of the terminal branches of the sciatic nerve (sacral plexus). The perineal nerve and the dorsal nerve of the penis (clitoris) are the two terminal branches of the pudendal nerve (sacral plexus).

32) a – The corpus cavernosum is a shaft or column of erectile tissue in the male and female genitalia. The dorsal nerve of the penis (clitoris), along with the perineal nerve, is a terminal branch of the pudendal nerve. The posterior scrotal (labial) nerves are branches of the perineal nerve.

33) e – The medial dorsal cutaneous nerve is the origin of dorsal digital nerves that supply the dorsal surface of the medial side of the great (toe #1) and adjacent sides of toes #2 and #3. The adjacent sides of toes #1 and #2 are supplied by the deep peroneal nerve. The adjacent sides of toes #3 and #4, #4 and #5 are supplied by the intermediate dorsal cutaneous nerve. The plantar surface of all toes is innervated by plantar nerves.

34) c – The cremaster muscle elevates the testis (pleural of testicle). The ischiocavernosus, bulbospongiosus, and superficial transverse perinei muscles are all supplied by the perineal nerve, a terminal branch of the pudendal nerve.

35) c – Muscles innervated by the tibial nerve generally function to flex the leg, plantar flex the foot, and flex the toes.

36) b – The L1 spinal nerve is the lowest spinal nerve to supply the abdominal wall. The L1 ventral ramus is the origin of branches that form the ilioinguinal and iliohypogastric nerves. Both supply skin of the anterior lower abdomen and upper thigh. The L1 ventral ramus also gives a branch that combines with a L2 ventral ramus to form the genitofemoral nerve, a member of the lumbar plexus.

37) e – The deep peroneal nerve supplies the tibialis anterior, extensor digitorum longus, extensor hallucis longus, peroneus tertius, and extensor digitorum brevis muscles. Both the sphincter muscle of urethra and deep transverse perinei muscle are innervated by the dorsal nerve of the penis (clitoris). The cremaster muscle is innervated by the genitofemoral nerve. Finally, The bulbospongiosus muscle is supplied by the deep branch of the perineal nerve. The perineal nerve should not be confused with a peroneal nerve.

38) d – The pudendal nerve serves as the origin of the inferior rectal nerves before dividing into its two terminal branches, the perineal nerve and dorsal nerve of the penis (clitoris). Because the inferior cluneal nerves arise from the posterior femoral cutaneous nerve, they are formed from ventral rami branches of the S1, S2, and S3 spinal segments. The anterior scrotal (labial) nerves are branches of the ilioinguinal nerve. They therefore are derived from the L1 ventral ramus.

39) c – When present, the accessory obturator nerve is formed by branches of the L3 and L4 ventral rami. The L2 ventral ramus may also contribute. Due to an ambiguity, these branches cannot be said to belong to either anterior or posterior divisions of the lumbar plexus. The accessory obturator nerve provides innervation to the pectineus muscle and hip joint. The sartorius muscle is innervated by the femoral nerve.

40) d – The deep peroneal nerve, along with the superficial peronial nerve, is a terminal branch of the common peroneal nerve. The deep peroneal nerve supplies five muscles and the dorsal skin of the adjacent sides of toes #1 and #2. This includes the lateral side of toe #1 and medial side of toe #2. Supplied muscles include the tibialis anterior, extensor digitorum longus, extensor hallucis longus, peroneus tertius, and extensor digitorum brevis muscles. Both the ischiocavernosus and bulbospongiosus are perineal muscles supplied by the deep branch of the perineal nerve. Finally, the medial dorsal cutaneous nerve is a branch of the superficial peroneal nerve.

41) c – The interosseous nerve of leg is a sensory nerve that travels down the leg between the

tibia and fibula, supplying the interosseous membrane between these two bones. The medial sural nerve combines with a branch of the common peroneal nerve, the peroneal communicating nerve, to form the sural nerve. The lateral sural cutaneous nerve is a branch of the common peroneal nerve that supplies skin of the lateral calf. Finally, the lateral dorsal cutaneous nerve is the distal continuation of the sural nerve along the lateral side of the foot.

42) d – The medial plantar nerve, along with the lateral plantar nerve, is a terminal branch of the tibial nerve. The medial plantar nerve supplies four muscles and skin of the medial sole and plantar surface of the medial 3 1/2 toes. This includes plantar skin of the medial side of toe #1 and adjacent sides of toes #1 and #2, #2 and #3, #3 and #4. The four supplied muscles include the abductor hallucis, flexor hallucis brevis, flexor digitorum brevis, and first lumbrical muscles. Dorsal skin of the medial side of toe #1 and lateral side of toe #2 is innervated by the medial dorsal cutaneous nerve.

43) b – The obturator nerve is formed by branches of the anterior divisions of the L2, L3, and L4 ventral rami. It supplies muscles that adduct the thigh and skin of the medial thigh. Muscles innervated include the pectineus (shared with femoral nerve), obturator externus, adductor brevis, adductor longus, gracilis, and the deep (anterior) portion of the adductor magnus muscles. The obturator internus muscle is supplied by the nerve to obturator internus. The sartorius muscle is innervated by the femoral nerve.

44) c – The superficial peroneal nerve, along with the deep peroneal nerve, is a terminal branch of the common peroneal nerve. It innervates the peroneus longus and peroneus brevis muscles and becomes a cutaneous sensory nerve approximately midway between the knee and foot. The superficial peroneal nerve divides into the medial and intermediate dorsal cutaneous nerves, which supply skin of the top or dorsum of the foot. The medial dorsal cutaneous nerve is the origin of dorsal digital nerves that supply dorsal skin of the medial

side of the great toe (toe #1) and adjacent sides of toes #2 and #3. The intermediate dorsal cutaneous nerve is the origin of dorsal digital nerves that supply the adjacent sides of toes #3 and #4, #4 and #5. The adjacent sides of toes #1 and #2 are supplied by the deep peroneal nerve. The lateral dorsal cutaneous nerve is the distal continuation of the sural nerve. It supplies skin of the lateral foot and lateral side of toe #5.

45) c – The femoral nerve supplies skin of the anterior thigh and muscles that flex the thigh and extend the leg. Supplied muscles include the psoas major, iliacus, pectineus (shared with obturator), sartorius, and the quadriceps femoris muscle group (consisting of rectus femoris, vastus lateralis, vastus intermedius and vastus medialis muscles). The adductor brevis muscle is innervated by the obturator nerve. The cremaster muscle is supplied by the genitofemoral nerve.

46) a – After giving off the inferior rectal nerves, the pudendal nerve divides into its two terminal branches, the dorsal nerve of the penis (clitoris) and perineal nerve. The perineal nerve subsequently serves as the origin of the posterior scrotal (labial) nerves. The anterior scrotal nerves are branches of the ilioinguinal nerve.

47) b – The medial dorsal cutaneous nerve is the medial branch of the superficial peroneal nerve. It is the origin of dorsal digital nerves that supply the dorsal surface of the medial side of the great toe (toe #1) and adjacent sides of toes #2 and #3. The adjacent sides of toes #1 and #2 are supplied by the deep peroneal nerve. The intermediate dorsal cutaneous nerve is the lateral branch of the superficial peroneal nerve. It is the origin of dorsal digital nerves that supply the dorsal surface of the adjacent sides of toes #3 and #4, #4 and #5. The lateral dorsal cutaneous nerve is the distal continuation of the sural nerve along the lateral side of the foot. It supplies the lateral side of toe #5. The medial plantar nerve supplies skin of the medial sole and plantar surface of the medial 3 1/2 toes. This includes plantar skin of the medial side of toe #1 and adjacent sides of toes #1 and #2, #2 and #3, #3 and #4. The lat-

eral plantar nerve supplies the plantar skin of the adjacent sides of toes #4 and #5 and the lateral side of toe #5 and (lateral 1 1/2 toes).

48) b – The ilioinguinal nerve is formed by a L1 ventral ramus branch. The anterior scrotal (labial) nerves are branches of the ilioinguinal nerve. The posterior scrotal (labial) nerves are branches of the perineal nerve, which is a terminal branch of the pudendal nerve (S2, S3, S4). The genitofemoral nerve is formed by a combination of a L1 ventral ramus branch and a branch of the anterior division of the L2 ventral ramus. The femoral nerve is formed by branches of the posterior divisions of the L2, L3, and L4 ventral rami.

49) b – The perineal nerve, along with the dorsal nerve of the penis (clitoris), is a terminal branch of the pudendal nerve. The perineal nerve is the origin of the posterior scrotal (labial) nerves and the deep perineal nerve. The deep perineal nerve innervates the ischiocavernosus, bulbospongiosus, and superficial transverse perinei muscle (superficial transverse muscle of perineum). The corpus cavernosum is not a muscle, but a shaft or column of erectile tissue that is innervated by the dorsal nerve of the penis (clitoris). The deep transverse perinei muscle is also supplied by the dorsal nerve of the penis (clitoris).

50) d – The sural nerve is formed by the combination of a common peroneal nerve branch, the peroneal communicating nerve, and a tibial nerve branch, the medial sural nerve. The sural nerve supplies skin of the posterior calf and lateral side of the foot. The word *sura* refers to the calf. The lateral sural nerve is a common peroneal branch that supplies skin of the lateral calf. The medial dorsal cutaneous nerve is a branch of the superficial peroneal nerve.

51) d – The iliohypogastric nerve is formed by a L1 ventral ramus branch. The lateral branch of iliohypogastric nerve supplies skin of the lateral buttocks. The cremaster muscle is supplied by the genitofemoral nerve. The anterior scrotal (labial) nerves are branches of the ilioinguinal nerve.

52) d – The sciatic nerve is formed by a tibial and peroneal component, both of which later become separate nerves. The peroneal component of the sciatic nerve innervates the short head of the biceps femoris muscle. The tibial component innervates the semitendinosus muscle, semimembranosus muscle, long head of the biceps femoris muscle, and the superficial (posterior) portion of the adductor magnus muscle. The adductor longus is innervated by the obturator nerve. The sartorius muscle is innervated by the femoral nerve.

53) e – A branch of the L4 ventral ramus combines with the entire L5 ventral ramus to form the lumbosacral trunk. This nerve represents the only lumbar contribution to the sacral plexus. It travels down to combine with sacral branches and form the superior gluteal nerve, inferior gluteal nerve, and sciatic nerve. The superior gluteal nerve is formed by a branch of the lumbosacral trunk (L4, L5) that combines with a S1 ventral ramus branch. The inferior gluteal nerve is formed by ventral rami branches from the L5 portion of the lumbosacral trunk, S1 spinal root, and S2 spinal root (L5, S1, S2). After giving branches to the two gluteal nerves, the lumbosacral trunk combines with branches from the ventral rami of S1, S2, and S3 to form the sciatic nerve.

54) c – The deep peroneal nerve supplies the tibialis anterior, extensor digitorum longus, extensor hallucis longus, peroneus tertius, and extensor digitorum brevis muscles. The extensor hallucis brevis muscle is the portion of the extensor digitorum brevis muscle that extends to the great toe. The peroneus longus muscle is innervated by the superficial peroneal nerve. The abductor hallucis muscle is supplied by the medial plantar nerve.

55) d – The femoral nerve is formed by branches of the *posterior* divisions of the L2, L3, and L4 ventral rami. It supplies skin of the anterior thigh and muscles that flex the thigh and extend the leg. Supplied muscles include the psoas major, iliacus, pectineus (shared with obturator), sartorius, and the quadriceps femoris muscle group (consisting of rectus femoris, vastus lateralis, vastus intermedius and vastus medialis

muscles). In addition, it supplies skin of the medial leg (below knee) and foot via the saphenous nerve. The sural nerve is a cutaneous nerve formed by branches from the common peroneal and tibial nerves. The word *sura* refers to the calf. The gracilis muscle is innervated by the obturator nerve.

56) b – The superficial peroneal nerve divides into the medial and intermediate dorsal cutaneous nerves, which supply skin of the top or dorsum of the foot. The lateral dorsal cutaneous nerve is the distal continuation of the sural nerve along the lateral side of the foot. The medial sural nerve is a branch of the tibial nerve.

57) a – The lateral plantar nerve, along with the medial plantar nerve, is a terminal branch of the tibial nerve. The lateral plantar nerve is responsible for innervation of 14 foot muscles and plantar skin of the lateral 1 1/2 toes. Ten of the fourteen muscles supplied by the lateral plantar nerve happen to be either interosseous or lumbrical muscles. Innervated muscles include the quadratus plantae, abductor digiti minimi pedis, flexor digiti minimi pedis, adductor hallucis, the three lateral lumbrical muscles (#2, #3, #4), all three plantar interosseous muscles (#1, #2, #3), and all four dorsal interosseous muscles (#1, #2, #3, #4). Skin of the medial side of toe #4 is innervated by the medial plantar nerve.

58) d – The perineal nerve, along with the dorsal nerve of the penis (clitoris), is a terminal branch of the pudendal nerve. The perineal nerve is the origin of the posterior scrotal (labial) nerves and the deep perineal nerve.

The deep perineal nerve innervates the ischiocavernosus, bulbospongiosus, and superficial transverse perinei muscle (superficial transverse muscle of perineum). The inferior rectal nerves are branches of the pudendal nerve prior to its division into terminal branches. Do not confuse the peroneal nerves with the perineal nerve. The common peroneal nerve is a terminal branch of the sciatic nerve. It subsequently divides into the deep and superficial peroneal nerves.

59) c – The anterior femoral cutaneous nerves are branches of the femoral nerve. They therefore are formed by branches of the posterior divisions of the L2, L3, and L4 ventral rami. The lateral femoral cutaneous nerve is formed by branches of the posterior divisions of the L2 and L3 ventral rami. The posterior femoral cutaneous nerve is formed by ventral rami branches from the S1, S2, and S3 spinal segments (sacral plexus). The inferior cluneal nerves are branches of the posterior femoral cutaneous nerve.

60) d – The superficial peroneal nerve divides into the medial and intermediate dorsal cutaneous nerves, which supply skin of the top or dorsum of the foot. The intermediate dorsal cutaneous nerve is the lateral branch and is the origin of dorsal digital nerves that supply the dorsal surface of the adjacent sides of toes #3 and #4, #4 and #5. The medial side of toe #1 (great toe) and adjacent sides of toes #2 and #3 are innervated by the medial dorsal cutaneous nerve. The deep peroneal nerve supplies the dorsal skin of the adjacent sides of toes #1 and #2.

"The art of medicine consists in amusing the patient while nature cures the disease."

– Voltaire

CHAPTER THIRTEEN

CONCLUSION AND INTRODUCTION TO THE WEB-BASED LEARNING APPLICATIONS

Any student who has reached this point by reading every chapter and working through all quizzes and exams should be greatly commended. A significant amount of material has been covered and it required a lot of motivation and self-discipline on your part. Completing this course not only expands your knowledge base, but qualifies you as a "serious" student; one that is likely to find success in future studies. Furthermore, it identifies you as an individual who is likely to reap great benefits from the entire *Medtutor* system of courses. The purpose of this chapter is to describe how to maximize your learning experience with the course's various online applications.

The biggest challenge associated with medical education is related to the volume of information. There simply is not enough time to gain a comprehensive understanding of the new terminology and facts introduced in a semester-based course using traditional means. The *Medtutor* books are designed to introduce and teach the maximum amount of information that can be digested by self-study. **Medtutor.com** serves as the one centralized learning center for all courses. Virtually every piece of information that is presented in the texts is incorporated in the web-based applications. These applications include individual course final exams, randomized exams, flashcards, interactive posters, and crossword puzzles, all of which allow the user to track their progress and review information in a fun and innovative fashion. In addition to being viewable on conventional computers, *Medtutor* applications are also designed to be compatible for use with mobile devices. All activities allow for heavy customization since the student can direct the system as to which book(s) and/or chapter(s) to pull information from.

The best way to learn is to be tested. The peripheral nerve course is not considered complete until the web-based **final exam** is taken and a score is issued. This comprehensive exam should be approached in the same way a final exam in a formal course would and it is imperative not to take it until you are thoroughly prepared. Like the final exam of the other *Medtutor* books, you will only get one opportunity to take it. Before taking the exam, you should review all of the material and retake all quizzes and chapter tests. Draw out and label anatomic structures and fiber compositions. Problem areas should be identified and targeted. Place the poster in a location convenient for frequent viewing and repetitively attempt to identify *all* nerves. Once you feel adequately prepared, schedule a particular date and time to take the exam. At least three hours of uninterrupted time should be set aside in order to complete it. Be sure to get plenty of sleep the night before and employ the same rituals that have helped you with previous exams. The more you put into taking this exam, the greater the reward you attain. To incite maximal effort in preparation, a unique **medtutor.com tee-shirt** will be given free of charge to any student who scores greater than 70% correct on the final exam.

In order to take the exam, you will need to go to the interactive website, **Medtutor.com,** and register. If previously unregistered, you will be granted 30 days of free access to the site, providing additional learning opportunities with the use of the interactive applications. If you wish to continue your subscription after 30 days, you may do so for a nominal subscription fee. The timed final exam consists of 180 questions displayed in the same format as those found in the book's quizzes and chapter tests. However, all final exam questions are new and have not been previously seen in the chapters. The exam is administered in two ninety-minute segments and a break is permitted in-between them. The exam can seem long but it is designed to mimic medical board exams in which mental fatigue often plays a role. At the conclusion of the test, you will immediately obtain a score and answers and detailed explanations are also provided. Every question is grouped into a particular category, so you will know how well you did in every segment of the course. You can also direct the website to send an e-mail that verifies your score on the final exam to any individual, school, or admissions committee of your choosing.

As opposed to the terminal component of the course, the final exam should be viewed as a bridge to more advanced learning. Missed or uncertain questions require review. Areas of deficiency can be identified and future work can be directed at those areas with the use of the web-based applications. It is imperative that the material is actually *learned* and not just memorized long enough to get through the final exam. You have expended a great deal of time and effort to reach this point. Do not miss out on this opportunity to learn; most of the work is behind you. Repetitive exposure will solidify your knowledge base.

The **randomized exam system** is a separate web-based interactive application that includes a database of thousands of board-type questions related to information contained in this book. Each question is affiliated with a specific chapter or category. The student can sporadically and repeatedly prompt the system to randomly assimilate a test of a desired number of questions. As directed by the student, this exam may contain questions specific to a particular chapter, a group of chapters, the entire book, or even to a mixture of other *Medtutor* books and their chapters. Furthermore, the student can also direct the system to assemble exams solely from questions the student has never seen before, questions previously passed, questions previously failed, or a combination of all question subcategories. Problem areas can be identified and future exams can target those areas.

To facilitate tracking, a progress bar and a score bar are provided for each pool of questions that are associated with a particular chapter. This allows the student to instantaneously know where he or she currently stands within each category of information at any given time. Out of the total number of questions available for each chapter or category, the system displays the percentage of questions that have previously been answered by the student. This percentage is displayed as a *progress* bar. Out of the questions that have previously been answered, the system also displays the percentage that was answered correctly. This is displayed as a *score* bar. Like the final exam, each randomized exam is timed and graded upon completion. Answers and detailed explanations are provided. The number of questions and percentage correct for each of the various categories are also displayed. Upon completion of an exam, if so desired, the student can then direct the system to immediately create another randomized exam of desired specifications or participate in a different teaching application.

The **flashcard application** also possesses customizable properties that help the student efficiently manage information and learn. Thousands of flashcards related to virtually every fact presented in the course are available. Numerous flashcards contain color-enhanced images of anatomic structures. The student directs the system as to the number and type of flashcards to display during a particular sitting. Like the questions that appear in a randomized exam, flashcards may be studied based on a specific chapter, a group of chapters, the entire book, or a group of other *Medtutor* books and book chapters. Upon completion of a particular set of cards, the student may prompt the system to display the same set of cards backwards in order to show the back of each card first. This reinforces recall and promotes learning. Alternatively, the student may direct the system to initially present the back of each card from the onset. The student has the ability to pass or fail him/herself on each flashcard. Failed flashcards are placed in a personalized databank that can be accessed at any time. With review, cards that are subsequently marked as "passed" are removed from the databank; "failed" cards remain.

Interactive posters are a novel and efficient way to learn and are unique to **Medtutor.com**. The website contains several interactive posters, including four that are associated with this course. Two interactive posters replicate the peripheral nerve poster and two replicate the skeleton poster. Other posters are associated with other *Medtutor* courses. The student can go to the interactive poster page and click on the poster of choice. A legend of the selected poster appears in the bottom left of the screen and the student can click on the region of the poster that is to be reviewed. The chosen region then enlarges on the screen.

In each of the two peripheral nerve interactive posters, displayed nerves are only associated with nerve numbers; nerve names are not present. One poster is considered a *name-only* poster. When the student attempts to identify a particular nerve and moves the cursor over the nerve number, the nerve name appears on the computer screen. Thus, a relatively large number of nerve names can be tested in a short period of time, ideal for a quick review immediately before an exam. The second poster is considered a *comprehensive* poster, which is especially conducive to teaching peripheral nerve anatomy and function. When prompt-

ed by the student, the comprehensive poster provides slides that depict nerve names, images of supplied muscles, muscle names, images of supplied skin, and nerve fiber compositions. Each slide also includes an instruction box that allows the student to display additional information that exists or return to the poster. The slides create an efficient mechanism for testing and learning.

With the use of the *comprehensive* peripheral nerve poster, the student first attempts to identify a nerve by moving the cursor over a nerve number and clicking on it. A slide appears containing the name of the nerve and an instruction box that reads "show supplied muscles." After considering the muscles supplied by the nerve, the student can click on the instruction box. If the nerve is a somatic motor nerve or a mixed nerve, an image appears with the innervated muscles color-enhanced and associated with numbers. No muscle names are present. The instruction box on this slide would read "show muscle names." Even if the student did not initially know the supplied muscles, a second chance is given to identify them by image, promoting learning. After consideration, the student can click on the instruction box and a new image appears containing muscle names in place of numbers. As required, additional instruction boxes on subsequent slides may read "show deeper muscles" or "show distal muscles." When each box is clicked on, an image appears that displays the information. The last of the series of muscle image slides contains an instruction box that reads "show supplied skin." Upon clicking on this box, an image appears that displays the area of skin supplied by the nerve. If no skin is supplied, a slide informs the student that the nerve is a motor nerve and no skin is supplied.

The instruction box on the initial slide of a somatic sensory nerve or an autonomic nerve will also read "show supplied muscles," even though these nerves do not innervate striated muscles. This ensures that no clues or hints are given to the student. Upon clicking on the instruction box, a slide appears that informs the student that no skeletal muscles are supplied by the nerve. With a somatic sensory nerve, the slide additionally states that the nerve is a sensory nerve and contains an instruction box that reads "show supplied skin." After consideration, the student can click on the box and an image of the supplied skin appears. With an autonomic nerve, the slide also states that the nerve is an autonomic nerve and the instruction box reads "show composition." After considering sympathetic versus parasympathetic and preganglionic verses postganglionic, the student can click on the box and a slide appears that displays the information. An instruction box on the last slide for both somatic and autonomic nerves reads "return to poster." This notifies the student that he or she is at the tail-end of the sequence of slides for that particular nerve and can return to the poster to consider the name and innervations of another nerve.

The use and navigation of the two skeleton interactive posters is similar to the two peripheral nerve posters. A notable difference is that the bones of the *name-only* version of the skeleton poster are associated with red and black dots instead of numbers. When the cursor is moved over a red dot, the name of the bone appears on the screen. When positioned over a black dot, the name of the associated surface anatomy detail appears. Various notches, foramina, heads, necks, tubercles, and tuberosities are examples of surface anatomy details that may be displayed. Similar to the peripheral nerve posters, bones of the *comprehensive* skeleton poster are associated with numbers. This poster displays bone names, images of bone surface details, names of bone details, images of muscle origins and insertions, and muscle names when prompted by the student. With the comprehensive versions of the peripheral nerve and skeleton posters, an audio application can furnish the correct pronunciation of anatomic structures as the names appear on the screen. The efficiency and effectiveness of these interactive posters as learning tools cannot be over-empha-sized.

The **medical crossword puzzles** constitute another innovative teaching application at **Medtutor.com**. The puzzles are an infor-mal way to continually review and learn new material. As with other applications, the system can be directed to create a puzzle specific to information contained in this book or some combina-tion of other *Medtutor* books. If the answer to a crossword ques-tion is not known, the application provides a short explanation when requested. Additionally, crossword puzzles can be worked online or printed and worked while away from the computer. The student can return to the internet site to check answers and obtain explanations. Once a puzzle is completed, the system can immedi-ately create a new puzzle as directed by the student. Among other utilities, the medical crossword puzzle application is a fun and effective means to consistently review and maintain a tangible knowledge base long after the texts are finished. There is a signif-icant amount of fundamental medical information presented in the *Medtutor* series; even working just one puzzle a day would great-ly benefit any practitioner in a health-related profession.

With mastery of the peripheral nerve material, you will want to continue your expansion of medical knowledge. At this stage, the two *Medtutor* books that would be most beneficial include *The Cranial Nerves* and *Medical Terminology: an Innovative and Successful Approach*. All *Medtutor* products, including books and posters, can be obtained at **Medtutor.com**.

The Cranial Nerves serves to simplify and consolidate the complex material of cranial nerve anatomy and is the perfect companion to the peripheral nerve text. The book is accompanied by a unique poster that depicts every cranial nerve branch; over 270 nerves are labeled. The text starts with the basics of neu-roanatomy, allowing for feelings of intimidation and confusion to be replaced with confidence and understanding. The cranial nerve material found in the Peripheral Nerve text is reorganized and reviewed, and a more in-depth description is provided. Subjects covered include brain stem nuclei, cranial nerve fiber composi-tions, ganglia, branches, and innervations. The medical terms dis-cussed are introduced and explained in a succinct fashion and mnemonic devices are interspersed throughout to promote quick absorption of the material. Chapter tests with thoroughly explana-tory answer keys are utilized to promote efficient and independ-ent learning. The text is also complimented by the same internet exercises as this course, including a 180 question comprehensive final exam and two interactive posters that replicate the cranial nerve poster that accompanies the text. With effort and the use of this course, even beginner students find themselves converted to cranial nerve "experts."

There is little doubt that the most efficient mechanism to pre-pare for any medical career is to master medical language. Rather than relying on the rote memorization of individual words, ***Medical Terminology: An Innovative and Successful Approach*** focuses on teaching Greek and Latin combining forms (prefixes, suffixes, and word roots). The text demonstrates how to break down complex terms into their components, allowing the student to instantaneously deduce the meaning of words that he or she has never seen before. The unique book design allows for very effi-cient study sessions, easy quick reference, and maximum porta-bility. Definitions and examples are given in carefully laid out charts, and the coil binding allows the text to remain in the per-fect position during intermittent periods of extensive study.

By going to the *Medtutor* website and accessing the interac-tive applications of the *medical combining forms course,* the stu-dent is presented with a variety of formats that increase exposure to word forms and accelearate the learning experience. As profi-ciency improves, advancement can be made to the applications of the *medical terminology course.* This course goes beyond the book by introducing thousands of new medical terms that the stu-dent can interpret and learn with the newly acquired knowledge of combining forms. Definitions are given and the combining form components are reviewed for each medical term. The stu-dent obtains the dual benefit of developing an expertise in com-bining forms while also learning medical terminology. A whole new language soon becomes unlocked. Each internet course con-tains a 180 question final exam that can be found on the website. As with the final exams of other *Medtutor* courses, the student can use the website to send a separate e-mail that verifies the score on each exam to any designated invididual or organiza-tion.

The customizable web-based applications and training pro-grams include randomized exams, flashcards, and crossword puz-zles. The website tracks the individual student's progress, allow-ing each student to tailor the exercises to focus on particular prob-lem areas. As an additional benefit, flashcards of the *medical ter-minology course* contain an audio application that can provide the correct pronunciation of medical terms when requested by the student. Learning medical terminology by merely reading a ter-minology book is often fruitless; the material is dull and monot-onous and there is no realistic reason to think a student will remember a particular word unless repeatedly exposed to it. This system offers a diverse and fun way to address this problem. When used in tandem, the text and website provide a dynamic and highly effective way to master medical language with significant advantages over other terminology books.

Other *Medtutor* courses are available at **Medtutor.com**. The goal of each is to provide a system that is convenient and con-ducive to a lifetime of learning. The texts and posters provide information in an easy to understand format and the web-based applications give a recreational and repetitive exposure to the medical facts. Health-related careers can be very challenging and the more information a practitioner knows, the higher the quality of care he or she can provide. If you don't use it, you lose it and the *Medtutor* courses are designed to help you both learn and maintain your knowledge in the most efficient way possible.

HALF AND HALF REVISITED

1) **24 true vertebrae:** Half (12) articulate with ribs (T1 – T12), half (12) do not (C1 – C7 and L1 – L5).

2) **8 carpal bones:** Half (4) are in the proximal row, half (4) are in the distal row.

3) **6 named sympathetic nerves that supply structures of the trunk** branch from the sympathetic chain and are not associated with spinal nerves. The upper half (3) are cardiac (heart). The lower half (3) are splanchnic (viscera).

4) **8 muscles are supplied by the trigeminal nerve:** Half (4) are muscles of mastication (temporalis, masseter, lateral pterygoid, medial pterygoid). Half are not (tensor tympani, tensor veli palatini, anterior belly of digastric, mylohyoid).

5) **12 cranial nerves:** The first half (CN I – VI) supplies the nose and eye (the trigeminal nerve also supplies other structures). The second half (CN VIII – XII) has other responsibilities.

6) **8 cervical spinal nerves:** The first half (C1 – C4) forms the cervical plexus. The second half (C5 – C8) forms the brachial plexus (along with the T1 spinal nerve).

7) **12 intercostal nerves:** The first half (T1 – T6) are confined to the thorax. The bottom half (T6 – T12) eventually leave to supply the abdominal wall.

8) **The function of the obturator nerve is to $A_1D_2D_3U_4C_5T_6$ and it supplies 6 muscles:** Half (3) have "adduct" in their names (adductor brevis, adductor longus, adductor magnus [deep (anterior) portion]). Half (3) do not (pectineus [shared with femoral nerve], obturator externus, gracilis).

9) **The femoral nerve supplies 8 muscles:** Half (4) flex the thigh. The other half (4) form the quadriceps femoris muscle group and extend the leg. Both motions propel the lower extremity in an anterior (or forward) direction.

INDEX

branch to lumbosacral trunk, 432-33
branch to obturator nerve, 430, 433
branch to phrenic nerve, 303
branch to supraclavicular trunk, 303
branch to tensor fasciae latae, 439f
brevis, definition of, 353
bridegrooms palsy, 381
broad ligament, 94, 95f
Broca's area, 220f
bronchi, 75f, 106, 165, 239
bronchial arteries, 75
bronchial smooth muscles, 165, 169, 171
bronchial tree, 73, 106, 196f-197f
bronchial veins, 75
bronchioles, 74-75, 106
bronchitis, 325
bronchoconstriction, 169, 206
bronchomediastinal trunks, 97-98
bronchopulmonary segments, 75-76, 106
bronchus, 73f, 416
BTL (bilateral tubal ligation), 94, 107
buccal branch from facial nerve, 237, 256
buccal nerve, 229f
buccinator muscle, 229f, 237, 313f-314f, 314f
bucket handle tear, 57
bulbospongiosus (bulbocavernosus) muscle,
        440, 440f
bulbourethral glands, 95, 96f
bupivacaine, 145
bursa, definition of, 416
bursa pharyngea, 301f
bursitis, 416
buttocks, 438-39, 439f, 462

C1⁻ channels, 130-31
C1 spinal segment, 305
C1 ventral rami, 302, 328
C1 vertebra (atlas bone), 37, 58, 179, 271
    illustration of, 23f, 34f, 37f
C2 dorsal ramus (third occipital nerve), 305f
C2 spinal segment, 304-5
C2 ventral rami branches, 303, 328
C2 ventral ramus, 302, 304-5
C2 vertebra (axis bone), 37, 271, 289
    illustration of, 23f, 37f
C3 dorsal ramus, 304, 305f
C3 spinal segment, 303, 305
C3 ventral rami branches, 303
C3 ventral ramus, 328
C3 vertebra, 289
C4 dorsal ramus, 305f
C4 spinal segment, 305
C4 ventral rami branches, 303, 328
C4 vertebra, 289
C5 spinal segment, 303, 305, 343
C5 ventral rami, 303-4
C5 vertebra, 272f
C6 vertebra, 272f, 289
C7 vertebra, 23f, 34f, 272f, 289
C8 spinal cord segment, 271-72, 291
C8 vertebra, 289
Ca⁺⁺ (calcium), 123, 130
caecum, 195f
calcaneus (heel bone), 46, 58, 445
    illustration of, 34f, 46f-47f
calcium (Ca⁺⁺81), 123, 130
calf muscle (gastrocnemius), 443f-445f, 444,
        450-51
calix, definition of, 92
calvaria, 35
cancer, 97

capillary beds, 71, 73, 75, 92
    illustration of, 73f
capitate bone, 45, 45f
capitis, definition of, 7, 8f
capsule of the kidney, 92
caput, definition of, 7
Carbocaine (mepivacaine), 145
carbohydrates, 87, 165, 206, 208
carbon dioxide, 75, 165, 239, 326
cardia, 85f
cardiac notch, 85, 85f
cardiac plexus, 85, 181, 315, 410
    illustration of, 85f, 184f, 196f
cardiac plexus nerve, 183
cardiac sphincter, 85, 85f
cardiac tamponade, 105
carina, 74
carotid arteries, 71f-72f, 72, 78f, 303f-304f
carotid artery sinus, 238
carotid body, 239
carotid branch from glossopharyngeal nerve
        (afferent nerve of Hering), 239, 313
carotid plexus, 196f
carotid pulse, 411, 417
carotid sinus, 239, 313
carpal bones, 34f, 44-45, 48, 58
carpal tunnel syndrome, 380
carpi, definition of, 353
carpus (wrist), 44-45, 58, 353-54, 361, 370-71,
        380
    illustration of, 353f
cartilage, 54, 57, 74-75, 106
cartilage ring of trachea, 316f
cartilago triticea, 315f
catabolic processes/catabloism, 165, 206
catheter, 458
cations, 121, 147
caudad, definition of, 5
cauda equina, 273, 274f, 460
caudal, 5, 5f-6f
caudate lobe of the liver, 88, 88f
caudate nucleus, 99, 107
cecum, 86, 86f-87f
celiac ganglion, 181-83
    illustration of, 182f, 184f, 192f, 196f-197f
celiac plexus, 182, 411
    illustration of, 184f, 192f, 196f
cell body. *see* soma
cellulitis, 416
central nervous system (CNS), 98-99, 137-39
    about, 107
    see also autonomic nervous system (ANS)
central vein, 88
cephalad, definition of, 5, 8f
cephalic, definition of, 5, 5f-6f, 7, 8f
cerebellar peduncles, 99, 107
cerebellum, 99, 107
    illustration of, 23f, 99f, 274f
cerebellum function, tests of, 254
cerebral hemispheres, 99
cerebrospinal fluid (CSF), 70, 105, 460
    see also spinal cavity
cerebrum, 99, 99f, 107
cervical, definition of, 7, 8f, 24
cervical artery, 305f
cervical branch from facial nerve, 237, 256
cervical canal, 94
cervical dorsal rami, 281, 301, 304-5, 305f
cervical enlargement, 274f
cervical ganglia and branches, 181
cervical lymph nodes, 97

cervical plexus, 274, 291, 301-3
    illustration of, 274f, 305f
cervical spinal nerves, 179-81, 281, 291
cervical vertebrae, 36-37, 36f-37f, 271
    see also specific vertebrae
cervicothoracic ganglion (stellate ganglion),
        181, 183, 184f, 196f
cervix, 7, 24, 94, 94f-95f
cesarean section (C-section), 146, 458-61
chambers of the heart, 71
chemoreceptors, 239, 313
chest wall, 397-99, 399f
chewing, 228
CHF (congestive heart failure), 325-26
chicken pox, 290
chloroprocaine, 145
cholangitis, 415-16
chole, definition of, 88-89, 106
cholecystokinin, 89, 106
chol(o), definition of, 416
chondroglossus muscle, 241, 311
chorda tympani, 228f, 236, 241f, 313
choroid, 169, 170f
choroid plexus of 3rd ventricle, 23f
chronic nerve compression, 379
chronic obstructive pulmonary disease
        (COPD), 325-26
chyle, 97
chyme, 85
cilia, 170, 193, 207
ciliary body (muscle), 170, 170f, 193, 196f-197f
ciliary ganglion, 193, 196f-197f, 208
circulatory system, 71-73, 72f-73f, 92f-93f,
        181f
    see also specific arteries or veins
cisterna chyli, 97, 97f-98f
citric acid (Krebs) cycle, 165-67, 204
clavicle, 34f, 44, 44f
clavicular facet, 38f
clavicular portion of pectoralis major, 360f
claw hand, 380
clitoris, dorsal nerve of, 440-41, 461f, 462
clonus, 254-55
closed cavities, 69-70
cluneal, definition of, 433
cluneal nerves, 464
CN 1. *see* olfactory nerve
CN II. *see* optic nerve
CN III. *see* oculomotor nerve
CN IV. *see* trochlear nerve
CN IX. *see* glossopharyngeal nerve
CNS. *see* central nervous system
CN V. *see* trigeminal nerve
CN VI. *see* abducens nerve
CN VII. *see* facial nerve
CN VIII. *see* vestibulocochlear nerve
CN X. *see* vagus nerve
CN XI. *see* accessory nerve
CN XII. *see* hypoglossal nerve
coagulation abnormalities, 460
cocaine, 145
coccygeal articular surface, 37f
coccygeal nerve, 179, 272
coccyx (coccygeal vertebrae), 36, 48, 271-72
    illustration of, 34f, 36f-37f, 94f, 274f
cochlea, 238, 238f, 258
cochlear root, 238, 258
cochlear (spiral) ganglion, 238
collecting ducts, 92
collecting tubule, 92